P9-CDF-228

NO LONGER~
the property of
Whitaker Library

THE TEACHER/TUTOR RESOURCE BOOK

ACADEMIC LANGUAGE NOTEBOOKS
THE LANGUAGE OF MATH

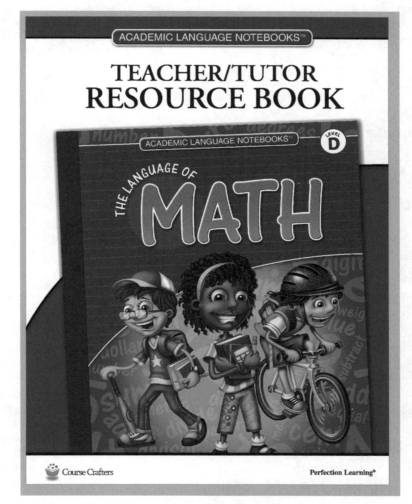

LEVEL D

Course Crafters   **Perfection Learning**®

Whitaker Library
Chowan University
One University Place
Murfreesboro, NC 27855

THE DEVELOPMENT TEAM

Authors	*Suzanne Irujo and Alex Ragan*
Editorial Director	*Alex Ragan*
Project Editor	*Mary McKeon*
Developmental Editors	*Monica Harari Schnee and Rosalyn Reiff*
Writers	*Ellen Balla, Stephen Currie, June Edelstein, Pam Halloran, Susan Leeming, Lisa Panka, and Dale Zevin*
Art Consultant and Designer	*Thomasina Webb*
Production Editor	*Melissa Urszinyi*
Artists	*Ken Bowser, AC Kreader, Andy Levine, Tyler Martin, Ryan Sias, and Thad Tichenor*

ESL Consultants

Margo Gottlieb
Mimi Met
Lydia Stack

Educator Reviewers

Susan Brandon
Katherine Bourdon
Jodi Crandall
Nell Forgacs
Holly Kharitonashvili

Linda Lawrence
Dawn Mushkin
Graciela Trillas
Arthur Raynes
Claudia Torres Yakos

Math Reviewers

Debra Coggins
Kathy Ross
Maria Torres

CREATED AND DEVELOPED BY:

Course Crafters, Inc.
3 Washington Square
Haverhill, MA 01830
Phone: 978-372-3446 x228
Fax: 978-372-3660
www.coursecrafters.com

PUBLISHED BY:

Perfection Learning® Corporation
1000 North Second Avenue, P.O. Box 500
Logan, Iowa 51546
Phone: 1-800-831-4190
Fax: 1-800-543-2745
www.perfectionlearning.com

©2008 by Course Crafters, Inc.

All rights reserved. No part of this book my be reproduced, stored in a retrieval system, or transmitted in any form or by any means, electronic, mechanical, photocopying, recording, or otherwise, without prior permission of the publisher.

Printed in the United States of America

76686 4

ISBN-13: 978-0-7891-7196-2
ISBN-10: 0-7891-7196-1

1 2 3 4 5 6 LT 12 11 10 9 8 7

AUTHORS

Dr. Suzanne Irujo has been a teacher and teacher educator in the fields of bilingual education, ESL, and foreign language education for 30 years. Her public school experience includes teaching elementary bilingual education and ESL, teaching high school ESL and Spanish, and administering a K-12 ESL program. As a teacher educator, she taught ESL, foreign language, and bilingual methodology courses and supervised student teachers at Boston University, where she also taught courses in linguistics, first language acquisition, bilingualism and biliteracy, and second language acquisition. Dr. Irujo holds an Ed.D. in applied psycholinguistics, an M.Ed. in bilingual education, and a B.A. in Spanish. She is the author of *Teaching Bilingual Children: Beliefs and Behaviors* (Heinle & Heinle, 1998), series editor of the four-volume series *Integrating the ESL Standards Into Classroom Practice* (TESOL, 2000) and co-editor of *Collaborative Conversations Among Language Teacher Educators* (TESOL, 2004).

Alex Ragan holds a Master of Education degree (Ed.M.), Specialized, from the Harvard Graduate School of Education. He founded and acts as editor-in-chief for *The ELL Outlook,* a bi-monthly e-newsletter focusing on the education of English language learners (ELLs). Alex also contributes various articles to *The ELL Outlook* on such topics as determining text difficulty and using modified texts in ELL classrooms. He recently authored an article with Dr. Nonie Lesaux investigating the effects of ELL program entry and exit criteria at the district, state, and national levels, which was published in the Educational Policy Analysis Archives. Alex is also the editorial director at Course Crafters.

Math Consultants

Kathy Ross has been in education for 35 years. She taught mathematics, was a mathematics resource teacher for grades K-8, and then served as the K-12 Mathematics Supervisor in Jefferson Parish Public School System until her retirement. Kathy was an author on Addison Wesley's secondary mathematics series and was a contributing writer on the Scott-Foresman/Addison Wesley middle school mathematics series. She has a B.S. from the University of New Orleans and a MST in Mathematics Education from Loyola University.

Debra Coggins is a mathematics education consultant with experience advising districts, coaching teachers, writing professional materials, and developing and delivering professional development. Her most recent professional publication is *English Language Learners in the Mathematics Classroom* (Corwin Press, 2007), on which Debra is the lead writer. Debra has a Masters in Mathematics Education from the University of California at Berkeley and mathematics specialist, elementary, and mathematics teaching credentials. She has 17 years teaching experience in grades K-12.

María Torres has served as a school administrator, a classroom teacher, and a program administrator and supervisor of student teachers in higher education. María has over fifteen years experience working with a private, non-profit organization where she delivers training and technical assistance in mathematics content and pedagogy in a six-state region. She holds a B.S. in Secondary Education with mathematics and social studies specializations and a Master's degree in Educational Supervision with a mathematics specialization.

TABLE OF

About the Program

Unit 1 *Place Value and Number Sense*

Unit 2 *Mental Math and Estimation*

Unit 3 *Multiplication and Division Number Sense*

Unit 4 *Multiplication and Division of Whole Numbers*

CONTENTS

v

PROGRAM OVERVIEW

THE STUDENT LEARNING SYSTEM

The Student Worktext

The Student Worktext is at the core of the Student Learning System. Each Student Worktext includes 30 modules tied to topics in the math curriculum.

As students finish each lesson of a module, they organize the completed Student Worktext pages, along with their additional work and notes, into their *Academic Language Notebook* (*ALN*).

A three-ring binder for each student, supplied with the *ALN* program, includes tabs for the modules. This encourages students to create a portfolio of their work, and to practice learning skills along with academic language.

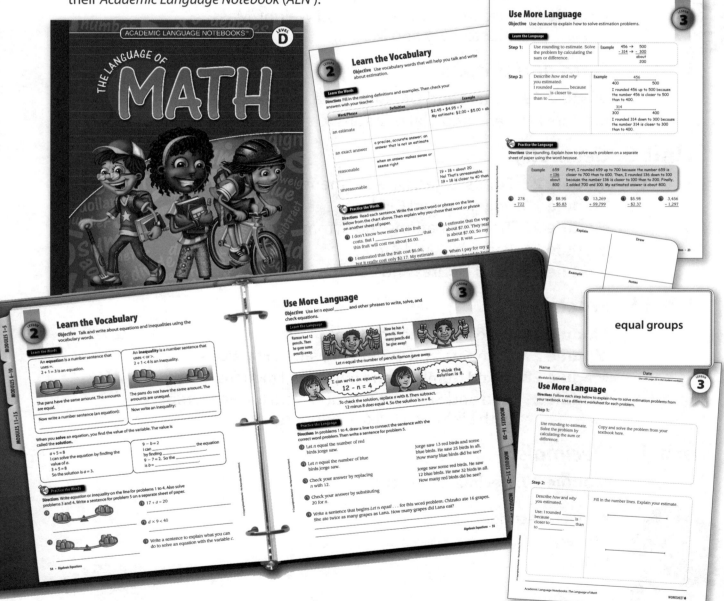

The Student Learning System also includes Student Vocabulary Cards, organizing tabs, notebook paper, and Student Worksheets.

THE TEACHER TOOLKIT

The Teacher/Tutor Resource Book (TTRB)

The Teacher/Tutor Resource Book (TTRB) is designed for all ELL teachers, tutors, and aides—even those with little or no experience with these students. All lessons follow a simple, predictable format: Introduce, Teach and Learn, Review and Practice, and Assess and Intervene.

Research-based ELL Best Practices are directly translated into teacher practice in each TTRB lesson plan—through suggested teacher talk, models for differentiated instruction, and assessment rubrics.

The Teacher Toolkit also includes an ELL Best Practice Audio CD, Teacher Transparencies, an Assessment Handbook, and a Teacher Resource CD-ROM .

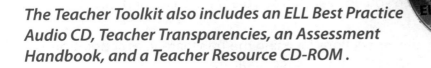

ADDITIONAL PROGRAM MATERIALS

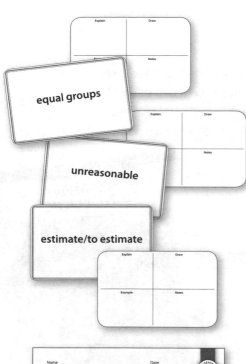

Student Vocabulary Cards

WHAT:

The Student Vocabulary Cards provide space for each student to write examples, make notes, create their own definitions, and draw. There are vocabulary cards for each of the 30 modules in *ALN*, approximately 180 per grade level.

WHEN:
- Use when you see ⬛ in the Teacher/Tutor Resource Book.
- Use when your students need additional vocabulary practice or review.

HOW:
- Various activities with the Vocabulary Cards are suggested throughout modules in the Teacher/Tutor Resource Book.
- Additional vocabulary building activities can be found at the end of the Teacher/Tutor Resource Book.

Included with the Teacher Toolkit:

Student Worksheets - Extra Practice

WHAT:

Reproducible worksheets for students that focus on the most challenging academic language in the module. There is one worksheet for every module in *ALN*, 30 in all for each grade.

WHEN:
- Use when you see ⬛ in the Teacher/Tutor Resource Book.
- Use when your students need extra academic language practice.

HOW:

Follow the instructions for using the worksheets at point-of-use in the Teacher/Tutor Resource Book.

Teacher Transparencies

WHAT:

The Teacher Transparencies reproduce important illustrations, charts, diagrams, and other teaching aids and activities from the Student Worktext and Teacher/Tutor Resource Book. There are two transparencies for every module in *ALN*, 60 per grade level.

WHEN:
- Use when you see ⬛ in the Teacher/Tutor Resource Book.
- Use when you need an activity, diagram, chart, or problem set.

HOW:

Follow the instructions for using the Transparencies at point-of-use in the Teacher/Tutor Resource Book.

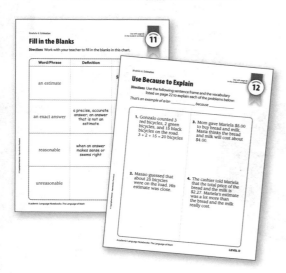

Teacher Resource CD-ROM

WHAT:
The Teacher Resource CD-ROM contains additional program materials for the teacher. The CD-ROM contains the Assessment Management System, PDF versions of Student Worksheets and Teacher Transparencies, Lesson-Level Assessment Rubrics, and additional resources.

WHEN:
- Use when you need to print Student Worksheets, find PDFs of Teacher Transparencies, or find additional resources for your classroom.
- Use when you want to assess and monitor your students' progress.

HOW:
Follow the instructions on the CD-ROM.

Assessment Handbook

WHAT:
The Assessment Handbook is a guide for assessing and tracking student progress in learning the academic language of math. It includes an overview of the assessments in *ALN*, instructions for using the assessment management system, and reproducible copies of Lesson-Level Assessment Rubrics.

WHEN:
Use when you have a question about assessing your students using *ALN*.

HOW:
First read about the overview of assessments in *ALN*. Then check and record your students' progress using the Lesson-Level Assessment Rubrics. Finally, track and analyze student assessment data using the management system on the Teacher Resource CD-ROM.

ELL Best Practices Audio CD

WHAT:
Recording of the six ELL Best Practices on an audio CD.

WHEN:
Use when you want to learn about ELL best practices and you don't have time to read—in your car, at home, after class.

HOW:
Listen to the ELL Best Practices Audio CD.

WHO IS *ALN* FOR?

The Academic Language Notebooks are designed for English language learners (ELLs) at the intermediate and advanced levels of English language proficiency. The specific names for various levels of English language proficiency may differ based on the state students are educated in and the English language proficiency test used in your state or district. If you know students' tested proficiency levels, use those to determine whether *ALN* is appropriate or not. If you do not have a proficiency designation, the following descriptions can help:

Intermediate level English language learners:

- need repetition in order to understand complex speech.
- have restricted vocabulary and limited command of language structure.
- speak in simple, appropriate, comprehensible sentences, but with frequent grammatical errors.
- comprehend and use some academic vocabulary.
- have trouble comprehending and producing complex sentences and academic language.
- show great variety in reading comprehension, depending on their familiarity with the themes, concepts, or genres of the text.
- read most successfully when they have background knowledge on which to build.
- begin to write a variety of texts, with some complexity and coherence.
- still use many nonconventional features in their writing.

Advanced level English language learners:

- have language skills that are adequate for most daily communication.
- produce occasional errors in language structure or word use.
- have difficulty understanding and using words with multiple meanings, and figurative or idiomatic language.
- have occasional difficulty producing and understanding complex structures or abstract language.
- read with fluency.
- may not understand texts where facts are decontextualized or vocabulary is abstract or has multiple meanings.
- can read independently, but with occasional comprehension problems when reading grade-level text.
- can write personal and academic text independently, but with difficulty.
- can produce writing where language structure, vocabulary use, and organization begin to look somewhat native-like.
- errors persist in speaking and writing, but do not usually interfere with communication.

Source: Adapted from *PreK-12 English Language Proficiency Standards*, Teachers of English to Speakers of Other Languages, Inc.

WHAT IS ACADEMIC LANGUAGE?

Academic English is the language ELLs need in order to succeed in academic settings. Academic English differs from the social English that students use to carry on conversations about everyday situations. Academic language is needed to understand, talk, and write about abstract, decontextualized concepts. It is crucial for understanding textbooks, solving problems, and doing well on standardized tests. Without explicit and frequent attention to the academic language of mathematics, ELLs will not have the academic language skills needed to succeed in mainstream math classes.

The academic language of math includes vocabulary, both specialized math vocabulary and everyday words with additional math meanings (such as *table, point,* or *set*). It also includes grammar, such as translating word order into mathematical symbols (the sentence *The number a is 5 less than the number b.* isn't $a = 5-b$, but $a = b-5$), and language use, such as knowing how to explain a mathematical process.

Teaching Academic Vocabulary

To teach academic vocabulary:

- **Make the meanings of words explicit and clear.** Demonstrate meaning through visuals, examples, and contextualized activities before introducing formal definitions.

- **Actively involve students in vocabulary learning by linking meaningful, hands-on activities with vocabulary learning.** Puzzles and games are helpful for getting students to use the vocabulary in sentences, and for relating the words to the math they are learning.

- **Expose students to vocabulary as much as possible, as many times as possible.** ELLs need multiple repetitions in different contexts in order to gain a deep understanding of new terms. Repeat the vocabulary as much as you can, in as many meaningful ways as possible.

Teaching Academic Grammar

To teach academic grammar:

- **Introduce grammar points in context.** Provide multiple examples in contexts that students are familiar with. Point out how the language works, but do not give extensive grammatical explanations.

- **Focus on grammar throughout a math lesson.** Call students' attention to how you use a grammar point while you are teaching math. Provide activities where students have to use the language while they are doing math.

- **Do not correct students' grammar mistakes.** Instead, model the correct structure by rephrasing what students say when you respond to them.

Where to Learn More

Bielenberg, B., & Fillmore, L.W. (2005). The English they need for the test. *Educational Leadership, December 2004/January 2005*.
   Read the article online at: http://www.barrow.k12.ga.us/esol/The_English_They_Need_for_the_Test.pdf
Irujo, S. (2007). Teaching math to English language learners: Can research help? *The ELL Outlook, 6(2)*.
   Read the article online at: http://www.coursecrafters.com/ELL-Outlook/2007/mar_apr/ELLOutlookITIArticle1.htm
Zwiers, J. (2005). The third language of academic English. *Educational Leadership, December 2004/January 2005*.

ELL BEST PRACTICE #1
Comprehensible Language

What Is Comprehensible Language?

Comprehensible language, both oral and written, is language that can be understood by language learners. What constitutes comprehensible language varies according to students' English language proficiency, native language proficiency, and previous schooling in math. Increased attention must be paid to comprehensible language when students have less English language proficiency and less previous schooling in math.

How to Create Comprehensible Language

Language can be made more comprehensible by modifying the way lessons are presented. You can create comprehensible language in classrooms by:

- **Adapting and modifying teacher talk.** As much as possible, avoid the use of idiomatic language and complex sentence structures. Keep sentences short, to the point, and focused on the lesson objective. When teaching key ideas, paraphrase the same information in various ways.

- **Associating new vocabulary and language structures with concrete materials.** When modeling or presenting a task, associate specific language explicitly with each part of the task as it is modeled. Write on the board, point to a visual, or demonstrate with math manipulatives as you orally describe what you are doing.

When you are using *ALN*, look for BP 1 **for an example of comprehensible language that you can implement in your classroom.**

> **Point to *enough*.** Say: Enough *means* as many or as much as I need. Point to a large pile of paper and a small group of pencils. Say: *I have enough paper for today. I don't have enough pencils for today.* Write *enough* on the board and point out that the spelling and the pronunciation don't match. Practice pronouncing the word, as necessary. Ask students to talk with their partners about times when they have or don't have enough time or money. Have a few volunteers share.

ELL BEST PRACTICE #2
Assessing, Activating, and Building Background Knowledge

What Is Background Knowledge?

Background knowledge is the knowledge and skills that students already have about a specific topic. Background knowledge is like the foundation of a house. Without sufficient background knowledge, students will be unable to successfully learn what they are being taught. To determine whether or not further background knowledge must be built before starting a lesson, teachers need to find out what individual students already know about the topic that will be taught in the lesson.

How to Assess, Activate, and Build Background Knowledge

To assess, activate, and build background knowledge, follow these three steps:

1. **Find out what students know and don't know.** Think about both the language and math skills that students will need to know before they learn about a new topic. (In *ALN*, look for the Prerequisite Background Knowledge box on the first page of every module of the Teacher/Tutor Resource Book.) Ask students simple questions or have students complete a simple activity, and informally assess students.

2. **Link what students already know to what they will be learning about a topic.** Based on what students already know, make connections between their existing knowledge and skills and concepts from the new topic. Remind students about other lessons that may have been done earlier in the year. Connect new knowledge to experiences they've had at home or in their daily lives.

3. **Build additional background as necessary.** If students don't have enough background knowledge or skills, you may need to review or reteach key concepts before introducing new ones. Sometimes this can be done quickly, in the form of a mini-lesson, before beginning a new lesson. If students lack a substantial amount of background knowledge due to interrupted prior schooling, they may need additional intervention.

When you are using *ALN*, look for BP 2 for an example of assessing, activating, and building background knowledge.

> **BP 2 Ask:** *What units do you use to measure liquids or to measure how heavy something is at home? Do you use different units to measure things at the supermarket or at the doctor's office?* Elicit responses. Remind students that there are different units of measurement for capacity and mass or weight.

> **Introduce the concept of comparison.** Say: *When we want to find the difference between two things, we compare them. For example, we say Carol is hungrier than Mardy or Mike has bigger feet than Edie.* Ask students for other examples of what can be compared.

ELL BEST PRACTICE #3
Performance Assessment

What Is a Performance Assessment?

Performance assessments measure what students are able to do on specific tasks. Unlike multiple-choice standardized tests, performance assessments can measure how well students are performing at the time of testing _and_ over a longer period of time. When assessing the academic language of math, a performance assessment could mean having a student explain how a word problem was solved, comparing and contrasting different types of shapes, or following directions to correctly shade a fraction of a shape.

How to Conduct Performance Assessments

To plan and create performance assessments to track student progress, follow these three steps:

1. **Decide what you want to assess.** A performance assessments should evaluate how well a student can accomplish the objective of the lesson. Performance assessments should assess either academic language or content, but should not try to assess both at the same time. In _ALN_, all assessments are based on lesson-specific objectives and focus on assessing the Main Idea of the module and the academic language of math.

2. **Choose or create an assessment task.** Performance assessment may be based on the tasks that students complete during a lesson. You may also want to design separate assessment tasks. These tasks should be similar, but not the same as, the activities used to teach the objective during the lesson. If there are multiple parts to a lesson objective, make sure the task tests all these parts. _ALN_ includes at least one written performance assessment at the end of every lesson.

3. **Track students' progress over time.** Collect results of assessment tasks in the short-term and long-term in a notebook or a journal. This will allow you to see patterns over time, monitor students' yearly progress, and indicate when intervention is necessary to help a struggling student. In _ALN_, use the Assessment Management System to track students' progress by module and over the course of a year.

When you are using _ALN_, look for **BP 3** for an example of a performance assessment.

> **BP 3 Read aloud the Main Idea with students.** Ask students if they understand the Main Idea. Have them hold their thumbs straight up if they think they completely understand the concept, hold their thumbs straight down if they feel completely confused, and point their thumbs to the side if they think they understand some, but not all. Use this information to help you determine how quickly or slowly to proceed through the lesson.

ELL BEST PRACTICE #4
Interaction

What Is An Interactive Classroom?

In an interactive math classroom, students talk with other students about math topics. They also talk with the teacher in ways that go beyond just answering the teacher's questions. This provides students with non-threatening ways to use and expand their language. Instead of making use of teacher-centered lessons, interactive classrooms provide ample opportunities for students to work with other students, which combines learning math concepts with learning new language.

How to Create Interactive Language Learning Activities

To create a more interactive classroom:

- **Limit the amount of teacher talk.** Be aware of how much time you are talking versus how much time each student is talking. The more time teachers spend talking to the class, the less time students are able to use the language they need to be learning. As a general goal, aim to have students talking to each other about the math topic for at least half of class time.

- **Facilitate interaction in pairs and small groups.** For example, when you ask the whole class a question, have student partners discuss the question with each other before calling on a volunteer to share the answer with the class. When pairs of students have solved a problem together, have them compare their answer with another pair before going over the problem with the whole class.

- **Make sure that all interaction is meaningful.** Students should use and practice solving real math problems using real language. For example, if students are learning how to use *if. . .then* statements, they should practice using this structure by describing real-life multiplication problems rather than making *if. . .then* statements about non-math related situations or things.

When you are using *ALN*, look for **BP|4** for an example of an interactive activity.

> **BP|4** **Have pairs choose tagged classroom items and use play money to count out the cost and change** as they practice the question frames: *How much does it cost? It costs _____. What is your change? My change is _____.*

> **BP|4** **Review regular and irregular past tense verbs by having students sort them.** Create two columns on the board: *–ed* and *change the word*. Write these verbs on sticky notes, mix them up, and stick them to the board: *stay, return, visit, arrive, start, last, come, leave, do, is, go, begin.*
>
> **Model the activity.** Choose a sticky note, say the verb, say it in the past tense, and put it in the correct column. Use the verb to ask and answer a question in the past tense. Invite pairs of volunteers to participate by choosing a sticky note and putting it in the correct column. Student 1 asks the past tense question. Student 2 answers using the past tense verb.

ELL BEST PRACTICE #5
Higher-Order Thinking

What Is Higher-Order Thinking?

Higher-order thinking enables students to think critically, solve increasingly complex math problems, and think creatively. Critical thinking is just as important for ELLs as it is for any student. ELLs need to be given the chance to answer questions that involve more than simple factual recall. They need to analyze, synthesize, interpret, and evaluate new information they are learning. While ELLs may lack English language proficiency, they can and should be given tasks that encourage higher-order thinking skills.

How to Encourage Higher-Order Thinking with ELLs

One of the greatest challenges with ELLs is encouraging higher-order thinking while taking into account their lack of English language proficiency and potential lack of math background knowledge.

Following these suggestions can help:

- **Use comprehensible language as much as possible.** If students are unable to understand what you are asking, their ability to answer questions using higher-order thinking skills will be severely limited. Rephrase higher-order questions and directions for activities in various ways. Support what you are saying with demonstrations, models, and visuals.

- **Encourage students to think critically even though they may lack English language proficiency.** Above all, ELLs need to know that thinking is not dependent on English language proficiency and their ability to express themselves in English will grow over time. If possible, allow students to express their thinking in ways that are not verbal—with pictures, by acting out what they are thinking, by using a combination of verbal and visual presentations, or by using the native language if there is somebody who can interpret it. When they do express their thinking verbally in English, focus on the content, not the form, when you respond or assess students.

When you are using *ALN*, look for **BP 5** **for an example of higher-order thinking.**

> **BP 5 Use counters to model the Grouping Property of Addition.** Write *8 + (1 + 1) =* and *(8 + 1) + 1=* on the board. Have volunteers solve the problems, making sure they get the same answer. (10) Ask students: *Did you think both answers would be the same? Why or why not?* Say: *We can group numbers in different ways and still get the same answer. This is called the Grouping Property.* Write *Grouping Property* on the board above the two number sentences the volunteers just solved.

ELL BEST PRACTICE #6
Hands-On Activities

Why Are Hands-On Activities Important for Language Learning?

Hands-on materials make language more comprehensible. By explicitly associating new language with hands-on materials, the meaning of academic math language can be directly supported by concrete objects that students can see and manipulate. ELLs will also more easily learn language because of the built-in redundancy—if they don't understand the meaning of a word or phrase, the visual representation provides support.

How to Create Hands-On Activities that Support Academic Language Learning

To develop hands-on activities that will support language learning, use these steps:

- **Use hands-on materials that support the math topic and vocabulary being taught.** Think of math materials that directly represent a math concept or vocabulary word. Some examples include base-ten blocks, place value charts, number lines, fraction strips, counting rods, play money, clocks, calendars, thermometers, and rulers.

- **Connect specific language to specific hands-on materials.** Hands-on activities can help students learn math concepts, but for students to also learn math language, a direct connection must be made between the hands-on activity and the language that goes with it. As you model how to complete an activity, emphasize the language that explains what is being done. Structure the activities so students have to use the language themselves while they do the task.

When you are using *ALN*, look for **BP 6** for an example of hands-on activities.

Where to Learn More About the ELL Best Practices

Colorín Colorado. (2007). Using informal assessments with English language learners.
Read the article at: http://www.colorincolorado.org/educators/assessment/informal

Gibbons, P. (2002). *Scaffolding Language, Scaffolding Learning: Teaching Second Language Learners in the Mainstream Classroom.*
Portsmouth, NH: Heinemann.

Echevarria, J.E., Vogt, M.E., & Short, D.J. (2004). *Making Content Comprehensible for English Learners: The SIOP Model.* Boston, MA: Pearson Education, Inc.

Carl, K., & Rosen, M. (1994). Using alternative assessments with English language learners. Evaluation Assistance Center East, George Washington University. Read the article online at: http://www.ncela.gwu.edu/pubs/lists/altern.htm

Krashen, S.D. (1981). *Second Language Acquisition and Second Language Learning.*
Download the entire book online at: http://www.sdkrashen.com/SL_Acquisition_and_Learning/index.html

Kuhlman, N. (2006). Using performance-based assessments in the ELD classroom. *The ELL Outlook, 4(4).*
Read the article at: http://www.coursecrafters.com/ELL-Outlook/2005/sep_oct/ELLOutlookITIArticle1.htm

North Central Regional Education Laboratory (n.d.). *Building on Prior Knowledge and Meaningful Student Contexts/Cultures.*
Read the articles online at: http://www.ncrel.org/sdrs/areas/issues/students/learning/lr100.htm

O'Malley, J.M., & Valdez Pierce, L. (1996). *Authentic Assessment of English language learners: Practical Approaches for Teachers.*
Reading, MA: Addison Wesley.

HOW AND WHEN TO USE *ALN*

Follow these steps to use the *Academic Language Notebooks* in your classroom.

BEFORE THE MATH TEXTBOOK/CURRICULUM

STEP 1
Pick a topic from your math textbook.

Your MATH Textbook

STEP 2
Pick a corresponding ALN module.

ALN: The Language of Math

STEP 3
Pre-Teach the Main Idea and Essential Vocabulary with ALN.

IN YOUR CLASSROOM

DURING THE MATH TEXTBOOK/CURRICULUM

STEP 4

Use your math textbook/curriculum.

Now go back to your own math textbook/curriculum!

AFTER THE MATH TEXTBOOK/CURRICULUM

STEP 5

Build additional language and problem solving strategies with ALN.

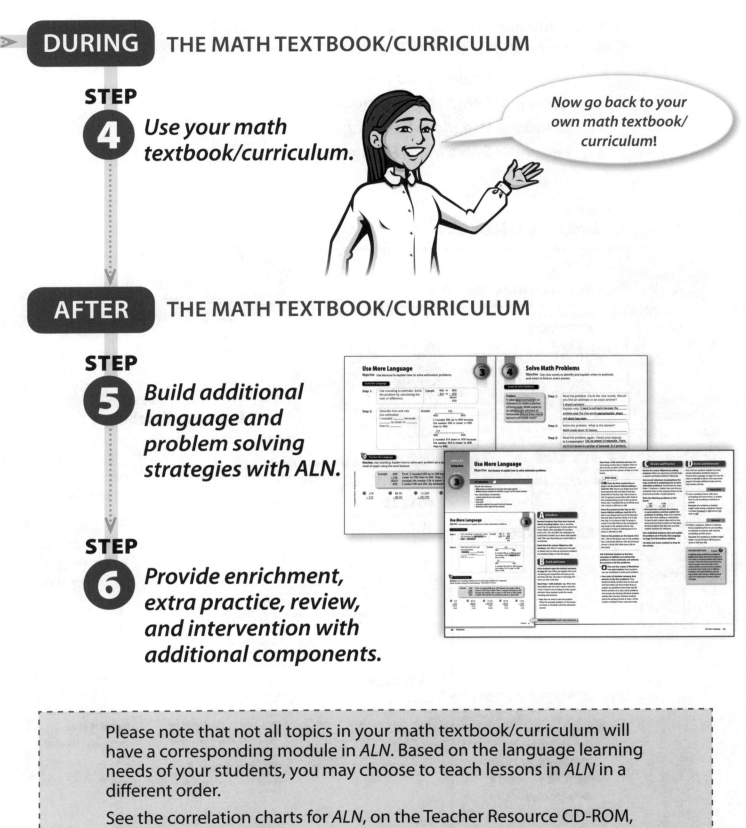

STEP 6

Provide enrichment, extra practice, review, and intervention with additional components.

Please note that not all topics in your math textbook/curriculum will have a corresponding module in *ALN*. Based on the language learning needs of your students, you may choose to teach lessons in *ALN* in a different order.

See the correlation charts for *ALN*, on the Teacher Resource CD-ROM, to learn more.

STUDENT WORKTEXT

In *ALN*, there are four lessons per module, all of which complement a topic from the math textbook/curriculum:

Lesson 1: Understand the Main Idea
Lesson 2: Learn the Vocabulary
Lesson 3: Use More Language
Lesson 4: Solve Math Problems

Lesson 1: Understand the Main Idea

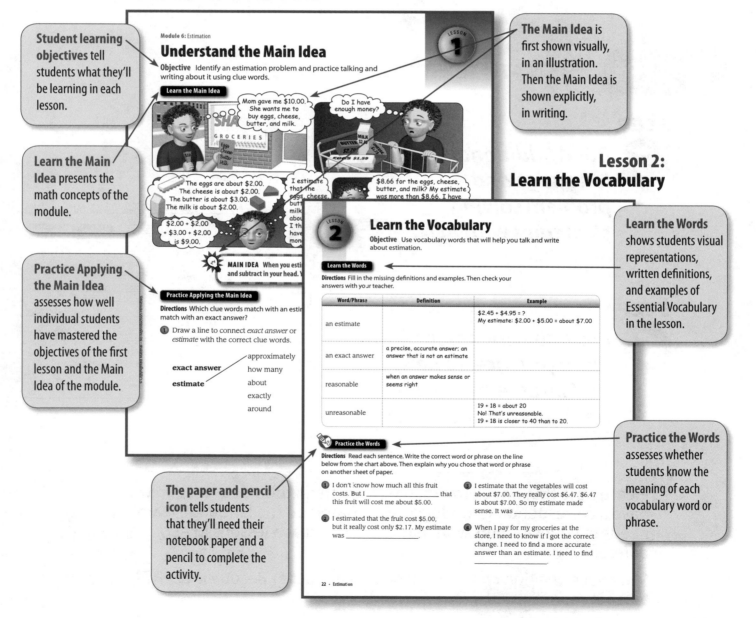

Student learning objectives tell students what they'll be learning in each lesson.

Learn the Main Idea presents the math concepts of the module.

Practice Applying the Main Idea assesses how well individual students have mastered the objectives of the first lesson and the Main Idea of the module.

The Main Idea is first shown visually, in an illustration. Then the Main Idea is shown explicitly, in writing.

Lesson 2: Learn the Vocabulary

Learn the Words shows students visual representations, written definitions, and examples of Essential Vocabulary in the lesson.

Practice the Words assesses whether students know the meaning of each vocabulary word or phrase.

The paper and pencil icon tells students that they'll need their notebook paper and a pencil to complete the activity.

WALK-THROUGH

Lesson 3:
Use More Language

Illustrations in **Learn the Language** model language use in real-life contexts.

In **Practice the Language**, students demonstrate what they've learned about the language taught in this lesson.

Model problems mimic grade-level math problems from math textbooks/ curriculum so students are prepared for mainstream classroom work.

Lesson 4:
Solve Math Problems

Learn to Solve Problems teaches students strategies for understanding and solving grade-level math problems.

Step-by-step problem solving sequence models language and mathematical concepts needed to solve the problem.

Practice activities have students complete simpler questions first, followed by more complex questions that involve higher-order thinking.

Practice Solving Math Problems assesses how well students meet lesson objectives and solve grade-level-appropriate word problems.

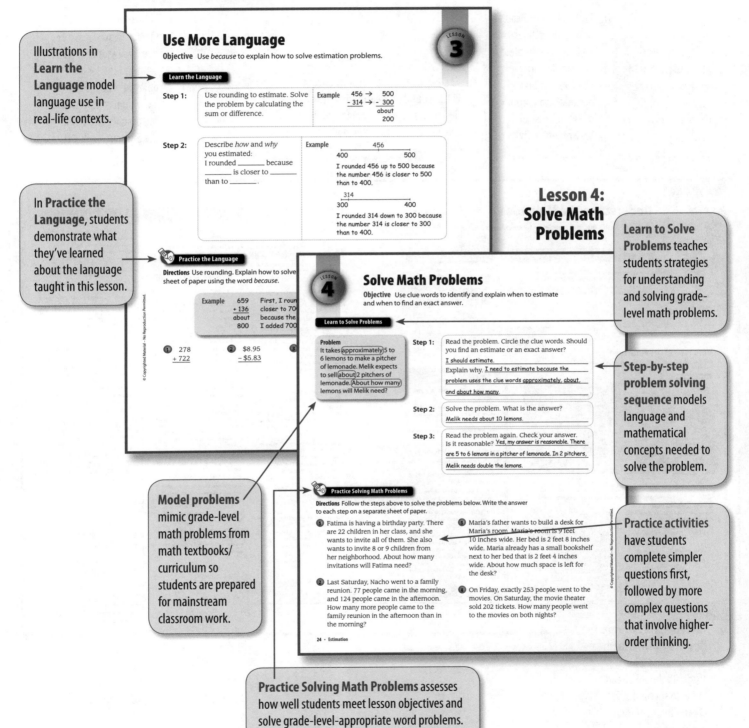

Use More Language

Objective Use *because* to explain how to solve estimation problems.

Learn the Language

Step 1: Use rounding to estimate. Solve the problem by calculating the sum or difference.

Example
$$456 \rightarrow 500$$
$$- 314 \rightarrow - 300$$
$$\text{about}$$
$$200$$

Step 2: Describe *how* and *why* you estimated:
I rounded _____ because _____ is closer to _____ than to _____.

Example   456
400   500
I rounded 456 up to 500 because the number 456 is closer to 500 than to 400.

314
300   400
I rounded 314 down to 300 because the number 314 is closer to 300 than to 400.

Practice the Language

Directions Use rounding. Explain how to solve ___ sheet of paper using the word *because*.

Example   659   First, I roun___
+ 136   closer to 70___
about   because the___
800   I added 700___

① 278   ② $8.95
+ 722   - $5.83

Solve Math Problems

Objective Use clue words to identify and explain when to estimate and when to find an exact answer.

Learn to Solve Problems

Problem
It takes approximately 5 to 6 lemons to make a pitcher of lemonade. Melik expects to sell about 2 pitchers of lemonade. About how many lemons will Melik need?

Step 1: Read the problem. Circle the clue words. Should you find an estimate or an exact answer?
I should estimate.
Explain why. I need to estimate because the problem uses the clue words approximately, about, and about how many.

Step 2: Solve the problem. What is the answer?
Melik needs about 10 lemons.

Step 3: Read the problem again. Check your answer. Is it reasonable? Yes, my answer is reasonable. There are 5 to 6 lemons in a pitcher of lemonade. In 2 pitchers, Melik needs double the lemons.

Practice Solving Math Problems

Directions Follow the steps above to solve the problems below. Write the answer to each step on a separate sheet of paper.

① Fatima is having a birthday party. There are 22 children in her class, and she wants to invite all of them. She also wants to invite 8 or 9 children from her neighborhood. About how many invitations will Fatima need?

② Last Saturday, Nacho went to a family reunion. 77 people came in the morning, and 124 people came in the afternoon. How many more people came to the family reunion in the afternoon than in the morning?

③ Maria's father wants to build a desk for Maria's room. Maria's room is 9 feet 10 inches wide. Her bed is 2 feet 8 inches wide. Maria already has a small bookshelf next to her bed that is 2 feet 4 inches wide. About how much space is left for the desk?

④ On Friday, exactly 253 people went to the movies. On Saturday, the movie theater sold 202 tickets. How many people went to the movies on both nights?

24 · Estimation

© Copyrighted Material – No Reproduction Permitted.

TEACHER/TUTOR RESOURCE BOOK

Lesson 1: *Understand the Main Idea*

Understand the Main Idea should always be taught <u>before</u> lessons in the math textbook/curriculum.

Time clock indicates how long each lesson will take to complete. Time indicated does not include optional Intervention or Extension and Enrichment activities.

ELL Best Practice box introduces the ELL best practice featured in the module, describing how to integrate this best practice throughout the module.

The assessment rubric in each lesson measures how well students have achieved the lesson objectives based on individual completion of the practice activity in the Student Worktext.

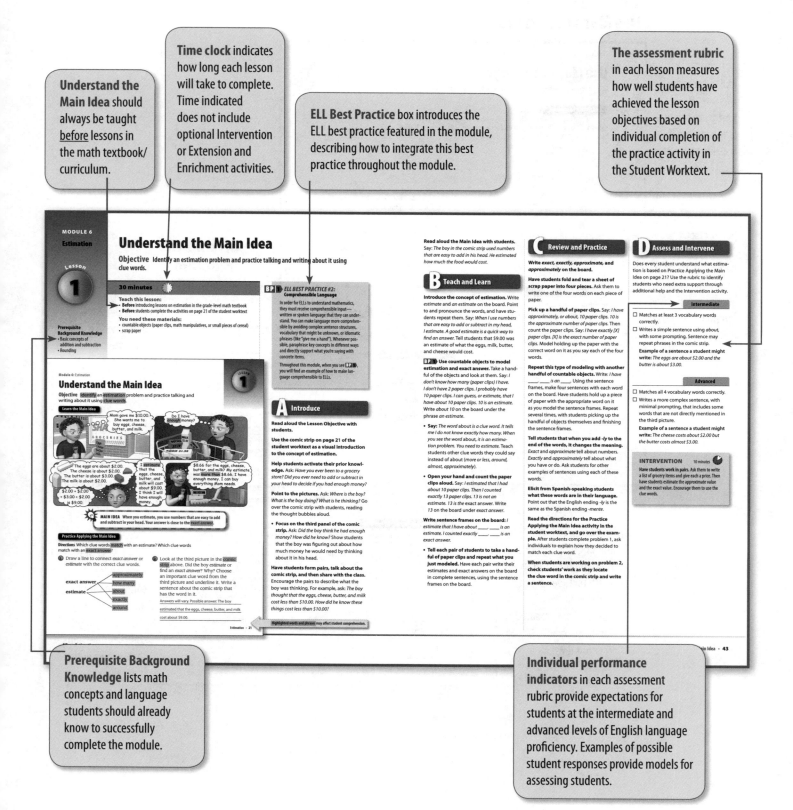

Prerequisite Background Knowledge lists math concepts and language students should already know to successfully complete the module.

Individual performance indicators in each assessment rubric provide expectations for students at the intermediate and advanced levels of English language proficiency. Examples of possible student responses provide models for assessing students.

WALK-THROUGH

Lesson 2: *Learn the Vocabulary*

List of **Essential Vocabulary** shows words and phrases that are explicitly taught to students in the lesson. These words and phrases are essential for understanding textbook lessons on the topic of the module.

List of **Additional Vocabulary** provides other words and phrases that ELLs may not know and may need to learn to be successful in this lesson.

Teacher Transparency icons alert teachers to the use of a transparency at point-of-use in the lesson.

Learn the Vocabulary should always be taught <u>before</u> lessons in the math textbook/curriculum.

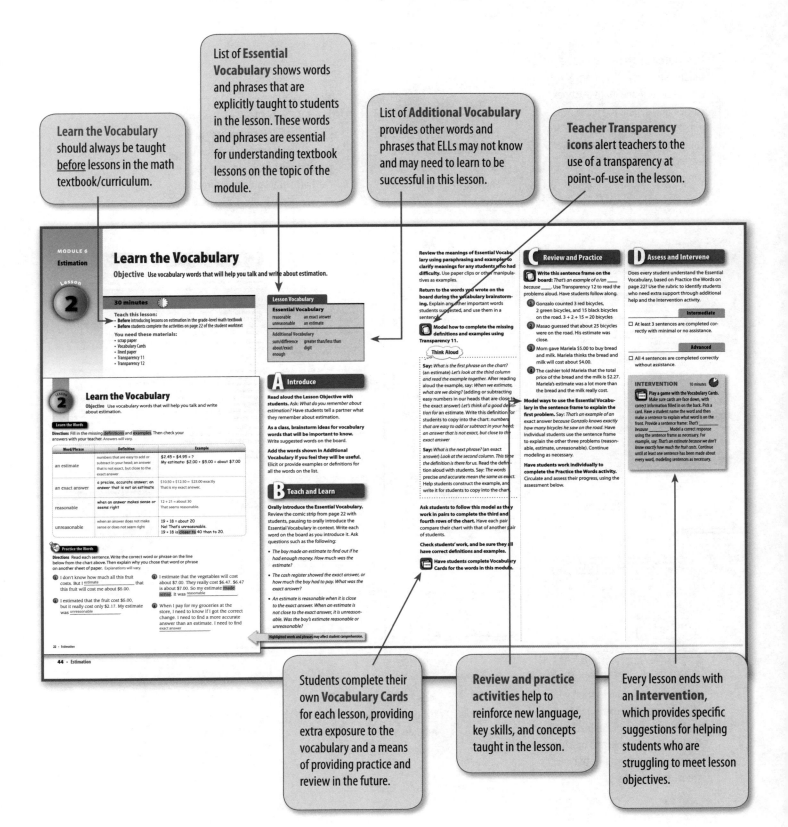

Students complete their own **Vocabulary Cards** for each lesson, providing extra exposure to the vocabulary and a means of providing practice and review in the future.

Review and practice activities help to reinforce new language, key skills, and concepts taught in the lesson.

Every lesson ends with an **Intervention**, which provides specific suggestions for helping students who are struggling to meet lesson objectives.

TEACHER/TUTOR RESOURCE BOOK

Lesson 3: *Use More Language*

Use More Language should be taught either before, during, or after lessons in the math textbook/curriculum, depending on what's indicated here. Generally, Use More Language lessons are taught after lessons in the math textbook/curriculum.

Review activities activate prior knowledge and build additional background necesssary for students to succeed in the lesson.

Think Alouds allow teachers to model the thinking process and the academic language needed to solve math problems and use mathematical language correctly.

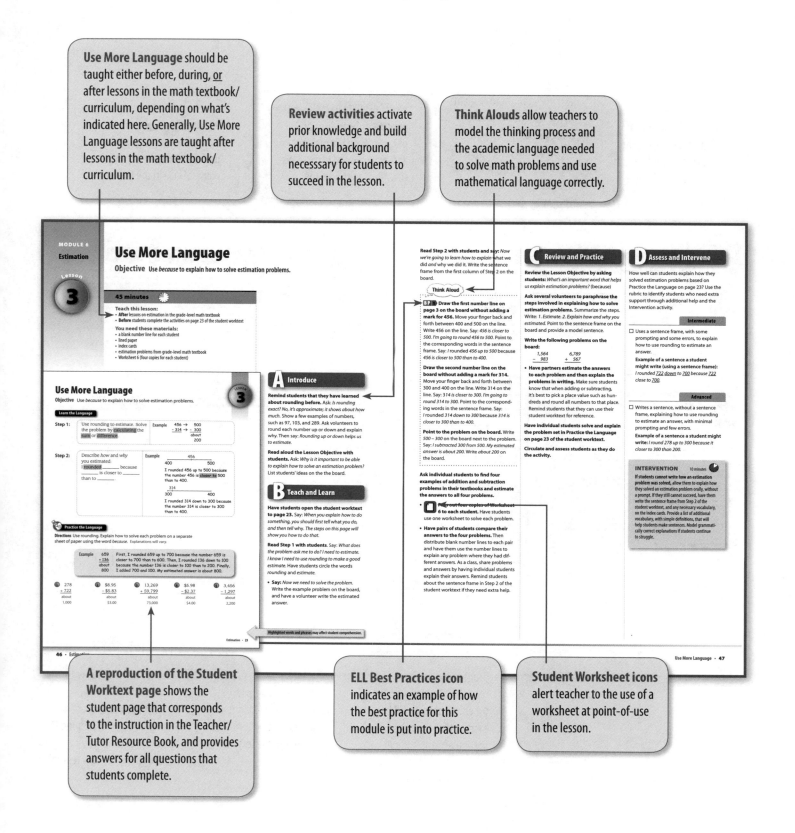

A reproduction of the Student Worktext page shows the student page that corresponds to the instruction in the Teacher/Tutor Resource Book, and provides answers for all questions that students complete.

ELL Best Practices icon indicates an example of how the best practice for this module is put into practice.

Student Worksheet icons alert teacher to the use of a worksheet at point-of-use in the lesson.

WALK-THROUGH

Lesson 4: *Solve Math Problems*

Solve Math Problems should always be taught __after__ lessons in the math textbook/curriculum.

List of materials needed includes Teacher Transparencies, Vocabulary Cards, and Student Worksheets, as well as other materials used in the lesson.

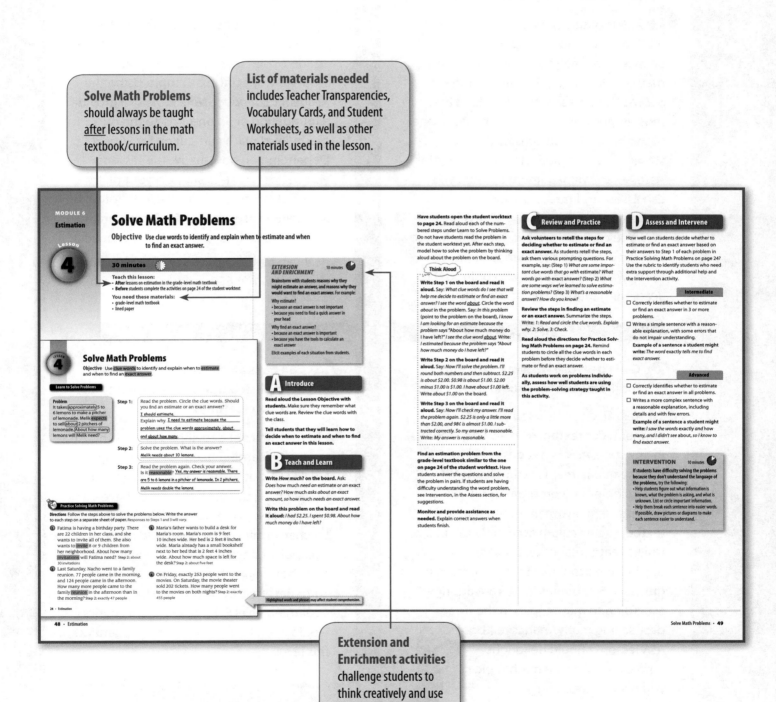

MODULE 6

Estimation

Lesson 4

Solve Math Problems

Objective Use clue words to identify and explain when to estimate and when to find an exact answer.

30 minutes

Teach this lesson:
• **After** lessons on estimation in the grade-level math textbook
• **Before** students complete the activities on page 24 of the student worktext

You need these materials:
• grade-level math textbook
• lined paper

Solve Math Problems

Objective Use clue words to identify and explain when to estimate and when to find an exact answer.

Learn to Solve Problems

Problem
It takes approximately 5 to 6 lemons to make a pitcher of lemonade. Melik expects to sell 2 pitchers of lemonade. About how many lemons will Melik need?

Step 1: Read the problem. Circle the clue words. Should you find an estimate or an exact answer?
I should estimate.
Explain why. *I need to estimate because the problem uses the clue words approximately, about, and about how many.*

Step 2: Solve the problem. What is the answer?
Melik needs about 10 lemons.

Step 3: Read the problem again. Check your answer. Is it reasonable? *Yes, my answer is reasonable. There are 5 to 6 lemons in a pitcher of lemonade. In 2 pitchers, Melik needs double the lemons.*

Practice Solving Math Problems

Directions Follow the steps above to solve the problems below. Write the answer to each step on a separate sheet of paper. Responses to Steps 1 and 3 will vary.

1 Fatima is having a birthday party. There are 22 children in her class, and she wants to invite all of them. She also wants to invite 8 or 9 children from her neighborhood. About how many invitations will Fatima need? Step 2: about 30 invitations

2 Last Saturday, Nacho went to a family reunion. 77 people came in the morning, and 124 people came in the afternoon. How many more people came to the family reunion in the afternoon than in the morning? Step 2: exactly 47 people

3 Maria's father wants to build a desk for Maria's room. Maria's room is 9 feet 10 inches wide. Her bed is 2 feet 8 inches wide. Maria already has a small bookshelf next to her bed that is 2 feet 4 inches wide. About how much space is left for the desk? Step 2: about five feet

4 On Friday, exactly 253 people went to the movies. On Saturday, the movie theater sold 202 tickets. How many people went to the movies on both nights? Step 2: exactly 455 people

Highlighted words and phrases may affect student comprehension.

24 • Estimation

EXTENSION AND ENRICHMENT 10 minutes
Brainstorm with students reasons why they might estimate an answer, and reasons why they would want to find an exact answer. For example:

Why estimate?
• because an exact answer is not important
• because you need to find a quick answer in your head

Why find an exact answer?
• because an exact answer is important
• because you have the tools to calculate an exact answer

Elicit examples of each situation from students.

A **Introduce**

Read aloud the Lesson Objective with students. Make sure they remember what clue words are. Review the clue words with the class.

Tell students that they will learn how to decide when to estimate and when to find an exact answer in this lesson.

B **Teach and Learn**

Write *How much?* on the board. Ask: *Does how much need an estimate or an exact answer? How much asks about an exact amount, so how much needs an exact answer.*

Write this problem on the board and read it aloud: *I had $2.25. I spent $0.98. About how much money do I have left?*

Have students open the student worktext to page 24. Read aloud each of the numbered steps under Learn to Solve Problems. Do not have students read the problem in the student worktext yet. After each step, model how to solve the problem by thinking aloud about the problem on the board.

Think Aloud

Write Step 1 on the board and read it aloud. Say: *What clue words do I see that will help me decide to estimate or find an exact answer? I see the word about. Circle the word about in the problem.* Say: *In this problem (point to the problem on the board), I know I am looking for an estimate because the problem says "About how much money do I have left?" I see the clue word about.* Write: *I estimated because the problem says "About how much money do I have left?"*

Write Step 2 on the board and read it aloud. Say: *Now I'll solve the problem. I'll round both numbers and then subtract. $2.25 is about $2.00. $0.98 is about $1.00. $2.00 minus $1.00 is $1.00. I have about $1.00 left.* Write $1.00 on the board.

Write Step 3 on the board and read it aloud. Say: *Now I'll check my answer. I'll read the problem again. $2.25 is only a little more than $2.00, and 98¢ is almost $1.00. I subtracted correctly. So my answer is reasonable.* Write: *My answer is reasonable.*

Find an estimation problem from the grade-level textbook similar to the one on page 24 of the student worktext. Have students answer the questions and solve the problem in pairs. If students are having difficulty understanding the word problem, see Intervention, in the Assess section, for suggestions.

Monitor and provide assistance as needed. Explain correct answers when students finish.

C **Review and Practice**

Ask volunteers to retell the steps for deciding whether to estimate or find an exact answer. As students retell the steps, ask them various prompting questions. For example, say: (Step 1) *What are some important clue words that go with estimate? What words go with exact answer?* (Step 2) *What are some ways we've learned to solve estimation problems?* (Step 3) *What's a reasonable answer? How do you know?*

Review the steps in finding an estimate or an exact answer. Summarize the steps. Write: *1: Read and circle the clue words. Explain why. 2: Solve. 3: Check.*

Read aloud the directions for Practice Solving Math Problems on page 24. Remind students to circle all the clue words in each problem before they decide whether to estimate or find an exact answer.

As students work on problems individually, assess how well students are using the problem-solving strategy taught in this activity.

D **Assess and Intervene**

How well can students decide whether to estimate or find an exact answer based on their answers to Step 1 of each problem in Practice Solving Math Problems on page 24? Use the rubric to identify students who need extra support through additional help and the Intervention activity.

Intermediate

☐ Correctly identifies whether to estimate or find an exact answer in 3 or more problems.

☐ Writes a simple sentence with a reasonable explanation, with some errors that do not impair understanding.

Example of a sentence a student might write: *The word exactly tells me to find exact answer.*

Advanced

☐ Correctly identifies whether to estimate or find an exact answer in all problems.

☐ Writes a more complex sentence with a reasonable explanation, including details and with few errors.

Example of a sentence a student might write: *I saw the words exactly and how many, and I didn't see about, so I know to find exact answer.*

INTERVENTION 10 minutes
If students have difficulty solving the problems because they don't understand the language of the problems, try the following:
• Help students figure out what information is known, what the problem is asking, and what is unknown. List or circle important information.
• Help them break each sentence into easier words. If possible, draw pictures or diagrams to make each sentence easier to understand.

48 • Estimation

Solve Math Problems • 49

Extension and Enrichment activities challenge students to think creatively and use higher-order thinking.

FREQUENTLY ASKED QUESTIONS

Q How can *ALN* prepare my students for high-stakes tests and help me show adequate yearly progress?

A *ALN* is based on national and state mathematics and ESL/ELD standards and an extensive analysis of the mainstream math textbooks/curriculum in grades 3–5. *ALN* focuses on teaching ELLs the most important academic math language of textbooks, classrooms, and high-stakes tests. Coupled with use of the *ALN* Assessment Management System, you can assess and track how well individual students are doing on all 120 lessons in *ALN*. You can also print various graphs and reports. Year-end summaries can be used to show yearly progress in acquiring the academic language of mathematics.

Q I teach math and have ELLs in my class. How—and when—should I use ALN?

A *ALN* is designed to complement your mainstream math textbook/curriculum as needed, both before and after you teach students a specific math topic. Using the *Academic Language Notebooks* will provide a foundation or an on-ramp to the on grade-level math curriculum for your ELLs. Depending on how many *ALN* lessons you decide to use to support your math textbook/curriculum (from one to four), *ALN* can be used for a quick lesson or for more extensive support if students need it.

ALN can be used during small group time, during pull-out ESL periods, or after school.

Q Can I use *ALN* with my existing mathematics textbook/curriculum?

A Yes. *ALN* can be used with any mathematics textbook, in any classroom, in any state. *ALN* is not designed to replace mainstream textbooks. *ALN* is a supplementary program designed to help make mainstream mathematics textbook/curriculum accessible to ELLs. Unlike mathematics textbooks, *ALN* teaches the academic English of math in grades 3–5. Modules in *ALN* are arranged according to math topics in the three best-selling mathematics textbooks. *ALN* lessons should be taught before and after the math topic you plan on teaching.

Q Can ELLs at the beginning stages of English language proficiency use *ALN* successfully?

A *ALN* was not developed for the English language learning needs of beginning level ELLs, but beginning level ELLs could benefit from the program if they have additional support from a trained ESL teacher. Additional time should be given to vocabulary development. Interventions and additional activities in the Teacher/Tutor Resource Book can also help beginning level ELLs. Assessment rubrics would need to be modified for students at this level.

Q Can *ALN* replace my current math curriculum?

A No. *ALN* was designed to supplement, and to be used along with, your current math textbook/curriculum. *ALN* is not a stand-alone program or sheltered math program. *ALN* focuses on teaching ELLs the academic language of mathematics, while your math textbook/curriculum will continue to teach students mathematics content and skills.

Q I'd like to use *ALN* in an after school program I teach. Will *ALN* work? What about summer school?

A *ALN* can be used in both after school and summer school programs to teach the academic language of math at either the 3rd, 4th, or 5th grade levels. Since *ALN* is not a stand alone product, you'll need to use a math textbook/curriculum to teach mathematics concepts, operations, and problem solving. Since *ALN* is modular, you can teach students from 30 minutes to four hours per math textbook/curriculum topic. See the Implementation Guide for more information on using ALN in different programs and instructional settings.

Q The math textbook I use doesn't teach math topics in the same order as *ALN*. Can I still use *ALN*?

A Yes, you can. The modules in *ALN* are non-sequential, designed to be taught in any order. Because of this, *ALN* can be used with any math textbook/curriculum and in any order.

Q I'm a new teacher. I don't have any experience with ELLs. Can I use *ALN* or do I need special training?

A You do not need any specific training to use *ALN*. *ALN* was designed to be used by all types of teachers, including community-based tutors, teacher's aides, ELL teachers, and mainstream classroom teachers. Teachers are provided with specific step-by-step guidelines for implementing *ALN* in the classroom and for learning ELL best practices.

Q I really don't have much time to teach academic English, but I know it's important. How can I use *ALN* if I don't have much time?

A *ALN* is modular. It is designed to be plugged into the curriculum as needed. If you don't have much time, decide what your students are struggling with the most—the main idea, the vocabulary, sentence-level language, or the problem solving portion of a topic. Based on your students' needs, you may decide to use only one of the four lessons in *ALN* for a specific math topic, which will take only 30-45 minutes to complete in class.

I use a rule to add these fractions.

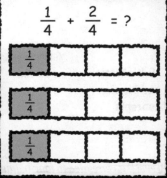

$$\frac{1}{4} + \frac{2}{4} = ?$$

PROGRAM SCOPE

MODULE NUMBER AND NAME	LESSON 1: UNDERSTAND THE MAIN IDEA	LESSON 2: LEARN THE VOCABULARY	LESSON 3: USE MORE LANGUAGE	LESSON 4: SOLVE MATH PROBLEMS
1. **Place Value**	Place value helps you read and write numbers and know the values of the digits in a number.	• digit • place value • value • period	Use *there are/are there* to ask and answer questions about place value.	Write correct number sentences when the problem includes word forms of large numbers.
2. **Compare and Order Whole Numbers**	You can use place value, a number line, or base ten blocks to compare and order numbers.	• to compare • to order • equal to (=) • greater than (>) • less than (<)	Use adjectives to compare and order numbers.	Cross out information that you do not need to solve math problems.
3. **Round Whole Numbers**	You can use a number line or rounding rules to round numbers.	• to round • to the nearest ____ • about • halfway between	Explain how you round numbers using the antonyms *round up* and *round down,* and the word *because.*	Solve word problems using real-world information.
4. **Money**	Start with the largest bills and the largest coins to count money. Count on (count up) to make change.	• dollar • bill • coin • cent • to make change • to count on (count up)	Ask and answer questions about making change using *if* clauses and *will* clauses.	Make a list of the coins you need to make change to help you solve problems.
5. **Mental Math**	You can add and subtract in your head in different ways.	• mental math • property • to break apart • compensation/ to compensate	Use root words to remember the meanings of the Commutative, Associative, and Identity properties. • Associative Property of Addition • Commutative Property of Addition • Identity Property of Addition	Explain how you break apart numbers or compensate (adjust) to solve a problem using mental math.
6. **Estimation**	When you estimate, you use numbers that are easy to add and subtract in your head. Your answer is close to the exact answer.	• reasonable • unreasonable • exact answer • estimate/to estimate	Use *because* to explain how to solve estimation problems.	Use clue words to explain when to estimate and when to find an exact answer.
7. **Multiplication and Division Concepts**	Multiplication and division are opposites.	• array • equal groups • fact family • inverse operations	Talk and write about equal groups in multiplication and division, using the words *every, each,* and *all.*	Decide whether to multiply or divide to solve word problems.

Level D is correlated to fourth grade math textbooks and curriculum.

MODULE NUMBER AND NAME	LESSON 1: UNDERSTAND THE MAIN IDEA	LESSON 2: LEARN THE VOCABULARY	LESSON 3: USE MORE LANGUAGE	LESSON 4: SOLVE MATH PROBLEMS
8. **Multiplication Properties and Division Rules**	You can use the properties of multiplication and the rules of division to multiply and divide more easily.	• Zero Property of Multiplication • Identity Property of Multiplication • Commutative Property of Multiplication • Associative Property of Multiplication	Identify what the word *number* refers to in phrases such as *a number, any number, that number,* and *what number.*	Analyze what the problem really asks, and explain your answer.
9. **Multiplication and Division Facts**	There are many different ways to find multiplication and division facts.	• multiple • pattern	Use regular and irregular past tense verbs and *so* to describe how you found a product or quotient.	Decide whether to multiply or divide.
10. **Model Multiplication by 1- and 2-Digit Numbers**	When you multiply, you can break apart the numbers into tens and ones to help find the products.	• Distributive Property • to regroup _____ as _____ • partial product	Use *by* plus *–ing* to explain how to find products using the Distributive Property.	Solve problems that use words you don't know.
11. **Model Division by 1- and 2-Digit Divisors**	When you divide things into equal groups, sometimes you have something left over.	• remainder • to bring down • left/left over	Read and write division problems in number sentences and long form.	Explain why a remainder is reasonable or unreasonable.
12. **Mental Math and Estimation with Multiplication and Division**	You can use patterns of zeros, or estimation, or both, to multiply and divide in your head.	• compatible numbers • underestimate • overestimate • divisible	Describe patterns for multiplying and dividing with zeros, using synonyms of *because.*	Explain why you chose rounding or compatible numbers to estimate the answer in multiplication and division problems.
13. **Algebraic Expressions**	An expression uses numbers and symbols to show a problem.	• algebra • expression • symbol • to simplify • to evaluate • variable • unknown (N, Adj)	Use words and phrases that unknown variables may represent.	Act out a problem to help you write an expression.
14. **Algebraic Equations**	To solve an equation, you need to find the value of the variable.	• equation • inequality • to solve/solution	Use *let n equal* _____ to and other phrases to write, solve, and check an equation.	Write equations to help solve problems.

PROGRAM SCOPE

MODULE NUMBER AND NAME	LESSON 1: UNDERSTAND THE MAIN IDEA	LESSON 2: LEARN THE VOCABULARY	LESSON 3: USE MORE LANGUAGE	LESSON 4: SOLVE MATH PROBLEMS
15. Patterns and Functions	You can write rules for patterns and write equations to show the rules.	• rule • function table (input/output table) • to extend	Describe how to extend a function table, using *when* and *if*.	Make a function table to solve a problem.
16. Time	You can use time to tell how long something will take to do or how long it will be until something happens.	• analog clock • digital clock • elapsed time	Use *since* and *until* to talk about elapsed time.	Decide what unit of time to use to find elapsed time.
17. Measures of Length (Customary and Metric)	We use units of length to measure and compare how long things are.	• units of measure • linear units • customary • metric	Use *about* and *actually* to describe estimating and measuring using customary and metric linear units. • inch (in.) • centimeter (cm) • foot (ft) • decimeter (dm) • yard (yd) • meter (m) • mile (mi) • kilometer (km) • millimeter (mm)	Decide whether to multiply or divide to solve problems where you change from one customary unit of length to another.
18. Measures of Capacity and Weight/Mass (Customary and Metric)	Units of capacity, weight, and mass can be used to measure and compare things.	• capacity • to hold • weight • to weigh • mass	Use *greater than, less than,* and *equal to* to compare units of capacity, weight, and mass. • fluid ounce (fl oz) • pound (lb) • ton (T) • cup (c) • milliliter (mL) • pint (pt) • liter (L) • quart (qt) • gram (g) • gallon (gal) • kilogram (kg) • ounce (oz)	Explain how to change units to solve a multistep problem.
19. Collect and Organize Data	When you collect data, you can organize and display it in different ways.	• data • survey • tally chart • line plot • stem-and-leaf plot	Use word associations to remember vocabulary words. • range • outlier • mean • median • mode	Tell if a statement about data on a chart or plot is correct or not, and explain why.

MODULE NUMBER AND NAME	LESSON 1: UNDERSTAND THE MAIN IDEA	LESSON 2: LEARN THE VOCABULARY	LESSON 3: USE MORE LANGUAGE	LESSON 4: SOLVE MATH PROBLEMS
20. **Read and Make Graphs**	You can use different kinds of graphs to organize data and compare data in different ways.	• graph • scale • interval	Describe the scale and interval of a graph using *large enough* or *small enough*.	Choose a particular kind of graph to use to help you solve a problem, and explain your choice.

21. **Points, Lines, Line Segments, Rays, and Angles**	We can use geometry to describe things in our world.	• geometry
		• line
		• point
		• angle
		• line segment
		• endpoint
		• ray
			Use geometric terms to describe and identify drawings.
			
			• parallel lines • vertex/vertices
			• intersecting lines • right angle
			              • obtuse angle
			• perpendicular lines • acute angle
			              • straight angle
				Understand sentences that have many different phrases in them.

22. **Polygons and Circles**	You can classify and name polygons and circles in different ways.	• plane figure • polygon • regular polygon	Classify and name shapes. • triangle • rhombus • quadrilateral • right triangle • pentagon • obtuse triangle • hexagon • acute triangle • octagon • equilateral triangle • rectangle • square • isosceles triangle • trapezoid • scalene triangle • parallelogram	Solve problems that are in the form of riddles.
23. **Transformations and Symmetry**	You can move shapes to see if they are the same, or fold them to see if the two sides match.	• transformation • translation • reflection • rotation • congruent • symmetry	Use the ending –*tion* to make nouns from verbs, and write the two related words.	Identify true and false statements with *always, sometimes,* and *never.*
24. **Perimeter and Area**	You can use different ways to find the distance around a figure or find the number of square units that cover a figure.	• perimeter • area • square unit • formula	Use *alike* and *different* to compare and contrast perimeter and area.	Use information you know to help you solve problems with words you don't know.

PROGRAM SCOPE

MODULE NUMBER AND NAME	LESSON 1: UNDERSTAND THE MAIN IDEA	LESSON 2: LEARN THE VOCABULARY	LESSON 3: USE MORE LANGUAGE	LESSON 4: SOLVE MATH PROBLEMS
25. Solid Figures and Volume	Solid figures have three measurements. You can make models of solid figures. You can find how much space is inside solid figures.	• solid figure • face • edge • net • volume • cubic unit	Use riddles to describe solid figures. • rectangular prism • cone • cube • cylinder • sphere • pyramid • triangular	Understand the use of the phrase *can be* with a verb in word problems.
26. Read and Write Fractions	Fractions name equal parts of a whole, equal parts of a group of objects, or points on a number line.	• fraction • numerator • denominator • group (set) • whole (region)	Use *is* and *are* to ask and answer questions about fractions.	Use *would* to answer questions with *suppose* in word problems.
27. Compare and Order Equivalent Fractions	Equivalent fractions name the same amount; you can use them to compare and order fractions.	• equivalent fraction • simplest form • common factor	Describe rules for finding equivalent fractions using the synonyms *other than* and *except*.	Identify information you do not need to solve problems.
28. Mixed Numbers and Improper Fractions	Some fractions have a value that is equal to or greater than one.	• mixed number • improper fraction	Give and follow commands, to rename improper fractions and mixed numbers.	Solve multistep problems that use fractions greater than 1.
29. Add and Subtract Fractions and Mixed Numbers with Like and Unlike Denominators	You use different rules to add and subtact different kinds of fractions.	• like denominators • unlike denominators	Use prefixes and suffixes to show relationships among words that tell about fractions.	Explain what is wrong when solutions to problems are not correct.
30. Decimal Concepts	Decimal numbers and fractions both show parts of a whole.	• decimal • decimal point • tenths • hundredths • thousandths	Write and follow directions about decimals.	Explain your answers to word problems.

LEVEL D, MODULES 1–30

Academic Language Notebooks: *The Language of Math*

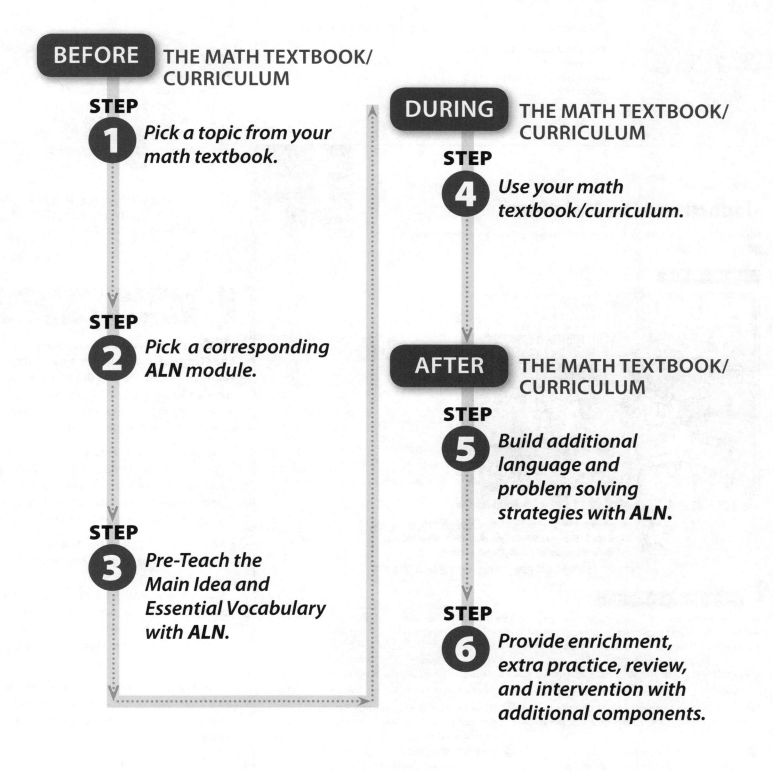

BEFORE THE MATH TEXTBOOK/ CURRICULUM

STEP 1 *Pick a topic from your math textbook.*

STEP 2 *Pick a corresponding ALN module.*

STEP 3 *Pre-Teach the Main Idea and Essential Vocabulary with ALN.*

DURING THE MATH TEXTBOOK/ CURRICULUM

STEP 4 *Use your math textbook/curriculum.*

AFTER THE MATH TEXTBOOK/ CURRICULUM

STEP 5 *Build additional language and problem solving strategies with ALN.*

STEP 6 *Provide enrichment, extra practice, review, and intervention with additional components.*

Understand the Main Idea

Objective Use place value to read and write numbers and identify the values of the digits.

45 minutes ⏱

Teach this lesson:
- **Before** introducing lessons on place value in the grade-level math textbook
- **Before** students complete the activities on page 1 of the student worktext

You need these materials:
- Transparency 1
- One or more pedometers
- Index cards

Prerequisite Background Knowledge
- Ability to count to 100 in English
- Basic concepts of place value

BP 2 ***ELL BEST PRACTICE #2:***
Assessing, Activating, and Building Background Knowledge

English language learners may have difficulty transferring what they learned previously in school or informally at home to what they are currently learning in school. As you introduce place value, elicit examples of identifying the values of digits and reading and writing large numbers that reflect familiar situations from students' experiences (population counts of community and school, distances in miles, seats in stadiums, etc.). Be sure students are able to count to 100 in English and have mastered basic concepts of place value.

Throughout this module, when you see **BP 2**, this is an example of assessing, activating, and building background knowledge.

Module 1: Place Value

Understand the Main Idea

Objective Use place value to read and write numbers and identify the values of the digits.

Learn the Main Idea

Wow! I walked 9,842 steps today!

Mom, I walked nine thousand eight hundred forty-two steps today! That's 9 thousands + 8 hundreds + 4 tens + 2 ones!

Place Value Helps You Know the Value of Digits			
Thousand	Hundreds	Tens	Ones
9	8	4	2
$9 \times 1,000$	8×100	4×10	2×1
9,000	800	40	2

MAIN IDEA Place value helps you read and write numbers and know the values of the digits in a number.

Practice Applying the Main Idea

Directions Study the pictures above and read the example below. Then answer each question using a complete sentence. Be sure to use the word *because* in your answer. Write your answers on a separate sheet of paper.

Example What is the value of the digit 2 in the number 9,842? The value is 2 because 2 is in the ones place.

1. What is the value of the digit 4 in the number 9,842? The value is 40 because it is in the tens place.

2. What is the value of the digit 8 in the number 9,842? The value is 800 because it is in the hundreds place.

3. What is the value of the digit 9 in the number 9,842? The value is 9,000 because it is in the thousands place.

4. Why is it important to understand place value? It is important because place value helps you read and write numbers correctly.

A Introduce

BP 2 **Help students activate their prior knowledge about basic concepts of place value.** Encourage them to share what they know about using place value to read and write numbers and about using place value to tell the values of digits in numbers.

- **Say:** *Think about your everyday life. How does knowing how place value works help you in school or in a store?* Have student pairs discuss their experiences with place value and then share with the group.

- **Write 485 and 458 on the board.** Say: *If your school has a total of 485 students and your cousin's school has a total of 458 students, how can you explain to your cousin that your school has more students, although he says that both number have the same digits?* If necessary, tell students the meaning of *digits*.

- **Ask students for other examples where it's important to understand how place value works (for example, when buying food or clothes).**

Highlighted words and phrases may affect student comprehension.

Read aloud the Lesson Objective. Tell students that the objective of this lesson is to help them use place value to read and write numbers, and to help them identify the values of the digits in a number. Say: *Place value helps us understand the value of a place in a number. The place of a digit in a number determines its value or worth.*

Ask a student to read aloud the Main Idea of the lesson on page 1 in the student worktext.

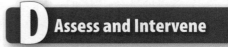

B Teach and Learn

Write the numbers 365 and 3,650 on the board. Point to each one, and ask: *How many digits are there in this number?* (3, 4) *Who can read this number aloud?* Call on volunteers to take turns reading the numbers aloud. Say: *You can read these numbers correctly because you know about place value. When you change the place of a digit in a number, you know how much each digit in the number is worth.*

Draw a simple place value chart on the board like the one pictured on the right-hand side of page 1 of the student worktext. Point to the place value chart, and say: *A place value chart helps you read and write large numbers.*

- **Fill in the number *365* in the appropriate columns on the place value chart.** As you say the value of each digit, point to its place in the chart. Say: *In 365, the digit 3 has a value of 300 because it is in the hundreds column. The digit 6 has a value of 60 because it is in the tens column. The digit 5 has a value of 5 because it is in the ones column.*

- **Then erase *365* from the place value chart.** Follow the same procedure with the numbers 3,650, 36,500, and 365,000. Say: *The digits are in different places, so they have different values. When you change the place of a digit in a number, the value of the number changes.*

Use pedometers to talk about place value. Say: *Pedometers are just like place value charts. They give you information about the value of digits in a number.*

- **Hold up a pedometer, and ask the following questions:** *How many of you have seen or used a pedometer? What is a pedometer used for?* (to count how many steps someone has taken or how far they have

walked) *What information does a pedometer provide?* (It tells how many steps a person has taken.)

- **Pass several pedometers around the room.** Have small groups talk about how they might use pedometers, and answer the questions together as they look at the pedometers.

Have students study the first picture on page 1 of the student worktext. *Ask: What did the girl in the picture find out after looking at her pedometer? How many steps did she walk that day?*

- **Then ask students various questions about the value of each digit on the pedometer.** For example, ask: *How did the girl know how to read the number on her pedometer? How did the girl know to say 9,000 when she read the digit 9? How did she know to say 40 when she read the digit 4?*

- **If students are having difficulty answering your questions, make sure they are able to determine the value of every digit on the pedometer in the picture.** Use a place value chart to explain the value of every digit.

Focus students' attention on the second picture in the worktext. Have a student volunteer read the text aloud. Write *9,842* on the board. Say: *There are two other ways of writing 9,842 besides using digits.* Then write the following: *Nine thousand, eight hundred forty-two* and *9 thousands + 8 hundreds + 4 tens + 2 ones*

Write *5,682* and *9,842* on the board. Have students work in groups of three to write these numbers in a place value chart. Ask groups of students various prompting questions like: *How many thousands are in 5,682? What does the 2 mean in 4,312?*

C Review and Practice

Review the concept of place value with students. Write the number *967* on the board. Remind students that each digit in the number 967 has a different value. To illustrate this point, have volunteers write the value of each digit on a place value chart.

Have students work in pairs to practice identifying the value of digits in a large number on Transparency 1. Tell them their answers should be in complete sentences on their own sheets of paper.

- **First, go over the directions in the transparency.** Make sure students understand that they need to draw their own place value charts to answer each question.

- **Circulate among the pairs to assess the accuracy of their work.** After they write their answers, discuss the answers as a whole group in preparation for the next activity with similar questions.

Read aloud the directions for the Practice Applying the Main Idea activity on page 1 of the student worktext. Have students do the activity independently.

D Assess and Intervene

Do students know the value of digits in a number based on Practice Applying the Main Idea on page 1? Use the rubric to identify students who need extra support through additional help and the Intervention activity.

Intermediate

- ☐ Answers 2 of questions 1–3 correctly.
- ☐ Answers question 4 with a phrase that mentions reading or writing numbers.

  Example of a sentence a student might write: *Help read and write numbers.*

Advanced

- ☐ Answers 3 of questions 1–3 correctly.
- ☐ Answers question 4 in a complete sentence that mentions reading and writing numbers.

  Example of a sentence a student might write: *Place value is important because helps read and write numbers.*

INTERVENTION 10 minutes

If students are having difficulty using place value to read and write high-value numbers, have them work with a partner. Have them search on the Internet or look in an encyclopedia or world almanac, and read and write population counts of various cities in their home state. Have them write the numbers on index cards. Then help them identify the place values of the digits in each number.

Lesson

2

Learn the Vocabulary

Objective Talk and write about place value by using the vocabulary words.

30 minutes

Teach this lesson:
- **Before** introducing lessons on place value in the grade-level math textbook
- **Before** students complete the activities on page 2 of the student worktext

You need these materials:
- Worksheet 1
- Vocabulary Cards
- Written clues for vocabulary scavenger hunt

Lesson Vocabulary

Essential Vocabulary

digit	place value	value
period		

Additional Vocabulary

standard form	expanded form	word form
tens	ones	hundreds
thousands	ten thousands	millions
hundred thousands		

LESSON **2**

Learn the Vocabulary

Objective Talk and write about place value using the vocabulary words.

Learn the Words

Word/Phrase	Definition	Example
digit	a symbol used to write numbers	0, 1, 2, 3, 4, 5, 6, 7, 8, 9
value	how much something is worth	This diamond ring has a value of $5,000.00.
place value	the value we give to the place where a digit is in a number	The place value of the 2 in 263 is hundreds. The value of the 2 is 200.

The place value example table:

Hundreds	Tens	Ones
2	6	3
2 × 100	6 × 10	3 × 1
200	60	3

Word/Phrase	Definition	Example
period	each group of three digits in a number, starting from the right and separated by a comma	

The period example table:

Hundred Thousands	Ten Thousands	Thousands		Hundreds	Tens	Ones
7	6	9	,	2	6	3

Practice the Words

Directions Answer these questions in a complete sentence. Use a separate sheet of paper.

1. What is the symbol used to write a number? It is a digit.

2. What punctuation mark do you use to separate 3 digits in a row? You use a comma.

3. What is the word for 3 digits in a number that are separated by a comma? The word is period.

4. What is the phrase used for the worth of the place of a digit based on its position in a number? It is place value.

A Introduce

BP 2 Help students activate their prior knowledge. Ask: *What are some words and phrases you remember about place value from Lesson 1?* Have students discuss words and phrases they remember with a partner, and then share responses with the class. Write students' responses on the board. (Responses should include *digit, value, place value*.)

Focus students' attention on page 2 of the student worktext. Read aloud the Lesson Objective with students.

Tell students that this lesson will teach vocabulary that will help them understand place value. Choose words from the Additional Vocabulary box that you think will be useful to talk about place value. Elicit or provide examples of definitions for all the words on the list.

Highlighted words and phrases may affect student comprehension.

 Teach and Learn

Orally introduce the Essential Vocabulary for this module. Point to each word or phrase, model its pronunciation, and have students repeat.

- **Focus on the chart on page 2 of the student worktext.** Make sure students understand the chart headings.

- **Have a student volunteer read the first vocabulary word (*digit*) and the definition and example provided.** Ask: *How many symbols for numbers are there?* (10) *What are they?* (0, 1, 2, 3, 4, 5, 6, 7, 8, 9) Point out that numbers are made of digits, like words are made of letters.

- **Have another student read the second row.** Say: *When we talk about the value of something, we're talking about its worth. For example, if I say, "The value of this textbook is $26.00," that means the textbook costs $26.00.*

- **Have a third student read the third row.** Ask students to create sample questions with the phrase *place value*, using the following question and answer frame: *What is the place value of ____ in the number ____? The place value of ____ is ____. Its value is ____.* For example: *What is the place value of 2 in the number 263? The place value of 2 in 263 is hundreds. Its value is 200.*

- **Read aloud to students the fourth row on the chart.** Point out that in English the word *period* has many meanings (including: the punctuation mark used to mark the end of a sentence, a long interval of time in history, and the length of time that a student spends in a particular class).

- **Explain that, in mathematics, a period is a group of three digits in a number, separated by a comma.** Point to the place value chart on page 2 of the student worktext. Focus students' attention on the number 769,263 in the example column on the chart. Explain the place value of each digit in each period.

- **Then say:** *3 is in the ones column, 6 is in the tens column, 2 is in the hundreds column. They make one period. 9 is in the thousands column, 6 is in the ten thousands column, and 7 is in the hundred thousands column. This makes another period.*

Write the following three numbers on the board: *87,240; 523,076; 1,907,610.* Have students underline the numbers in each period in each number.

Ask student volunteers to read aloud the three numbers on the board and to identify the value of each digit. Help students identify the millions place value if they are unfamiliar with it.

📇 **Have students work with a partner to complete the Vocabulary Cards for the words in this module.**

 Review and Practice

Review the Essential Vocabulary with students. Have student pairs come up with definitions of each term using their own words. Then have pairs exchange their definitions with another pair and provide example sentences for each term.

🔲 **Have students play Walk-Around Bingo to practice the Essential Vocabulary.** Distribute Worksheet 1 to every student, and explain the activity instructions.

- **Say:** *Each of you has the same worksheet. Vocabulary words or phrases are in the left column. You will walk around the room and have 6 other students fill in the 6 empty boxes on your worksheet and sign their name. Each person you meet can only fill in 1 box. Let's see who can get all 6 boxes filled in correctly by 6 different students. When you finish, call out "Bingo!"* When a student calls out "Bingo!," check his or her answers before proclaiming winner status.

Have students work independently to complete the Practice the Words activity in their student worktext on page 2. Make sure that students understand the directions. Then circulate around the room, check their progress, and assess them with the following rubric.

 Assess and Intervene

Can students understand and use the Essential Vocabulary based on Practice the Words on page 2 of the student worktext? Use the rubric to identify students who need extra support through additional help and the Intervention activity.

☐ Answers 3 of questions 1–4 correctly.
☐ Answers are written in complete sentences or phrases, and may contain errors.
  Example of a sentence a student might write: *Use comma.*

Advanced

☐ Answers 4 of questions 1–4 correctly.
☐ Answers are written in clear complete sentences with few or no errors.
  Example of a sentence a student might write: *You use comma.*

INTERVENTION 10 minutes

If students are having difficulty understanding or defining an essential word or phrase, have them go on a vocabulary scavenger hunt. Before class, hide words and phrases related to clues in a stack of cards. Read each clue aloud. Then have students search for the word or phrase that answers the clue.

Clue: It's a group of three digits in a number. It starts from the right and is separated by a comma. What is it?

Clue: 3 is one. 8 is another. What are they?

Clue: It's the worth of a digit because of its location in a number! What is it?

(Words to be hunted are: *period, digits, place value*)

Use More Language

Objective Use *there are/are there* to ask and answer questions about place value.

---

30 minutes

Teach this lesson:
• **After** lessons on place value concepts in students' grade-level math textbook
• **Before** students complete the activities on page 3 of the student worktext

You need these materials:
• sheet of paper plus crayons or markers for each student
• hat or bag
• Index cards

Use More Language

Objective Use *there are/are there* to ask and answer questions about place value.

LESSON 3

Learn the Language

How many _____ are there in _____?
There are _____ in _____.

Practice the Language

Directions Answer questions 1 and 2 in complete sentences. Then write a question to answer questions 3 and 4.

1 How many thousands are there in the thousands place of 295,260?

There are 5 thousands in 295,260.

_____

2 How many ten thousands are there in 295,260?

There are 9 ten thousands in 295,260.

_____

3 There are 2 hundred thousands in 295,260.

How many hundred thousands are there in 295,260?

_____

4 There are more ten thousands in 295,260 than in 432,576.

Are there more ten thousands in 295,260 than in 432,576?

A Introduce

BP 2 **Brainstorm with students situations when it might be important for them to understand place value.** Write students' ideas on the board in a list. Provide several examples, such as buying a car or renting an apartment.

Tell students that it's very important for everyone to understand place value. Place value can help when you need to ask or answer questions involving large numbers in the thousands, ten thousands, hundred thousands, and millions.

BP 2 **Say:** *When your family looks for a used car, truck, or van, what are some questions your parents ask?* (How many miles are there on the odometer? Are there more than one hundred thousand miles on the odometer?)

Point to the Lesson Objective on page 3 of the student worktext, and read it aloud. Tell students they will be using *are there* and *there are* as they ask and answer questions about place value.

Highlighted words and phrases may affect student comprehension.

Place Value • 3

B. Teach and Learn

Divide the class into pairs of students. Have pairs look at the pictures on page 3 of the student worktext and then read the speech bubbles. Have one student read the speech bubble for the teacher, and the other student read the speech bubble for the student. Then have the pairs answer the following questions: *What is the teacher asking? What is the girl telling the teacher?*

As a class, read the speech bubbles aloud, modeling proper pronunciation. Go over answers to the two questions by summarizing the two illustrations on page 3. Say: *The teacher wants to know how many ten thousands are in 295,260.* Write *295,260* on the board, and circle the *9*. Then say: *The girl is using a place value chart.* (If necessary, review how to use a place value chart to determine the value of each digit in a number.)

Introduce use of *are there/there are* to form questions and answers about place value. Write the following question and answer frames on the board: *How many ____ are there in ____? There are ____ in ____.* Highlight the phrases *are there* and *there are* by underlining them. Tell students that we use the phrase *are there* in questions and *there are* in answers.

Model using the question and sentence frames to ask and answer a question. Write the following number on the board: *65,781.* Say: *I want to find out how many hundreds are in 65,781.* Circle the *7* in *65,781.*

- **Say:** *To make a question, I need to use a question word and the phrase* are there. Point to the question frame on the board. Say: *How many hundreds are there in 65,781?* Write this question on the board.

- **Follow a similar procedure to answer the question.** Tell students that we use *there are* to form an answer. Point to the answer frame on the board. Say and write: *There are 7 hundreds in 65,781.*

Have each student work with a partner. Have them ask and answer each other's questions about the following large numbers you write on the board: *380,624; 705,918; 5,643,098.*

Circulate throughout the room. Provide pairs with any assistance they might need (for example, by pointing to the question and answer frames, further modeling questions and answers, etc.).

C. Review and Practice

Review asking and answering questions about place value with students. Ask a volunteer to explain when to use *are there* versus *there are.* Say: *Do we ask* How many dogs there are? *(no) Do we use* are there *or* there are *to answer that question?* (*there are*) Make sure the question and answer frames are still written on the board.

Give the class further practice making questions. Say: *Did you know that an African elephant weighs approximately 13.5 tons?*

- **Ask students:** *Who knows how many pounds there are in a ton?* (There are 2,000 pounds in a ton.) *That means that an African elephant weighs 27,000 pounds. How much would 2 elephants weigh?* (54,000 pounds)

- **Ask:** *How many thousands are there in the thousands place in 54,000 pounds?* (4) *How many ten thousands are there in 54,000?* (5)

- **Write the following on the board:** *There are 2,000 pounds in a ton.* Have a volunteer make a question that corresponds with the sentence. (How many pounds are there in a ton?)

Explain to students that they are now going to work in groups of four to play a game. Prepare and play the game in the following way:

- **Divide the class into groups of four.** In each group, two students will create an answer with *There are ____ in ____.* while the other two students will make up a question with *How many ____ are there in (large number)?* Have students write their questions and answers on individual sheets of paper.

- **As groups come up with questions and answers, go around the room.** Answer any questions group members might have. Make sure students are writing questions and answers correctly and that they make sense.

- **As a class, play the game.** Put all the questions and answers in a hat or a bag. Choose one randomly, and read it aloud several times. Working at the same time, groups will write a correct question or answer. When they finish, group members should raise their hands. Give 10 points for every correct answer. Repeat this game several times.

Read the directions to the Practice Language activity on page 3 in the student worktext. Have students work independently to complete the activity. Make sure students know they can use a place value chart and/or the question and answer frames if they need help. Circulate, and assess students as they work.

D. Assess and Intervene

How well can students ask and answer questions about place value using *are there/there are* based on Practice the Language on page 3? Use the rubric to identify students who need extra support through extra help and the Intervention activity.

Intermediate

- ☐ Identifies the correct digit in 3 of questions 1–4.
- ☐ Uses the question and answer frames to write complete sentences with only minor errors.

Advanced

- ☐ Identifies the correct digit in 4 of questions 1–4.
- ☐ Uses the question and answer frames to write complete responses with no errors.

INTERVENTION   10 minutes

If students are having trouble using the phrases *there are/are there,* have them work in pairs. Have each student write both phrases on two separate index cards. Have students practice asking and answering questions about place value in large numbers. Each time a student asks a question, he or she holds up the card that says "Are there" and proceeds to ask the question. The first student in the group to know the correct answer holds up the card that says, "There are" and gives the answer. For example: *Are there more ten thousands in 495,278 or in 832,572? There are more ten thousands in 495,278.*

Lesson

Solve Math Problems

Objective Write correct number sentences when the problem includes word forms of large numbers.

30 minutes

Teach this lesson:
• **After** lessons on place value in students' grade-level math textbooks
• **Before** students complete the activities on page 4 of the student worktext

You need these materials:
• place value charts
• Transparency 2

EXTENSION AND ENRICHMENT   10 minutes

Work with students to write a brief (one para-graph) newspaper article about the number of miles a typical solo driver travels daily, monthly, and yearly in their town or city. Have students write the number of miles in standard form in a chart, and in word form in the text of the article.

LESSON
4

Solve Math Problems

Objective Write correct number sentences when a problem includes word forms of large numbers.

Learn to Solve Problems

Problem In 2004, there were three hundred seventy thousand, nine hundred eighty-six people in Snowball, Colorado. During 2005, two thousand more people moved to Snowball. And in 2006, four thousand more people moved there. How many people in all lived in Snowball, Colorado in 2006?

	Think	Write
Step 1:	Read the problem. Underline the question. What do I have to do?	I need to add the people who moved to Snowball in 2005 to the number that lived there in 2004 to find out how many lived there in 2006.
Step 2:	Circle the facts.	I'll circle how many people lived in Snowball in 2004, the number that moved there in 2005 and in 2006.
Step 3:	Write a number sentence. Solve the problem. Then write your answer in word form.	370,986 + 2,000 + 4,000 = 376,986 three hundred seventy-six thousand, nine hundred eighty-six people

Practice Solving Math Problems

Directions Follow steps 1 to 3 above to solve the word problems below. Be sure to write your answer in word form. Show your work on a separate sheet of paper. All answers should be in word form.

1. The tallest mountain in the world is Mount Everest. It is twenty-nine thousand, thirty-five feet tall. Mount McKinley is twenty thousand, three hundred twenty feet tall. How many feet taller is Mount Everest than Mount McKinley? 29,035 − 20,320 = 8,715

2. The football stadium has ten thousand, five hundred seats. Eight hundred three seats are empty. How many football fans are at the game? 10,500 − 803 = 9,697

3. Juan's family lives in Los Angeles, California. They drive to Guadalajara, Mexico every December to visit their relatives—a round trip of two thousand, six hundred miles. How many miles will they drive in all if they take this trip two years in a row? 2,600 + 2,600 = 5,200 miles

4. An American man, Gregory Dunham, built a motorcycle that weighs six thousand, five hundred pounds! How many pounds would two of these motorcycles weigh? 6,500 + 6,500 = 13,000

A Introduce

Say: *Usually you solve math problems in stan-dard form, using numbers.* Write these numbers on the board: *12,239; 97,258; 457,567.*

Say: *In other problems, you have to put numbers in word form.* Write the following examples of numbers in word form on the board directly underneath the previous examples you wrote: *twelve thousand, two hundred thirty-nine; ninety-seven thousand, two hundred fifty-eight; four hundred fifty-seven thousand, five hundred sixty-seven.* Have students practice writing the word form of several numbers you write on the board.

BP 2 **Remind students that they have learned many tools and tips to help them solve word problems.** Ask: *What are some tools and tips that you remember?* Have them discuss with another student and then share with the class.

Write their responses on the board as a list. If the following are not provided by the students, discuss them, and add them to the list on the board:

• Circle facts

• Locate questions by finding question marks

• Decide which operation(s) [addition, subtrac-tion, multiplication, division] is (are) needed

• Use pictures, drawings, counters, charts, graphs, or number sentences

• Use a place value chart

Highlighted words and phrases may affect student comprehension.

- Estimate an answer
- Try to figure out what unknown words mean
- Take long sentences apart
- Identify unnecessary information

Tell students that in this lesson they will learn how to use facts and number sentences to solve problems that include word forms of large numbers. Point to the numbers you wrote on the board as examples.

Read aloud the Lesson Objective with students. Tell students that they will learn to write correct number sentences when the problem includes word forms of large numbers.

B Teach and Learn

Have students open their student worktexts to page 4 and look at the problem in Learn to Solve Problems. Write the problem on the board. Tell students that this is a word problem that has large numbers.

Show students how to solve the problem in the student worktext by using a Think Aloud:

Think Aloud

Read aloud the problem on page 4. Say: *This problem looks difficult, but if we look at it closely, we will be able to solve it.* Provide students with a few minutes to read the problem again in silence.

Focus students' attention on the chart on page 4 of the student worktext. Say: *Notice the two headings, Think and Write. Now let's think through the problem and see if we can solve it.*

Write Step 1 on the board, and read it aloud. Say: *First, I am going to read the problem again.* Read the problem again, slowly. Say: *Then I need to underline the question. I know that a question mark always means that there is a question, so I'll look for the question mark! I found it:* How many people lived in Snowball, Colorado in 2006? *Now I need to underline this question.* Underline the question on the board. Ask: *What do I need to do? I need to add to find my answer.*

Write Step 2 on the board, and read it aloud. Say: *The problem tells me that 370,986 people lived in Snowball in 2004. I need to circle that fact.* Circle *three hundred seventy*

thousand, nine hundred eighty-six people in the problem. Say: *The problem also tells me that 2,000 more people moved to Snowball in 2005. I need to circle that fact, too.* Circle *two thousand more people* in the problem. Say: *The problem tells me that 4,000 more people moved to Snowball in 2006. So I need to circle that fact, too.* Circle *four thousand more people* in the problem on the board.

Write Step 3 on the board, and read it aloud. Say: *I need to write a number sentence. I know it's going to be an addition problem because the question asks, "How many people in all?" I need to add 370,986 + 2,000 + 4,000.* Point to each circled part of the question as you write *2004 = 370,986; 2005 = + 2,000 people; 2006 = + 4,000;* and *370,986 + 2,000 + 4,000 = .* Write and say: *The total is 376,986.*

Have pairs of students write in the blank space next to Step 3 the number 376,986 using the word form. Go around the class to check that students are writing the word form of the number correctly.

Display Transparency 2. Have students form groups of four to read and solve the first problem. Have the groups use the step-by-step method in the student worktext. When the small groups have completed the problem, have them share their answers with the whole class.

C Review and Practice

To review the three steps used to write correct number sentences, ask students to retell the three steps using their own words. Prompt students with questions, such as: *What do I do in Step 1? What do I do in Step 2? What do I do in Step 3?*

Have pairs of students work together to solve the second problem on Transparency 2. Remind them to follow the steps outlined in the student worktext. As students work, go around the room assessing progress and modeling, using Think Alouds, as necessary.

You also might want to select one problem from the students' grade-level math textbook that is similar to the one on page 4 of the student worktext. Write this problem on the board or tell students to turn to the specific page in their textbooks.

Read aloud the directions for Practice Solving Math Problems on page 4. As students work on the problems individually, go around and check how well they have learned the problem-solving strategy. Then assess them with the following rubric.

D Assess and Intervene

How well can students write correct number sentences when the problem includes word forms of large numbers, based on Practice Solving Math Problems on page 4? Use the rubric to identify students who need extra support through extra help or the Intervention activity.

Intermediate

☐ Writes number sentences correctly in standard form for 4 of questions 1–4.

☐ Writes the answer correctly in word form for 3 of the 4 problems.

Advanced

☐ Writes number sentences correctly in standard form for 4 of questions 1–4.

☐ Writes the answer correctly in word form for all 4 of the problems.

INTERVENTION   15 minutes

If students have difficulty writing the standard word form of numbers that contain zero, have them use place value charts. Provide them with some large numbers in word form. Invite students to read the word form and then fill in each place on the chart with digits. For places that have no digits filled in, they write a zero. Have pairs of students compare their completed charts with one another and decide if they are both correct. Check their work.

Lesson

1

Prerequisite Background Knowledge
- Basic understanding of place value
- Ability to use number lines and base-ten blocks

Understand the Main Idea

Objective Describe ways to compare and order numbers.

30 minutes

Teach this lesson:
- **Before** introducing material on comparing and ordering numbers in students' grade-level math texts
- **Before** students complete page 5 of the student worktext

You need these materials:
- Transparency 3
- base-ten blocks
- lightweight ball or a small beanbag
- index cards

BP 3 **ELL BEST PRACTICE #3:**
Performance Assessment

English language learners often know more than they can demonstrate on standard reading- and writing-based assessments. For this reason, it can be more effective to evaluate their learning based on observations of their performance on daily classroom tasks. Pay attention to how well students compare and order numbers in the context of the activities in this module. Use rubrics, checklists, and other observational tools to check students' work on these authentic tasks.

Throughout this module, when you see **BP 3**, this is an example of a performance assessment.

Module 2: Compare and Order Whole Numbers

Understand the Main Idea

LESSON 1

Objective Describe ways to compare and order numbers.

Learn the Main Idea

You can compare and order numbers in three different ways.

1. You can use place value.	Tens / Ones: 5 / 8 Tens / Ones: 5 / 4	58 is greater than 54. 54 is less than 58.
2. You can use a number line.	Number line from 70 to 80, marks at 73, 76, 78	These numbers are in order from least to greatest: 73, 76, 78.
3. You can use base-ten blocks.	base-ten blocks	22 is less than 31. 31 is greater than 22.

MAIN IDEA You can use place value, a number line, or base-ten blocks to compare and order numbers.

Practice Applying the Main Idea

Directions Read the sentences for questions 1 to 3. Circle the word that correctly completes the sentence. On a separate sheet of paper, write the sentence again with the right word. Answer question 4 on this page.

1. Araf uses a (number line/scale) to compare 43 and 57. Araf uses a number line to compare 43 and 57.

2. Hugo uses (multiplication/base-ten blocks) to order 17, 23, and 20. Hugo uses base-ten blocks to order 17, 23, and 20.

3. Gia uses a place value chart to compare (two numbers/two shapes). Gia uses place value to compare two numbers.

4. Write a sentence about a time when you needed to compare or order numbers.

Possible answers: I needed to know if my basketball team won the game. I was trying to find out which shirt cost more money.

A Introduce

Read aloud the Lesson Objective with students. Tell them that in this lesson, they will learn different ways to compare and order numbers.

Write the words *place value, number line,* and *base-ten blocks* on the board. Have students read the words aloud. Say: *These are all math words that can help us order and compare numbers. What do you think they mean?*

- **Have students work with a partner.** Have them fold a sheet of paper into thirds and write each word from the board at the top of one of the sections.

- **Ask students to talk with their partners about these words.** Have them write or draw in each column to describe or tell something they know about each word.

- **Ask volunteers to share ideas with the class.** Establish that place value has to do with how people write numbers, that number lines show numbers in an organized way, and that base-ten blocks can be used to model numbers.

Read aloud the Main Idea with students. Explain that the words *place value, number line,* and *base-ten blocks* will be important in this lesson to help them compare and order numbers.

Highlighted words and phrases may affect student comprehension.

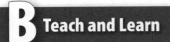

B Teach and Learn

Write the numbers *58* and *54* on the board. Point to 58 and have students name the number. Repeat for 54.

- **Say:** *These numbers are not the same. They are not equal. One is greater than the other.* Remind students that *greater* means *more.* Then say: *If one number is greater, then the other is _____.* Let students fill in the word *less.*

- **BP 3 Put students in groups of three.** Point to the numbers on the board. Say: *Which number is greater? Which number is less?* Have groups answer the question and write a brief explanation of how they know. Ask volunteers to share their ideas with the class. Then have students each write two numbers on a piece of paper. Have them take turns showing their numbers to their group and asking: *Which number is greater? Which number is less?*

Read aloud the first sentence at the top of the student worktext. Tell students that they might already know the words *compare* and *order* from previous math instruction. Ask volunteers to tell what they know about these words.

Explain that *comparing* and *ordering* are very much alike. Say: *When you have two numbers, you compare them. When you have more than two numbers, you order them.* Explain that ordering numbers means putting them in order.

Indicate the list of words on the board. Explain that students can use any of the three methods to compare the two numbers. Point out students who used one of these methods in their group work to determine which number was greater.

Use this Think Aloud to walk students through Learn the Main Idea:

Think Aloud

Point to the first row of the table on page 5 of the student worktext. Say: *When we use place value, we write digits in different places to show how much they are worth. How many tens are in 58? (5) How many ones are in 58? (8) There are 5 tens and 8 ones. So we write the digit 5 in the tens place and the digit 8 in the ones place.* Point out that this has been done in the worktext. Repeat this process with 54.

Then say: *58 and 54 each have 5 tens. But 58 has 8 ones, and 54 has 4 ones. So 58 has more ones. 58 is greater. If 58 is greater, then 54 is less.* Read the two sentences in the right column with students. Point out that they can say both *58 is greater than 54* and *54 is less than 58.*

Call attention to the next row. Point out that there are three numbers this time, not just two. Say: *I am trying to order the numbers 78, 73, and 76. This number line shows the numbers from 70 to 80.*

 **Present Transparency 3 to the class.** Say: *Let's write these numbers on the number line.*

- **BP 3 Ask students to help you find and mark the numbers.** Have them explain how they know where the numbers go. Once the numbers are in place, explain that the greatest number is on the right and the least number is on the left. Say: *I can put these numbers in order from least to greatest. The order is 73, 76, 78.*

- **Repeat with numbers *47, 43,* and *44* on the second number line.** Explain that the greatest number is always on the right and the least number is always on the left.

Draw students' attention to the last row of the table on page 5. Distribute base-ten blocks to partners. Have students model the two numbers *22* and *31.*

- **Say:** *Using base-ten blocks is like using place value. We start with the greater place. That is the tens place. Which number has more tens? (31) So 31 is greater than 22.* Repeat with 18 and 21, then with 46 and 47.

C Review and Practice

Review the three ways to compare and order numbers. Write the numbers *12, 24,* and *36* on the board. Have a volunteer place these numbers on a place value chart and a number line. Have another volunteer model the numbers with base-ten blocks.

Ask two other students to put the three numbers in order on the board. Have them explain which method they used and why. Say: *Place value, number lines, and base-ten blocks are three ways we can compare and order numbers.*

BP 3 Use a game to review the ways to compare and order numbers. Toss a ball or a beanbag to a student and say: *Place value!* Direct the student to toss the item back to you, saying *Number line!* or *Base-ten blocks!* Repeat with other students, saying one of the three methods and having them respond with another.

Read aloud the directions for Practice Applying the Main Idea on page 5. Explain that students will write a complete sentence for each one. Have students work independently to finish each item.

D Assess and Intervene

Can students identify ways to compare and order numbers, based on Practice Applying the Main Idea on page 5? Use the rubric to identify students who need extra support through additional help and the Intervention activity.

Intermediate

- ☐ Identifies and circles the correct word in at least 2 of questions 1–3.
- ☐ Sentence in question 4 describes a situation in which comparing or ordering numbers is called for but may include several errors that don't affect meaning.

Example of a sentence a student might write: *I need know my team win the game.*

Advanced

- ☐ Identifies and circles the correct word in questions 1–3.
- ☐ Sentence in question 4 clearly describes a situation in which comparing or ordering numbers is called for and contains few errors.

Example of a sentence a student might write: *I wanted to find if more people were in Ms. Gold's class or more was in our class.*

INTERVENTION   5 minutes

If students cannot identify the correct words in Practice Applying the Main Idea, reread the Main Idea with them. Say *place value, number line,* and *base-ten blocks* in turn and have students point to the corresponding pictures in the student worktext. Then have them make an index card for each method, with the word on one side and a sketch on the other. Ask them to answer each item again, this time using the cards to help.

Lesson

2

Learn the Vocabulary

Objective Talk and write about comparing and ordering numbers using the vocabulary words.

30 minutes

Teach this lesson:
- **Before** students are introduced to comparing and ordering numbers in their grade-level math textbooks
- **Before** students complete the activities on page 6 of the student worktext

You need these materials:
- 3 pencils for each pair of students
- Vocabulary Cards
- base-ten blocks

Lesson Vocabulary

Essential Vocabulary

| to compare | to order | equal to (=) |
| greater than (>) | less than (<) | |

Additional Vocabulary

| digit | in order | to line up |
| greater/greatest | less/least | longer/longest |

A Introduce

Read aloud the Lesson Objective with students. Tell them that in this lesson, they will learn about words that describe comparing and ordering numbers. Ask: *What words do you think would be useful to use when comparing numbers? How about comparing baseball cards? Stickers?*

Have students work in small groups. Ask groups to choose a recorder, then brainstorm words and phrases that are useful in comparing and ordering numbers. Have the recorder write them down. Groups can share their lists with the class. Write words and phrases on the board as they are mentioned.

Check to see that all the Essential Vocabulary words are on the board. Since most of these words were introduced in the previous lesson, many of them should be listed. Add any that do not appear.

Choose words from the Additional Vocabulary that you think will be useful. Elicit or provide examples or definitions for all the words on the list.

Read each word aloud and have students read it back to you. Remind students that these words are important in comparing and ordering numbers.

LESSON **2**

Learn the Vocabulary

Objective Talk and write about comparing and ordering numbers using the vocabulary words.

Learn the Words

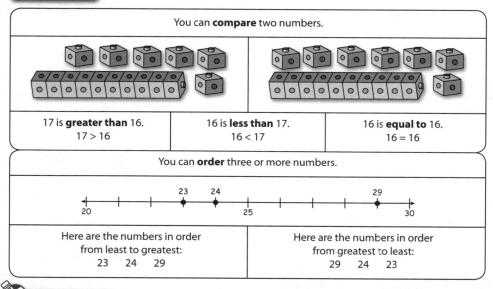

You can **compare** two numbers.

17 is **greater than** 16.
17 > 16

16 is **less than** 17.
16 < 17

16 is **equal to** 16.
16 = 16

You can **order** three or more numbers.

Here are the numbers in order from least to greatest:
23   24   29

Here are the numbers in order from greatest to least:
29   24   23

Practice the Words

Directions In questions 1 to 5, find and circle the hidden vocabulary words. Then draw a line to connect each word on the left to a sentence on the right so all the sentences make sense. For question 6, write a sentence to explain your answer on a separate sheet of paper.

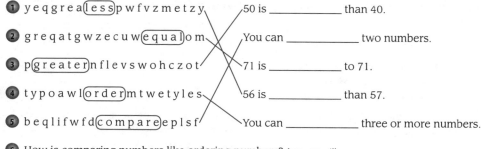

1. y e q g r e a (l e s s) p w f v z m e t z y   50 is _____ than 40.

2. g r e q a t g w z e c u w (e q u a l) o m   You can _____ two numbers.

3. p (g r e a t e r) n f l e v s w o h c z o t   71 is _____ to 71.

4. t y p o a w l (o r d e r) m t w e t y l e s   56 is _____ than 57.

5. b e q l i f w f d (c o m p a r e) e p l s f   You can _____ three or more numbers.

6. How is comparing numbers like ordering numbers? Answers will vary.

6 · Compare and Order Whole Numbers

Highlighted words and phrases may affect student comprehension.

B | Teach and Learn

Circle the words *compare* and *order* in the list of words on the board. Remind students that one of these words is used with two numbers and that the other is used with three numbers or more. Ask students which is which. (If students have difficulty remembering the difference, have them focus on the second syllable of the word *compare,* which sounds like *pair*, meaning *two.)*

Read aloud the first sentence on page 6 of the student worktext. Then call students' attention to the pictures below it. Invite students to tell what they see. Elicit that the pictures show base-ten blocks that model the numbers *16* and *17*.

- **Draw students' attention to the three boxes below the pictures.** Have a volunteer read aloud the text in the first box. Remind students that they used the phrase *greater than* in the previous lesson and that it means *more than*.

- **Emphasize that the symbol > means *is greater than*.** Point out that the two sentences in the box are read the same way and mean the same thing, although they are written differently. Repeat with the second box, noting that the symbol < means *is less than*.

- **Point out that it is easy to confuse the symbols < and >.** Invite students to share their strategies for keeping the two symbols straight. You might offer this suggestion: *One end of each symbol has one point. The other end has two points. The end with more points goes next to the number that is greater.*

- **Continue with the third box, on the far right.** Say: *Two numbers can be the same. We say they are equal.* Stress that we say *greater than* and *less than*, but *equal to*.

Read aloud the sentence about ordering numbers. Have students study the picture of the number line and tell what they see.

Explain that *ordering numbers* is the same as *putting numbers in order*. Call three students of different heights to the front of the room. Help them stand in order of height or have classmates direct them to stand that way.

- **Say**: *The order is [Sonja], [Kumari], [Chen]. They are* in order *from shortest to tallest.* Show the progression by moving your hand on an upward slope from the shortest student to the tallest.

- **Then say:** *I can say the names in order another way, too.* Slide your hand on a downward slope, beginning with the tallest child. Say: *This order is from tallest to shortest: [Chen], [Kumari], [Sonja].*

BP 3 Have pairs of students practice ordering items. Ask them to order the lengths of three pencils. Have one student touch the pencils in order from shortest to longest; have the other student touch them to show the progression from longest to shortest. As they work, have students use the sentence frame: *The pencils are in order from ____ to ____.*

Return to Learn the Words in the text and focus students' attention on the last set of boxes. Explain that the numbers there are like the line of pencils. Emphasize that both boxes give the numbers in order, but that one goes from least to greatest and the other from greatest to least. Have students point to the least number in each list (23), to the greatest number (29), and to the number that is between least and greatest (24).

Have students make Vocabulary Cards for the words in this lesson.

C | Review and Practice

Divide the class into groups of five to practice using the vocabulary words. First, play a demonstration round. Call five students to the front of the room. Give each student a Vocabulary Card. Then have students take turns using their vocabulary word in a sentence, such as *I know that 5 is greater than 3* or *Jorge needs to* compare *two numbers*. Students get a point for an acceptable sentence. Have students play within their assigned groups.

Read aloud the directions for Practice the Words at the bottom of page 6 of the student worktext. Tell students that they may find other words hidden in the lines of letters, but that they are looking for vocabulary words. Encourage students to use the information in Learn the Words at the top of the page to help them decide which word goes with which sentence. Then point out that they will need to write a complete sentence for question 6.

BP 3 Have students work on their own to answer the questions on page 6. As students work, take notes on their approach to the assignment. Note, for example, whether they need to use the Learn the Words box above for support and whether they work confidently or tentatively.

D | Assess and Intervene

Can all students use the vocabulary words, based on Practice the Words on page 6 of the student worktext? Use the rubric to identify students who need extra support through additional help and the Intervention activity.

Intermediate

- ☐ Finds and circles all 5 words and matches at least 3 with the correct sentence.
- ☐ The sentence describes the basic similarity between ordering and comparing, but may include errors that do not affect meaning.

  Example of a sentence a student might write: *Compare and order both about how big is numbers.*

Advanced

- ☐ Finds and circles all 5 words and matches each with the correct sentence.
- ☐ The sentence has few errors, if any, and uses the word *because* to describe how comparing and ordering are alike.

  Example of a sentence a student might write: *They are alike because each help you find the numbers that is greater and that is less.*

INTERVENTION   10 minutes

If students have difficulty connecting the words *greater* and *less* to the appropriate sentences, they may be uncertain about basic concepts of place value. Offer students guided instruction with base-ten blocks. Help them model and read the numbers in the sentences (50 and 40, 56 and 57) and review how to determine which number in each pair is greater and which is less.

Lesson

3

Use More Language

Objective Use adjectives to compare and order numbers.

---

30 minutes

Teach this lesson:
- **After** students complete work on comparing and ordering numbers in their grade-level math textbooks
- **Before** students complete the activities on page 7 of the student worktext

You need these materials:
- index cards
- classroom objects of different sizes, such as a paintbrush, a paper clip, a pencil, and a book
- Worksheet 2

EXTENSION AND ENRICHMENT   15 minutes

Have students create a time line showing important events in world history. Help students use books and the Internet to find the years in which historic events took place. Then have them write the events and the corresponding years on index cards and add a one-sentence description of why the event was important. Finally, have students work together to order the events by year. Display the resulting time line in the classroom.

Use More Language

Objective Use adjectives to compare and order numbers.

Learn the Language

4,721 is greater than 4,523.

But 5,107 is the greatest.

4,721   4,523   5,107

You can use words like *greater than* and *greatest* to compare and order numbers.

6 inches

10 inches   3 inches

The orange ribbon is longer than the striped ribbon. The dotted ribbon is the longest.

The kitten has more legs than the bird. The insect has the most legs.

_____ is _____ than _____.
_____ is the _____.

_____ has _____ _____ than _____.
_____ has the _____ _____.

Practice the Language

Directions Write the correct words to complete the sentences. Use the picture.

1 Use words that are related to *tall*.
Dimble is ___taller___ than Hank. Baboo is the ___tallest___.

2 Use words that are related to *few*.
Hank has ___fewer___ antennas than Dimble. Baboo has the ___fewest___ antennas.

3 Write two sentences on your own about the picture. Use words that are related to *old*.
Possible answer: Baboo is older than Dimble. Hank is the oldest.

Dimble	Hank	Baboo
15 feet tall	7 feet tall	17 feet tall
165 years old	212 years old	172 years old

Highlighted words and phrases may affect student comprehension.

Compare and Order Whole Numbers • 7

LESSON 3

A Introduce

Activate background knowledge by displaying a short object, like a paper clip, and a longer object, like a paintbrush. Ask: *What's this?* (It's a paintbrush.) *What do we use it for?* (We use it for painting pictures.)

- **Say:** *One of these is short. The other one is long. Which one is short? Which one is long?* Challenge students to find another object in the room that is short and another one that is long. Explain that *long* and *short* are adjectives, or describing words. Have students mention other adjectives. List them on the board.

Read aloud the Lesson Objective with students. Tell students that they will learn more about adjectives and forms of adjectives in this lesson.

B Teach and Learn

Call students' attention to the picture of the students on the top of page 7 in the student worktext. Ask volunteers to play the parts of the three children in the picture. Have them write the numbers on index cards, hold up the numbers, and say the words in the speech bubbles.

Ask students to identify the two under-lined words in the speech bubbles. (greater, greatest) Say: *These words are both related to the word* great. *They are* forms *of the word* great. Say that here, *great* means *large*.

- **Remind students that the word** *greater* **is used to compare two numbers.** Explain that *greatest* refers to three numbers or more.

Have students practice using the words *greater* **and** *greatest*. Have each student write a random four-digit number on an index card. Have them form pairs. Instruct the student with the greater number to say *My number is greater than your number*. Have students find a new partner and repeat. Then have students form groups of three. Have the student with the greatest number say: *My number is the greatest*.

Read aloud the text below the artwork on page 7 of the student worktext. Then focus students' attention on the two panels below the sentence. Divide the class into pairs. Have half the pairs study the example with ribbons and the other half study the example with animals. Have partners talk to each other about what they see and read aloud the sentences that describe the art.

- **Then have each pair work with a pair that has studied the other picture.** Have students take turns describing and explaining their assigned example to the other pair. Monitor conversations and offer help as needed.

Lead a follow-up conversation with the whole class. Ask students to explain how the two examples are alike and different. Encourage students to begin their explanations with: *They are alike/different because ____*. Elicit that both examples show comparisons and order-ing, but that the things being counted are different and that one example uses *is* while the other uses *has*.

Point out the sentence frames below the pictures. Connect them with the sentences in the ribbon and animal examples. Show students that the adjective belongs in the second blank space.

Write the following words on the board: *greater/greatest, longer/longest, more/most*. Explain that these words all have to do with comparing and ordering. Underline the end-ing *-er* in *greater* and *longer* and the ending *-est* in *greatest* and *longest*. Explain that many words used in making comparisons have these endings, but that not all do.

- **Have students generate other adjective pairs that can be used to compare num-bers and end in** *-er* **and** *-est*. If needed, offer base words such as *small, far,* and *few* and help students add endings to make *smaller/smallest, father/farthest,* and *fewer/fewest*. Write some of these word pairs on the board.

Write the words *less* **and** *least* **on the board.** Point out that like *more* and *most,* they do not fit the *-er/-est* pattern. Have students use the cards they created earlier with the four-digit numbers. Ask them to repeat the activity, only this time the student with the number that is less should say to his or her partner: *My num-ber is less than your number*. In a group of three, the one whose number is least should say: *My number is the least*.

C Review and Practice

Review the adjectives used to compare and order numbers. Work with students to make a list of adjectives on the board. Then hold up a short object, like a paper clip, and a long object, like a paintbrush. Have a volunteer compare the two objects using the sentence frame.

Say: *When we compare and order objects, we use words called adjectives. We add the* -er *and* -est *on the end of adjectives to help us make compari-sons correctly in English.* Have students call out various adjectives with different endings.

Distribute one copy of Worksheet 2 to each student. Read the directions aloud as students follow along. Explain that they need to draw appropriate pictures or write appropriate words. Emphasize that the words in each set are related to the first word given.

- **Have students check their answers with a partner.** Remind them to try to resolve any disagreements themselves before ask-ing for help from you. Go over the answers as a class.

Read aloud the directions for Practice the Language at the bottom of page 7 in the student worktext. Tell students to use the numbers in the picture to help them solve the problems. Point out that students will complete sentences in numbers 1 and 2, but that they will write two sentences of their own for number 3. Remind them that they may use the sentence frames on the page.

BP 3 **Have students complete the items on their own.** Circulate through the room and assess them. Then go over the answers after everyone has finished.

D Assess and Intervene

Can students use comparative and superla-tive adjective forms to compare and order numbers, based on the Practice the Language activity on page 7? Use the rubric to identify students who need extra support through ad-ditional help and the Intervention activity.

Intermediate

- ☐ Correctly fills in 3 or 4 of the missing words.
- ☐ Uses sentence frames to write 2 complete sentences comparing and ordering the ages of the aliens.

Advanced

- ☐ Correctly fills in all 4 of the missing words.
- ☐ Writes 2 complete and grammatically correct sentences to compare and order the ages of the aliens, without the need for sentence frames or prompting

INTERVENTION   5 minutes

If students have difficulty with the practice problems, they may not understand when to use adjective forms ending in *-er* and when to use forms ending in *-est*. To help, hold up a pencil and a book and ask students to identify which one is *smaller*. Emphasizing the *-er* ending of *smaller,* say: *Yes, the pencil is smaller than the book*. Write *smaller* on the board and underline the *er*. Then say: *We are comparing* two *objects, so we write* small *and then* two *more letters:* e *and* r. Repeat with three objects: the pencil, the book, and a paper clip. Establish that the paper clip is *the smallest*. Point out that there are *three* objects, so students should write *small* and then add the *three* letters *est*.

MODULE 2

Compare and Order Numbers

Lesson

4

Solve Math Problems

Objective Cross out information that you do not need to solve math problems.

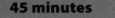

45 minutes

Teach this lesson:
- **After** introducing material on comparing and ordering numbers in students' grade-level math textbooks
- **Before** students complete the activities on page 8 of the student worktext

You need these materials:
- base-ten blocks
- Transparency 4
- various classroom objects, including a hammer

A Introduce

Read aloud the Lesson Objective with students. Explain that some word problems include information that is not needed.

Ask: *If you are going to buy milk at the store, what do you need to know?* (How much it costs. How much money I have.) *Do you need to know how much peanut butter costs? Do you need to know if I am wearing red sneakers?* Provide examples of other situations and ask students to offer humorous examples of unneeded information.

Then ask: *Have you ever solved a math problem that had extra information you didn't need? What did you do with that extra information?* Have volunteers tell about these problems and their solutions.

LESSON 4

Solve Math Problems

Objective Cross out information that you do not need to solve math problems.

Learn to Solve Problems

Problem
Pancho is (3,373) days old. John is (3,412) days old. Ms. Lee is (10,630) days old. Peter is (3,382) days old. Which boy is the oldest?

Step 1: Read the problem. Underline the question.

Step 2: Decide what you have to do. I have to order the ages of the boys.

Step 3: Circle the facts. Cross out the fact that is not necessary. Ms. Lee is not a boy. I do not need Ms. Lee's age to solve the problem. I can cross it out.

Step 4: Order the numbers to solve the problem. From least to greatest, the numbers are: 3,373; 3,382; 3,412.
John is the oldest boy.

Practice Solving Math Problems

Directions Follow steps 1 to 4 above to solve the word problems below. Write the answers in complete sentences on a separate sheet of paper.

1. Carla lives (2,792) miles from the place where she was born. Lei lives (5,034) miles from the place where she was born. Nava lives (2,905) miles from the place where she was born. Lei lives (X) miles from the fire station. <u>Which girl lives the closest to the place where she was born?</u> Carla lives closest.

2. There are (25,802) people in Centerville. There are (25,044) people in Round Lake. There are (25,890) people in Grove City. <u>Are there more people in Centerville or in Grove City?</u> There are more people in Grove City.

3. Ms. Carrion's class raised ($112) for the fourth grade trip. Ms. Thomas's class raised ($108) for the fourth grade trip. Mr. Cho's class raised ($119) for the fourth grade trip. This year the students will go on their trip by bus. <u>Which of the three classes raised the least money?</u> Ms. Thomas' class raised the least money.

4. Oak Street School has (1,034) students. About (580) of these students are girls. Mrs. Hamada has (1,050) stickers to give to the students at the school. <u>Does she have enough to give one sticker to each student?</u> Yes, she has enough to give one sticker to each student.

8 • Compare and Order Whole Numbers

B Teach and Learn

Have students look at the problem on page 8 of the student worktext. Ask a volunteer to read the problem aloud. Say that people usually do not measure their ages in days, but that it is not hard to find out the number of days a person has been alive. Tell them you can multiply the years by 365 and the months by 30 to get an estimate. Add that most fourth grade students are between 3,000 and 4,000 days old.

Check students' comprehension of the numbers in the problem by asking questions, such as: *How many days old is Pancho? How many days old is Ms. Lee?* (3,373; 10,630) Help students read and say the numbers correctly.

Say: *You need some of this information to solve the problem. But you do not need all of it.* Tell students they will use the steps on page 8 to find unneeded information.

Highlighted words and phrases may affect student comprehension.

Model how to solve the problem by using the following Think Aloud:

Think Aloud

Call student's attention to the first step. Have a volunteer read it aloud.

Say: *First, I'll read the problem. Then, I will underline the question. The question usually comes at the end of a word problem. What other clue helps you to know which part is the question?* Elicit that questions end with question marks. Help students find the question.

Point out that the question in the problem on page 8 is already underlined. Tell students that they will need to find and underline the questions themselves as they solve the word problems on this page.

Have students read Step 2. Say: *The question asks me to find out which boy is the oldest. I can find out which boy is oldest by ordering the ages of the boys.* Remind students that they compare two numbers but order three numbers or more.

Continue to Step 3. Say: *I need to circle the facts. But one of the facts in the problem is not needed. Let me see if I can find the fact I don't need.* Copy all four names and the corresponding numbers of days onto the board, saying the names and numbers as you do so.

- **Review the question.** Say: *Aha! The question asks me to find the oldest boy. But not all these people are boys. Which person is not a boy?* Elicit that Ms. Lee is not a boy.

- **Say**: *It is interesting to see how many days old Ms. Lee is. But it does not help me to solve this problem. I can cross this information out. I don't need it.* Cross out the information about Ms. Lee that you wrote on the board.

Say: *Now, I can go on to the last step.* Have a volunteer read Step 4 aloud. Have students close their books. Ask them to work with a partner to order the numbers on the board and determine which of the three boys is the oldest. Provide base-ten blocks for students to use if needed.

- **Have pairs share their answers with classmates.** Ask them to describe how they solved the problem. Encourage them to use time-order words like *first, next,* and *last,* as well as make use of comparing and place value words such as *greater, less, the thousands place,* and *digit.*

Briefly review the steps with students. Point out that three of the steps require a written answer. Some steps also ask students to underline or circle information in the problem.

Give students a chance to practice these steps. Have students form groups of four. Display Transparency 4. Review the steps together. Then point out the first problem under the steps. Have someone in each group copy the problem on a piece of paper.

- **Have the first student in each group read the problem aloud, then find and underline the question.** Have others in the group check that student's work. Then have the first student pass the paper to the next student, who carries out Step 2, writing the answer in a complete sentence. Continue, round-robin style, until each group has completed all four steps. Tell students that they should refer to the steps on the transparency as they work. Also point out the model problem in the student worktext on page 8 and have them use it as a guide, if needed.

- **Have students continue with the second problem.** Have them change roles so each student is working on a different step than before. Assign groups to compare answers with those of another group when they have completed both problems.

- **Wrap up.** Lead a general discussion about how students identified the unnecessary information and how they solved the problem. Ask them: *Which step was easiest? Which was hardest?*

Review and Practice

Direct pairs of students to review and practice the steps on page 8 in the student worktexts. One student can say the first part of the step and the other student can finish it.

BP 3 **Then read aloud the directions for Practice Solving Math Problems.** Remind students that they should follow the steps in their student worktexts. Have students solve these problems individually. Circulate, assessing how well students follow the steps and how easily they can identify the unnecessary information. Take notes as you observe students working. Go over the answers with students when the entire class has completed the assignment.

Assess and Intervene

How well can students identify unnecessary information to help them solve problems, based on Practice Solving Math Problems on page 8? Use the rubric to identify students who need extra support through additional help and the Intervention activity.

Intermediate

☐ Correctly identifies and crosses out unneeded information in at least three of the problems.

☐ Writes the answers to steps 2–4 in complete sentences, which may include errors that do not impede communication.

Example of a sentence a student might write: *Class of Ms. Thomas raise least.*

Advanced

☐ Correctly identifies and crosses out unneeded information in all four of the problems.

☐ Writes the answers to steps 2–4 in complete sentences with few errors.

Example of a sentence a student might write: *Ms. Thomas class raise least money.*

INTERVENTION 5 minutes

If students struggle to find the unnecessary information in these problems, they may benefit from simple, concrete examples of what *need* means. Display a pencil and a hammer. Say: *I need the pencil so I can write. I do not need the hammer to write. The hammer will not help me if I want to write something.* Then ask students to tell which object they need to pound a nail. Summarize by saying *I need a hammer to pound a nail. I do not need a pencil to pound a nail. The pencil will not help me if I want to pound a nail.* Repeat with other pairs of objects, focusing on the different uses of each. Then return to the problem at the top of page 8. Say: *I need to know how old Pancho is to solve the problem. But I do not need to know how old Ms. Lee is. That information will not help me solve this problem.*

Understand the Main Idea

Objective Use a number line or rounding rules to round numbers.

40 minutes 🕐

Teach this lesson:
- **Before** introducing lessons on rounding in students' grade-level math textbook
- **Before** students complete the activity on page 9 of the student worktext

You need these materials:
- index cards with 4 numbers written on them to round to the hundreds and thousands

Prerequisite Background Knowledge
- Concept of place value
- Place names through millions

BP 4 ⟩ **ELL BEST PRACTICE #4:**
Interaction

For English language learners, extensive interaction with others promotes acquisition of new knowledge. Active engagement in the learning process facilitates the development of the new concept of rounding. New language needed to communicate about rounding is acquired and practiced by interaction with the group and with the text. Teachers who facilitate this kind of engagement through pair, small-, and large-group interaction will enable students to take risks with the new language of rounding whole numbers.

Throughout this module, when you see **BP** 4 , this is an example of an interactive activity.

Module 3: Round Whole Numbers

Understand the Main Idea

LESSON
1

Objective Use a number line or rounding rules to round numbers.

Learn the Main Idea

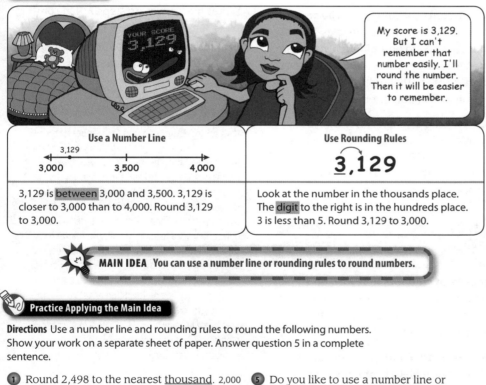

My score is 3,129. But I can't remember that number easily. I'll round the number. Then it will be easier to remember.

Use a Number Line	Use Rounding Rules
3,129 ◄──┼──────┼──────┼──► 3,000　3,500　4,000	3,129
3,129 is between 3,000 and 3,500. 3,129 is closer to 3,000 than to 4,000. Round 3,129 to 3,000.	Look at the number in the thousands place. The digit to the right is in the hundreds place. 3 is less than 5. Round 3,129 to 3,000.

💡 **MAIN IDEA** You can use a number line or rounding rules to round numbers.

✏️ **Practice Applying the Main Idea**

Directions Use a number line and rounding rules to round the following numbers. Show your work on a separate sheet of paper. Answer question 5 in a complete sentence.

1️⃣ Round 2,498 to the nearest <u>thousand</u>. 2,000

2️⃣ Round 2,764 to the nearest <u>thousand</u>. 3,000

3️⃣ Round 2,134 to the nearest <u>hundred</u>. 2,100

4️⃣ Round 2,658 to the nearest <u>hundred</u>. 2,700

5️⃣ Do you like to use a number line or rounding rules when rounding? Explain why.

Answers will vary. I like to use a number line because I can see all of the numbers. OR I like rounding rules because I know which numbers are less than 5 or more than 5.

A **Introduce**

Read aloud the Lesson Objective with students. Say: *Sometimes when we talk about numbers, we do not need to say the exact number. We can say a number that is very close to it.*

Activate background knowledge about place value. Say: *When we talk about rounding numbers, we need to know place value.* Write the number *3,129* on the board. Write the sentence frame *What is the place value of _____?* on the board. Ask: *What is the place value of the 3?* (thousands) *What is the place value of the 1?* (hundreds) *What is the place value of the 2?* (tens) *What is the place value of the 9?* (ones)

Have students work with a partner. Ask each student to write a number with four digits on a sheet of paper. Have students exchange papers with their partner. Have them use the sentence frame on the board to ask each other questions about their numbers.

Point to the drawing of the computer screen on page 9 of the student worktext. Ask: *What is the girl doing?* (playing a computer game) *What does the number on the screen mean?* (it shows the number of points she got)

Highlighted words and phrases may affect student comprehension.

Read the text in the speech bubble aloud. Ask: *What can the girl do to remember the number of points?* Invite students to brainstorm different ways to remember the score (think of a number close to the nearest ten, hundred, thousand). Explain that you can round or find a number close to the score by using a number line or rounding rules.

Point to the number line. Say: *The girl uses a number line that shows 3,000, 3,500, and 4,000. She wants to see which number is closer to 3,129.* Ask students to tell which number is closer to 3,129. (3,000)

Point to the last panel. Read the caption aloud. Say: *When we use rounding rules, we look at the digits in a number and their place value. If a digit is 5 or more, we round up. If it is 4 or less, we round down.*

Read the Main Idea aloud with students. Ask students what they know about place value and digits from previous math classes.

B Teach and Learn

Write the words *number line* and *rounding rules* on the board. Model how to use each one using a Think Aloud, as follows:

Think Aloud

Draw a number line on the board. Under the number line, write the numbers *3,000, 3,500,* and *4,000.* Say: *I want to find out which number is closer to 3,129. I can use a number line. I will mark 3,129 on my number line.* Write *3,129* in the appropriate place on the number line. *I will mark it between 3,000 and 3,500. I see that 3,129 is closer to 3,000 than to 4,000. So I can round 3,129 to 3,000 because it is closer than 4,000.*

Point to *rounding rules* on the board. Write *3,129* on the board underneath it. Say: *Rounding rules help me decide if I should round up or round down. The rules tell me to use digits and their place value. I have to look at the digit to the right of the thousands place. That is the rounding place. What is the digit in the rounding place?* (1) Circle *1* on the board. Say: *A rounding rule tells me that if the digit in the rounding place is 5 or more, I round up. If the digit in the rounding place is 4 or less, I round down.* Write these rules on the board. Ask: *Is this digit 4 or less?* (yes) *So I should round down. I round 3,129 down to the nearest thousand, which is 3,000.*

Write 8,576 on the board and have students copy it. Guide students to round the number to the nearest thousand using a number line and again using rounding rules. Remind students how to use each method of rounding if necessary, but do not provide answers. Check their work and provide assistance as needed.

Have students work in pairs. Ask each pair to round the number 5,829 to the nearest thousand. Assign half the pairs to use rounding rules and half to use number lines. Match a pair that used rounding rules with a pair that used a number line. Have them compare their answers and say how they found out the answer.

C Review and Practice

To help students review the concept of rounding, write *478* on the board. Ask: *What can I do to round 478 to the nearest hundred?* (use a number line or rounding rules) *If I use a number line, what numbers should I mark on the number line?* (400, 450, 500) Draw the number line on the board. *Is 478 closer to 400 or 500?* (500) *How can I use rounding rules to round 478?* Point to the rounding rules on the board, and read them chorally. Then ask volunteers to help you round 478. Ask them to come to the board. Ask them to circle the *7* and decide whether it is 5 or more or 4 or less. Guide them to round up to 500.

BP 4 Divide the class into pairs. Give each pair of students an index card with two numbers in the thousands and two in the hundreds. Tell them to round to the closest hundred or thousand. Remind students that they can use a number line or rounding rules. Have students show their work on paper.

Have students share their work with the class. Ask them to explain how they knew to round up or round down. On the board, make a two-column chart with the headings Round Up and Round Down. As students share their answers, write the numbers that rounded up in the "Round Up" column, and the numbers that rounded down in the "Round Down" column. Point out that all of the numbers with 4 or lower in the rounding place rounded down, and all of the numbers with 5 or higher in the rounding place rounded up.

Read the directions for the Practice Applying the Main Idea activity. Point out that students will make their own number lines, and they can choose to use the number line or rounding rules to solve each problem.

D Assess and Intervene

How well do students understand rounding concepts based on Practice Applying the Main Idea on page 9? Use the rubric to identify students who need extra support through additional help and the Intervention activity.

Intermediate

☐ Correctly rounds numbers using number lines or rounding rules in 3 of the problems.

☐ Explains in a short sentence which tool was used to round and how the tool was used. Sentence may contain errors.

Example of a sentence a student may write: *I round number use number line and 2,498 is close to 2,000.*

Advanced

☐ Correctly rounds numbers using number lines or rounding rules in all 4 problems.

☐ Writes sentences clearly explaining which tool was used to round and how.

Example of a sentence a student may write: *I used a number line to round. I can see all numbers from small to large.*

INTERVENTION 5 minutes

If students are having difficulty using a number line and rounding rules to round to the nearest hundred or thousand, have students make a number line with marks in the hundreds. Have them draw a place value chart with a column for each place value. Say a number. Have students write the number on their paper and show where it falls on the number line. Then have students draw arrows on the number line in both directions from the given number. The shortest arrow shows what they should round to. Now, have students write the number on the place value chart. Tell them to underline the place they are rounding to, and circle the place to the right. Discuss the rounding rules and have students draw an arrow to show rounding up or down.

Lesson

2

Learn the Vocabulary

Objective Talk and write about rounding using the vocabulary words.

---

40 minutes

Teach this lesson:
- **Before** introducing lessons on rounding in students' grade-level math textbook
- **Before** students complete the activities on page 10 of the student worktext

You need these materials:
- index cards that have questions including the vocabulary words written on them (1 per student)

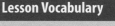

Lesson Vocabulary

Essential Vocabulary

| about | to round | to the nearest |

halfway between

Additional Vocabulary

nearer	nearest	increase
digit*	closer	closest
place		

* - Term that has a Vocabulary Card.

LESSON

2

Learn the Vocabulary

Objective Talk and write about rounding using the vocabulary words.

Learn the Words

Directions Fill in the missing words. Then check your answers with your teacher.

to round: to replace a number with another number that tells about how many or how much	**to the nearest _____:** to round to the closest number in the tens place, or hundreds place, or thousands place, and so on
There are 24 eggs. Round ____ 24 to the nearest ten.	Round 5,496 **to the nearest** hundred. The nearest _____ hundred is 5,500.
about: not the exact number, but close to that number	**halfway between:** exactly in the middle of two things or two numbers
There are about ____ 120 peanuts in the jar.	15 is halfway between _____ 10 and 20.

Practice the Words

Directions Answer the questions below using the words above. Then use a separate sheet of paper to draw a number line and answer question 5.

1. What did you do if you rounded 1,276 to 1,300?

   I rounded to the nearest hundred.

2. What number is halfway between 2,500 and 2,600?

   2,550 is halfway between 2,500 and 2,600.

3. The number of students in our grade is 92 or about _____ 90.

4. 3,862 rounded to the nearest thousand is 4,000.

5. Draw a number line from 8,000 to 9,000.

   a. Fill in the number that is halfway between 8,000 and 9,000. Write a complete sentence describing the number. 8,500 is the number halfway between 8,000 and 9,000.

   b. Write a number that is about as much as 8,473. Explain your answer. 8,470 (or 8,500; answers will vary) is about as much as 8,473. It is not exact, but it is close to it.

A Introduce

Read aloud the Lesson Objective with students. Ask: *What do you remember about rounding whole numbers? What can you use to help you round numbers?* Have students discuss with a partner what they remember about number lines and rounding rules.

Have students make a list of words they think they will use to talk about rounding. Write the words on the board. Model using the words they suggest in sentences about rounding.

Choose words from the Additional Vocabulary box that you think will be useful. Add them to the list of words on the board. Elicit or provide examples or definitions for all the words on the list.

B Teach and Learn

Orally introduce the Essential Vocabulary. Look at the drawings on page 10 of the student worktext. Read each vocabulary word or phrase and definition aloud. Pause to paraphrase and explain the Essential Vocabulary. Then read the example sentences.

Write these numbers on the board: *14* and *16.* Write the word *round,* and say it out loud. Ask: *What number can we round 14 to?* (10) *What about 16?* (20) Have students round the numbers chorally with you.

Highlighted words and phrases may affect student comprehension.

Model and explain the other Essential Vocabulary as follows. Have students fill in the blanks in the example sentences at the appropriate time.

Think Aloud

Point to the illustration of the egg cartons. Count the eggs chorally. Say: *I see that there are 24 eggs in the egg cartons.* Write *24* on the board. *I want to round the number of eggs to the nearest ten. I see a 2 in the tens place.* Underline the *2*. *That means that I have to round down to 20 or round up to 30.* Write the number *20* and draw an arrow pointing down, and the number *30* with an arrow pointing up.

Say: *Is 20 the nearest ten or is 30 the nearest ten? I can use a number line or rounding rules to find out.* Draw a number line on the board with lines from 20 to 30. Say: *I will count to 24 and mark it.* Mark *24* on the number line. *I see that 24 is closer to 20 than to 30. So, if I round it to the nearest ten, I round it down to 20.*

Say: *I can use rounding rules. I know that I round down if the number is 4 or less than 4. So I round down to the nearest ten and my answer is 20.* Remind students that the word *nearest* in math has the same meaning as when they say *nearest to school* or *nearest to me.*

Point to the illustration of the jars. Say: *There are about 100 peanuts in the jar. I know that the exact number is 116, but 100 is about or is close to 116 and it is easier to remember. So about means that it is not an exact number, but it is close to that number.*

Return to the number line on the board. Count from 20 to 25 and circle *25*. Say: *I see that 25 is halfway between 20 and 30. That means that it is right in the middle of the two tens. 25 is not closer to 20 or to 30. I can also tell because the word* halfway *has two smaller words, half and way. Half tells me that it is between 2 points. Halfway between tells me that it is right in the middle. 25 is not nearer to 20 or to 30. It is halfway between. If I want to round 25 to the nearest 10, I have to use rounding rules.*

BP 4 Have pairs of students work together. Ask them to find a number that is halfway between 1,500 and 2,000. Then have them explain to their partner how they found the number. Next, ask each student to

round the number to the nearest hundred. Have them explain to their partner how they rounded the number.

 Have students complete Vocabulary Cards for the words in this module.

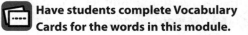

C Review and Practice

Review the Lesson Objective. Ask students: *What are important words that you use when you talk about rounding?* (*to round* and *to the nearest*)

BP 4 Play a game to help students practice lesson vocabulary. Start by dividing the class into groups of four students.

- **Give each group a set of four index cards that have questions written on them.** The questions should involve the four Essential Vocabulary words. For example, *What number is halfway between 100 and 200? [Sam] has 401 cards. About how many cards does he have? What is 3,178 rounded to the nearest thousand? What is 591 rounded to the nearest hundred?*

- **Have students place the cards upside down in a pile.** Each student in the group picks a card. They must read the card aloud to the group. Then all of the students in the group should work together to solve the problem. Once they arrive at an answer, the student who picked the card should write the group's answer in a complete sentence on the other side of the card. They should properly use the vocabulary term that was in the question in their answer. Groups should repeat this process until all cards have been used.

- **Collect the cards from each group.** Review the answers the group gave so you can determine how well students understood each vocabulary term.

Introduce the Practice the Words activity in the student worktext. Make sure that students understand the directions. Tell them that they will have to use a separate sheet of paper. Have students complete the activity individually. Check students' work.

D Assess and Intervene

Can all students talk and write about rounding using the Essential Vocabulary? Use the rubric to identify students who need extra support through additional help and the Intervention activity.

Intermediate

☐ Answers at least 3 of questions 1–4 correctly.

☐ Answers both parts of question 5 correctly but answer may contain some errors.

Example of a sentence a student might write: *8,500 not exact to 8,473, but close.*

Advanced

☐ Answers 4 of questions 1–4 correctly.

☐ Clearly answers both parts of question 5 correctly in complete sentences.

Example of a sentence a student might write: *8,500 not exact number, but close to 8,473.*

INTERVENTION 5 minutes

Some students may have difficulty using the vocabulary words in sentences. To give students additional practice, write the vocabulary word on one side of an index card and the sentence frame on the reverse. For example:

- **to round:** When I _____ a number, I change the number for another number _____ to it. (round, close)
- **to the nearest _____:** I look at the place value and round to the number _____ to it. (closest)
- **about:** This number is not exact, but it is _____ as much as the exact number. (about)
- **halfway between:** The number in the middle is exactly _____ these two numbers. (halfway between)

Distribute to students to complete. Read the sentences with students. Allow students to keep the index cards to review.

Lesson

3

Use More Language

Objective Explain how you round numbers using the antonyms *round up* and *round down,* and the word *because.*

40 minutes ⏱

Teach this lesson:
- **After** lessons on rounding in students' grade-level math textbook
- **Before** students complete the activities on page 11 of the student worktext

You need these materials:
- Transparency 5
- dice

Use More Language

Objective Explain how you round numbers using the antonyms *round up* and *round down* and the word *because.*

LESSON **3**

Learn the Language

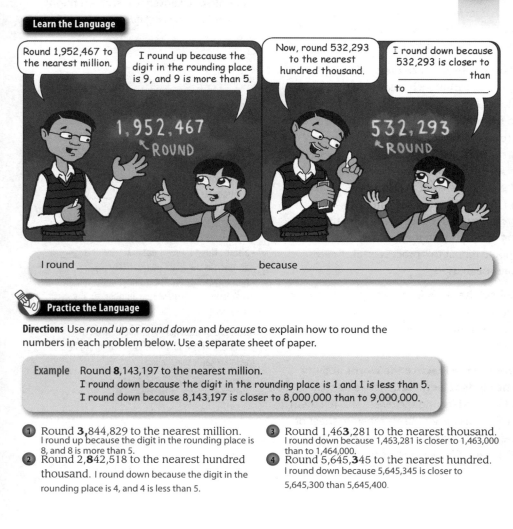

I round _____ because _____.

Practice the Language

Directions Use *round up* or *round down* and *because* to explain how to round the numbers in each problem below. Use a separate sheet of paper.

> **Example** Round **8,**143,197 to the nearest million.
> I round down because the digit in the rounding place is 1 and 1 is less than 5.
> I round down because 8,143,197 is closer to 8,000,000 than to 9,000,000.

① Round **3,**844,829 to the nearest million.
I round up because the digit in the rounding place is 8, and 8 is more than 5.

② Round 2,**8**42,518 to the nearest hundred thousand. I round down because the digit in the rounding place is 4, and 4 is less than 5.

③ Round 1,46**3,**281 to the nearest thousand.
I round down because 1,463,281 is closer to 1,463,000 than to 1,464,000.

④ Round 5,645,**3**45 to the nearest hundred.
I round down because 5,645,345 is closer to 5,645,300 than 5,645,400.

A Introduce

Read aloud the Lesson Objective with students. Ask students to work with a partner to use gestures in order to demonstrate the following antonyms: *up, down, big, small, tall, short, slow, fast.* Say: *When you show the meaning of these words, you use opposite gestures and actions.*

Say: *Antonyms are words that are opposites.* Write the following list on the board, and ask volunteers to come up and say and write the antonym: *big, sad, ugly, easy, good, nearest, long.*

Remind students that they have learned how to round up and down in the previous lessons. Ask: *Why do you think we use opposites to explain how we round numbers?* List students' ideas on the board.

B Teach and Learn

Have students open the student worktext to page 11. Say: *When you round numbers, you use the digit in the rounding place, or a number line, and decide if you have to round up or down. To explain what you did and why, you use the word* because.

Point to the first picture. Write *1,952,467* on the board, and read it out loud. Say: *This is a big number! There are many digits. When we have big numbers like this one, we choose which digit to round to. Then we decide if we need to round up or down.*

Highlighted words and phrases may affect student comprehension.

Read the first speech bubble chorally.
Ask: *What is the teacher asking the girl to do?* (round to the nearest million) Underline the number in the millions place. (1)

Read the second speech bubble chorally.
Ask: *How does the girl know she has to round up?* (the digit in the rounding place is 9, and 9 is more than 5) Circle the *9*.

BP 4 Have students read the speech bubbles in the second illustration. Invite volunteers to figure out the answer. Then ask students to read the answer aloud. Allow them to discuss and explain in their own words why they rounded down.

Say: *When you round numbers, you round up or down according to the digit in the rounding place.* Point up as you say *round up* and point down as you say *round down.* Say: *If the number is less than 5, you round down. If it is 5 or greater, you round up.* Now say a number between 1 and 10. Have students point up if they should round up. Have them point down if they should round down. Repeat several times until all students are pointing in the right direction for each cue.

Use Transparency 5 to model how to use *because* to explain how you round numbers. Say: *Look at the cities in the left column and the numbers in the right column. These numbers tell us how many people live in each city.*

- **Model how to round up or down and use *because* as follows:**

> **Think Aloud**

> **Say:** *I need to round the population of Philadelphia to the nearest ten thousand.* Write *1,463,281* on the board. Ask: *What should I do first? I need to look at the digit in the ten thousands place.* Underline the 3. Say: *The digit in the rounding place is 3.* Point to the sentence frame in the student worktext. Say: *I round up because it is greater than 5.* Write *I round down because 3 is less than 5.* on the board. Say: *So I will round 1,463,281 down to 1,460,000.* Write *1,460,000* on the board underneath the first number. Say: *The population of Philadelphia is about 1,460,000.*

Ask students to look at the population for San Antonio on Transparency 5. Tell them to look at the number in the ones place. Ask: *If we want to round this number to the nearest ten, should we round up or down?* (round up)

Why? (because the digit in the rounding place is 9) Have students use the sentence frame on Transparency 5 to answer the question in a complete sentence.

BP 4 Have students work in small groups. Tell them to write the population of San Antonio from the transparency on a sheet of paper. Then have them look at each digit and identify its place value. Have them use the place value chart in their math textbooks for reference if necessary.

- **Assign each group a rounding place in the number, and have them circle their digit.** Have them decide whether to round up or down. Then have the students in each group write a sentence using *because* to explain why they rounded up or down. Have a volunteer in each group share their work with the class.

C Review and Practice

Review the Lesson Objective by asking students: *Why is it useful to use antonyms when you want to explain how to round?* (Because they are opposites. Sometimes I round up. Sometimes I round down.)

Divide students into pairs. Assign each pair a city from Transparency 5. Ask them to look at the population of the city and write it on a sheet of paper. Have them choose a digit to round up and choose another digit to round down. Have students use the sentence frame with *because* to explain how they rounded the numbers. Ask volunteers to share their work with the class.

BP 4 Divide the class into groups of three students. Give each group a die and some blank paper. Have each student roll the die twice. The students write down the numbers they roll on the blank paper until they form a six-digit number. Have each group work together to round the number to the nearest hundred thousand and hundred. Have the groups show their work and write their answer using *because* to explain how they rounded their numbers. Repeat this process as many times as time permits.

After this group work, have students work individually to complete the Practice the Language activity on page 11 in the student worktext. Circulate, and assess students as they work on the activity.

D Assess and Intervene

How well can students use *round up* and *round down*? How well can they use *because* to explain how they rounded in Practice the Language on page 11? Use the rubric to identify students who need extra support through additional help and the Intervention activity.

Intermediate

☐ Rounds at least 3 numbers correctly in questions 1–4.

☐ Answers questions in complete sentences explaining how they round using *because*, with minimal errors that do not impede comprehension.

Advanced

☐ Rounds 4 numbers correctly in questions 1–4.

☐ Answers questions in complete sentences explaining how they round using *because*, with no errors.

INTERVENTION   5 minutes

If students are having trouble using the antonyms *round up* and *round down* and the word *because* to explain how to round, first explain the meaning of *opposite*: two words that have very different meanings, such as *clean* and *dirty*. Then show with a gesture the opposite movement of *up* and *down*. Write the sentence frame "I round _____ because the digit in the rounding place is greater than/less than _____." Give students the following instructions, and ask them to use the sentence frame to explain how they rounded: Round 213 to the nearest hundred; round 1,972 to the nearest thousand; round 47 to the nearest ten; round 81,624 to the nearest ten thousand.

Lesson
4

Solve Math Problems

Objective Solve math problems using real-world information.

---

35 minutes

Teach this lesson:
- **After** lessons on rounding concepts in students' grade-level math textbook
- **Before** students complete the activities on page 12 of the student worktext

You need these materials:
- Worksheet 3
- Transparency 6
- Large map of the United States

Give pairs of students a real-world number that is related to a school activity, such as the number of items collected for a food drive or the number of students in school. (The number should be in the thousands.) Ask students to round the number to the nearest ten, hundred, and thousand. Have students write their answers in complete sentences. Students can demonstrate on the board how they rounded to each place on the board and explain to the class what they did.

LESSON
4

Solve Math Problems

Objective Solve word problems using real-world information.

Learn to Solve Problems

Problem Los Angeles, California is 2,794 miles from New York City, New York. San Francisco, California is 2,930 miles from New York City. Pasadena, California is 2,442 miles from New York City. Las Vegas, Nevada is 2,572 miles from New York City. Round each number to the nearest hundred. Which city in California is the farthest away from New York City?

	Think	Write
Step 1:	Read the problem. Underline the questions. Decide what you have to do.	I need to round each number to the nearest hundred. I also need to find out which city in California is the farthest away from New York City.
Step 2:	Circle the facts. What else do you need to know?	I need to know which cities are in California.
Step 3:	Round the distances to the nearest hundred. Solve the problem.	I will round the numbers to the nearest hundred for the 3 cities in California. 2,794 rounds up to 2,800. 2,930 rounds down to 2,900. 2,442 rounds down to 2,400. San Francisco is the farthest away from New York City.

Practice Solving Math Problems

Directions Follow steps 1 to 3 above to answer the questions below. Write your answers in complete sentences on a separate sheet of paper.

1. Houston, Texas is 1,675 miles from New York City. Miami, Florida is 1,328 miles from New York City. Round the numbers to the nearest hundred. Which city is farther away from New York City? Houston is farther away from New York City than Miami.

2. Dallas, Texas is 1,604 miles from New York City. El Paso, Texas is 2,147 miles from New York City. Round the numbers to the nearest hundred. Which city is closer to New York City? Dallas is closer to New York City than El Paso.

3. Look at question 1. How far is it from New York City to the city that is in Florida? It is 1,328 miles from New York City to Miami, Florida.

4. How does rounding help you look at the distances? Answers will vary. Rounding helps me because it makes the numbers easier to think about.

Introduce

Read aloud the Lesson Objective with students. Explain what real-world information is. Say: *Real-world information is facts or things that are real, that you know about the world. They include things that will help you in your everyday life.*

Brainstorm a list of real-world information that students encounter in math lessons. Guide students to the following information: time, distance, width, length, weight, capacity, and temperature.

Display a map of the United States. Explain that reading a map allows us to find out important real-world information. People read maps all the time to figure out where they need to go and how far one city or town is from another. Say: *Reading a map to find out the distances is one example of using real-world information. What other real-world information can you think of?*

BP 4 **Have students share their experiences in reading maps.** Some students may have read a map in social studies classes. Students may be familiar with a world map, a textbook map, or a classroom globe.

Highlighted words and phrases may affect student comprehension.

B Teach and Learn

Write this problem from the worktext on the board, and read it aloud: *Los Angeles, California is 2,794 miles from New York City, New York. San Francisco, California is 2,930 miles from New York City. Pasadena, California is 2,442 miles from New York City. Las Vegas, Nevada is 2,572 miles from New York City. Round each number to the nearest hundred. Which city in California is farthest away from New York City?*

Point to the two sentences before the question in the problem, and read them aloud. Tell students that what you need to do in a word problem is not always in question form. The questions you need to answer do not always have a question word and a question mark. Remind students to look for directions or sentences that tell them what to do.

If possible, have students look at the map for visual reference when solving the problem. Point out each city on the map. Trace a line from each city to New York City. Point out the state labels of California, Nevada, and New York.

Have students look at the numbered steps on page 12. Read aloud each numbered step under Learn to Solve Problems. After each step, model how to use real-world information to solve problems by thinking aloud.

Think Aloud

Write Step 1 on the board, and read the problem aloud. Say: *What are the questions I need to answer in this problem? I know that some questions do not have a question mark, that they are directions. The questions are:* Round each number to the nearest hundred. Then tell which city in California is closest to New York City. Which city in California is farthest away from New York City? *I will underline those questions.* Underline the questions on the board. Say: *Now I need to decide what to do.*

Write Step 2 on the board. Read it aloud. Say: *First I will circle the distances.* Circle the distances in the problem on the board. Reread the last question in the problem aloud. Say: *The distances from each city to New York City are information that I need. So I will circle all of the numbers. What else do*

I need to know? I need to know which cities are in California. I can look at the map if I need help. I see that Los Angeles, San Francisco, and Pasadena are in California. Circle all the cities in California in the problem on the board. Point to Las Vegas in the problem. Say: *Las Vegas is not in California. It is in Nevada.*

Write Step 3 on the board. Say: *I need to round the distances for the 3 cities in California. I do not need to round the distance for the city in Nevada.* Write the distances on the board. Then say: *Now, I have to round each distance to the nearest hundred. Los Angeles is 2,794 miles from New York City. That rounds up to 2,800.* Write *2,800* underneath *2,794.* Say: *San Francisco is 2,930 miles from New York City, so it rounds down to 2,900.* Write *2,900* underneath *2,930.* Say: *Pasadena is 2,442 miles from New York City. That rounds down to 2,400.* Write *2,400* underneath *2,442.* Finally, say: *Now I will order the numbers to see which city is closest and which city is farthest away from New York City. 2,400, 2,800, and 2,900. Pasadena is the closest to New York City and San Francisco is the farthest away.*

Present Transparency 6 to the class. Divide the class into small groups of three and four students. Tell students to follow the steps on the transparency, or on page 12 of their student worktexts, to solve the problem on the transparency. If necessary, students can use a map for reference. Have them discuss rounding and how to solve the problem in their groups. When completed, have them present their work to the class.

Walk around to groups, monitoring and providing assistance as needed. Explain correct answers when students complete their work.

C Review and Practice

Review the steps for solving problems with the class. Have volunteers retell the steps to round to the nearest hundred. Ask students prompting questions. For example: (Step 1) *What do you do first?* (Step 2) *Do all questions have question marks?* (Step 3) *What can you do to help you find the closest and the farthest distance?*

Divide the class into pairs. Give each student a copy of Worksheet 3. Have the pairs discuss how to solve the problem. Then have each student work individually to solve the problem. When the students have finished, they can share with their partner how they solved it.

Have students individually complete Practice Solving Math Problems in the student worktext. Circulate, and assess how well students are able to use the facts to solve the problems.

D Assess and Intervene

How well can students use real-world information to solve problems that involve rounding based on Solve Math Problems on page 12? Use the rubric to identify students who need extra support through additional help and the Intervention activity.

Intermediate

☐ Answers 3 of questions 1–4 correctly.

☐ Writes sentences that answer the questions but may have some errors that interfere with meaning.

Example of a sentence a student might write: *Rounding help because I see numbers easier.*

Advanced

☐ Answers 4 of questions 1–4 correctly.

☐ Writes sentences that clearly answer the questions.

Example of a sentence a student might write: *Rounding helps because I make numbers easy and look at the distances better.*

INTERVENTION 5 minutes

If students have trouble understanding the complexity and language of the problem, help students divide the questions into smaller steps: (1) Round each number to the nearest hundred. (2) Order the numbers from least to greatest. (3) Name the closest city to New York City. (4) Name the farthest city from New York City.

Lesson

1

Understand the Main Idea

Objective Identify and count different forms of money and change, starting from the greatest value.

45 minutes

Teach this lesson:
- **Before** introducing lessons on counting money and making change
- **Before** students complete the activities on page 13 of the student worktext

You need these materials:
- books
- play money bills and coins, 2 bags to put them in
- index cards with drawings of familiar items and prices, 1 card per student
- Transparency 7

Prerequisite Background Knowledge
- Names and values of U.S. coins and bills

BP 5 **ELL BEST PRACTICE #5:** **Higher-Order Thinking**

English language learners are capable of using higher-order thinking, but at times they are hindered by their inability to express their thinking verbally. As you ask questions about money, counting money, and making change, move beyond simply identifying how to do these activities and learning the language to describe them. Help students make inferences, analyze, and interpret what they are learning in terms of language and content.

Throughout this module, when you see **BP 5**, you will find an example of using higher-order thinking with students.

Module 4: Money

Understand the Main Idea

Objective Identify and count different forms of money and change starting from the greatest value.

LESSON 1

Learn the Main Idea

I want to buy this book. How much is it?

The book is $3.65.

I don't know if I can buy the book. I need to count my money. $3.00, $3.25, $3.50, $3.60, $3.70, $3.80, $3.90, $4.00. I have $4.00. I can buy the book.

Here is your change. $3.65, $3.75, $4.00.

Thank you!

MAIN IDEA Start with the largest bills and the largest coins to count money. Count on to make change.

Practice Applying the Main Idea

Directions Look at each picture. In problems 1 and 2, count the money and write a sentence to tell how much money you have. In problems 3 and 4, tell how much money you have. Show how you count your change. Write a complete sentence to tell how much change you get. Use a separate sheet of a paper.

① $20, $22, $22.75, $22.85, $22.90. I have $22.90.

② $10.00, $11, $11.75, $11.85. I have $11.85.

③ I have $10.00. $8.00, $9.00, $10.00. My change is $3.00.

④ I have $20.00. $7.00, $8.00, $9.00, $10.00. My change is $14.00.

A Introduce

Read aloud the Lesson Objective with students.

Help students activate their background knowledge. Ask: *Did you ever count your money before or after you bought something? What happened? How did you count it?* Elicit several responses from students.

BP 5 **Say:** *It is important to count your money before you buy something. It is important to count your change. Why?*

Use the artwork on page 13 of the student worktext as a visual introduction to adding money, making change, and telling which bills and coins have greater and less value.

- **Give pairs of students time to look at the comic strip.** Have pairs describe what they see to each other.

- **Point to the girl in the left hand panel and the right hand panel.** Ask: *Where is she? What is she doing? What do you think she wants to buy?*

- **BP 5** **Have students look at panels 2 and 3.** Ask: *Can the girl buy the book? How do you know? What does the woman give the girl? What does the girl do?*

Highlighted words and phrases may affect student comprehension.

Money • 13

- **Chorally read aloud the text in each frame with students.** Summarize what happened in the comic strip: *The girl asked the price. She bought a book. The woman gave her change.*

- **Model acting out the comic strip.** Use play money and a book as you read aloud the text. Then have pairs use play money and a book to act out the comic strip.

Read aloud the Main Idea with students. Ask students what they know about counting money and making change from their own lives or previous math classes.

B Teach and Learn

Model how to order bills starting with the greatest value using a Think Aloud.

> ### Think Aloud
>
> **Place the following play money bills on a table so everyone can see**: $20, $10, $5, $1. Mix up the money so it is not in order. Point to each bill and say: *This is _____ dollar(s).*
>
> **Say:** *I want to order the money. I will start with the greatest value. That's $20.00.* Move the $20 bill to the first place. *What values come next? $10.00, $5.00, $1.00.* Move each bill as you name it. *Now I have ordered the money. I started with the greatest value and finished with the smallest value. $20.00, $10.00, $5.00, $1.00.*

Display Transparency 7 for students to see bills, coins, and their respective values.

Divide the class into small groups. Distribute play bills for $20, $10, $5, $1. Write the following sentence frame on the board: *I started with _____ because it has the greatest value.* Have students order the money starting with the greatest value, taking turns saying each dollar amount, and completing the sentence frame.

Repeat the procedure for these play coins: $1 coin, quarter, dime, nickel, penny. Have the groups order the coins, take turns naming the value of each coin, and completing this sentence frames: *I started with _____ because it has the greatest value.*

Model how to count money using bills. Students should have their play bills and coins in front of them, ordered from greatest to least value. Say: *When we count money, we start with the greatest value.* Point to each dollar value as you count. Say: *$20.00, $30.00, $35.00, $36.00. I have $36.00.* Repeat, and have students chorally count the money with you.

Repeat the activity for counting the coins. ($1.91)

Place a variety of coins in one bag and different play bills in another bag. Model the activity. Say: *Take 3 coins from this bag and 3 bills from this bag.* Take the play money from the bags. Model putting it in order and counting it. Write this question frame on the board, and model completing it: *How much money do you have? I have $_____.* Have pairs take the money, order it, count it out loud, and take turns completing the question frame.

Model how to make change. Show students a $10.00 bill and a book with a price tag of $3.00. Say: *I want to buy this book. I will pay with $10.00. The price of the book is $3.00. How much change will I get? I start with the cost, $3.00, and count until I reach the amount I pay with.* Count using dollar bills. As you put them in front of you say: *$4.00, $5.00, $6.00, $7.00, $8.00, $9.00, $10.00.* Say: *My change is $7.00.* Repeat the activity with the class as you count up chorally to count the change.

Repeat the activity, using both bills and coins. Model how to count on to make change from $10.00 with costs such as $3.25 or $5.75. Say: *I have $_____.* Count on to make change as you put the bills and coins in front of you. Invite students to count the money chorally with you.

C Review and Practice

Ahead of time, make index cards showing familiar items with prices. Prices should include dollars and cents. The prices should be easy to make change from $10.00. Include items such as markers, pencils, books, crayons, and erasers. Have at least one card for each student.

- **Have students work in pairs.** Model the activity. Say: *You have $10.00 to spend.* One student chooses a card and uses play bills and coins to show how much the item costs and orders the money starting with the greatest value. The student counts it aloud for his or her partner and says: *The _____ costs _____.*

- **The other student uses play bills and coins to show how much change he or she should get.** Use the frame: *I get _____ in change.*

Read aloud the directions for the Practice Applying the Main Idea activity. Check students' work. Share and discuss students' answers.

D Assess and Intervene

Does every student understand how to order and count money and make change based on the Practice Applying the Main Idea on page 13? Use the rubric to identify students who need extra support through additional help and the Intervention activity.

Intermediate

- ☐ Correctly identifies and orders the money in #1 and 2 and writes the totals.
- ☐ Writes sentences for #3 and 4 that tell how much money they have and how much change they have. Sentences may contain some errors that interfere with meaning.

  Example of an answer a student might write: *Money is $24.50. I have change is $14.*

Advanced

- ☐ Correctly identifies and orders the money in #1 and 2 and writes the totals.
- ☐ Writes clear sentences for #3 and 4 that tell how much money they have and how much change they have. Errors do not interfere with meaning.

  Example of an answer a student might write: *I have $24.50. My change are $14.*

> **INTERVENTION**   10 minutes
>
> **If students are having trouble counting on from a cost,** explain that we try to get to amounts that are easier and quicker to count. For example, from $2.31, we add pennies first to get to $2.35. Then we can add one nickel instead of having to add five pennies. From $2.40, we can add one dime instead of ten pennies. Have students write $3.38 on a sheet of paper. Ask students to think of what easier value they can count up to. Ask: *Is it easy to count from $3.43? Is it easier to count from $3.40?*

Learn the Vocabulary

Objective Talk about counting bills and coins and making change using the vocabulary words.

---

45 minutes

Teach this lesson:
- **Before** introducing lessons on counting money and making change in students' grade-level math textbook
- **Before** students complete the activities on page 14 of the student worktext

You need these materials:
- index cards
- glass jar
- play coins and bills
- real coins
- Transparency 8
- Vocabulary Cards

Lesson Vocabulary

Essential Vocabulary

dollar	bill	coin
cent	to make change	to count on (up)

Additional Vocabulary

decimal point*   dollar sign ($)   cent sign (¢)
value*

* - Terms that have Vocabulary Cards.

LESSON
2

Learn the Vocabulary

Objective Talk and write about counting bills and coins and making change using the vocabulary words.

Learn the Words

Word/Phrase	Definition	Example
dollar	a unit of money that is worth 100 cents	The symbol for **dollar** is $.
bill	a piece of paper money	Each **bill** has a different value.
coin	a flat, round piece of metal used as money	 These **coins** also have different values.
cent	a unit of money; there are 100 cents in 1 dollar	1 cent The symbol for **cent** is ¢.
to make change	to give back the extra money when a person buys an item and pays more than the price of the item	I have $2.00. The book costs $1.75. The cashier has to **make change** and give me back 25¢.
to count on (up)	to start with the price of the item you buy and add coins and bills until you get to the total paid	The pencils cost $1.70. I pay with $2.00. I **count on** by 10 cents to count my change. I count: $1.70, $1.80, $1.90, $2.00.

Practice the Words

Directions Complete the story. Then draw a picture and use a complete sentence to answer the question about the story on a separate sheet of paper.

> Mel has a jar with money in it. He shakes the jar. He can hear the metal coin___s, but he can't hear the paper bill___s. He takes his money out and counts it. He counts $9.45, nine dollar___s and forty-five cent___s. He wants to buy a game that costs $9.35. He counts on___ to see how much money he will have left after he buys the game. When he goes to the store, he gives the cashier his money. The cashier has to make change___ and give Mel back the right amount of money.
>
> What will Mel's change be? Mel's change will be 10¢.

A | Introduce

Read aloud the Lesson Objective with students. Ask: *What do you know about counting money? About making change?* Have students write on an index card any important words they know when talking about counting money and making change. Partners place check marks next to words that they both wrote and then share their words with the class.

As a class, brainstorm ideas for vocabulary words that will be important to know. Write suggested words on the board and add the Essential Vocabulary to the list.

Choose words from the Additional Vocabulary box that you think will be useful. Write the words on the board. Elicit or provide examples or definitions for all these words.

B | Teach and Learn

Orally introduce the Essential Vocabulary as explained below. Review the artwork on the right side of page 14 with students, pausing to explain Essential Vocabulary words.

Have students use play money and work with you as you explain and demonstrate word meanings. Write each word on the board, and model its pronunciation. Read each definition and explanation aloud as you point to the key illustrations. Then have students read each word, definition, and explanation chorally with you.

> Highlighted words and phrases may affect student comprehension.

- **Write the word *dollar* on the board. Have students hold up a $5.00 bill.** Say: *We use dollars to buy things. Prices are often in dollars.* Ask: *How much is this worth?* (five dollars)

- **Write *bill* on the board.** As students hold up a bill, ask: *What is this bill made from?* (paper)

- **Write *coin* on the board.** Have students hold up a play coin. Say: *This is a coin. Coins are made from metal. Coins have different values. We use coins to buy things of smaller value.* If possible, show students a real coin so they can feel the metal. Write each coin value on the board and chorally say it as you show the coin: *penny 1¢, nickel 5¢, dime 10¢, quarter 25¢, half dollar 50¢, dollar coin $1.00.* Write this question frame on the board: *What is the value of this coin? The value of this coin is _____.* Model completing it, and have students use the information on the board to answer.

- **BP 5** **Write the word *cent*.** Hold up a penny with students. Say: *This is one cent. A cent is also called a penny. We need 100 cents to make a dollar.* Ask: *How many cents (pennies) do we need to make a quarter (dime, nickel)?* Write the following sentence frame on the board, and model completing it: *We need _____ cents to make a _____.* Have students use the sentence frame to answer.

- **Write *to make change* on the board.** Say and show: *I have $5.00. I buy a box of crayons for $2.00. I get money back from the salesperson.* Together count up with students using play money. Say: *$2.00, $3.00, $4.00, $5.00.* Then count the bills together. Say: *A salesperson makes change when you pay more than something costs. He or she gives you money back.*

Divide the class into small groups. Write on the board: *You have $10.00. The markers cost $3.00.* Read the sentences chorally. Tell students you need to make change. Together, make change and then count the change. Ask: *What did you do?* (I made change.) *What is your change?* (My change is $7.00.) Provide additional examples.

Repeat the procedure using coins and bills. Model first, and then have students in the group make change for $10.00 as you say different amounts: *$2.00, $5.50, $8.00.*

Model the meaning of the phrase *to count on* using a Think Aloud. If your students' math textbook uses the phrases *count up*, use that phrase instead of *count on*.

Think Aloud

Write *to count on* on the board. Say: *I want to buy a notebook. I only have a five-dollar bill. The price is $2.00. I pay with $5.00. The salesperson gives me my change. Now I have to count my change to see if it is correct. I start with the cost of the notebook and count on until I reach the amount of money that I paid with. $2.00, $3.00, $4.00, $5.00.*

Have students work with a partner to role-play salesperson and customer. Write these prompts on the board: *How much does it cost? It costs _____. Here is your change.* Have them take turns paying and making change using play coins and bills. Have students count out loud as they make change. Circulate, and assist as necessary.

Return to the words you wrote on the board during the vocabulary brainstorming. Review the Essential and Additional Vocabulary, and any important words and meanings students suggested.

Display Transparency 8. Together complete the rhyme using the Essential Vocabulary. (answers: dollars, coin, cent, dollar, make change, count up) Then read the rhyme chorally.

Have students complete the Vocabulary Cards for this module.

C   Review and Practice

Give pairs of students play coins and bills. Act out or show what each Essential Vocabulary word means with students using play money. For example, say: *Coin,* and hold up a play coin. Say: *This is a coin.* Repeat for each Essential Vocabulary word and have students repeat the context sentences after you.

BP 5 **Play a guessing game with students.** Hold up the play money. Have students guess what the word is by completing the following sentence frame. Write it on the board and have students use it when answering: *That ___ is worth _____.* (bill, X dollars; or coin, X cents)

Introduce the Practice the Words Activity in the student worktext. Show students a glass jar, and demonstrate how paper money doesn't make noise but coins do. Read aloud the directions and the story, pausing at each blank. Do not allow students to verbally complete the story. Have students work independently to complete the story and answer the questions.

D   Assess and Intervene

Does every student understand the Essential Vocabulary in Practice the Words on page 14? Use the rubric to identify students who need extra support through additional help and the Intervention activity.

Intermediate

☐ At least 4 words correctly filled in to complete the story.

☐ Question about the story answered correctly using a simple phrase.

Example of an answer a student might write: *Mel's change 10¢.*

Advanced

☐ Story completed, using all Essential Vocabulary words correctly.

☐ Question about the story answered correctly using complete sentences.

Example of an answer a student might write: *He has 10¢ left.*

INTERVENTION   10 minutes

Some students may be confused by homophones, or words that have more than one meaning. Give the definition for the homophone, and then ask students to give the math definition. Say: *Bill can be a boy's name. What does* bill *mean in math? Sent is the past tense of send and means to make something or someone go away. What does* cent *mean in math? Change is something that does not stay the same. What does* change *mean in math?* Have students make sentences using both meanings.

Lesson

3

Use More Language

Objective Ask and answer questions about making change using the words *if* and *will*.

---

45 minutes

Teach this lesson:
- **After** lessons on counting money and making change in students' grade-level math textbook
- **Before** students complete activities on page 15 of the student worktext

You need these materials:
- play coins and bills
- index cards
- students' textbooks

Use More Language

LESSON 3

Objective Ask and answer questions about making change using the words *if* and *will*.

Learn the Language

I have a $10 bill. I want to buy the markers and drawing pad. If I spend $6.00 and pay with $10, how much change will I get?

I will buy markers and a drawing pad for $6.00. If I spend $6 and pay with $10, I will get $4.00 change.

If I spend _____ and pay with _____, how much change will I get?

If I spend _____ and pay with _____, I will get _____ change.

Practice the Language

Directions In problems 1 and 2, write how much money you have. Then write how much change you will get. In problem 3, write a question to go with the answer. Use the question and sentence frames above.

Example
If I spend $52.00, and I pay with 1 fifty-dollar bill and 1 five-dollar bill, how much money do I have, and how much change will I get?

I have $55.00. If I spend $52.00 and pay with $55.00, I will get $3.00 change.

1 If I spend $3.45, and pay with 3 one-dollar bills and 2 quarters, how much money do I have, and how much change will I get?

I have $3.50. If I spend $3.45 and pay with $3.50, I will get 5¢ change.

2 If I spend $21.49, and pay with 1 twenty-dollar bill, 1 one-dollar bill, and 2 quarters, how much money do I have, and how much change will I get?

I have $21.50. If I spend $21.49, and pay with $21.50, I will get 1¢ change.

3 I have $14.20. If I spend $14.19 and pay with $14.20, I will get 1¢ change.

If I spend $14.19, and pay with 1 ten-dollar bill, 3 one-dollar bills, 3 quarters, 2 dimes, 1 nickel, and 20 pennies, how much money do I have, and how much change will I get?

A Introduce

Introduce *if* and *will* clauses using familiar examples. Write these sentence frames on the board: *If I am thirsty, I will ____. If I am hungry, I will ____. If I am tired, I will ____.*

- **Underline the word *if*, and explain that this word shows something that might happen.** Underline *will*, and explain that this word shows something in the future. Say: *When we put these two parts of a sentence together, the second part says what* will *happen in the future if the first part happens.*

- **Model the first sentence starter by saying and writing:** *If I am thirsty, I will drink water.* Invite students to complete the sentence with other *will* clauses, such as: *I will get some milk.* Invite students to complete the other sentences and write their answers on the board. Read each one aloud. Ask students to think of other situations that fit the sentence starters above. Write them on the board and read them aloud.

Read aloud the Lesson Objective with students. Remind them that in Lessons 1 and 2 they learned how to count on to make change. They started with the greatest amount and ended with the least amount when counting money. They counted on to make change, starting with the cost and ending with the amount paid.

Have students find a few examples of problems with counting money and making change in their math textbooks. Use play money to solve the problems with students.

Highlighted words and phrases may affect student comprehension.

B Teach and Learn

Focus students' attention on Panel 1 on page 15 of the student worktext. Write the question frame on the board. Have a student volunteer read aloud what the girl says. Have another student come to the board and complete the question frame. Read the completed question chorally with the class.

Focus students' attention on Panel 2. Write the sentence frame on the board. Have a volunteer read aloud what the girl says. Have another student come to the board and complete the sentence frame. Read the completed sentence chorally with the class. Have a pair of student volunteers read the completed questions and answers.

Write on the board: *If I spend $20.98, and I pay with $21.00, I will get _____ change.* Read this aloud, and then have students look at page 15 of the student worktext.

- **Remind students that both parts of the sentence depend on each other.** Say: *When we put these two parts together, the second part shows what will happen in the future if the first part happens.*

Read aloud the directions for Practice the Language. Walk students through the example using a think aloud:

> **Think Aloud**
>
> **Read aloud the example problem.** Ask: *If I spend $52.00, and I pay with 1 fifty-dollar bill and 1 five-dollar bill, how much change will I get?* Say: *I spent $52.00.* Write *$52.00* on the board.
>
> **Say:** *The problem says I pay with 1 fifty-dollar bill and 1 five-dollar bill.* Write *$50.00* and *$5.00* on the board, or hold up play money. Say: *I start with the greatest value, the fifty-dollar bill, and then add the five-dollar bill. 50 + 5 = 55. I have $55.00.* Write *$55.00* on the board. Say: *I will pay with $55.00.*
>
> **Say:** *I need to find out how much change I will get. I will start with the price of $52.00. Then I will count on until I get to the amount I paid.* Use play money as you count: *$52.00, $53.00, $54.00, $55.00. Now I will count the money to see how much change I will get. I will get $3.00 change.*

Say: *I will use the sentence frame to write my answer.* Write on the board: *If I spend $52.00 and pay with $55.00, I will get $3.00 change.*

Provide additional examples, such as: *If I spend $19.98, and I pay with 1 ten-dollar bill and 2 five-dollar bills, how much change will I get? If I spend $11.65, and I pay with 3 five-dollar bills, how much change will I get?* Together with students, read each question chorally.

Have students work in small groups. Write two similar problems to the ones above on the board. Have groups follow the steps you explained in the Think Aloud. Students write the answers on a separate sheet of paper, using a sentence with *if* and *will* clauses. Have students share their answers. Discuss answers, and explain incorrect answers. Remind students how to count money by starting with the greatest value, and how to count change, starting with the cost and ending with the amount you paid.

Have students work in pairs. Starting with a $20 bill, have pairs decide how much they will pay for something and then use the question frame to write a question. Then have pairs exchange questions with another pair and answer the questions.

C Review and Practice

Before having students complete the Practice the Language activity, review the directions. Write a sample question on the board, such as: *If I spend $25.32, and pay with 1 ten-dollar bill, 2 five-dollar bills, and 6 one-dollar bills, how much change will I get?*

- **Have students work with a partner.** Have them use play money to solve the problem. ($0.68) Monitor and assist as necessary.

After this pair work, have students complete the Practice the Language activity on page 15 in the student worktext. Circulate, and assess students as they do the activity.

D Assess and Intervene

How well can students answer questions using sentences with *if* and *will* clauses based on the Practice the Language activity on page 15? Use the rubric to identify students who need extra support through additional help and the Intervention activity.

Intermediate

- ☐ Answers at least 1 question correctly using sentence frames.
- ☐ Asks and answers questions using sentence frames. Errors do not affect comprehension.

  Example of an answer a student might write: *Have $55.00. If I spend $52.00, and pay with $55.00, I will get $3.00 for change.*

Advanced

- ☐ Answers at least 2 questions correctly.
- ☐ Asks questions and writes sentences using *if* and *will* correctly with minimal errors.

  Example of an answer a student might write: *I have $55.00. If I spend $52.00, will get $3.00 change.*

INTERVENTION 15 minutes

If students are having trouble answering the questions in the Practice the Language activity, have them write the simplified versions of the steps on separate index cards. Together read each step, and use play coins and bills to complete each step. Underneath the step on the index card, students write a sentence that describes what they did. For example: *I have $_____.* Write this sentence frame on the board: *If I spend _____, I will get _____.* Using the information on the index cards, help students fill in the blanks to complete sentences with *if* and *will* clauses for each question on page 15 of the student worktext.

Solve Math Problems

Objective Make a list of coins that you need to make change to help you solve problems

45 minutes

Teach this lesson:
- **After** lessons on counting money and making change
- **Before** students complete the activities on page 16 of the student worktext

You need these materials:
- play coins and bills
- Worksheet 4
- Transparency 7
- Three word problems on making change

Solve Math Problems

Objective Make a list of coins that you need to make change to help you solve problems.

Learn to Solve Problems

Problem I want to buy a zoo poster for $5.29. If I pay with a $10.00 bill, how much change will I get?

Step 1: Read the problem. Underline the question. Circle the facts.

Step 2: Start with the cost and count on to the amount paid. $5.29, $5.30, $5.40, $5.50, $5.75, $6.00, $7.00, $8.00, $9.00, $10.00
Make a list of coins and bills. 1¢, 10¢, 10¢, 25¢, 25¢, $1.00, $1.00, $1.00, $1.00

Step 3: Count the coins and bills on your list to answer the question.
I count the coins and bills to answer the question. I start with $1.00, the greatest value, and end with the pennies, the smallest value. $1.00, $2.00, $3.00, $4.00, $4.25, $4.50, $4.60, $4.70, $4.71.
I will get $4.71 change.

Practice Solving Math Problems

Directions Follow steps 1 to 3 above to solve the problems below. Show your work on a separate sheet of paper. Answer the questions in complete sentences below.

1. Shian and Reyna want to buy a soccer ball for $9.98. If they pay with a $20.00 bill, how much change will they get?
$10.00, 1¢, and 1¢. Shian and Reyna will get $10.02 change.

2. Evilisse wants to buy some fish food for her fish for $5.39. If she pays with a $10.00 bill, how much change will she get?
$4, 25¢, 25¢, 10¢, 1¢. Evilisse will get $4.61 change.

3. Luis wants to buy a birthday present for his mother for $6.89. If he pays with 1 five-dollar bill and 2 one-dollar bills, how much change will he get?
10¢, 1¢. Luis will get 11¢ change.

4. Carmen wants to buy some seeds to plant in her garden for $2.59. If she pays with 2 one-dollar bills and 3 quarters, how much change will she get?
10¢, 5¢,1¢. Carmen will get 16¢ change.

16 · Money

EXTENSION AND ENRICHMENT

10 minutes

Work with students to write a problem that includes how much money they have, what they buy, how much it costs, and how much change they will get. Write this incomplete problem on the board, fill it in, and then use play money to solve it: _____ has $_____. He wants to buy _____. It costs _____. He will get _____ change. After solving the problem, ask: *Why is it important to count your money before and after you buy something?* (so you know you have enough money to buy the item you want; so you know you've gotten the correct amount of change back from your purchase)

A Introduce

Read aloud the Lesson Objective with students. Explain that making lists of coins they will need to make change will help students solve word problems. Say: *Do you remember when we used play money to help us count money and make change? In this lesson, you will just make a list of the coins and bills and use your lists to help you answer questions about how much change someone will get.*

B Teach and Learn

Write this problem on the board, and read it aloud: *I want to buy a zoo poster for $5.29. If I pay with a $10.00 bill, how much change will I get?* Have students open their student worktexts to page 16 and look at Learn to Solve Problems. Tell students that the numbered steps will help them list the coins in a money math problem.

Highlighted words and phrases may affect student comprehension.

Model how to solve the problem by using a Think Aloud:

Think Aloud

Write Step 1 on the board. Say: *First I read the problem.* Read the problem out loud. *Next I need to underline the question "how much change will I get?"* Underline the question. *Then I need to circle the facts.* Circle *$5.29* and *$10.00*.

Write Step 2 on the board, and read it aloud. Say: *What is the cost? The zoo poster costs $5.29. I need to count on from $5.29 to the amount I paid. I start at $5.29 and add to get a number that is easy to work with. I keep counting on until I get to the amount of money I paid, $10.00. OK, $5.29. I need a penny. That makes $5.30.* (write *1¢*) *I need a dime. That makes $5.40.* (write *10¢*) *I need another dime to get to $5.50.* (write *10¢*) *Next, I need two quarters: $5.75, $6.00* (write *25¢, 25¢*) *Now I can add bills. I need $4.00.* (write *$1.00, $1.00, $1.00, $1.00*) *Here are the coins and bills I need: 1 penny (1¢), 2 dimes (10¢, 10¢), 2 quarters (25¢, 25¢), and 4 one-dollar bills ($1, $1, $1, $1).*

Write Step 3 on the board, and read it aloud. Say: *Now I can count the coins and bills to see how much change I will get. I start with the greatest value and end with the smallest value. I start with $1.00, $2.00, $3.00, $4.00, $4.25, $4.50, $4.60, $4.70, $4.71. I will get $4.71 change.* Write these numbers on the board as necessary to support students.

Choose three word problems involving making change from the grade-level math textbook. Write these problems on the board, or have students keep their textbooks open.

- **Display Transparency 7 as a visual aid for support to solve problems.**

- **Divide the class into groups of three.** Give each group copies of Worksheet 4, which shows the chart on page 16 of the student worktext. Pairs should solve all three problems and use one worksheet for each problem. Have each student take turns writing. All answers should be in complete sentences.

- **As students work, circulate and help students as necessary.** Model instruction similar to that shown in the Think Aloud above. If students need additional assistance, first have them use play money to count out their change. Then have them use the play money to make their lists. In addition, allow students to use their worktexts as a reference.

C Review and Practice

Give students more practice making lists to show the bills and coins they will get as change. Divide the class into pairs, and have them follow the steps on the worksheet by listing the coins and bills they would get back as change.

Write money word problems on the board. Example: *Lin and Lee want to buy a book for their mother for $7.99. If they pay with a $20.00 bill, how much change will they get?*

- **Read the problem aloud.** Have the pairs complete the following sentence frame to tell how much change Lin and Lee will get: _____ will get _____ change. Students' choice of coin combinations may vary, so list all correct responses on the board and explain if necessary.

- **Provide additional examples.** Monitor students' work to make sure they understand the steps and are solving the problems correctly.

Read aloud the directions for Practice Solving Math Problems in the student worktext. Circulate, and assess how well they are using the strategy taught in this lesson and writing complete sentences to answer each problem.

D Assess and Intervene

How well can students list the coins needed to make change and write a complete sentence to answer the question, based on Practice Solving Math Problems on page 16? Use the rubric to identify students who need extra support through additional help and the Intervention activity.

Intermediate

☐ At least 3 lists are accurately written to represent the change in 3 word problems.

☐ Answers are written in simple, complete sentences, with only minimal errors.

Example of an answer a student might write: *He get $10.02 changed.*

Advanced

☐ All lists are accurately written to represent the change in all word problems.

☐ Answers are clearly written in complete sentences with no errors that affect meaning. Answers use the future tense, *will*.

Example of an answer a student might write: *They will get 55¢ change.*

INTERVENTION 15 minutes

Are students having difficulty counting up with bills and coins of different values? Have students practice counting up by fives, tens, and twenty-fives. Give students a small stack of nickels or play five-dollar bills, and have them practice counting up by fives. Next, have students count up using dimes or play ten-dollar bills. Then, have them count up using quarters. Give the students a stack of mixed bills and coins. Ask the students to line up the bills and coins in order of value on the desk in front of them. Then, have them count up starting with the smallest coin or bill.

Understand the Main Idea

Objective Follow a model to add and subtract in your head in two ways.

30 minutes

Teach this lesson:
- **Before** introducing lessons of mental math in students' grade-level math textbooks
- **Before** students complete the activities on page 17 of the student worktext

You need these materials:
- manipulative objects such as base-ten blocks, counters, and beans
- Transparency 9

Prerequisite Background Knowledge
- Basic concepts of addition and subtraction

BP 6 ELL BEST PRACTICE #6:
Hands-On Activities

Hands-on activities can help English language learners learn academic concepts and language in ways that are not dependent on how much English they understand, read, speak, or write. The mental calculations needed for doing math in one's head are more difficult when done in, or translated from, another language. Concrete objects are very helpful for remembering what was done during various degrees in mental calculation. As students progress from simple to more complex math problems, be sure to provide the hands-on manipulatives they need to be successful.

Throughout this module, when you see **BP 6**, you will find an example of hands-on activities.

Module 5: Mental Math

Understand the Main Idea

Objective Follow a model to add and subtract in your head in two ways.

Learn the Main Idea

She thinks: 25 + 64 = ? That's hard to do in my head. I'll **break the numbers apart:**

$$25 = 20 + 5$$
$$64 = 60 + 4$$

Add the tens: 20 + 60 = 80
Add the ones: 5 + 4 = 9
Add the sums: 80 + 9 = 89
So, 25 + 64 = 89.

He thinks: 60 − 18 = ? That's hard to do in my head. I'll **use an easier number:** 20 is close to 18, and it's easier to subtract.
Subtract: 60 − 20 = 40
Adjust: I subtracted 2 extra ones. I have to adjust. I'll add 2 extra ones: 40 + 2 = 42
So, 60 − 18 = 42.

MAIN IDEA You can add and subtract in your head in different ways.

Practice Applying the Main Idea

Directions In questions 1 to 3, add or subtract in your head. Then write down the steps you used. In question 4, answer the question in a complete sentence. Use a separate sheet of paper.

1. Tell how to add 72 + 26 in your head. Use breaking apart. Break apart: 72 = 70 + 2; 26 = 20 + 6. Add tens: 70 + 20 = 90. Add ones: 2 + 6 = 8. Add sums: 90 + 8 = 98.

2. Tell how to add 72 + 26 in your head. Use adjusting. Use an easier number. Adjust: 72 is close to 70, so 70 + 26. Add: 70 + 26 = 96. Adjust: I didn't add enough. I need to add 2 more. 96 + 2 = 98.

3. Tell how to subtract 46 − 12 in your head. Use adjusting. Use an easier number. Adjust: 12 is close to 10, so 46 − 10. Subtract: 46 − 10 = 36. Adjust: I didn't subtract enough. I need to subtract 2 more. 36 − 2 = 34.

4. Why is it important to be able to add and subtract in your head? It is important because sometimes you need to add or subtract and don't have a pencil and paper or a calculator.

A Introduce

Read aloud the Lesson Objective with students. Tell students that they will learn steps to follow to help them add and subtract in their heads.

Help students activate their prior knowledge. Ask: *Have you ever needed to add or subtract, but didn't have a pencil or paper with you? Where were you? What did you need to find out? What did you do?*

Direct students to the illustration on the left of page 17 in the student worktext. Ask: *What is the girl doing?* (buying a pen and a notebook) *What does she need to find out?* (the total) *How can she find out the total?* (add)

Focus students' attention on the illustration on the right. Ask: *What is the boy doing?* (buying a pencil) *What does he want to find out?* (how much money he will have left) *What can he do to find out?* (subtract)

- **Tell students that the boy and girl in the pictures are going to try to solve the problems in their head.** Say: *They are not going to use paper, pencil, or a calculator to help them do the problems. In this lesson, you'll learn about two different ways to solve math problems in your head.*

Highlighted words and phrases may affect student comprehension.

Read aloud the Main Idea on page 17 in the student worktext. Tell students that the objective of this lesson is to help them learn different ways to add and subtract in their heads.

B Teach and Learn

Point to the illustration on the left on page 17 of the student worktext. Ask: *What two numbers does the girl want to add?* Write *25 + 64* on the board. Ask a student volunteer to read aloud what the girl is saying. Write the word *break apart* on the board.

- **Ask:** *What's another way to say* break apart? (separate, divide, split in two)

- **Ask:** *What do you do when you break apart numbers? When numbers have 2 digits, we can break them apart into tens and ones.* Write *48 = 40 + 8* on the board. Have pairs of students write and break apart other 2-digit numbers.

- **Say:** *The girl wants to add 25 + 64 in her head. She decides to break apart the numbers. Then she can add the tens and ones separately. Why does she add the tens and ones separately?* (it's easier to do the math in her head)

- **Ask:** *How can you break apart 25?* Write *25 = 20 + 5* on the board. *How can you break apart 64?* Write *64 = 60 + 4.*

Say: *After the girl breaks apart the addends 25 and 64, she adds the tens.* Define *addends* if necessary. Say: *It is usually easier to add the tens first when you are adding in your head.* Write on the board and read aloud: *20 + 60.* Say: *Can you add 20 + 60 in your head? What is the answer?* (80) Write the answer on the board.

Say: *Then she adds the ones.* Write on the board: *5 + 4.* Ask: *Can you add 5 + 4 in your head? What is the answer?* (9) Write the answer on the board.

Say: *Then she adds the two sums and gets the answer to the problem. Can you add 80 + 9 in your head?* Write *80 + 9 = 89* on the board.

BP 6 **Have groups of four students check the girl's answer by using base-ten blocks, counters, or beans.**

Tell students that you can also break apart numbers to subtract in your head.

Point to the illustration on the right-hand side of the page. Ask a student volunteer to read aloud the text of the boy's speech bubble. Say: *The boy also does math in his head. But he is*

doing it a different way. Instead of breaking apart numbers, he will adjust the numbers.

- **Ask:** *What does it mean to adjust something?* (change it to make it better, like adjusting pillows or blankets, or a seat belt) Say: *When you adjust numbers, you change them so they work better in the problem.*

- **Say:** *The boy wants to subtract 18 from 60.* Write *60 − 18* on the board. *Subtracting 18 from 60 is hard to do in your head. He uses another number that is easier to subtract in his head.*

- **Write 60 − 20 on the board.** Ask: *Why does he subtract 20 from 60?* (20 is close to 18, it is easy) *Can you subtract 20 from 60 in your head? What is the answer?* (40) *But subtracting 20 was too much. One pencil only costs 18 cents. What does he need to do?* (he needs to adjust the number) *How does he adjust the number?* (he subtracted too much so he needs to put it back; he adds 2.) *40 + 2 = 42. So 60 − 18 is 42.*

Have students work in pairs. Write *56 − 32* on the board. Have students discuss how to do the math in their head. Use prompting questions like: *How can you break apart the numbers? How can you adjust the numbers?*

C Review and Practice

Review the concepts of breaking apart and adjusting. Write the following number problems on the board and discuss how to solve the problems:

$$36 + 42 \qquad 47 - 31$$

Display Transparency 9. Tell students they will work in pairs. Walk students through the steps for breaking apart numbers and for adjusting sums or differences. Have one student in each pair choose an addition problem. Then tell students that they will break apart the numbers to find the sum. The other student will adjust the numbers to find the sum.

- **Have pairs compare their answers.** If students have different answers, have them talk through the steps to find out what went wrong.

- **Next have the other student in each pair choose a subtraction problem.** Have the first student find the difference by adjusting a number, and the other student use breaking apart.

- **BP 6** **Suggest that students use base-ten blocks, counters, or beans to check their answers throughout this activity.**

Read aloud the directions for the Practice Applying the Main Idea activity in the student worktext. Remind students to use the problems at the top of the page as a model. Have students work independently. Circulate and assess them while they are working.

D Assess and Intervene

Can students use words and numbers to tell how to solve addition and subtraction problems in their heads based on Practice Applying the Main Idea on page 17 of the student worktext? Use the rubric to identify students who need extra support through additional help and the Intervention activity.

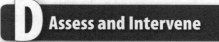

Intermediate

- ☐ Answers 2 of questions 1–3 correctly, but may not include explanations of how to adjust.
- ☐ Gives at least one valid reason for why mental math is important.

Advanced

- ☐ Answers all 3 of questions 1–3 correctly, including explanations of how to adjust.
- ☐ Gives two reasons, or one reason with details, for why mental math is important.

INTERVENTION   10 minutes

If students are having trouble remembering the steps needed to break apart or adjust numbers, have them copy the steps from the transparency onto separate sheets of paper. Mix up the papers. Give students a problem and have them put the correct steps in sequence. Then scaffold students as they use the steps to orally explain how to add or subtract in their heads.

Lesson

2

Learn the Vocabulary

Objective Talk and write about adding and subtracting mentally using vocabulary words.

30 minutes

Teach this lesson:
- **Before** introducing lessons on mental math in students' grade-level math textbooks
- **Before** students complete the activities on page 18 of the student worktext

You need these materials:
- Vocabulary Cards
- index cards

Lesson Vocabulary

Essential Vocabulary

mental math	property
to break apart	compensation/to compensate

Additional Vocabulary

addend	order (noun)	sum
difference	to adjust	

LESSON

2

Learn the Vocabulary

Objective Talk and write about adding and subtracting mentally using vocabulary words.

 Learn the Words

Directions Fill in the blanks below.

Word/Phrase	Definition	Draw/Write
mental math	doing math in your head	Draw a picture of yourself doing mental math on a separate piece of paper.
to break apart	to rewrite a number as the sum of two other numbers	Break apart the numbers: 67 + 28 $67 + 3 = 70 \qquad 28 - 3 = 25$ $70 + 25 = 95$
compensation/ to compensate	changing numbers to adjust for adding or subtracting too many or not enough	Compensate: 67 − 28 $67 + 2 = 69 \qquad 28 + 2 = 30$ $69 - 30 = 39$
property	something that is always true about an operation	Write the names of the three properties of addition: 1. Order Property 2. Grouping Property 3. Zero Property

Practice the Words

Directions Match each word or phrase from the first column with the correct example or definition from the second column. For question 5, write your answer on a separate sheet of paper.

1. property _c___ a. changing numbers to adjust for adding or subtracting too many or not enough

2. mental math _D___ b. to rewrite a number as the sum of two other numbers

3. to break apart _B___ c. something that is always true about an operation

4. compensation _A___ d. doing math in your head

5. Write a complete sentence to explain a situation where you might use mental math.
   Answers will vary.

Introduce

Call students' attention to page 18 of the student worktext. Read aloud the Lesson Objective with students.

Ask: *What words and phrases do you remember about doing math in your head?* (break apart, adjust) Write the words on the board. Say: *You learned about breaking apart and adjusting numbers. We're going to use these phrases and some new ones to talk about doing math in your head.*

Write on the board: *mental math, property, to break apart, compensation, to compensate.* Have students say the words after you. Then have students discuss the meanings of the terms with a partner. When they are finished, ask them to check with another pair to see if they understand the words correctly. Tell students that they will learn more about these words in this lesson.

Choose words from the Additional Vocabulary box that you think will be useful. Add these words to the list on the board. Elicit or provide examples or definitions for all the words on the list.

Highlighted words and phrases may affect student comprehension.

Teach and Learn

Introduce the Essential Vocabulary orally. Refer students to the chart on page 18 of the student worktext and read aloud the headings of the three columns –Word/Phrase, Definition, Draw/Write.

Focus students' attention on the phrase *mental math* in the chart. Say: *Mental math is a way of doing math problems in your head. The word* mental *is an adjective. It describes the noun* math. *The word* mental *means it is about the mind or brain. You will be solving math problems in your mind!*

- **Have students draw a picture of themselves in the space provided in the last column.** Ask volunteers to draw their pictures on the board. Students may draw a thought bubble or a light bulb over their head to show that they are thinking.

Remind students that they learned about "breaking apart" to do mental math. Have a student volunteer read aloud the definition for the phrase *to break apart*.

- **Ask:** *What's another way to say* break apart? (to separate, to take apart) *Do you remember how the girl on page 17 solved the problem in her head? She broke apart the numbers in the addition problem 67 + 28 to come up with the sum.* Remind students that a *sum* is the answer to an addition problem. *What did she do with the addends 67 and 28?* Remind students that an *addend* is any of the numbers that are added. Have students fill in the information requested in the space provided in the last column.

Ask students to recall how the boy in Lesson 1 did mental math. (he adjusted the numbers) Remind students that he performed the two problems in his head in a different way than the girl. Write the subtraction problem from page 17 on the board: *59 − 13.* Ask: *What did he do to find the difference, or the answer when subtracting the two numbers?* Explain to students that adjusting numbers is the same as compensating. Have students pronounce the word *compensate* after you. Ask a student volunteer to read the definition of the phrase *compensation/to compensate* from the chart.

Read aloud the definition for *property* on the chart. Ask students if they remember the names of the three properties of addition.

Have students work in pairs to try to orally recall the names. (Order Property, Grouping Property, Zero Property) Have a volunteer pair provide the names. Write the names of the properties on the board, and then read them aloud as a class.

- **Have students fill in the properties they know in the last column.** Tell students they will learn more about these properties in the next lesson. Students may know that the Order Property is sometimes called the Commutative Property, the Grouping Property is sometimes called the Associative Property, and the Zero Property is sometimes called the Identity Property. If students use these alternate names, write them down next to the common names.

📇 **Have students complete Vocabulary Cards for the words in this lesson.**

Review and Practice

📇 **To review the vocabulary terms, have students work in groups of three.** They will play the game The Professor.

- **Student A will be the professor**. Students B and C will be the students. Students B and C take turns showing one Vocabulary Card to the professor. The professor has to say the word and then write a complete sentence correctly on an index card using the word or phrase.

- **Emphasize that the sentence provided should show an understanding of the vocabulary term.** Have students rotate roles so each student in the group gets to be the professor.

- **Circulate as the groups work, checking students' written answers.**

Read aloud the directions for the Practice the Words activity at the bottom of page 18 of the student worktext. Tell students that they will work independently. They will read the word or phrase in the first column and look for its matching definition in the second column. Then they will write the letter of the correct definition on the line after the vocabulary word. Make sure students cover up the top part of the page as they work.

Circulate as students work, giving assistance as needed to individual students.

Assess and Intervene

Can students use the new vocabulary to talk about adding or subtracting mentally, based on Practice the Words on page 18 of the student worktext? Use the rubric to identify students who need additional support through extra help and the Intervention activity.

Intermediate

☐ Matches at least 2 of the 4 words with the correct example or definition.

☐ Writes a sentence that shows understanding of when mental math is used, but may be incomplete and contain errors; errors may make comprehension difficult, but do not affect meaning.

Example of a sentence a student might write: *I use mental math when I needs find out money at store.*

Advanced

☐ Matches all 4 of the words with the correct example or definition.

☐ Writes a sentence that clearly demonstrates an understanding of when mental math is used. Errors do not affect comprehension.

Example of a sentence a student might write: *I use mental math when I need to find out how much something costs at store.*

INTERVENTION 10 minutes 🕐

If students have difficulty matching vocabulary words with their definitions, give each student four index cards. Have students write the definitions of each of the four vocabulary words on page 18 of the student worktext on one side of an index card. Have students work with a partner. Students take turns reading the definitions and guessing the vocabulary terms. When they have guessed all four, have them check their answers by looking at page 19. Have them copy the vocabulary word or phrase on the back of the appropriate index card. Have partners take turns saying the words and giving the meanings. Finally, have students look at the meanings and try to write a number sentence example for each term.

Lesson

3

Use More Language

Objective Use root words to remember the meanings of the Commutative, Associative, and Identity Properties.

| 30 minutes | |

Teach this lesson:
- **After** lessons on mental math in students' grade-level math textbook
- **Before** students complete the activities on page 19 of the student worktext

Lesson Vocabulary

Associative Property of Addition
Commutative Property of Addition
Identity Property of Addition

A Introduce

Call student's attention to page 19 in the student worktext. Have them work with a partner to discuss what they see.

Read aloud the Lesson Objective with students. Explain that in this lesson they will discuss three properties of addition. On the board write the title *Three Properties of Addition*. Ask: *What is a property?* (something that is always true about an operation) Say: *In this lesson, you will learn these properties of addition.* Underneath the title, write: *Commutative Property, Associative Property,* and *Identity Property*. Say each property out loud as you write it down, and have students repeat after you.

Tell students that these addition properties will help them do math in their heads. The properties will be useful when students don't have a pen, pencil, or paper and need to add or subtract something.

Draw a picture of a tree and its roots on the board. Point to the roots in the drawing. Ask: *Do you know what a root is? It is the part of the tree that is underground. Roots are the support or foundation of the tree.*

Ask: *What do you think a "root word" is? A root word is the simplest form of a word. Other words are formed from root words. The word happiness has the root word happy.* Ask students for other examples of root words they may know.

Use More Language

Lesson

3

Objective Use root words to remember the meanings of the Commutative, Associative, and Identity Properties.

Learn the Language

Properties explain why you can break numbers apart and add in any order.

Addition Property	Definition	Example
Commutative Property **commute** — to exchange or change places	You can add two numbers in any order. The sum is the same.	3 + 6 = 6 + 3 9 = 9
Associative Property **associate** — to join	You can change the grouping of numbers you add. The sum is the same.	(5 + 2) + 7 = 14 5 + (2 + 7) = 14
Identity Property **identical** — same	The sum of any number and zero is that same number.	4 + 0 = 4 0 + 398 = 398

Practice the Language

Directions Find and circle the hidden name of an addition property in questions 1 to 3. Then draw a line to connect each word to the number problem that is an example of that property. Answer question 4 in a complete sentence.

1. M O E I K W O (ASSOCIATIVE) W O C X L K ———— 2 + 8 = 8 + 2

2. B R X S (IDENTITY) B K L P E I N J F L C U J K P ———— (9 + 6) + 5 = 9 + (6 + 5)

3. N S C A I T P Q U A (COMMUTATIVE) R N D ———— 17 + 0 = 17

4. Why is it helpful to know roots of some words?

   Answers will vary.

   _____

   _____

Highlighted words and phrases may affect student comprehension.

Write the root words *port* (carry), *mit* (send), and *graph* (write) on the board. Have students come up with other words that have these words in them (port: airport, portable; mit: transmit, commit, submit; graph: telegraph, photograph).

B Teach and Learn

Call students' attention to the three-column chart on page 19 of the student worktext. Point to the left column titled *Addition Property* and to the first property listed, *Commutative Property*. Model the words aloud, and have students repeat. Ask: *What do you think the root word of* commutative *is?* (commute)

- **Say:** *The root word* commute *means to exchange or change places.* Tell students that a commuter is a person who travels from home to work and then returns from work to home. He or she changes places.

- **Say:** *What are some other words or phrases that have the root word* commute? *What do they mean?* (commuter train, commuter bus, commuter traffic) *Do any of you commute to school? Do you commute by car or by bus?* (Take a count.) *Do your parents commute to work?* (Ask for hands.) *How do they commute to work?* (Take a count.)

- **Explain that the Commutative Property of Addition means that you can exchange the places of any two numbers when you add.** You can add in any order. For example, $3 + 6 = 6 + 3$. The sum (9) will still be the same. Remind students that this property is also called the Order Property. Have students work in pairs to think of two other examples of the Commutative Property.

Use a similar approach to explain the root words for the other two properties. Model saying the words aloud, and have students repeat. Then ask students to find the root word, and explain the meaning of the root word.

- **Say:** *When we associate, we join a group. What are some other words or phrases that have the root word* associate? (association, like the PTA [Parent Teacher Association]) *The Associative Property of Addition is about groupings of numbers. When you add, the addends can change their groups, and the sum will stay the same.*

Write the example from page 19 in the worktext on the board: $(5 + 2) + 7 = 5 + (2 + 7)$ Say: *The sum* (14) *will still be the same.* Remind students that another term for the Associative Property is the Grouping Property. Have students work in pairs to write two more examples of the Associative Property.

- **Ask:** *What do you think the root of* Identity *is?* (iden) *The root* iden *means same, equal, or alike. Do any of you have an identical twin? What do you know about identical twins?* (they look exactly alike) *What are some other words or phrases that have the root* iden? (identity, identification)

- **Explain that the Identity Property of Addition means that the sum of any number plus zero is that same number.** When you add zero to a number, the number keeps its identity—it stays the same! For example, $4 + 0 = 4$. Remind students that the Identity Property of Addition is also called the Zero Property. Have students work in pairs to write two more examples of the Identity Property.

Have students fill out Vocabulary Cards for the three properties of addition.

C Review and Practice

Review the meanings of the three properties of addition by using root words. Have students work with partners to play an alliteration game. Say the letter *I*. Have one student write the root word they learned that starts with *I* (iden). Then have the partner write words with that root. Next, partners work together to write the property name (for example: iden; identity, identification, identify; Identity Property). Do the same with letters *A* and *C*.

Read aloud the directions for the Practice the Language activity at the bottom of page 19 of the student worktext. Tell students that they are to look at the lines of letters to find the hidden names of the three properties of addition they learned in this lesson.

Encourage students to use the information from the Learn the Language chart to help them find the words. Then have students decide which word goes with each number problem. Tell them they will have to write a complete sentence to answer number 4.

Remind students they are to work independently on the activity. Go through the room and assess them while they are working.

D Assess and Intervene

Can every student remember the meanings of the three properties of addition and recognize which number problems are examples of each, based on Practice the Language on page 19 of the student worktext? Use the rubric to identify students who need extra support through additional help and the Intervention activity.

Intermediate

- ☐ Finds/circles at least 2 addition properties. Matches at least 2 addition properties with correct number problems.
- ☐ Writes phrases or a sentence giving a logical reason, although errors may impede clarity. **Example of a sentence a student might write:** *Root is help for more word.*

Advanced

- ☐ Finds/circles all 3 addition properties. Matches 3 addition properties with correct number problems.
- ☐ Writes a complete sentence giving a clear, logical reason, with few errors. **Example at a sentence a student might write:** *If I know root of word, I can know other words with same root.*

INTERVENTION 5 minutes

If students have difficulty associating the name of the addition property to a number example, write a digit from 0–9 on each of 10 large index cards. Have each of 10 students in the audience "be" a different number by "wearing" (or holding) a number. Call out one of the addition properties and have "numbers" come to the front of the room and form an example of that property. Two numbers can get together to form a two-digit number. If there are fewer than 10 students, line up all the cards on the chalkboard or whiteboard tray or a desk, and have students put them in order to show each property.

Solve Math Problems

Objective Explain how you break apart numbers or compensate to solve a problem using mental math.

30 minutes

Teach this lesson:
- **After** lessons on mental math in students' grade-level math textbook
- **Before** students complete the activities on page 20 of the student worktext

You need these materials:
- Worksheet 5
- Transparency 10
- base-ten blocks, counters, or beans

EXTENSION AND ENRICHMENT   10 minutes

Have small groups of students create and present skits studying situations in which they have to use mental math. Provide examples to encourage students to be funny and creative, such as: *A boy and his mother went to the store to buy new clothes. They took $50 and a calculator to the store with them. On the way, they dropped the calculator. They wanted to buy a shirt for $18 and pants for $24. Did they have enough money?*

Solve Math Problems

Objective Explain how you break apart numbers or compensate to solve a problem using mental math.

Learn to Solve Problems

> **Problem** Ana has $75.00. She wants to buy in-line skates for $43 and a helmet for $29. Does Ana have enough money?

One Way! Breaking Apart Numbers

$43 + $29

Step 1:	43 = 40 + 3 29 = 20 + 9
Step 2:	Add the ones: 3 + 9 = 12
Step 3:	Add the tens: 40 + 20 = 60
Step 4:	Add the sums: 12 + 60 = 72

Another Way! Compensating Numbers

$43 + $29

Step 1:	Add 1 to 29 to get 30: 1 + 29 = 30
Step 2:	Add 43 + 30 to get 73.
Step 3:	Then subtract 1 from 73: 73 − 1 = 72

> Ana has enough money either way! Plus, she has $3.00 left over!

Practice Solving Math Problems

Directions Solve these word problems in your head. On the lines, write the answer in a complete sentence. On a separate sheet of paper, tell which strategy you used and show how you used it to solve the problem. Answer question 4 on a separate sheet of paper.

1 Huy ran five days each week last year. He ran 260 days out of 365 days. How many days did he not run? _____

Huy did not run 105 days.

2 Lita likes to write poems. Last summer she wrote 48 poems. This summer she wrote 56 poems. How many poems did she write all together? _____

Lita wrote 104 poems all together.

3 750 people attended a performance of a school play. 553 of the seats were taken by students. How many seats were left for other students? _____

197 seats remained for other people.

4 Tell about a situation where you might need to use mental math to add or subtract. Write a complete sentence.
I might use mental math when I don't have paper, pencil, or pen handy, when I am at the store buying something, when I am counting ants or fireflies, etc.

Highlighted words and phrases may affect student comprehension.

B Introduce

Have students turn to page 20 in their student worktexts.

Read aloud the Lesson Objective with students. Tell students that in this lesson they will be using mental math to solve word problems. Remind them of the two main ways to add and subtract, or to compute, in their heads: breaking apart numbers, and compensating by adjusting numbers.

Have pairs of students read the problem at the top of page 20. Have partners tell each other what the problem is about.

Ask: *How much money does Ana have?* ($75.00) *What does she want to buy?* (skates and a helmet) *How do you know how much they cost?* (the prices are in the problem)

Teach and Learn

Read the problem on page 20 aloud, or have a volunteer read it. Check students' comprehension of the problem by asking: *What kind of skates does Ana want?* (in-line skates) *What does she plan to wear on her head?* (a helmet)

Say: *The question usually comes at the end of a word problem.* Ask: *What is the question?* (Does Ana have enough money?)

Explain that there are two ways this problem can be solved using mental math. Point out the two columns: *One Way! Breaking Apart Numbers* and *Another Way! Compensating Numbers.*

Walk students through the first strategy, breaking apart numbers, by asking questions such as: *How does Ana break apart $43 + $29? What does she do in Step 2? What does she do in Step 3? What does she do in Step 4 to get her answer?*

BP 6 Walk students through the second strategy, compensating numbers, by asking: *How does Ana adjust the numbers $43 + $29? What does she do in Step 2? What does she do in Step 3 to get her answer?* Emphasize that Ana added $1 extra in Step 1. Say: *Now she has to compensate, or adjust, by subtracting that extra $1.* Explain that sometimes we have to add when we compensate, and sometimes we have to subtract. If students aren't sure which to do, they should draw the problem or model it with counters. Then ask: *Does Ana have enough money? What will Ana buy? What will her change be?*

Assign students to work in groups of four. Write these problems on the board: *94 + 16* and *38 + 23*. Have each group discuss which strategy to use. Then have group members work together to solve each number problem. When the group is finished solving the problem, have them tell another group why they chose the strategy they did. Tell them to see if they followed the same steps and if their answers agree.

Display Transparency 10. Have students work in pairs and use mental math to solve the word problems. Have them write the word problems on a sheet of paper and then choose one of the two strategies as they follow the steps to solve each problem:

1. Miko wrote 97 poems last year. This year she has written 24 poems. How many poems has she written in all? (121)

2. Brian delivered newspapers to 86 families in his neighborhood last year. 17 families have moved away. How many families does he deliver papers to this year? (69)

3. Tatsuo played in 26 chess tournaments last year. That is 14 more tournaments than he played in the year before. How many games did Tatsuo play in all during the last 2 years? (38)

- **When the groups are finished solving the problems, ask volunteers to come to the front of the room and explain how they reached their answers.**

Review and Practice

Distribute Worksheet 5 to students. Explain to students that they will individually do each problem on the worksheet and then check with a partner to see if they solved the problems correctly and if they followed the right steps.

- **Have each student decide which of the two strategies he or she will use.** Have students work individually to solve the problems.

- **When students have finished both problems, have them check with a partner to compare answers and discuss their reasoning.**

For further practice using the steps, have student pairs write word problems of their own. Tell students to think about which strategy students need to use: breaking apart numbers or compensating by adjusting numbers. After they have written their problems, have them exchange problems with another pair and solve them. Collect the word problems, and make a class Word Problem Book for each student to take home and practice the strategy with their family.

Read aloud the directions for Practice Solving Math Problems on page 20. Remind students to follow the steps on the top part of the page.

BP 6 Make available to students base-ten blocks, counters, or beans to help them solve these word problems on their own.

Circulate around the room, assessing how well students are following the steps.

Review the answers with students when they have completed both problems.

Assess and Intervene

Were students able to solve word problems in their head and to tell why they chose a certain strategy? Were they able identify a personal situation for using mental math? Use the rubric to identify students who need extra support through additional help and the Intervention activity.

Intermediate

☐ Correctly solves 2 out of 3 word problems, identifies the strategy used, and explains how the strategy was used.

☐ Can identify a personal situation where mental math might be used, but the response is not a complete sentence and/or has errors.

Example of a sentence a student might write: *I might need use mental math when no paper.*

Advanced

☐ Correctly solves 3 out of 3 word problems, identifies the strategy used, and explains how the strategy was used.

☐ Can write a complete sentence, with few errors, about a personal situation where mental math might be used.

Example of a sentence a student might write: *I might need use mental math when I don't have paper or pen.*

INTERVENTION   5 minutes

If students are having difficulty solving word problems using compensation (or adjusting), write the following on the board: *186 − 47*

To the left, write:

What you think:
  1) It's easy to subtract 50.
  2) I subtracted 3 too many, so I will add 3.

To the right, write:

What you say:
  1) 186 − 50 = 136
  2) 136 + 3 = 139
So, 186 − 47 = 139

Understand the Main Idea

Objective Identify an estimation problem and practice talking and writing about it using clue words.

30 minutes

Teach this lesson:
- **Before** introducing lessons on estimation in the grade-level math textbook
- **Before** students complete the activities on page 21 of the student worktext

You need these materials:
- countable objects (paper clips, math manipulatives, or small pieces of cereal)
- scrap paper

Prerequisite Background Knowledge
- Basic concepts of addition and subtraction
- Rounding

BP 1 **ELL BEST PRACTICE #2:**
Comprehensible Language

In order for ELLs to understand mathematics, they must receive comprehensible input—written or spoken language that they can understand. You can make language more comprehensible by avoiding complex sentence structures, vocabulary that might be unknown, or idiomatic phrases (like "give me a hand"). Whenever possible, paraphrase key concepts in different ways and directly support what you're saying with concrete items.

Throughout this module, when you see **BP 1**, you will find an example of how to make language comprehensible to ELLs.

Module 6: Estimation

Understand the Main Idea

LESSON **1**

Objective Identify an estimation problem and practice talking and writing about it using clue words.

Learn the Main Idea

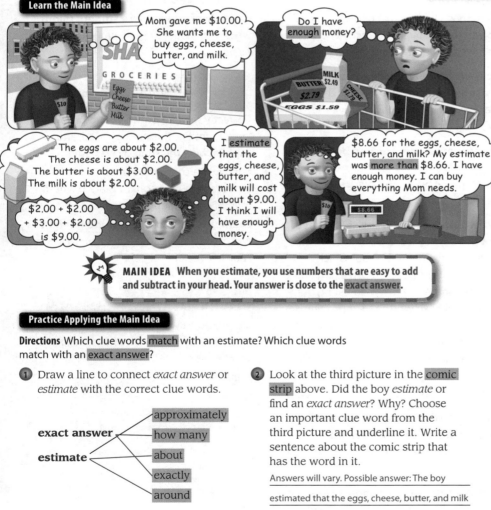

MAIN IDEA When you estimate, you use numbers that are easy to add and subtract in your head. Your answer is close to the exact answer.

Practice Applying the Main Idea

Directions Which clue words match with an estimate? Which clue words match with an exact answer?

1. Draw a line to connect *exact answer* or *estimate* with the correct clue words.

exact answer
estimate

- approximately
- how many
- about
- exactly
- around

2. Look at the third picture in the comic strip above. Did the boy *estimate* or find an *exact answer*? Why? Choose an important clue word from the third picture and underline it. Write a sentence about the comic strip that has the word in it.

Answers will vary. Possible answer: The boy

estimated that the eggs, cheese, butter, and milk

cost about $9.00.

A Introduce

Read aloud the Lesson Objective with students.

Use the comic strip on page 21 of the student worktext as a visual introduction to the concept of estimation.

Help students activate their prior knowledge. Ask: *Have you ever been to a grocery store? Did you ever need to add or subtract in your head to decide if you had enough money?*

Point to the pictures. Ask: *Where is the boy? What is the boy doing? What is he thinking?* Go over the comic strip with students, reading the thought bubbles aloud.

- **Focus on the third panel of the comic strip.** Ask: *Did the boy think he had enough money? How did he know?* Show students that the boy was figuring out about how much money he would need by thinking about it in his head.

Have students form pairs, talk about the comic strip, and then share with the class. Encourage the pairs to describe what the boy was thinking. For example, ask: *The boy thought that the eggs, cheese, butter, and milk cost less than $10.00. How did he know these things cost less than $10.00?*

Highlighted words and phrases may affect student comprehension.

Read aloud the Main Idea with students.
Say: *The boy in the comic strip used numbers that are easy to add in his head. He estimated how much the food would cost.*

 Teach and Learn

Introduce the concept of estimation. Write *estimate* and *an estimate* on the board. Point to and pronounce the words, and have students repeat them. Say: *When I use numbers that are easy to add or subtract in my head, I estimate. A good estimate is a quick way to find an answer.* Tell students that $9.00 was an estimate of what the eggs, milk, butter, and cheese would cost.

BP 1 **Use countable objects to model estimation and exact answer.** Take a handful of the objects and look at them. Say: *I don't know how many (paper clips) I have. I don't have 2 paper clips. I probably have 10 paper clips. I can guess, or estimate, that I have about 10 paper clips. 10 is an estimate.* Write *about 10* on the board under the phrase *an estimate*.

- **Say:** *The word* about *is a clue word. It tells me I do not know exactly how many. When you see the word* about, *it is an estimation problem. You need to estimate.* Teach students other clue words they could say instead of *about* (*more or less, around, almost, approximately*).

- **Open your hand and count the paper clips aloud.** Say: *I estimated that I had about 10 paper clips. Then I counted exactly 13 paper clips. 13 is not an estimate. 13 is the* exact answer. Write *13* on the board under *exact answer.*

Write sentence frames on the board: *I estimate that I have about ____. ____ is an estimate. I counted exactly ____. ____ is an exact answer.*

- **Tell each pair of students to take a handful of paper clips and repeat what you just modeled.** Have each pair write their estimates and exact answers on the board in complete sentences, using the sentence frames on the board.

C Review and Practice

Write *exact, exactly, approximate,* and *approximately* on the board.

Have students fold and tear a sheet of scrap paper into four pieces. Ask them to write one of the four words on each piece of paper.

Pick up a handful of paper clips. Say: *I have approximately, or about, 10 paper clips. 10 is the approximate number of paper clips.* Then count the paper clips. Say: *I have exactly [X] paper clips. [X] is the exact number of paper clips.* Model holding up the paper with the correct word on it as you say each of the four words.

Repeat this type of modeling with another handful of countable objects. Write: *I have ____. ____ is an ____.* Using the sentence frames, make four sentences with each word on the board. Have students hold up a piece of paper with the appropriate word on it as you model the sentence frames. Repeat several times, with students picking up the handful of objects themselves and finishing the sentence frames.

Tell students that when you add *-ly* to the end of the words, it changes the meaning. *Exact* and *approximate* tell about numbers. *Exactly* and *approximately* tell about what you have or do. Ask students for other examples of sentences using each of these words.

Elicit from Spanish-speaking students what these words are in their language. Point out that the English ending *-ly* is the same as the Spanish ending *-mente.*

Read the directions for the Practice Applying the Main Idea activity in the student worktext, and go over the example. After students complete problem 1, ask individuals to explain how they decided to match each clue word.

When students are working on problem 2, check students' work as they locate the clue word in the comic strip and write a sentence.

D Assess and Intervene

Does every student understand what estimation is based on Practice Applying the Main Idea on page 21? Use the rubric to identify students who need extra support through additional help and the Intervention activity.

Intermediate

☐ Matches at least 3 vocabulary words correctly.
☐ Writes a simple sentence using *about,* with some prompting. Sentence may repeat phrases in the comic strip.

  Example of a sentence a student might write: *The eggs are about $2.00 and the butter is about $3.00.*

Advanced

☐ Matches all 4 vocabulary words correctly.
☐ Writes a more complex sentence, with minimal prompting, that includes some words that are not directly mentioned in the third picture.

  Example of a sentence a student might write: *The cheese costs about $2.00 but the butter costs almost $3.00.*

INTERVENTION 10 minutes

Have students work in pairs. Ask them to write a list of grocery items and give each a price. Then have students estimate the approximate value and the exact value. Encourage them to use the clue words.

Learn the Vocabulary

Objective Use vocabulary words that will help you talk and write about estimation.

30 minutes

Teach this lesson:
- **Before** introducing lessons on estimation in the grade-level math textbook
- **Before** students complete the activities on page 22 of the student worktext

You need these materials:
- scrap paper
- Vocabulary Cards
- lined paper
- Transparency 11
- Transparency 12

Lesson Vocabulary

Essential Vocabulary

reasonable	an exact answer
unreasonable	an estimate

Additional Vocabulary

sum/difference	greater than/less than
about/exact	digit
enough	

Learn the Vocabulary

Objective Use vocabulary words that will help you talk and write about estimation.

Learn the Words

Directions Fill in the missing definitions and examples. Then check your answers with your teacher. Answers will vary.

Word/Phrase	Definition	Example
an estimate	numbers that are easy to add or subtract in your head; an answer that is not exact, but close to the exact answer	$2.45 + $4.95 = ? My estimate: $2.00 + $5.00 = about $7.00
an exact answer	a precise, accurate answer; an answer that is not an estimate	$10.50 + $12.50 = $23.00 exactly That is my exact answer.
reasonable	when an answer makes sense or seems right	12 + 21 = about 30 That seems reasonable.
unreasonable	when an answer does not make sense or does not seem right	19 + 18 = about 20 No! That's unreasonable. 19 + 18 is closer to 40 than to 20.

Practice the Words

Directions Read each sentence. Write the correct word or phrase on the line below from the chart above. Then explain why you chose that word or phrase on another sheet of paper. Explanations will vary.

1. I don't know how much all this fruit costs. But I __estimate__ that this fruit will cost me about $5.00.

2. I estimated that the fruit cost $5.00, but it really cost only $2.17. My estimate was __unreasonable__.

3. I estimate that the vegetables will cost about $7.00. They really cost $6.47. $6.47 is about $7.00. So my estimate made sense. It was __reasonable__.

4. When I pay for my groceries at the store, I need to know if I got the correct change. I need to find a more accurate answer than an estimate. I need to find __exact answer__.

A Introduce

Read aloud the Lesson Objective with students. Ask: *What do you remember about estimation?* Have students tell a partner what they remember about estimation.

As a class, brainstorm ideas for vocabulary words that will be important to know. Write suggested words on the board.

Add the words shown in Additional Vocabulary if you feel they will be useful. Elicit or provide examples or definitions for all the words on the list.

B Teach and Learn

Orally introduce the Essential Vocabulary. Review the comic strip from page 22 with students, pausing to orally introduce the Essential Vocabulary in context. Write each word on the board as you introduce it. Ask questions such as the following:

- *The boy made an estimate to find out if he had enough money. How much was the estimate?*

- *The cash register showed the exact answer, or how much the boy had to pay. What was the exact answer?*

- *An estimate is reasonable when it is close to the exact answer. When an estimate is not close to the exact answer, it is unreasonable. Was the boy's estimate reasonable or unreasonable?*

Highlighted words and phrases may affect student comprehension.

22 · Estimation

Review the meanings of Essential Vocabulary using paraphrasing and examples to clarify meanings for any students who had difficulty. Use paper clips or other manipulatives as examples.

Return to the words you wrote on the board during the vocabulary brainstorming. Explain any other important words students suggested, and use them in a sentence.

 Model how to complete the missing definitions and examples using Transparency 11.

Think Aloud

Say: *What is the first phrase on the chart?* (an estimate) *Let's look at the third column and read the example together.* After reading aloud the example, say: *When we estimate, what are we doing?* (adding or subtracting easy numbers in our heads that are close to the exact answer) *Let's think of a good definition for* an estimate. Write this definition for students to copy into the chart: *numbers that are easy to add or subtract in your head; an answer that is not exact, but close to the exact answer*

Say: *What is the next phrase?* (an exact answer) *Look at the second column. This time the definition is there for us.* Read the definition aloud with students. Say: *The words* precise *and* accurate *mean the same as exact.* Help students construct the example, and write it for students to copy into the chart.

Ask students to follow this model as they work in pairs to complete the third and fourth rows of the chart. Have each pair compare their chart with that of another pair of students.

Check students' work, and be sure they all have correct definitions and examples.

 Have students complete Vocabulary Cards for the words in this module.

C Review and Practice

 Write this sentence frame on the board: *That's an example of a /an ____ because ____.* Use Transparency 12 to read the problems aloud. Have students follow along.

1 Gonzalo counted 3 red bicycles, 2 green bicycles, and 15 black bicycles on the road. $3 + 2 + 15 = 20$ bicycles

2 Masao guessed that about 25 bicycles were on the road. His estimate was close.

3 Mom gave Mariela $5.00 to buy bread and milk. Mariela thinks the bread and milk will cost about $4.00.

4 The cashier told Mariela that the total price of the bread and the milk is $2.27. Mariela's estimate was a lot more than the bread and the milk really cost.

Model ways to use the Essential Vocabulary in the sentence frame to explain the first problem. Say: *That's an example of an* exact answer *because Gonzalo knows exactly how many bicycles he saw on the road.* Have individual students use the sentence frame to explain the other three problems (reasonable, estimate, unreasonable). Continue modeling as necessary.

Have students work individually to complete the Practice the Words activity. Circulate and assess their progress, using the assessment below.

D Assess and Intervene

Does every student understand the Essential Vocabulary, based on Practice the Words on page 22? Use the rubric to identify students who need extra support through additional help and the Intervention activity.

Practice the Words on page 22

Intermediate

☐ At least 3 sentences are completed correctly with minimal or no assistance.

Advanced

☐ All 4 sentences are completed correctly without assistance.

INTERVENTION 10 minutes

Play a game with the Vocabulary Cards. Make sure cards are face down, with correct information filled in on the back. Pick a card. Have a student name the word and then make a sentence to explain what word is on the front. Provide a sentence frame: *That's _____ because _____.* Model a correct response using the sentence frame as necessary. For example, say: *That's an estimate because we don't know exactly how much the fruit costs.* Continue until at least one sentence has been made about every word, modeling sentences as necessary.

Lesson
3

Use More Language

Objective Use *because* to explain how to solve estimation problems.

---

45 minutes

Teach this lesson:
- **After** lessons on estimation in the grade-level math textbook
- **Before** students complete the activities on page 23 of the student worktext

You need these materials:
- a blank number line for each student
- lined paper
- index cards
- estimation problems from grade-level math textbook
- Worksheet 6 (four copies for each student)

Use More Language

Objective Use *because* to explain how to solve estimation problems.

LESSON 3

Learn the Language

Step 1:

Use rounding to estimate. Solve the problem by calculating the sum or difference.	**Example**	$456 \rightarrow 500$ $- 314 \rightarrow - 300$ about 200

Step 2:

Describe *how* and *why* you estimated: I rounded _____ because _____ is closer to _____ than to _____ .	**Example**	456 400 500 I rounded 456 up to 500 because the number 456 is closer to 500 than to 400. 314 300 400 I rounded 314 down to 300 because the number 314 is closer to 300 than to 400.

Practice the Language

Directions Use rounding. Explain how to solve each problem on a separate sheet of paper using the word *because*. Explanations will vary.

Example	659 + 136 about 800	First, I rounded 659 up to 700 because the number 659 is closer to 700 than to 600. Then, I rounded 136 down to 100 because the number 136 is closer to 100 than to 200. Finally, I added 700 and 100. My estimated answer is about 800.

① 278 + 722 about 1,000	② $8.95 − $5.83 about $3.00	③ 13,269 + 59,799 about 73,000	④ $5.98 − $2.37 about $4.00	⑤ 3,456 − 1,297 about 2,200

A Introduce

Remind students that they have learned about rounding before. Ask: *Is rounding exact? No, it's approximate; it shows about how much.* Show a few examples of numbers, such as 97, 103, and 289. Ask volunteers to round each number up or down and explain why. Then say: *Rounding up or down helps us to estimate.*

Read aloud the Lesson Objective with students. Ask: *Why is it important to be able to explain how to solve an estimation problem?* List students' ideas on the the board.

B Teach and Learn

Have students open the student worktext to page 23. Say: *When you explain how to do something, you should first tell* what *you do, and then tell* why*. The steps on this page will show you how to do that.*

Read Step 1 with students. Say: *What does the problem ask me to do? I need to estimate. I know I need to use rounding to make a good estimate.* Have students circle the words *rounding* and *estimate.*

- **Say:** *Now we need to solve the problem.* Write the example problem on the board, and have a volunteer write the estimated answer.

Highlighted words and phrases may affect student comprehension.

Read Step 2 with students and say: *Now we're going to learn how to explain what we did and why we did it.* Write the sentence frame from the first column of Step 2 on the board.

> **Think Aloud**

BP 1 **Draw the first number line on page 3 on the board without adding a mark for 456.** Move your finger back and forth between 400 and 500 on the line. Write 456 on the line. Say: *456 is closer to 500. I'm going to round 456 to 500.* Point to the corresponding words in the sentence frame. Say: *I rounded 456 up to 500 because 456 is closer to 500 than to 400.*

Draw the second number line on the board without adding a mark for 314. Move your finger back and forth between 300 and 400 on the line. Write 314 on the line. Say: *314 is closer to 300. I'm going to round 314 to 300.* Point to the corresponding words in the sentence frame. Say: *I rounded 314 down to 300 because 314 is closer to 300 than to 400.*

Point to the problem on the board. Write *500 – 300* on the board next to the problem. Say: *I subtracted 300 from 500. My estimated answer is about 200.* Write *about 200* on the board.

Ask individual students to find four examples of addition and subtraction problems in their textbooks and estimate the answers to all four problems.

- 📄 **Pass out four copies of Worksheet 6 to each student.** Have students use one worksheet to solve each problem.

- **Have pairs of students compare their answers to the four problems.** Then distribute blank number lines to each pair and have them use the number lines to explain any problem where they had different answers. As a class, share problems and answers by having individual students explain their answers. Remind students about the sentence frame in Step 2 of the student worktext if they need extra help.

C Review and Practice

Review the Lesson Objective by asking students: *What's an important word that helps us explain estimation problems?* (because)

Ask several volunteers to paraphrase the steps involved in explaining how to solve estimation problems. Summarize the steps. Write: *1. Estimate. 2. Explain how and why you estimated.* Point to the sentence frame on the board and provide a model sentence.

Write the following problems on the board:

$$1,564 - 983$$

$$6,789 + 567$$

- **Have partners estimate the answers to each problem and then explain the problems in writing.** Make sure students know that when adding or subtracting, it's best to pick a place value such as hundreds and round all numbers to that place. Remind students that they can use their student worktext for reference.

Have individual students solve and explain the problem set in Practice the Language on page 23 of the student worktext.

Circulate and assess students as they do the activity.

D Assess and Intervene

How well can students explain how they solved estimation problems based on Practice the Language on page 23? Use the rubric to identify students who need extra support through additional help and the Intervention activity.

Intermediate

☐ Uses a sentence frame, with some prompting and some errors, to explain how to use rounding to estimate an answer.

Example of a sentence a student might write (using a sentence frame): *I rounded 722 down to 700 because 722 close to 700.*

Advanced

☐ Writes a sentence, without a sentence frame, explaining how to use rounding to estimate an answer, with minimal prompting and few errors.

Example of a sentence a student might write: *I round 278 up to 300 because it closer to 300 than 200.*

INTERVENTION 10 minutes

If students cannot write how an estimation problem was solved, allow them to explain how they solved an estimation problem orally, without a prompt. If they still cannot succeed, have them write the sentence frame from Step 2 of the student worktext, and any necessary vocabulary, on the index cards. Provide a list of additional vocabulary, with simple definitions, that will help students make sentences. Model grammatically correct explanations if students continue to struggle.

Lesson

4

Solve Math Problems

Objective Use clue words to identify and explain when to estimate and when to find an exact answer.

30 minutes

Teach this lesson:
- **After** lessons on estimation in the grade-level math textbook
- **Before** students complete the activities on page 24 of the student worktext

You need these materials:
- grade-level math textbook
- lined paper

EXTENSION AND ENRICHMENT 10 minutes

Brainstorm with students reasons why they might estimate an answer, and reasons why they would want to find an exact answer. For example:

Why estimate?
- because an exact answer is not important
- because you need to find a quick answer in your head

Why find an exact answer?
- because an exact answer is important
- because you have the tools to calculate an exact answer

Elicit examples of each situation from students.

LESSON **4**

Solve Math Problems

Objective Use clue words to identify and explain when to estimate and when to find an exact answer.

Learn to Solve Problems

Problem
It takes (approximately) 5 to 6 lemons to make a pitcher of lemonade. Melik expects to sell (about) 2 pitchers of lemonade. (About how many) lemons will Melik need?

Step 1: Read the problem. Circle the clue words. Should you find an estimate or an exact answer?
I should estimate.
Explain why. <u>I need to estimate because the problem uses the clue words approximately, about, and about how many.</u>

Step 2: Solve the problem. What is the answer?
Melik needs about 10 lemons.

Step 3: Read the problem again. Check your answer. Is it reasonable? <u>Yes, my answer is reasonable. There are 5 to 6 lemons in a pitcher of lemonade. In 2 pitchers, Melik needs double the lemons.</u>

Practice Solving Math Problems

Directions Follow the steps above to solve the problems below. Write the answer to each step on a separate sheet of paper. Responses to Steps 1 and 3 will vary.

1. Fatima is having a birthday party. There are 22 children in her class, and she wants to invite all of them. She also wants to invite 8 or 9 children from her neighborhood. About how many invitations will Fatima need? **Step 2:** about 30 invitations

2. Last Saturday, Nacho went to a family reunion. 77 people came in the morning, and 124 people came in the afternoon. How many more people came to the family reunion in the afternoon than in the morning? **Step 2:** exactly 47 people

3. Maria's father wants to build a desk for Maria's room. Maria's room is 9 feet 10 inches wide. Her bed is 2 feet 8 inches wide. Maria already has a small bookshelf next to her bed that is 2 feet 4 inches wide. About how much space is left for the desk? **Step 2:** about five feet

4. On Friday, exactly 253 people went to the movies. On Saturday, the movie theater sold 202 tickets. How many people went to the movies on both nights? **Step 2:** exactly 455 people

A Introduce

Read aloud the Lesson Objective with students. Make sure they remember what clue words are. Review the clue words with the class.

Tell students that they will learn how to decide when to estimate and when to find an exact answer in this lesson.

B Teach and Learn

Write *How much?* on the board. Ask: *Does* how much *need an* estimate *or an* exact answer? How much *asks about an exact amount, so* how much *needs an exact answer.*

Write this problem on the board and read it aloud: *I had $2.25. I spent $0.98. About how much money do I have left?*

Highlighted words and phrases may affect student comprehension.

Have students open the student worktext to page 24. Read aloud each of the numbered steps under Learn to Solve Problems. Do not have students read the problem in the student worktext yet. After each step, model how to solve the problem by thinking aloud about the problem on the board.

> **Think Aloud**

Write Step 1 on the board and read it aloud. Say: *What clue words do I see that will help me decide to estimate or find an exact answer? I see the word about.* Circle the word *about* in the problem. Say: *In this problem* (point to the problem on the board), *I know I am looking for an estimate because the problem says "About how much money do I have left?" I see the clue word about.* Write: *I estimated because the problem says "About how much money do I have left?"*

Write Step 2 on the board and read it aloud. Say: *Now I'll solve the problem. I'll round both numbers and then subtract. $2.25 is about $2.00. $0.98 is about $1.00. $2.00 minus $1.00 is $1.00. I have about $1.00 left.* Write *about $1.00* on the board.

Write Step 3 on the board and read it aloud. Say: *Now I'll check my answer. I'll read the problem again. $2.25 is only a little more than $2.00, and 98¢ is almost $1.00. I subtracted correctly. So my answer is reasonable.* Write: *My answer is reasonable.*

Find an estimation problem from the grade-level textbook similar to the one on page 24 of the student worktext. Have students answer the questions and solve the problem in pairs. If students are having difficulty understanding the word problem, see Intervention, in the Assess section, for suggestions.

Monitor and provide assistance as needed. Explain correct answers when students finish.

C | Review and Practice

Ask volunteers to retell the steps for deciding whether to estimate or find an exact answer. As students retell the steps, ask them various prompting questions. For example, say: (Step 1) *What are some important clue words that go with* estimate? *What words go with* exact answer? (Step 2) *What are some ways we've learned to solve estimation problems?* (Step 3) *What's a reasonable answer? How do you know?*

Review the steps in finding an estimate or an exact answer. Summarize the steps. Write: *1: Read and circle the clue words. Explain why. 2: Solve. 3: Check.*

Read aloud the directions for Practice Solving Math Problems on page 24. Remind students to circle all the clue words in each problem before they decide whether to estimate or find an exact answer.

As students work on problems individually, assess how well students are using the problem-solving strategy taught in this activity.

D | Assess and Intervene

How well can students decide whether to estimate or find an exact answer based on their answers to Step 1 of each problem in Practice Solving Math Problems on page 24? Use the rubric to identify students who need extra support through additional help and the Intervention activity.

Intermediate

☐ Correctly identifies whether to estimate or find an exact answer in 3 or more problems.

☐ Writes a simple sentence with a reasonable explanation, with some errors that do not impair understanding.

Example of a sentence a student might write: *The word* exactly *tells me to find exact answer.*

Advanced

☐ Correctly identifies whether to estimate or find an exact answer in all problems.

☐ Writes a more complex sentence with a reasonable explanation, including details and with few errors.

Example of a sentence a student might write: *I saw the words* exactly *and* how many, *and I didn't see* about, *so I know to find exact answer.*

INTERVENTION   10 minutes

If students have difficulty solving the problems because they don't understand the language of the problems, try the following:
- Help students figure out what information is known, what the problem is asking, and what is unknown. List or circle important information.
- Help them break each sentence into easier words. If possible, draw pictures or diagrams to make each sentence easier to understand.

Lesson

1

Prerequisite Background Knowledge
• Basic concepts, vocabulary, and facts of multiplication and division

Understand the Main Idea

Objective Explain why multiplication and division are opposites.

30 minutes 🕐

Teach this lesson:
• **Before** introducing lessons on multiplication and division concepts in the grade-level math textbook
• **Before** students complete the activities on page 25 of the student worktext

You need these materials:
• counters

 **ELL BEST PRACTICE #2:**
Assessing, Activating, and Building Background Knowledge

English language learners often have difficulty connecting what they have learned at home or in previous schooling with what they are learning in school. Teachers can help ELLs make this connection by using activities that connect students' basic knowledge of multiplication and division to the idea of opposites. Use concrete examples from home and community activities that students are familiar with to help students connect to the abstract concept of inverse operations.

Throughout this module, when you see **BP 2**, you will find an example of how you can assess, activate, and build background knowledge.

Module 7: Multiplication and Division Concepts

Understand the Main Idea

LESSON

1

Objective Explain why multiplication and division are opposites.

Learn the Main Idea

Divide to find how many groups or how many in each group.

Four children play a game. They share 20 game pieces equally. Each player gets 5 game pieces.
20 ÷ 4 = 5

Multiply to find how many altogether.

The game is finished. Each player puts back 5 game pieces. There are 20 game pieces.
4 × 5 = 20

💡 **MAIN IDEA** Multiplication and division are opposites.

Practice Applying the Main Idea

Directions Look at the pictures above. Answer the questions using complete sentences.

1 How many groups of game pieces are there?
There are 4 groups of game pieces.

2 How many game pieces are there in each group?
There are 5 game pieces in each group.

3 Fill in the multiplication sentence.
4 × 5 = 20
number of groups × number in each group = total game pieces

4 Fill in the division sentence.
20 ÷ 4 = 5
total game pieces ÷ number of groups = number in each group

5 Why are multiplication and division opposites?
Division is used to separate things into equal groups.
Multiplication is used to put equal groups together.
Multiplication and division undo each other.

A Introduce

Read aloud the Lesson Objective with students.

BP 2 Help students activate their background knowledge. Ask: *Have you ever shared a group of objects or things with friends? Let's say that you have a bowl of cherries. How would you share the cherries with your friends? How could you be sure that each person gets the same amount?* Listen to several students' ideas. Say: *When we share a group of objects equally, each person gets the same number of objects.*

BP 2 Direct students' attention to the illustrations on page 25 of the student worktext. Say: *The children are playing a game that uses game pieces. Have you ever played a game like this? What does it look like the children are going to do with the game pieces?*

Have pairs of students describe the pictures to one another. Ask them to compare what is happening with the game pieces in both illustrations. Then invite partners to share their observations with the class.

Highlighted words and phrases may affect student comprehension.

Multiplication and Division Concepts • 25

Direct students' attention to the first illustration. Ask: *How many game pieces are there?* (20) *How many players are there?* (4) *What will the players do with the game pieces?* (divide them into equal groups)

Now focus on the second illustration. Ask: *What are the children doing with the game pieces now?* (putting them back) *How many game pieces does each player have?* (5) *How many game pieces are there altogether?* (20)

Give students time to compare the total number of game pieces in each illustration. They should discover that the total is the same in both.

BP 2 Read both captions aloud chorally. Then read aloud the Main Idea with students. Say: *The words* big *and* small *are opposites.* Good *and* bad *are opposites, too.* Ask: *What are opposites?* Have pairs of students list as many opposites as they can and share them with the class.

B Teach and Learn

Model how to divide the counters into equal groups by thinking aloud.

> **Think Aloud**

Ask: *How many game pieces are the players sharing?* (20) Use counters to represent the 20 game pieces. Place 20 counters in four rows, with five counters in each row. Ask: *How many rows do I have?* (4) *How many counters are in each row?* (5) *Now I will separate the rows to form four equal groups. I made four equal groups with five counters in each group.*

Say: *I started with 20 counters. I divided them into four equal groups. Each group got five counters. Twenty divided by four equals five. This is what the players do with the game pieces.*

Point to the groups of counters. Explain: *We used division to separate the counters into equal groups. We can use multiplication to do the opposite of what we did with division. We can multiply to combine, or put together, the groups.*

Push the groups of counters together to form one large group. Invite volunteers to come up and arrange the counters in four rows to match the starting configuration.

Ask: *Has the number of counters changed?* (no) *What happens when you separate 20 objects into four groups?* (you get four groups of five objects) *What happens when you combine four groups of five objects?* (you get a total of 20 objects)

C Review and Practice

Review the multiplication and division situations presented on page 25. Say: *Twenty game pieces are divided into five groups of four.* On the board, write: $20 \div 5 = 4$. Tell students that this sentence is read as *twenty divided by five equals four.* Then write the multiplication sentence $4 \times 5 = 20$ on the board. Say: *Four groups with five game pieces in each group makes a total of 20 game pieces.* Explain that the multiplication sentence is read as *four times five equals twenty.*

Divide the class into small groups. Give each group a set of 32 counters.

- **Tell students to use eight counters to make two equal groups.** Ask students to take turns describing the counters in terms of division. For example: *I divided eight objects into two equal groups. There are four objects in each group.*

- **Then have students combine the groups and describe what happened, using multiplication.** For example: *I combined two groups of four objects each to make a total of eight objects.*

- **Have the groups work together to write multiplication and division sentences.** Ask them to describe the number of groups, the number in each group, and the total. Use 12 objects and three groups, 18 objects and six groups, 24 objects and four groups, and 32 objects and eight groups.

Read the directions for the Practice Applying the Main Idea activity. Point out that this activity is similar to the one they have just done with you.

Check students' work. Share and discuss students' answers to the questions and assist as necessary.

D Assess and Intervene

Do all students understand that multiplication and division are opposites, based on Practice Applying the Math Idea on page 25? Use the rubric to identify students who need extra support through additional help and the Intervention activity.

Intermediate

- ☐ Answers questions 1 and 2 with the correct number of game pieces.
- ☐ Fills in at least 2 of the 3 words in each of questions 3 and 4 correctly.
- ☐ Writes a concrete explanation for question 5; it may be vague or unclear, but the concept of one undoing the other, or of opposites, is evident.

Example of sentences a student might write: *I multiply put groups together. I divide take apart. Same thing.*

Advanced

- ☐ Answers questions 1 and 2 with the correct number of game pieces.
- ☐ Fills in all 3 words in each of questions 3 and 4 correctly.
- ☐ Writes a clear general statement for question 5, including the idea of one operation undoing the other.

Example of sentences a student might write: *Multiplication put groups together. Division take groups apart. Division undo multiplication.*

INTERVENTION 5 minutes

If students are having difficulty understanding that multiplication and division are opposites, give each student 10 counters. Show how to divide the counters into two equal groups. Ask students how many counters there are, how many equal groups you made, and how many are in each group. Point to the counters and say: *Two groups of objects with five objects in each group equals 10 objects.* Ask students to use the 10 counters to make five equal groups. Again ask how many there are, how many groups there are, and how many are in each group. Have students combine the groups and describe this as a multiplication situation.

Lesson

2

Learn the Vocabulary

Objective Talk and write about multiplication and division using vocabulary words.

30 minutes

Teach this lesson:
- **Before** introducing lessons on multiplication and division concepts in the grade-level math textbook
- **Before** students complete the activities on page 26 of the student worktext

You need these materials:
- manipulatives such as counters, centimeter cubes, paper clips
- Vocabulary Cards
- Transparency 13

Lesson Vocabulary

Essential Vocabulary

| array | equal groups | fact family |

inverse operations

Additional Vocabulary

| row | column | undo, undoes |

related facts

LESSON

2

Learn the Vocabulary

Objective Talk and write about multiplication and division using the vocabulary words.

Learn the Words

Directions Fill in the missing words and numbers. Then check your answers with your teacher.

Word/Phrase	Definition	Example
array	an arrangement of objects in rows and columns	COLUMN ⭐⭐⭐⭐ / ⭐⭐⭐⭐ ◄ROW This __array__ has __2__ rows and __4__ columns.
equal groups	groups that all have the same number of objects	⭐⭐⭐ ⭐⭐⭐⭐ __2__ equal groups __4__ in each group
fact family	sets of facts that are related because they use the same numbers	$2 \times 4 = 8$ $3 \times \underline{5} = 15$ $4 \times 2 = 8$ $5 \times \underline{3} = 15$ $8 \div 2 = 4$ $15 \div \underline{3} = \underline{5}$ $8 \div 4 = 2$ $\underline{15} \div 5 = \underline{3}$
inverse operations	opposite operations, such as division and multiplication	$2 \times 4 = 8$ undoes $\underline{3} \times 5 = 15$ undoes $8 \div 2 = 4$ $15 \div \underline{3} = 5$

Practice the Words

Directions Use the vocabulary words above to complete the crossword puzzle.

Across

① When you divide, you make _____ groups.

③ Multiplication and division are opposites. They are _____ operations.

④ A group of related facts is a fact _____.

Down

② An _____ shows objects in rows and columns.

⑤ Write one or more sentences to compare multiplication and division. Use at least one other vocabulary word or phrase.

Possible answer: Multiplication and division are inverse operations. Multiplication puts equal groups together. Division separates objects into equal groups.

Crossword:
- 1 across: e q u a l
- r (2 down)
- 3 across: i n v e r s e
- a
- 4 across: f a m i l y

A Introduce

BP 2 Read aloud the Lesson Objective with students. Ask: *What do you know about multiplication and division? How are they the same? How are they different? When do you use multiplication? When do you use division?* Invite student pairs to tell each other what they know about these operations. As a class, brainstorm ideas for vocabulary words that will be important to talk about multiplication and division as inverse operations. List suggested words on the board.

Choose words from the Additional Vocabulary box that you think will be useful. Elicit or provide examples for all the words on the list.

B Teach and Learn

Orally introduce the Essential Vocabulary. Say each word and have students locate it on page 26 of the student worktext. Model the pronunciation and have students repeat after you.

On the board, draw a two-by-four *array* of stars, similar to the one on page 26. Say: *An array is a set of objects in rows and columns.* Move your arm left and right and up and down as you say: *Rows go across, or left and right. Columns go up and down.* Ask: *How many stars are in each row?* (4) Say: *Each row has the same number of stars. Each row is an equal group of stars.*

Highlighted words and phrases may affect student comprehension.

Ask: *How many stars are in each column?* (2) **Say:** *Each column has the same number of stars. Each column is an equal group of stars.*

On the board, draw two *equal groups* of four triangles that are not arranged in an array. Say: *We saw* equal groups *in the array of stars. Equal groups are not always arranged in arrays. They can be arranged in many different ways. Equal groups always have the same number of objects. That is why they are equal.* Ask students to describe the equal groups that you drew on the board.

Have students work in groups of three. Provide students with a variety of manipulatives, such as counters, centimeter cubes, and paper clips. Have each group use the objects to show equal groups of two, then four, then six.

Direct students' attention to the phrase *fact family* on page 26. Say: *A fact family shows all of the multiplication and division facts for a set of numbers. It is a family of numbers that are related, just like a family of parents, brothers, and sisters are related.* Ask: *What are the multiplication facts in this fact family?* ($2 \times 4 = 8$ and $4 \times 2 = 8$) *What are the division facts in this fact family?* ($8 \div 2 = 4$ and $8 \div 4 = 2$) *What are the numbers used in this fact family?* (2, 4, and 8) *How many numbers are part of this family?* (a fact family consists of three numbers)

Tell students that you can use a fact family to describe the array of stars. Say: *Two rows times four stars in each row equals a total of eight stars. Eight stars divided into two equal rows equals four stars in each row.* Ask students to use similar language to describe to a partner how the facts $4 \times 2 = 8$ and $8 \div 4 = 2$ relate to the array.

Think Aloud

BP 2 **Explain the meaning of *undo* by thinking aloud and using gestures.** Point to your clothing as you say: *When I get dressed in the morning, I button my shirt, zip my pants, and tie my shoes. When I get undressed at night, I unbutton my shirt, unzip my pants, and untie my shoes. I do the opposite of what I did in the morning to get dressed. I get undressed and* undo *everything I did.*

Write *undo* on the board and underline the prefix *un–*. Say: *In math, when we say division undoes multiplication, we mean that division does the opposite of multiplication. Can you think of two other operations in math that do the opposite?* (addition and subtraction)

Use the fact family on page 26 to discuss *inverse operations*. Explain: Inverse operations *are opposite operations. Multiplication and division are inverse operations. Division undoes multiplication, and multiplication undoes division. I can multiply two rows of stars by four stars in each row to find the total of eight. I can do the opposite and undo multiplication by dividing. If I divide the eight stars into two rows, I find that each row has four stars.*

Point to the array of stars on page 26 of the student worktext. Say: *This array shows equal groups. There are two rows of stars in the array, and each row has four stars. Is each row an equal group?* (yes) *There are four columns of stars in the array, and each column has two stars. Is each column an equal group?* (yes)

Model by thinking aloud how to undo operations.

Think Aloud

Say: *I can use multiplication to tell about the total number of stars. Two groups of four stars equals eight stars. I can divide to undo the multiplication. Eight stars divided into two equal groups equals four stars in each group.*

Have groups of three work together. Have them complete the blanks on the right side of page 26. Check their work.

📇 **Have students complete Vocabulary Cards for the words in this module.**

C Review and Practice

Review inverse operations. Divide the class into pairs. Provide each pair with a different set of numbers that can be used to create a fact family, for example 7, 4, and 28. Have them use the numbers to draw an array and write a fact family. Then ask each student to define a different Essential Vocabulary word as it relates to the completed written work.

🖼 **Use Transparency 13 to review and practice the vocabulary.** Divide the class into groups of three or four. Have groups answer the questions on the transparency. If necessary, define difficult vocabulary and help students understand the questions. Go over the answers as a class.

Introduce the Practice the Words activity in the student worktext. Make sure students understand how to complete the crossword puzzle. Have students complete the activity individually. Check students' work.

D Assess and Intervene

Does every student understand the Essential Vocabulary in Practice the Words on page 26? Use the rubric to identify students who need extra support through additional help and the Intervention activity.

Intermediate

☐ Correctly fills in at least 3 words in the puzzle.

☐ Answer to question 5 includes the concept of inverse operations, but may not be clear and complete.

Example of a sentence a student might write: *Inverse opposite, multiplication and division inverse.*

Advanced

☐ Correctly fills in all 4 words in the puzzle.

☐ Answer to question 5 includes the concept of opposites and demonstrates how the two are inverse operations.

Example of sentences a student might write: *When I multiply, put together. When I divide, separate. Opposite are inverse operations.*

INTERVENTION 10 minutes 🕐

📇 **If students are having difficulty discussing the concepts in context,** ask them to add visuals and model language to their Vocabulary Cards. For example, on the back side of the *array* card, they can draw an array and complete a sentence, such as the following: *This is an _____ with _____ columns and _____ rows.* Have students work with partners to practice verbalizing the concepts.

Use More Language

Objective Talk and write about equal groups in multiplication and division using the words *every*, *each*, and *all*.

30 minutes

Teach this lesson:
- **After** students complete lessons on multiplication and division concepts in the grade-level math textbook
- **Before** students complete the activities on page 27 of the student worktext

You need these materials:
- counters
- books from the classroom
- Transparency 14
- Worksheet 7

Use More Language

Objective Talk and write about equal groups in multiplication and division using the words *every, each,* and *all.*

LESSON **3**

Learn the Language

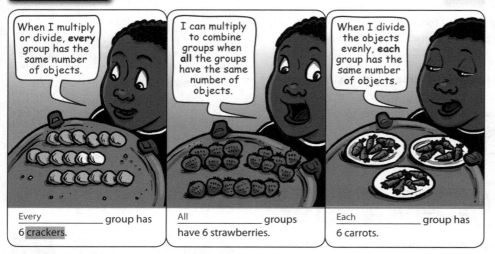

When I multiply or divide, **every** group has the same number of objects.

I can multiply to combine groups when **all** the groups have the same number of objects.

When I divide the objects evenly, **each** group has the same number of objects.

Every _____ group has 6 crackers.

All _____ groups have 6 strawberries.

Each _____ group has 6 carrots.

Practice the Language

Directions Look at the pictures of the pears below. Write complete sentences to describe the groups of pears. Use the words below in your sentences. Answer the last question in a complete sentence.

1 every Every basket has 6 pears. _____

_____

2 each Each basket has 6 pears. _____

_____

3 all All baskets have 6 pears. _____

_____

4 How many pears are there in all? Write a sentence or sentences to describe the groups and the total.

There are 4 baskets. Each basket has 6 pears. There

are 24 pears altogether.

_____

_____

Multiplication and Division Concepts • 27

A Introduce

Read aloud the Lesson Objective with students. Say: *Equal groups of objects can be combined to form a large group.* Ask: *What operation do we use to combine equal groups of objects?* (multiplication) Say: *A large group of objects can be separated into equal groups.* Ask: *What operation do we use to separate a large group of objects into equal groups?* (division)

BP 2 Ask volunteers to describe times when they separated something into equal groups or combined equal groups. After each description, have the rest of the class say chorally *multiplication* or *division.*

Explain that equal groups are the groups used in multiplication and division. Have students read the objective again and chorally repeat the three words at the end.

BP 2 Ask partners to make a sentence using one of these words. Call on volunteers to share their sentences. Tell students that in this lesson, they will practice using these words to talk about equal groups.

Highlighted words and phrases may affect student comprehension.

B. Teach and Learn

Divide the class into three or four groups.
Make sure that each group includes both boys and girls. Point to each group one at a time and say: Each *group has both boys and girls.* Every *group has both boys and girls.* You may want to repeat this two or three times, over-emphasizing the words *each* and *every.*

Now make a circular motion with your hands and say: All *groups have both boys and girls.* Repeat as necessary, emphasizing the word *all* and clearly pronouncing the *s* in *groups.*

Explain to students that all three of these sentences say the same thing, just in different ways.

Write the following sentence frames on the board:

Every group has _____.

Each group has _____.

All groups have _____.

Point out that when the word *group* is used with *each and every,* they should use the word *has.* *When the word* group *is used with* all, *they should use the word* have.

Read through the Learn the Language section at the top of page 27. Then read the text chorally with students.

Ask students to use *each, every,* and *all* to describe the groups of students in different ways. Provide examples, such as: Every *group has more than two students.* Then ask students to create similar sentences using the sentence frames on the board for *each, every,* and *all.*

Provide additional practice with the language while reviewing some of the vocabulary words from student worktext page 26. Draw an array with five rows and six columns on the board.

Model how to use the words by thinking aloud.

Think Aloud

Say: *I know that arrays show equal groups. I will look at the ways I can describe the groups.*

Move your hand across the array and say: *The array has five rows, and each row has six objects. That means that there are five groups of six objects.* Every *group has six objects.*

Each *group has six objects.* All *groups have six objects.*

Move your hand up and down the array and say: *The array has six columns, and each column has five objects. There are six groups of five objects.* Every *group has five objects.* Each *group has five objects.* All *groups have five objects.*

Have each student work with a partner.
Give each pair a set of counters. Ask partners to take turns making different equal groups of counters. Partners take turns describing the groups, using the words *each, every,* and *all.* Keep the sentence frames on the board for students to use as a reference.

Point to the illustration of the crackers on page 27. Invite a student to say the first sentence, using *every* in the blank. Repeat with the illustrations of strawberries and carrots.

C. Review and Practice

Review how to describe different groups, using *every, each* and *all* with Transparency 14.

- **Have students form groups of three.**
  Assign a scribe in each group to write sentences describing the group of objects on the transparency on a separate sheet of paper. Once students have completed the sentences ask them to assign a reader to share them with the class.

Divide the class into pairs. Give each pair a copy of Worksheet 7, which shows equal groups of objects. Have pairs say and write sentences using *each, every,* and *all* to describe the equal groups of objects.

- **Encourage students to practice oral language by reading their sentences to each other.** Some pairs may be able to write fact families for the pictures and use the pictures to practice multiplication and division vocabulary.

Read aloud the directions for the Practice the Language section. Ask: *What is the name of the fruit?* (pear) *What is the container that holds the fruit called?* (basket)

Have individual students complete the Practice the Language activity on page 27. Tell students that they may use either the word *group* or *basket* in their sentences.

D. Assess and Intervene

Are all students able to create complete sentences about equal groups using *each, every,* and *all,* based on Practice the Language on page 27? Use the rubric to identify students who need extra support through additional help and the Intervention activity.

Intermediate

☐ All of the first 3 sentences use the indicated words correctly, but sentences may be incomplete or have incorrect verb forms.

  Example of a sentence that a student might write: *All basket has 6 pear.*

☐ Uses phrases with some errors that do not hinder comprehension to correctly identify the number of baskets (or groups), the number of pears in each basket, and the number of pears altogether.

Advanced

☐ All of the first 3 sentences are complete, use correct verb forms, and use the indicated words correctly.

  Example of a sentence a student might write: *All baskets have same number of pears.*

☐ Uses complete sentences with minimal errors to correctly identify the number of baskets (or groups), the number of pears in each basket, and the number of pears altogether.

INTERVENTION   5 minutes

If students are confused by the use of plural and singular with the words *all, each* and *every,* display three groups of books with four books in each group. Tell students that each group has four books. Explain that when you say this, you are talking about one group at a time. Point to each group as you explain. Then point out that *all* groups have four books and explain that now you are talking about all of the groups together. Encourage students to describe other situations, using *each, every,* and *all.*

Solve Math Problems

Objective Decide whether to multiply or divide to solve word problems.

30 minutes

Teach this lesson:
- **After** students complete the lessons on multiplication and division concepts in their grade-level math textbooks
- **Before** students complete the activities on page 28 of the student worktext

You need these materials:
- scrap paper
- construction paper
- multiplication and division problems from grade-level textbook

Solve Math Problems

Objective Decide whether to multiply or divide to solve word problems.

Learn to Solve Problems

Problem	Sun used 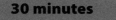dough to make cookies. She put the dough in 4 rows on the cookie sheet. Each row had 3 pieces of dough. How many cookies did Sun make?	

	Think	Write
Step 1:	Read the problem. Underline the question.	I need to find the number of cookies.
Step 2:	Decide what operation to use.	There are equal groups, so I can multiply or divide. Do I start with the total and separate it into equal groups? No. I do not know the total. I can't divide. Do I have to put the groups together to find the total? Yes. I will multiply.
Step 3:	Circle the facts.	There are 4 rows of dough. There are 3 pieces of dough in each row.
Step 4:	Write a number sentence and solve the problem.	I have to multiply to find how many in all. 4 × 3 = 12 Sun made 12 cookies.

Practice Solving Math Problems

Directions Follow steps 1 to 4 above to solve the problems below. Answer the questions in complete sentences. Show your work on a separate sheet of paper.

1 There are 5 boxes on a shelf. Each box holds 8 books. How many books are on the shelf? 5 × 8 = 40. There are 40 books in all.

2 Liz and her 2 brothers do yard work. They make $24.00 and they share the money equally. How much does each child get? $24.00 ÷ 3 = $8.00. Each child gets $8.00.

3 There are 36 markers in a box. Six friends share the markers equally. How many markers does each friend get? 36 ÷ 6 = 6. Each friend gets 6 markers.

4 A marching band has 7 rows. Each row has 6 people. How many people are in the band? 7 × 6 = 42. There are 42 people altogether.

5 How do you know when you have to multiply or divide when a problem has equal groups? When I know the total, I divide. When I don't know the total, I multiply.

Use construction paper to make a card for each number 1 through 9 and for the symbols ÷, ×, and =. On the board, write possible questions that students might ask about the numbers and symbols in multiplication and division facts. The following are some examples: *What do I mean? What is my name?* (factor, divisor, dividend, etc.) *Am I the total? Am I the number of groups? What is another fact in my family?*

Put students into groups of six. Have groups take turns selecting and holding up number and symbol cards to form a multiplication or a division fact. Each member of the group asks a question for the class to answer. Students may use the questions on the board or questions they create on their own.

A Introduce

BP 2 Write two simple word problems on the board: *There are 4 girls and each girl has 3 books. How many books?* and *5 boys divide $10.00 evenly. How much does each boy get?* Read the problems aloud. Ask students to talk with a partner about how they know what operation to use for each problem. Ask for volunteers to share their ideas.

Read aloud the Lesson Objective with students. Review the common situations that are used in division and multiplication. Give examples of each.

- **Multiplication:** Find the total amount when you know the number of groups and the number in each group.

- **Division:** Find the number of groups when you know the total and the number in each group.

- **Division:** Find the number in each group when you know the total and the number of groups.

Tell students that in this lesson, they will learn how to use the information in the problem to decide whether to multiply or divide.

Highlighted words and phrases may affect student comprehension.

 **Teach and Learn**

Write this problem on the board and read it aloud: *Sun used dough to make cookies. She put the dough in 4 rows on the cookie sheet. Each row had 3 pieces of dough. How many cookies did Sun make?*

BP 2 Ask if students have ever baked cookies. Did they place the dough in equal rows? Explain that drawing a picture might be helpful in this situation. On the board, draw an array of circles with four rows and three columns.

Model solving multiplication and division problems by thinking aloud. Have students open their student worktexts to page 28 and follow along as you model the steps.

Think Aloud

Write Step 1 and read it aloud. Say: *I'll look for a question word at the beginning and a question mark at the end. The question asks, "How many cookies did Sun make?" So I need to find out the number of cookies.* Underline the question in the problem on the board.

Write Step 2 and read it aloud. Say: *Now I need to ask myself some questions. Does the problem talk about equal groups? Yes, it does. Equal groups means I can multiply or divide. Do I start with the total and separate it into equal groups? No, I don't know what the total is. So I can't divide. Do I have to put the groups together to find a total? Yes, I have to find out how many cookies are on the sheet. So I have to multiply.* Write *multiply* on the board under the problem.

Write Step 3 and read it aloud. Say: *The facts are the number of rows of cookies and the number of cookies in each row.* In the problem on the board, circle the words *4 rows* and *Each row had 3 pieces.* Ask: *What do these numbers mean? The numbers describe an array with four rows and three 3 pieces of dough in each row.*

Write Step 4 and read it aloud. Say: *I know that I have to multiply, and I know that I have to use the numbers 3 and 4. Now I can write a multiplication sentence.* Write on the board: *3 × 4 = 12. The multiplication sentence tells me that Sun made 12 cookies.*

Find three simple multiplication and division word problems from the grade-level math textbook. Write the problems on the board. Allow students to work in pairs or small groups to solve the problems.

- **Suggest that one student copy each problem.** Then have the group read the problem chorally and work together to use the steps to solve the problem. Have students use page 28 in their worktexts as a guide.

Circulate among the groups and help out as needed. Assist with unfamiliar vocabulary as necessary.

 **Review and Practice**

Review the problems students solved from the math textbook. Invite volunteers to model the problem-solving process used to find the solution. Encourage students to describe alternative strategies and discuss how to check solutions, using inverse operations.

- **Ask students to identify any difficulties they had with the problems.** Model an appropriate thinking process to help eliminate these difficulties.

On the board, write the following division sentence: $48 \div 6 = 8$. Brainstorm with the class ideas about a word problem that could be solved using this fact. Together, decide on a situation to use in creating a word problem or use the following: *There are 48 children at soccer camp. They are divided into teams. Each team has 6 children. How many teams are there?*

Divide the class into small groups. Ask each group to create a multiplication or division word problem. You may provide number sentences for them or allow students to make up their own numbers. Circulate and assist as necessary. Make sure each group's problem makes sense before they write a final draft.

- **When students have completed the activity, switch problems among groups.** Have them solve the problems. Go over each group's solution with the class, correct any errors, and model any necessary changes in the solution processes.

Have students individually complete Practice Solving Math Problems in the worktext. As they work, observe how well

they follow the problem-solving process to determine whether to multiply or divide.

 **Assess and Intervene**

Do all students understand how to analyze word problems and decide whether to multiply or divide, based on Practice Solving Math Problems on page 28? Use the rubric to identify students who need extra support through additional help and the Intervention activity.

Intermediate

☐ Writes correct number sentences and answers in phrases or sentences for at least 3 of the 4 problems.

☐ Uses sentences or phrases to explain how to decide whether to multiply or divide; includes the concept of knowing the total or not.

Example of sentences a student might write: *Know total, divide. Not know total, multiply.*

Advanced

☐ Writes correct number sentences and complete sentence answers for all 4 problems.

☐ Uses complete sentences to explain how to decide whether to multiply or divide. Includes the concepts of equal groups and knowing the total or not.

Example of sentences a student might write: *When I know total, I divide. When I not know total, I multiply.*

INTERVENTION 10 minutes

If students are having difficulty determining whether to multiply or divide, have them write the facts from each problem. Tell them to put the largest number first, then a question mark, then the other number, and finally, an equals sign. Tell students that these are two of the three numbers in a fact family. Have them use their knowledge of basic facts or a multiplication table to find the third member in the fact family. Write that number after the equals sign. Then have students look at the number sentences and decide whether to put a multiplication or a division symbol in place of the question mark. Finally, have them reread the problem and decide if the symbol they chose makes sense.

Understand the Main Idea

Objective Explain how multiplication properties and division rules make it easier to multiply and divide.

---

45 minutes

Teach this lesson:
- **Before** introducing lessons on multiplication properties and division rules in students' grade-level math textbooks
- **Before** students complete the activities on page 29 of the student worktext

You need these materials:
- sticky notes with multiplication (Identity Property) problems and division (Number by Itself) problems
- classroom objects
- index cards

Prerequisite Background Knowledge
- Basic concepts and vocabulary of multiplication

BP 3 ELL BEST PRACTICE # 4:
Performance Assessment

English language learners often know more than what they can demonstrate on traditional reading- and writing-based assessments. Consequently, it is more effective to evaluate their learning based on daily observations of how they perform on classroom tasks. Observe how well students can use manipulatives to demonstrate different multiplication properties and division rules. Observe how they use the language in the lesson to express their ideas, even if they use simple phrases or short sentences. Record anecdotal notes during activities, and use the rubrics included in each lesson.

Throughout this module, when you see **BP 3**, this is an example of a performance assessment.

Module 8: Multiplication Properties and Division Rules

Understand the Main Idea

LESSON 1

Objective Explain how multiplication properties and division rules make it easier to multiply and divide.

Learn the Main Idea

There are 5 students. Each student gets 1 book. How many books do we need?

That's 5 students times one book for each student or 5 × 1 = 5. We need 5 books.

There are 5 students. There are 5 books. How many books do we each get?

That's 5 books divided by 5 students or 5 ÷ 5 = 1. Each student gets 1 book.

MAIN IDEA You can use the properties of multiplication and rules of division to multiply and divide more easily.

Practice Applying the Main Idea

Directions Read each question. Circle the correct number sentence in questions 1 to 4. Answer questions 5 and 6 in complete sentences.

1. There are 11 students on my soccer team. There are 11 soccer balls. How many soccer balls does each student get?
   (11 ÷ 11 = 1)   11 × 1 = 11

2. There are 10 fish. Each fish gets 1 fish bowl. How many fish bowls do they need?
   10 ÷ 10 = 1   (10 × 1 = 10)

3. There are 12 students. There are 12 cereal bars. How many cereal bars do they each get?
   12 × 1 = 12   (12 ÷ 12 = 1)

4. 20 friends each need a computer. How many computers do they need?
   (20 × 1 = 20)   20 ÷ 20 = 1

5. How does using the number 1 help you when you multiply? It helps me because my answer is always the other number and not 1.

6. How does dividing a number by itself help you? It helps me because I always get 1 for an answer.

Multiplication Properties and Division Rules · 29

A Introduce

Read aloud the Lesson Objective with students. Ask: *What is a rule?* (A rule tells you what you can and can't do.) *Why do you think it is important to know rules for multiplication and division?* (The rules make it easier to decide what to do.) *Is it easier to multiply or divide if we know the rules and how to do these operations?* (yes)

Help students activate prior knowledge. Ask: *When you have to share things with your friends, what do you do to find out how many things each one gets?* Say: *There are ____ students in our class. Each student needs one book. How many books do we need? That's ____ students times 1 book for each student, or ____ × 1 = ____. We need ____ books.*

Use the illustrations on page 29 of the student worktext as a visual introduction to using multiplication properties and division rules to multiply and divide more easily.

- **Focus students' attention on the panel on the left.** Ask: *What do you see? What does the girl need to do?* (She has to find out how many books they need). Chorally read the text in the panel with students.

Highlighted words and phrases may affect student comprehension.

- **Ask:** *How many students get books?* (5) *How many books does each student need?* (1) Say: *That's 5 students times 1 book each. That's 5 × 1 = 5. The group needs 5 books.*

- **Ask:** *What did he do to find how many books he needed?* (He multiplied the number of students by the number of books for each student.)

Focus students' attention on the panel on the right. Ask: *What do you see? What does the boy need to do?* (He has to find out how many books each student gets.) Chorally read the text in the panel with students. Ask students to count the children in the picture. Ask: *How many children are there?* (5) *How many books does each student get?* (1) *How did the girl find how many books each student gets?* (She divided the number of books by the number of students.)

Read aloud the Main Idea with students. Say: *Some rules are always true for multiplication and division. If you know the rules, they can make it easier to find the answer.*

B Teach and Learn

Invite three students to participate. On the board, write: *There are 3 students. Each student gets 1 glue stick. How many glue sticks do they need?* Give each of the three students one glue stick. Say: *We can write the number sentence 3 students × 1 glue stick = ? glue sticks. 3 × 1 = ?* Write the number sentence on the board, and read it aloud. Elicit from students that they need 3 glue sticks.

Explain to students that a property is a special quality or characteristic of something. A property of soap is that it cleans things. A property of multiplication tells you information about multiplication that will always be true.

- **Ask:** *What happens when we multiply a number by 1?* Elicit that when we multiply a number by 1, the answer is equal to that number. Ask: *Is this sometimes true, or is it always true?* (always) *The Identity Property of Multiplication is a property of multiplication because it is always true.*

- **Ask:** *If you know the Identity Property of Multiplication, how can it help you with multiplication?* Elicit that if you know the property, you can look at any problem that multiplies a number by 1 and know the answer.

Divide the class into groups of four. Have students multiply by 1 using four classroom items such as four pencils, four erasers, etc. Say: *How many are in your group?* (4) *Each of you gets 1 ____. What is the total number of ____? How do you write this in a multiplication sentence?*

Focus students' attention on division rules. Read the panel on the right of the student worktext again.

Invite five students to participate. Write on the board the following number sentence: *5 ÷ 5 = ?* Take five erasers and hand one to each student. Say: *When I divide the number of erasers by 5 students, I get 1 eraser for each student. So, 5 ÷ 5 = 1.* Write this number sentence on the board.

Say: *A rule of division says that when we divide a number by itself, the answer is always 1.* By itself *means by the same number.* Ask: *How can this rule help you solve division problems more easily?* (You can look at a problem and see that the rule applies, so you can solve it easily.)

Provide additional examples with other classroom items. Write their number sentences on the board. Ask: *What happens when we divide a number by itself?* (When we divide a number by itself, the answer is always 1.)

C Review and Practice

Review how multiplication properties and division rules can help you solve problems. For example: *There are eight children and each child gets one toy. How many toys do we need?* and *There are 10 cars. There are 10 drivers. How many drivers does each car have?*

- **Have students work with a partner.** Distribute sticky notes with simple multiplication and division problems on them to pairs. (Problems should use the Identity Property and dividing a number by itself.) Write *Multiply* and *Divide* on the board. Have one partner read a problem. Then have them discuss whether to use multiplication or division to solve it. Ask students if the multiplication properties and division rules they know will help them. Once the students come up with the operation, one of the partners goes to the front and places the sticky note in the corresponding column. Repeat the same procedure with the other problem.

BP 3 **Have pairs read their problems aloud.** Have them dictate the number sentence for each problem as you write it on the board.

Introduce the Practice Applying the Main Idea activity in the student worktext. Make sure students understand the directions. Have students complete the activity individually. Assess students' work.

D Assess and Intervene

Can every student explain why using the properties of multiplication or the rules of division makes it easier to multiply and divide based on Practice Applying the Main Idea on page 29? Can every student choose the correct operation? Use the rubric to help identify students who need extra support through additional help and the Intervention activity.

Intermediate

☐ Answers at least 3 of questions 1–4 correctly.

☐ Tells why the property of multiplication or the rules of division make it easier to multiply and divide for questions 5 and 6; answer may contain some errors that affect meaning.

Example of an answer a student might write: *Because the answers always the other number, not 1.*

Advanced

☐ Answers questions 1–4 correctly.

☐ Uses simple sentences in questions 5 and 6 to clearly explain why the property of multiplication or the rules of division make it easier to multiply and divide.

Example of an answer a student might write: *It helps me because 1 always is answer.*

INTERVENTION 10 minutes

If students are having trouble choosing the correct number sentence in Practice Applying the Main Idea, have students write the Identity Property of Multiplication on the front of an index card. On the back, have them write one example and a drawing for visual support. Do the same for the division rule of a number by itself. Have students identify what the numbers mean in each operation as they read it aloud with you. Then together, draw another example for each and write the number sentence. Finally, say a problem for each operation, and have the student come up with the number sentence and solve it independently.

Learn the Vocabulary

Objective Talk and write about multiplication properties and division rules using the vocabulary words and *because*.

---

45 minutes

Teach this lesson:
- **Before** introducing lessons on multiplication properties and division rules in students' grade-level math textbooks
- **Before** students complete the activities on page 30 of the student worktext

You need these materials:
- small manipulatives, such as buttons or erasers
- index cards
- sticky notes with 4, 2, and 5 written on them
- 1 set of parentheses made of construction paper
- Transparency 15

Lesson Vocabulary

Essential Vocabulary
Zero Property of Multiplication
Identity Property of Multiplication
Commutative Property of Multiplication
Associative Property of Multiplication

Additional Vocabulary
| property* | parentheses | itself |
| quotient | rule* | |

* - Terms that have Vocabulary Cards.

LESSON
2

Learn the Vocabulary

Objective Talk and write about multiplication properties and division rules using the vocabulary words and *because*.

Learn the Words

Phrase	Definition	Example
Zero Property of Multiplication	I can multiply any number by 0, and the product is always 0.	$10 \times 0 = 0$
Identity Property of Multiplication	I can multiply any number by 1 and the product is always that number.	$4 \times 1 = 4$
Commutative Property of Multiplication	I can change the order of the factors and the product is the same.	$7 \times 2 = 14$ $2 \times 7 = 14$
Associative Property of Multiplication	I can group the factors in different ways and the product is the same.	$5 (2 \times 3) = 30$ $(5 \times 2) \times 3 = 30$

Practice the Words

Directions Finish the sentence. Write the name of the multiplication property on a separate sheet of paper. Explain it using *because*. Then write your own example for each property.

1. $1 \times 22 = 22$
   This is an example of . . . the Identity Property of Multiplication

2. $9 \times (2 \times 3) = 54$ or $(9 \times 2) \times 3 = 54$
   This is an example of . . . the Associative Property of Multiplication

3. $11 \times 5 = 55$ or $5 \times 11 = 55$
   This is an example of . . . the Commutative Property of Multiplication

4. $12 \times 0 = 0$
   This is an example of . . . the Zero Property of Multiplication

---

A **Introduce**

Read aloud the Lesson Objective with students. Ask: *What do you remember about multiplying by 1 and dividing a number by itself?* Write *multiplication* and *division* on the board to form two columns. Write students' responses on the board under the appropriate word. Read them aloud.

As a class, brainstorm words that will be important to know. Write suggested words on the board underneath *multiplication* and *division*. Chorally read the words. Explain each one.

Choose words from the Additional Vocabulary that you think will be useful. Add them to the list on the board. Elicit or provide examples or definitions for all the words on the list.

B **Teach and Learn**

Orally introduce the Essential Vocabulary. Use the visuals on page 30 of the student worktext, pausing to explain each term. As you present each term, model its pronunciation, and have students repeat. After presenting each term, chorally read its meaning, and examples, and explain the visuals in Lesson 2.

- **Say:** *Remember that the word* property *means something that is always true about an operation.*

Highlighted words and phrases may affect student comprehension.

Present each vocabulary phrase in this manner:

- **Write and chorally read *Zero Property of Multiplication*.** Place five index cards in front of you. Say: *Our cards have no pictures. How many pictures are there in all?* Write *5 × 0* on the board. Say: *Five cards with zero pictures each equals zero pictures. Let's multiply by zero, or nothing. 5 × 0 = 0. Five times nothing equals nothing.* Provide similar examples, and write their number sentences on the board. Read them aloud. Say: *This is the Zero Property of Multiplication. When we multiply any number by zero, the answer is always zero.* Ask: *What is the Zero Property of Multiplication? What happens when we multiply a number by zero? What is 500 × 0? What is 789 × 0?*

Write and chorally read *Identity Property of Multiplication*. Circle the word *identity*. Say: *Who you are is your identity. Your identity is always the same. It never changes. When you multiply by 1, it is easy to see the identity of the other number. We multiplied a number times 1 in Lesson 1. Now we will learn the name of the property.*

- **Write: *1 × 4 = 4* on the board, and read it aloud.** Put four markers on one index card, and count them chorally. Say: *This index card has a group of markers.* Ask: *How many groups do you see?* (1) *How many markers are in this group?* (4) *How many markers are there all together? The number sentence for this is 1 × 4 = 4.* Provide additional examples, and write each one on the board. Ask: *What is the Identity Property of Multiplication? What happens when we multiply a number by 1?*

Write and chorally read *Commutative Property of Multiplication*. Ask: *What do we mean when we say change the order of the factors?* Place five index cards on the desk, with three erasers on each card. Ask: *How many erasers are there all together?* Have students give you the number sentence that represents what they see: *5 × 3.* Write it on the board. Ask: *How many index cards, or groups, do we have?* (5) *How many erasers are there in each group?* (3) *So 5 × 3 = 15.* Complete the number sentence on the board.

- **Say:** *Look at the number sentence. Now let's change the order of the factors.* Rearrange the cards and erasers so there are three cards with five erasers on each one. Make sure students see that you are using the same number of erasers. Say: *How many erasers are there in all now?* Point to the *3*, and guide students to say the new number

sentence: *3 × 5 = 15.* Write this on the board. Compare the two number sentences.

- **Ask:** *What happens when we change the order of the numbers when we multiply?* (The answer is the same.) Say: *This is the Commutative Property of Multiplication. When you multiply two numbers in any order, the answer, the product, is the same.* Ask: *What is the Commutative Property of Multiplication? What happens to the product when we change the order of the numbers we multiply?*

Write and chorally read *Associative Property of Multiplication*. Make a set of parentheses out of construction paper. Tape them on the board. Say: *These are parentheses. We use parentheses to separate groups of numbers when we use the Associative Property of Multiplication. We do the multiplication in the parentheses first.* Using sticky notes and parentheses, model aloud: *(4 × 2) × 5 = ?* Write *4 × 2 = 8* on the board. Say: *First I multiply what is inside the parentheses. Now I multiply 8 × 5 = 40.* Write this number sentence on the board.

Use the following Think Aloud to model the Associative Property of Multiplication.

Say: *This property says that I can group the factors in different ways and the product is the same. I will change the order of the factors so it is easier for me. I will group these factors like this: 2 × 5 × 4. I will put this number sentence in parentheses: (2 × 5). Now I write the other factor: × 4. So (2 × 5) × 4 = ? I multiply the factors in parentheses first: 2 × 5 = 10. Now 10 × 4 = 40. The product is the same.*

Divide the class into small groups. Ask them to copy the two number sentences from the board onto a sheet of paper. Ask the pairs to compare them and write their own definition for the Associative Property. Ask them to share their definitions with the class.

 Help students complete the Vocabulary Cards for this module. Clarify meanings using paraphrasing and manipulatives to demonstrate the properties.

Review and Practice

BP 3 **Use Transparency 15 to help students practice the Essential Vocabulary.** Explain to students that they first need to complete the sentence and then

decide which property the sentence is about. Make sure students know they can use their student worktext if they need help figuring out which property it is. Model completing the first sentence and naming the property if students need extra support.

Have students work in pairs. Ask them to use their Vocabulary Cards to create examples for each Essential Vocabulary phrase.

Introduce the Practice the Words Activity in the student worktext. Have students complete the activity independently. Assess students' work.

D Assess and Intervene

Does every student understand the Essential Vocabulary in Practice the Words on page 30? Use the rubric to identify students who need extra support through additional help and the Intervention activity.

Intermediate

☐ Correctly matches at least 2 phrases to the examples. Writes at least 2 number sentence examples of their own.

☐ At least 2 correct explanations are given, with simple phrases, some errors.

Example of an answer a student might write: *Because I can change order and get same answer.*

Advanced

☐ Correctly matches at least 3 phrases to the examples. Writes at least 3 number sentence examples of their own.

☐ At least 3 correct explanations given, simple sentences, few errors.

Example of an answer a student might write: *This is Associative Property because I put the factors in any order and get same answer. Because I can put numbers in any order and get same answer.*

INTERVENTION 5 minutes

If students are having difficulty understanding the different properties, write each property on one set of index cards and the meanings on another. Together, read each phrase and meaning. Have students close their eyes. Mix up the cards. Have students match them and read each property. Then have students write a number sentence for each one.

Lesson

3

Use More Language

Objective Identify what the word *number* refers to in phrases such as *a number, any number, that number,* and *what number.*

---

45 minutes

Teach this lesson:
- **After** students complete lessons on multiplication properties and division rules in their grade-level math textbooks
- **Before** students complete the activities on page 31 of the student worktext

You need these materials:
- counters or small manipulatives, such as buttons
- Transparency 16

A Introduce

Before introducing students to what the word *number* can refer to in different word problems, remind students of the meaning of the Identity Property of Multiplication.

- **Have students refer to Lesson 2 of their student worktexts.** Read the definition for the Identity Property chorally. Point out the phrase *that number,* and ask students what it means and how they know. Then explain that there are a lot of other phrases with a "little" word like *the, a, any,* or *that* plus the word *number.* These words can make a word problem more difficult to understand.

Read aloud the Lesson Objective with students. Say: *We will find out what the word* number *means, or refers to, in different problems.*

B Teach and Learn

Focus students' attention on the first sentence written on the board in the illustration on page 31 of the student worktext. Chorally read it, and then explain the illustration. Write on the board: *Any number divided by 1 is that number.*

Model how to identify *any number* and *that number* using a Think Aloud:

Think Aloud

Write on the board, and say: *You can't divide a number by 0.* Then say: *You can't put things in 0 groups. You can have any number of things, but you can't divide them by 0. So what can* a number *be here? It means* any number. *If I have 8 things, or 15 things, or 1,000 things, I can't divide them by 0. A number* in this sentence means *any number.*

Say: *Now you try it.* Write across the board: *Any number divided by 1 equals that number.* Have students create number sentences using the sentence above.

Use More Language

Objective Identify what the word *number* refers to in phrases such as *a number, any number, that number,* and *what number.*

Learn the Language

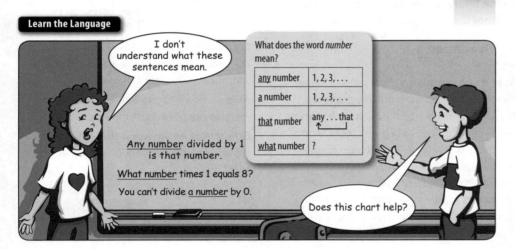

Practice the Language

Directions Complete each sentence with one of the phrases in the box. Then match the sentence with the example.

| a number | any number | that number | what number |

1. 8 multiplied by <u>what number</u> equals 8?

   b _____

   a. $5 \div 0 =$

2. 0 times <u>any number or a number</u> equals 0.

   d _____

   b. $8 \times 1 = 8$

3. Any number divided by 1 is <u>that number</u>.

   c _____

   c. $6 \div 1 = 6$

4. You can't divide <u>any number or a number</u> by 0.

   a _____

   d. $0 \times 3 = 0$

Highlighted words and phrases may affect student comprehension.

- **Draw empty boxes to represent** *any* **and** *that* **number as before:** □ *divided by 1 =* □

- **Have students choose** *any number.* Write the number in the box. Ask: *What is that number?* Invite a student to fill in the answer. Point out that any number and that number talk about the same number, by pointing out that these numbers are the same. Say: *When we see* any number *or* that number, *it means that we are talking about or referring to a number that is the same on both sides of the equal sign. So when you fill in the box, you have the same number on both sides.* Provide additional examples, and write them on the board. Ask: *When you see a word problem that asks about* any number *and* that number *what do you know?* (In this example *any number* and *that number* talk about the same number)

Focus students' attention on the second question in the illustration. Chorally read it, and explain the illustration. Use an empty box as before to represent *what number.* Write: *What number times 1 equals 8?*

> **Think Aloud**

Say: *This question asks* what number. *I can write a number sentence to go with this question.* Write the number sentence with the empty box on the board: □ × *1 = 8* Say: *In this sentence,* what number *is the number I need to figure out. I know that when I multiply any number by 1, the product is always* that number, *so* what number *here equals 8.* 8 × 1 = 8.

Have students work in small groups to practice division and multiplication by 1. Provide additional practice for each example by helping students create similar number sentence pairs. Write them on the board, and read them aloud. Say: *To divide by 0 means to put things into 0 equal groups. That's impossible. So when you say* You can't divide a number by 0, *it means that there is no number that you can divide by zero.*

Focus students' attention on the last sentence on the board in the illustration. Chorally read the sentence. Use a Think Aloud to explain dividing a number by 0.

> **Think Aloud**

Write on the board, and say: *You can't divide a number by 0.* Then say: *When you have zero markers and divide them by five students, the quotient is zero. What can* a number *be here? I will replace* a number *in the sentence with* 8 students. Write: *You can't divide 8 students by 0.* Say: *I think* a number *refers to 8 here, because it can't be 0. So,* 0 ÷ 8 = 0. (Write the number sentence on the board. Read it aloud.) A number *in this sentence means* any number *that isn't 0.*

Remind students that you can't divide a number by zero. Say: *Zero means nothing. If you have nothing, you can't divide it up into a number of equal groups.*

Review and Practice

Review multiplication properties and division rules from Lesson 2 and Lesson 3 using Transparency 16. Read aloud each sentence. Ask students to tell you if they are true or false. Have them use their student worktexts as a guide. Invite them to write *true* or *false* next to the sentences. Challenge students to change false sentences into true sentences by rewriting them. Write these on the transparency. (Answers: 1. true, 2. false, 3. true, 4. false, 5. false, 6. true)

Review the phrases in the chart at the top of page 31. Summarize that *any number* and *a number* both mean one number, but it doesn't matter what number it is. *That number* means the same number as one that came before in the sentence. *What number* means a number that you don't know.

- **Read aloud the first sentence on the blackboard in the picture on page 31.** Ask what *any number* means in this sentence. (it doesn't matter what number it is) Ask what *that number* means. (the same number as *any number*) Write examples: *6 divided by 1 is 6. 498 divided by 1 is 498.* Point out which numbers show *any number* and which numbers show *that number.* Elicit other examples.

- **Read the second sentence in the picture.** Ask: *What does* what number *mean?* (a specific number, but they don't know what it is) Write: *8 times 1 equals 8.* Point out the answer to *what number?*

- **Read the last sentence on the board.** Ask what *a number* means. (the same as *any number*) Give examples: *3 divided by 0; I can't do it.* Write *3 ÷ 0* on the board and draw a big X across it.

BP 3 Have pairs of students make a question or sentence with each of the four phrases on the chart, using the sentences in the picture as models. Provide assistance to be sure the sentences are correct. Have pairs exchange their papers with another pair and write examples for the sentences and answers for the questions. Provide assistance as needed.

Introduce the Practice the Language activity in the student worktext. Have students complete the activity independently.

D Assess and Intervene

Can students identify what the word *number* refers to in multiplication and division questions, based on Practice the Language on page 31? Use the rubric to identify students who need extra support through additional help and the Intervention activity.

Intermediate

- ☐ Completes at least 2 sentences correctly.
- ☐ Matches at least 3 sentences to the correct example.

Advanced

- ☐ Completes at least 3 sentences correctly.
- ☐ Matches all 4 sentences to the correct example.

INTERVENTION   10 minutes

If students are having difficulty choosing the correct phrase with the word *number,* have them write each word sentence as a number sentence, replacing the blank with a number that makes a correct equation. Then have them try each phrase on the blank to see if it makes sense.

Lesson
4

Solve Math Problems

Objective Analyze what the problem really asks, and explain your answer.

45 minutes

Teach this lesson:
- **After** lessons on multiplication properties and division rules in students' grade-level math textbooks
- **Before** students complete the activities on page 32 of the student worktext

You need these materials:
- Worksheet 8

EXTENSION AND ENRICHMENT   15 minutes

Ask students to write a story or a short paragraph about the students on page 29 of Lesson 1. Have them include why it is important to know and understand multiplication properties and division rules. Ask them to share their work. Be sure to remind students to include information about multiplication properties and division rules. Read the stories aloud, and then ask: *How did knowing multiplication properties and division rules help the children in our story? How can multiplication properties and division rules help us every day?*

LESSON
4

Solve Math Problems

Objective Analyze what the problem really asks and explain your answer.

Learn to Solve Problems

Problem   What number times 8 equals 48?
? × 8 = 48

	Think	Write
Step 1:	Read the problem. Ask yourself what you need to do.	"Times" means I have to multiply. But if I multiply 8 times 48, I get a number that is more than 48. That can't be right because 48 is the total or the product.
Step 2:	Think about what the question really means.	The question asks, "What number . . . ?" That means a number I don't know. I'll write a question mark. Then it says "times 8 . . . " I'll write that. Then it says "equals 48." I'll write that. ? × 8 = 48 Now I have a number sentence I can solve. I know that 5 × 8 = 40. And 6 × 8 = 48. The answer is 6.
Step 3:	Is my answer correct?	I can use division to check a multiplication problem. 48 ÷ 8 = 6, and 48 ÷ 6 = 8. My answer is correct.

Practice Solving Math Problems

Directions Follow steps 1 to 3 above to solve the problems below. Use a separate sheet of paper. Complete each sentence to tell what the answer is. Use *because* to explain your answer in a number sentence. Answer question 6 on a separate sheet of paper.

Example
<u>What number</u> divided by 8 equals 2? The number is <u>16</u>

because 16 ÷ 8 = 2 and 8 × 2 = 16.

① 10 times what number equals 50? The number is <u>5 because 10 × 5 = 50 and 50 ÷ 5 = 10.</u>

② What number divided by 5 equals 1? The number is <u>5 because 5 ÷ 5 = 1 and 1 × 5 = 5.</u>

③ 10 times what number equals 90? The number is <u>9 because 10 × 9 = 90 and 90 ÷ 10 = 9.</u>

④ What number divided by 7 equals 0? The number is <u>0 because 0 ÷ 7 = 0 and 7 × 0 = 7.</u>

⑤ What number times 3 equals 36? The number is <u>12 because 12 × 3 = 36 and 36 ÷ 3 = 12.</u>

⑥ How do you check if your answer is correct? Answers will vary, but should include using division to check a multiplication problem and using multiplication to check a division problem.

A **Introduce**

Read aloud the Lesson Objective with students. Say: *Remember when we asked ourselves what the word* number *meant in questions about multiplication and division? We read the questions many times. We looked at them carefully to understand. When we read a math problem or any other text, we want to read it carefully. We examine it so we can understand what it really means. In this lesson, we will learn to analyze and understand what a question means. Then we can think about what really happens when we use multiplication or division.*

B **Teach and Learn**

Write this problem on the board, and read it aloud: *What number times 8 equals 48?* Have students open their worktexts to page 32 and look at Learn to Solve Problems. Tell students that the numbered steps will help them understand the question and analyze it, or think about what they need to do to solve it.

Highlighted words and phrases may affect student comprehension.

Model solving problems by using a Think Aloud:

Think Aloud

Write Step 1 on the board, and read it aloud. Say: *What do I need to do? I need to read the problem first, and then I need to decide what to do. The question is: What number times 8 equals 48?* Write this question on the board. Say: *I know that times (×) means that I should multiply. But if I multiply 8 × 48, my answer is more than 48. And that number sentence is not right because I know that 48 is the total.*

Write Step 2 on the board, and read it aloud. Say: *The question says, What number times 8 equals 48?* Point to *what number* on the board, and say: What number *is the number that I need to find. I will write a number sentence. First I will write a question mark for the number I do not know. Then it says times 8, so I will write that. Then it says equals 48.* Write *? × 8 = 48* on the board. Say: *Now I have a number sentence. I can solve the problem. ? × 8 = 48. I know that 5 × 8 = 40, and 6 × 8 = 48. The answer is 6.* As you are speaking, write 6 × 8 = 48 on the board. Circle the 6.

Write Step 3 on the board, and read it aloud. Say: *Now I will check to see if my answer is correct. Does it make sense? I can use division to check a multiplication problem. If I divide 48 by 6, the answer is 8.* Write *48 ÷ 6 = 8* on the board. Say: *That's right. I get a reasonable answer. The number is 8, because 6 × 8 = 48.*

Choose 4 multiplication and division problems from students' grade-level math textbook that involve solving for missing numbers. Write them on the board, or allow students to keep their math textbooks open.

- **Divide the class into pairs.** Give each pair four copies of Worksheet 8. The worksheet has a version of the chart on page 32 of the student worktext that students can fill in. Pairs should solve all four problems from their math textbooks, using one worksheet for each problem. Have each student take turns writing. All answers should be in complete sentences, using the sentence frame: *The number is __ because ____.* (*The number is 12, because 12 × 4 = 48.*)

- **As students work, go around the room, helping students as necessary.** Model instruction similar to that shown in the Think Aloud. If students need additional help, write the sentence frame on the board: *The number is ____.* Have them complete that sentence frame before completing the sentence frame: *The number is ____ because ____.* Let students use their student worktexts for reference. Invite students to come up and write their answers on the board.

C Review and Practice

BP 3 Give students more practice choosing and explaining what operation to use in word problems. Write multiplication and division problems, such as: *What number times 4 equals 40? What number divided by 5 equals 10?*

- **Have pairs solve the problems.** Invite volunteers to write the number sentence on the board. Use questions to prompt students to think about what operation makes more sense: *If I multiply (divide), will I get the correct answer? Will I get a reasonable answer? What operation can I use to check my answer?*

- **As a class, go over each problem.** Encourage students who didn't volunteer earlier to come up with a partner and solve a problem together. As necessary, model your thinking process out loud, using language similar to the Think Aloud, if students have difficulty solving the problem and choosing the operation.

Have students individually complete Practice Solving Math Problems in the student worktext. Circulate, and assess how well they are using the problem-solving strategy outlined in the student worktext. Check to see if they are writing complete sentences using *because* to explain their answers.

D Assess and Intervene

How well can students analyze a question and explain their answer, based on Practice Solving Math Problems on page 32? Use the rubric to identify students who need extra support through additional help and the Intervention activity.

Intermediate

☐ Answers at least 4 of problems 1–5 correctly.

☐ Explanations include *because* and an appropriate number sentence.

☐ Answer to question #6 provides an appropriate explanation about a particular problem, but may not be complete; errors may make comprehension somewhat difficult.

Example of an answer a student might write: *Answer reasonable, I know 4 × 10 = 40.*

Advanced

☐ Answers problems 1–5 correctly.

☐ Explanations are formed with a complete sentence that includes *because* and an appropriate number sentence, with few errors and complete explanations.

☐ Answer to question #6 provides a general statement about using one operation to check the other.

Example of an answer a student might write: *I know the answer reasonable because multiplication check division.*

INTERVENTION 10 minutes

If students are having difficulty analyzing the problems, make sure they understand that they should first read the problem. Then have them find and underline the question. They should think about what happens if they use multiplication or division in the problem. Students should use the inverse operation to check if their answer is correct. Then they should write the number sentence with the answer, read it, and make sure it makes sense.

Understand the Main Idea

Objective Recognize different ways of finding multiplication and division facts.

Prerequisite Background Knowledge
- Concepts and vocabulary of multiplication and division
- Skip counting

45 minutes

Teach this lesson:
- **Before** introducing lessons on multiplication and division facts in students' grade-level math textbooks
- **Before** students complete the activities on page 33 of the student worktext

You need these materials:
- Transparency 17
- index cards—6 for each pair
- markers—2 for each pair

BP 4 ELL BEST PRACTICE #4:
Interaction

For English language learners, extensive interaction with teacher and text promotes acquisition of new knowledge and new language. Pair and small-group interaction will help ELLs better learn new concepts and practice vocabulary about multiplication and division facts.

Throughout this module, when you see **BP 4**, you will find an example of how you can make your classroom more interactive.

Module 9: Multiplication and Division Facts

LESSON **1**

Understand the Main Idea

Objective Recognize different ways of finding multiplication and division facts.

Learn the Main Idea

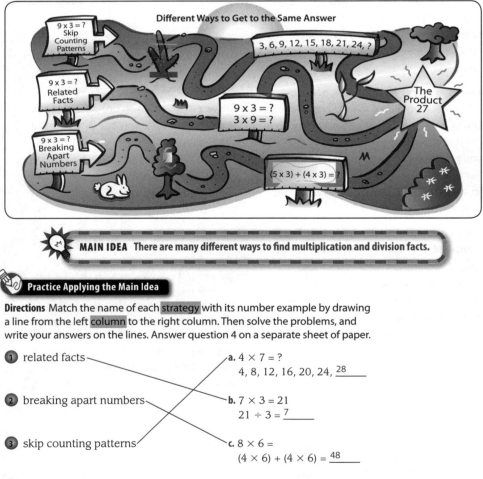

Different Ways to Get to the Same Answer

$9 \times 3 = ?$ Skip Counting Patterns

$9 \times 3 = ?$ Related Facts

$9 \times 3 = ?$ Breaking Apart Numbers

3, 6, 9, 12, 15, 18, 21, 24, ?

$9 \times 3 = ?$
$3 \times 9 = ?$

$(5 \times 3) + (4 \times 3) = ?$

The Product 27

MAIN IDEA There are many different ways to find multiplication and division facts.

Practice Applying the Main Idea

Directions Match the name of each strategy with its number example by drawing a line from the left column to the right column. Then solve the problems, and write your answers on the lines. Answer question 4 on a separate sheet of paper.

1. related facts

2. breaking apart numbers

3. skip counting patterns

a. $4 \times 7 = ?$
4, 8, 12, 16, 20, 24, __28__

b. $7 \times 3 = 21$
$21 \div 3 = $ __7__

c. $8 \times 6 = $
$(4 \times 6) + (4 \times 6) = $ __48__

4. Why is it important to know different ways of finding multiplication and division facts? Possible answer: I can figure out answers before I've memorized all the facts.

Multiplication and Division Facts · 33

A Introduce

Read aloud the Lesson Objective with students.

Have students brainstorm. Ask about the many ways and strategies they already know to find multiplication and division facts. (skip counting, patterns, multiplication properties, breaking apart, multiplication tables, related facts, number lines, using counters and arrays, repeated subtraction) Write students' responses on the board.

Have students work in groups of three. Ask them to think of examples of the different strategies that they already know. Have them write examples of the ones they know. Then have each group share their answers with another group.

Read the Main Idea together with students. Say: *You already know some ways to find multiplication and division facts. Now you will learn to recognize new ways in this lesson. You will also learn other ways in your math classes.*

Highlighted words and phrases may affect student comprehension.

B Teach and Learn

Focus students' attention on the illustration at the top of page 33 in their student worktext.

Have pairs of students discuss the illustration. Ask prompting questions: *Have you ever gone on a trip? Did your family use a roadmap? What do you use a roadmap for? What is different about the map here?* Ask them to report to the group what they talked about.

Say: *Roadmaps tell us ways that we can get from one place to another. This roadmap tells us different ways we can get to an answer. The street names are all math strategies—different ways you can get to the same multiplication facts.*

Have students look at the star on the right side of the page. Have them tell what is in it. Ask a volunteer to name the three different roads or paths to the destination: the product 27. Elicit that multiplication facts are used to get a product and these are all multiplication strategies.

Direct groups of four to work together. Have them study and check the number problems along each road. Ask: *Are the number problems correct? Is 27 the correct product for each one?* Elicit that the number problems are correct and that 27 is the correct product for each.

Display Transparency 17. Use it to go over the three ways to find multiplication and division facts. Have the students think of other examples for each way.

- **Keep the transparency on display as you write the following sentence frame on the board:** *I like to use <u>related facts</u> to find multiplication and division facts because <u>I can use the same numbers</u>.* Have students repeat the sentence after you. Have partners say it to each other. Ask volunteers to choose another way, and then help them finish the sentence. Have the other students repeat that sentence. Write that sentence on the board. Continue with the third way.

- **BP 4 Have pairs of students discuss which of the three routes on page 33 in the student worktext they like best.** Ask pairs to use the sentence frame on the board. Go around the room and assist students, as needed. Then ask pairs why they chose a certain way, and have them answer using the sentence frame.

- **BP 4 Have small groups of four work together.** Ask them to come up with other number examples of the three strategies. Write *Skip Counting Patterns, Related Facts,* and *Breaking Apart Numbers* on the board. Have a group representative come up and write some of the group's number examples under the correct headings.

C Review and Practice

To review the different ways of finding multiplication and division facts, write the following number sentences on the board. Ask students to tell which strategy they might use and why they would use it. Then, together, solve the problems.

$9 \times 4 = ?$ $18 \div 3 = ?$
$24 \div 4 = ?$ $7 \times 8 = ?$

BP 4 Play a matching game. Pass out 12 index cards and two markers to each pair of students. Have them write three number examples (such as the examples they wrote on Transparency 17) on six cards and the strategy name on the other six cards. They will write each strategy and number example twice. Ask two pairs of students to work together. Have them shuffle the cards and deal them out, three cards per player. The other cards go in a pile in the middle. Students take turns laying down one card at a time (and picking up a new card from the pile in the middle) until they see a match: a number example card that goes with its strategy. Whoever sees the match first takes those two cards. The one with the most cards at the end is the winner. Go around the room listening to students as they play and assisting as needed.

Read aloud the directions for the Practice Applying the Main Idea activity in the student worktext on page 33. Have students work independently to do the activity. Circulate, and assess how well students are matching strategies with number examples.

D Assess and Intervene

Can students recognize the different ways to find multiplication and division facts? Can they use a complete sentence to tell why it is important to know different ways to find multiplication and division facts? Use the rubric to identify students who need extra support through additional help and the Intervention activity.

Intermediate

☐ Correctly matches all 3 strategies and solves number problems.

☐ Responds in a phrase/sentence with minor errors about the importance of knowing different ways to find multiplication and division facts.

Example of a sentence a student might write: *Can check answer.*

Advanced

☐ Correctly matches all 3 strategies and solves number problems.

☐ Responds in a clear sentence with few errors about the importance of knowing different ways to find multiplication and division facts.

Example of a sentence a student might write: *I can check to see if answer is correct.*

INTERVENTION   10 minutes

If students are having difficulty finding multiplication and division facts in different ways, have them write the following phrases across a sheet of paper turned sideways: *Skip Counting Patterns, Related Facts, Breaking Apart Numbers.* Give the students some number sentences, such as $2 \times 3 = ?$, $4 \times 2 = ?$, and $3 \times 4 = ?$. Ask students to write the number sentence under the name of a strategies and then solve it using that strategy. Observe where the students are putting the sentences and how they are solving each one. Give more sentences as needed. Ask students to think of other sentences and add those to the lists. Have them keep their papers for future reference.

Lesson

2

Learn the Vocabulary

Objective Talk and write about multiplication and division facts using the
vocabulary words.

30 minutes ⏱

Teach this lesson:
- **Before** introducing lessons on multiplication and division facts in students'
  grade-level math textbooks
- **Before** students complete the activities on page 34 of the student worktext

You need these materials:
- Transparency 18
- sticky notes
- Vocabulary Cards
- index cards

Lesson Vocabulary

Essential Vocabulary	
multiple	pattern

Additional Vocabulary		
to break apart*	array	column
row	related facts	
multiplication table		

* - Terms that have Vocabulary Cards.

LESSON

2

Learn the Vocabulary

Objective Talk and write about multiplication and division facts using
the vocabulary words.

Learn the Words

A **pattern** is a set of numbers (or objects) in a
certain order. The order helps you predict, or
find out, what number comes next.

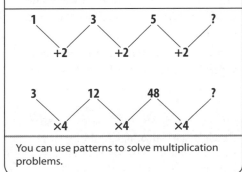

You can use patterns to solve multiplication
problems.

A **multiple** is the product of two numbers.

x	0	1	2	3	4	5	6	7	8	9
1	0	1	2	3	4	5	6	7	8	9
2	0	2	4	6	8	10	12	14	16	18
3	0	3	6	9	12	15	18	21	24	27

Move your finger across the row for 3.
Say aloud the multiples of 3: 3, 6, 9, 12, 15, 18,
21, 24, 27
Multiples are a kind of pattern.

Practice the Words

Directions Write the name of the correct vocabulary word (multiple or pattern) on
each line. Answer question 5 in a complete sentence.

1. The product of two numbers is called a
   <u>multiple</u>.

2. A set of numbers (or objects) in a certain
   order is a <u>pattern</u>.

3. A <u>multiple</u> of both 3 and 4
   is 12.

4. The order in a <u>pattern</u> helps
   you guess the number that comes next.

5. Why is knowing multiples useful when
   you divide and multiply?
   Possible answer: You can start with a multiple you
   know, 2 × 3 = 6, and keep counting by 3's until you
   get to your answer.

A Introduce

**Read aloud the Lesson Objective with
students.**

**Help students activate their prior knowl-
edge.** Ask: *What do you remember about how
to find multiplication and division facts?* Write
students' responses on the board. Ask: *Why is
it important to know these different ways?*

**Tell students that they will learn some
new vocabulary words to help them talk
and write about multiplication and division facts.**

Ask: *Where have we seen a pattern before?*
Have students look back at Skip Counting
Patterns on page 33. Say: *Look at the pattern
3, 6, 9, 12, 15, 18, 21, 24? How do you know which
number comes next?* Inform students they may
hear the word *pattern* when someone talks
about behavior (a behavior pattern) or a plan
for making clothing (a sewing pattern).

Write the word *multiple* on the board.
Underline *multi*. Ask: *Can you think of other
words that start with multi?* (multiply, multiplication) Say: *It is easy to confuse the spelling
and pronunciation of these words. The word
multiple is a noun that ends in e, and multiply
is a verb that ends in y.* Tell students they may
also hear the word *multiple* when someone
talks about multiple births (twins or triplets)
or multiple parking tickets (more than one).

**Choose words from the Additional Vocabu-
lary box that you think will be useful.** Elicit
or provide examples or definitions for all the
words on the list.

◁ Highlighted words and phrases may affect student comprehension.

B Teach and Learn

Focus students' attention on the left-hand panel on page 34 of the student work-text. Read the text above the illustrations. Ask: *What is a pattern?* (a set of numbers in a certain order) Ask: *What does the order help you do?* (It helps you predict what number comes next.)

Write *1, 2, 3, 4* on the board. Ask students: *What comes next?* (5) *How do you know?* (each number is 1 more) Do the same with *3, 6, 9, 12 ?* (15) Say: *There are other kinds of patterns. 1, 2, 3, 1, 2, 3, 1, 2, 3 is a repeating pattern.*

Focus students' attention on the first pattern in the panel on the left. Ask: *What number comes after 5? How do you know?* (7, because the pattern is 2 more) Focus attention on the second pattern. Ask: *What number comes next after 48?* (192, because the pattern is × 4)

BP 4 Write on the board the following patterns: *4, 8, 12, 16, ?; 3, 6, 9, 12, ?; 6, 12, 18, ?; and 7, 14, 21, ?* Have small groups of four find the next numbers in the patterns. Then have each group write two more patterns and share them with the class.

Focus students' attention on the multiplication table on the right-hand side of the page. Read the text above the multiplication table, and have students repeat the definition. Then read the text below the table. As you read, have students move their finger across the row, saying the multiples of 3 with you.

Write the following multiplication problems and stars on the board:

$4 \times 1 = 4$ ★★★★
$4 \times 2 = 8$ ★★★★ ★★★★
$4 \times 3 = 12$ ★★★★ ★★★★ ★★★★
$4 \times 4 = 16$ ★★★★ ★★★★ ★★★★ ★★★★

Say: *With these multiplication number sentences, you see arrays of stars. These arrays show that 4, 8, 12, and 16 are multiples of 4.* Have student volunteers come to the board, complete the problem, and draw arrays for $4 \times 5 = 20$ to $4 \times 9 = 36$. Write this sentence frame on the board: *These arrays show that ____ are multiples of ____.* Model the sentence, and have students say it after you. Ask student pairs to look at the arrays and talk about multiples using the sentence frame.

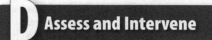 **Display Transparency 18.** Explain to students that a multiplication table can be used to multiply and divide, and to find patterns in both multiplication and division. Using your finger or a pointer, point out the location of a row and a column. Write *row* and *column* on the board, model their pronunciation, and have students repeat. Ask students whether a column goes up and down, or across. (up and down) A row? (across) Point out to students that the final *n* in the word *column* is silent.

- **Show students how you can find multiples of the number 4.** Tell them to look down the column where the number 4 appears and also look across the row where the number 4 appears. Have students read aloud all the multiples of 4 in chorus. Then have student pairs first locate with their fingers and then write on a sheet of paper the multiples of 5, 6, and 7 using the transparency.

- **Ask:** *How can you use the multiplication table to find a quotient of two numbers?* Elicit that you can go down a column of a certain number and across a row of a certain number to find a product. Then you can divide that number by one of the other numbers to find its quotient.

Have students complete the Vocabulary Cards for the words in this module.

C Review and Practice

Review the words *multiple* and *pattern* by writing the words on the board. Ask students to tell you a definition for each and to use each word in a sentence.

BP 4 Have students work with a partner. They will use the multiplication table on the transparency to find the product or quotient of the following four problems that you write on the board: $18 \div 2, 5 \times 5, 49 \div 7, 5 \times 9$

Write this sentence frame on the board: *To find the ____ of ____, I used a pattern of multiples of ____.* Write *product* and *quotient* under the first blank, 4×4 and $27 \div 9$ under the second blank, and *4* and *9* under the last blank. Model how to use the frame: *To find the product of 4 times 4, I used a pattern of multiples of 4. To find the quotient of 27 divided by 9, I used a pattern of multiples of 9.* Have

students repeat. Then have pairs of student use the frame to tell each other how they found the products and quotients in the four problems.

Have students work on their own to do the Practice the Words activity on page 34. Circulate around the room, and assess students as they are working.

D Assess and Intervene

Can every student talk and write about different ways of finding multiplication and division facts using the vocabulary in the Practice the Words activity on page 34? Use the rubric to identify students who need extra support through additional help and the Intervention activity.

Intermediate

☐ Chooses the correct vocabulary word in 3 out of 4 sentences.

☐ Writes a phrase or sentence with a few errors telling why multiples are useful when dividing and multiplying.

Example of a sentence a student might write: *You count many times multiple.*

Advanced

☐ Chooses the correct vocabulary word in 4 out of 4 sentences.

☐ Writes a complete sentence with few errors telling why multiples are useful when multiplying and dividing.

Example of a sentence a student might write: *Start with multiple you know and count to answer.*

INTERVENTION 5 minutes

If students have difficulty understanding the concepts *multiple* and *pattern*, play "True or False" using the Vocabulary Cards. Have students choose one of their cards, and read the word and the definition aloud. Give an example of the concept, which may be a true example or a false example. For instance: *3, 6, 9, 3, 6, 9, 3, 6, 9 is a pattern.* (T) *32 is a multiple of 5.* (F) Students write T or F on a slip of paper and hold it up so you can assess their understanding. Then have students give their own true and false examples.

Use More Language

Objective Use regular and irregular past tense verbs and *so* to describe how you found a product or quotient.

---

30 minutes

Teach this lesson:
- **After** lessons on multiplication and division facts in students' grade-level math textbook
- **Before** students complete the activities on page 35 of the student worktext

You need these materials:
- Vocabulary Cards
- Worksheet 9
- index cards

Use More Language

Objective Use regular and irregular past tense verbs and *so* to describe how you found a product or quotient.

LESSON
3

Learn the Language

Practice the Language

Directions Write past tense verbs from the word bank to complete the sentences. Write your choices in the blanks. Answer number 4 in a complete sentence on the lines below.

| broke | used | solved | thought | counted | looked | found | finished |

Example
What did you do to solve 7 × 4? To solve 7 × 4, I <u>used</u> a multiplication table.

1. What did you do to solve 7 × 4? To solve 7 × 4, I <u>broke</u> apart the 7 into (5 × 4) and (2 × 4).

2. How did you use the multiplication table to solve 7 × 4? To solve 7 × 4, I <u>looked</u> down column 4 and across row 7.

3. How did you solve 28 ÷ 7? To solve 28 ÷ 7, I <u>thought</u> about a related fact: 7 × 4 = 28, and 4 × 7 = 28. So 28 ÷ 7 = 4.

4. Write the steps you used to solve the following problem. Use this sentence frame: *To find/solve* _____, *I* _____. *So* _____. Use one of the verbs from the word bank.
7 × 9 = 63   63 ÷ 7 = ?
Answers will vary. To solve 63 ÷ 7, I used a related

fact, 7 × 9 = 63. So 63 ÷ 7 = 9.

Multiplication and Division Facts • 35

A Introduce

Ask students to tell you about something they did yesterday. As they describe what they did, write all of the verbs on the board, in two columns, with regular *–ed* verbs in one column and irregular verbs with other past tense forms in the second column. Continue eliciting past tense verbs until you have 4–5 verbs in each column.

Say: *All of these words are action words, or* verbs, *that tell about things that happened yesterday.* Yesterday *means that this is* past time, *that the things already happened.*

Point to the two columns of verbs on the board and say: *All of these verbs are past time verbs. How are the verbs in the first column different from the verbs in the second column?* Have students answer the question with a partner and share their answers. Summarize that the verbs in the first column end in *–ed,* while the verbs in the second column have different forms. Explain that past time verbs that end in *–ed* are called *regular verbs* because they follow a rule. The verbs in the second column are called *irregular verbs* because they don't follow the rule.

Read aloud the Lesson Objective with students. Tell students that in this lesson they will learn to describe how they found a product or quotient using different past-tense verbs.

Focus students' attention on the two girls on the left on page 35 of the student worktext. Ask students to work in pairs and talk about what they see in the picture without reading the words in the speech bubbles.

Highlighted words and phrases may affect student comprehension.

Have students talk about the two girls, their relationship, the setting, the time of day, and their activity. Tell students that these sisters are sharing how they solved both a multiplication and a division problem.

B Teach and Learn

Focus students' attention on the left-hand panel of the Learn the Language section on 35 of the student worktext. Read aloud the speech bubbles of both sisters.

Have students underline the question that Chi asks. Say: *Chi asks,* How did you solve 3 × 9 and 27 ÷ 9? *Is* How did you solve *the same as* How do you solve? *How is it different?* How do you solve *means the problem isn't solved yet.* How did you solve *means that the problem has already been solved.*

• **Have students circle and name all the things Chau said she did.** Ask students to look for the verbs that follow *I.* (broke, used) List these verbs on the board under the heading *Chau.* Then ask students to find and circle the verbs Chi said she did. Again, ask students to look for the verbs that follow the word *I.* (used [2x], thought, counted, looked [2x], found) List them on the board under the heading *Chi.*

Say: *Tell me something about those verbs. Are they about what the twins are doing now?* (no) *Are they about something they are going to do tomorrow?* (no) Elicit from students that the verbs are telling about what the twins did a little while ago. Say: *When you use past-tense verbs, you talk about things that happened in the past—2 weeks ago, last year, yesterday, or 5 minutes ago.*

Point out to students that regular past-tense verbs end in *-ed.* Say: *Most past-tense verbs are regular. They end in -ed. But the verbs we use most of the time are irregular verbs: do/ did, go/went, eat/ate, drink/drank, write/wrote, sleep/slept.*

Ask students to look at the verbs in the speech bubbles on page 35 and name the regular verbs. Write *Regular Verbs* and *Irregular Verbs* on the board. Write the regular verbs in the first column. (use/used, count/ counted, look/looked, solve/solved) Have students name the irregular verbs. (find/ found, break/broke, think/thought) Write them in the second column.

Read aloud the speech bubbles again. Have students clap their hands once as soon as they hear the word *so.*

BP 4 **Have students work in pairs.** Have them look for the word *so* in the speech bubbles on page 35 of the student worktext. Have them draw a triangle around the word *so* every time it appears. (3 times) Tell students that *so* means *for this reason,* or *therefore.* Say: *1 × 3 = 3. For this reason 3 × 1 = 3.* Have students repeat this sentence, using *so* instead of *for this reason.* Repeat the process using *therefore.* Point out that they will often use *so* to explain answers to math problems.

Write this sentence on the board: *To find the product of 3 × 9, I broke apart the 9 into 5 + 4, I multiplied 3 × 5 and 3 × 4, and I added the two products. So 3 × 9 = 27.* Have students read the sentence with you. Erase all but these sentence frames: *To find _____, I _____. So _____.*

Ask students to work in pairs. Have them use the sentence frames to explain how Chau and Chi used breaking apart and multiples to find products, and related facts and a multiplication table to find quotients. Ask the first student to read a number sentence, and the second student to explain how to solve it, without looking at the speech bubble. Then have the first student read the speech bubble. Both students should decide if what the second student said was correct. If not, that student should try again. Students should switch roles and continue until they have done all four problems.

C Review and Practice

Review using regular and irregular past-tense verbs. Write a present -tense verb on the board, and ask students to say it in the past tense. Write the past-tense form on the board as they say it.

Ask pairs of students to use the following sentence frame: *To find or solve_____, I _____. So _____.* Ask each pair to write a multiplication problem and a division problem and to use the sentence frames to explain how they found the product and the quotient.

BP 4 **Distribute Worksheet 9 to students.** Tell students to work with a partner. Have them write the past tense for each of these verbs used in math. Below the columns, have them write sentences using two of the regular and two of the irregular past-tense verbs.

Have students work independently to answer the questions in the Practice the Language activity on page 35 in the student worktext. Walk through the room, and assess them as they work.

D Assess and Intervene

Can students use *so* and the regular and irregular past-tense verbs to describe how they found a product or quotient? Use the rubric to identify students who need extra support through additional help and the Intervention activity.

Intermediate

☐ Chooses correct verb to complete 2 out of 3 sentences.

☐ Uses the sentence frames to describe how the problem was solved, with a correct past tense verb and *so,* and only minor errors.

Example of sentences a student might write: *To find 63 ÷ 7, I used fact relation. So 63 ÷ 7 = 9*

Advanced

☐ Chooses correct verb to complete 3 out of 3 sentences.

☐ Uses the sentence frames to describe how the problem was solved, with a correct past tense verb and *so,* with no errors.

Example of sentences a student might write: *To find 63 ÷ 7, I used a related fact. So 63 ÷ 7 = 9.*

INTERVENTION   10 minutes

If students are having difficulty using regular and irregular past-tense verbs and *so* to describe how they found a product or quotient, give students index cards and have them write one of the following words and phrases on each index card: *to find the product, to find the quotient, I broke apart, I used, a related fact, a pattern, a multiplication table, to solve, to find, of 4 × 6, of 3 × 4, of 8 ÷ 2, of 9 ÷ 3, so 3 × 4 = 12, so 8 ÷ 2 = 4, so 9 ÷ 3 = 3, so 4 × 6 = 24, I solved, I found, I looked across the row, I looked down the column.* Have students manipulate the cards to form sentences, such as: *To find the product of 3 × 4, I used a related fact (4 × 3). So 3 × 4 = 12.* Assist students as needed.

Solve Math Problems

Objective Decide whether to multiply or divide.

30 minutes

Teach this lesson:
- **After** lesson on multiplication and division facts in students' grade-level math textbooks
- **Before** students complete the activities on page 36 of the student worktext

You need these materials:
- multiplication table
- Vocabulary Cards
- counters and other manipulatives

EXTENSION AND ENRICHMENT   15 minutes

Have students work together with a partner to write a multiplication or a division word problem of their own. They can look for ideas In their math textbooks, but their problem must be original. Then have them exchange their problem with another pair and solve each other's problems. Collect the problems and put them together In a "Multiplication and Division Word Problems" book.

Solve Math Problems

Objective Decide whether to multiply or divide.

Learn to Solve Problems

> **Problem** (Six) students bought [three] tickets each to the new aquarium. They bought the extra tickets for their friends. <u>How many tickets did the students buy in all?</u>

Step 1: Read the problem. Underline the question.

Step 2: Find the facts. Circle the number of equal groups. Put a square around the number in each group. Put a triangle around the total.

Step 3: Think about the problem. Do you have to find the total? If yes, then multiply. Do you have to find the number of equal groups or the number in each equal group? If yes, then divide. What do you need to do?

I don't know the total. I need to find the total. I have to multiply.

Step 4: Write a number sentence. Solve the problem.

I will multiply. 6 × 3 = 18.

The students bought 18 tickets in all.

Practice Solving Math Problems

Directions Write *multiply* or *divide* in the blank to show what you need to do. Then solve each problem and write the answer in a complete sentence. Write out the steps for number 4 on a separate sheet of paper.

1. If there are 12 eggs in a dozen, how many eggs are there in 5 dozen?

   multiply; There are 60 eggs in 5 dozen.

2. Lana has 8 cookies. She wants to share the cookies with her 3 friends at lunch. How many cookies will each person get? Remember to include Lana!

   divide; Each person will get 2 cookies.

3. Roberto walks 4 miles in 1 hour. How many hours will it take him to walk 12 miles?

   multiply; It will take Roberto 3 hours to walk 12 miles.

4. Bao wants to buy ⑥ pieces of gum that cost [12] cents each. <u>How much money does Bao need to buy the gum?</u> To find the product, Bao needs to multiply. He multiplies 6 pieces of gum by 12 cents each to find the product. So 6 × 12 = 72 cents. Bao needs 72 cents to buy the gum.

A Introduce

Read aloud the Lesson Objective with students. Tell students that in this lesson they are going to read some word problems. They will learn steps to help them decide if they need to multiply or divide to solve the problems.

Activate students' background knowledge. Ask students to think about a recent math problem they had to solve. Ask: *Did you have to multiply to find the answer? Did you have to divide? How did you decide what to do?* Accept all answers.

Write this problem on the board: *Tania went shopping with her mother for school clothes. One shirt cost $11. Tania bought 5 shirts. How much did the shirts cost in all?*

Ask student pairs to talk about it and decide if they need to multiply or divide. Have students share their thinking with the class.

Direct students to the word problem in the Learn to Solve Problems section on page 36 of the student worktext. Read it aloud. Tell students that they will be learning four steps to help them solve this problem.

> Highlighted words and phrases may affect student comprehension.

Teach and Learn

Check students' understanding of the word problem on the top of page 36 of the student textbook. Ask questions, such as: *How many students bought tickets for the aquarium?* (6) *How many tickets did each student buy?* (3)

Model the steps to solve the problem using this Think Aloud.

> **Think Aloud**
>
> **Call students' attention to Step 1 in their worktexts and write it on the board.** Invite students to read it aloud with you. Summarize by saying: *First, I read the problem.* Write the problem on the board, and read it aloud. *Then, I underline the question. The question usually comes at the end of a word problem, and it has a question mark.* Help students find the question, and underline it on the board.
>
> **Read aloud Step 2 and write it on the board.** Say: *I have to find the facts. The facts are* six students *and* three tickets each. *I ask myself: Do I have equal groups? Each student bought the same number of tickets, so each student has an equal group of tickets. I will circle* six *because there are 6 students, so there are 6 equal groups of tickets.* Circle *six.* Say: *I need to put a square around the number in each group. Each student bought 3 tickets. So I will put a square around* three. Draw a square around *three.* Then say: *Can I put a triangle around the total? My answer is no. I don't know the total yet, so I can't put a triangle around it.*
>
> **Read Step 3 aloud, and write it on the board.** Ask: *What do I need to find out?* (the total) *If I have 6 groups of 3 tickets each, how do I find the total? Should I multiply or divide?* (multiply)
>
> **Continue to Step 4.** Ask a volunteer to read it aloud. Say: *I need to write a number sentence. So I write* 6 × 3 = ? Write the number sentence on the board. *Now I can solve the problem.* 6 × 3 = 18. *The students bought 18 tickets in all. Now I can put a triangle around the total.* Draw a triangle around *18 tickets.*

BP 4 In groups of four, have students summarize the steps for deciding whether to multiply or divide. Tell them they may use page 36 in their student worktexts. Have them write in their own words what they learned about how to decide whether to multiply or divide when they have a word problem. Walk around the room, and observe students as they do their summaries. When they are finished, have them share with the whole group.

Have students work in the same groups of four. Have them use the steps to solve a problem. Write the following problem on the board: *José plays basketball for the same amount of time every Monday, Tuesday, Thursday, and Saturday afternoon. He plays 32 hours in 4 weeks. How many hours does José play each week?*

When the groups are finished, discuss their answers and how they solved the problems.

Ask pairs of students to work together to write a math word problem. Tell them to be sure the problem is one that will need multiplication or division to solve it. When they finish writing, have them exchange problems with another pair. Then they can discuss the steps they used with that other pair.

Review and Practice

To review the lesson, ask students to recall the four steps. Prompt students with questions, such as: *What did I do in Step 1? What did I do in Step 2? What did I do in Step 3? What did I do in Step 4 to solve the problem?*

BP 4 Ask students to work with a partner to select a multiplication word problem and a division word problem from their math textbook. Have them use the Think Aloud model to decide if they need to multiply or divide to solve each problem.

Remind students of all the ways they've learned to solve multiplication and division problems. Review the ways addressed in Lesson 1 with students: breaking apart numbers, skip counting patterns, related facts, and multiplication tables.

Read aloud the directions for Practice Solving Math Problems on page 36 of the student worktext. Remind students that they will be working independently. Tell them it will be helpful if they follow the list of steps on page 36 as they do the problems.

Circulate around the room. Assess how well students are following the steps and solving the problems. Use the rubric below to assess them.

Assess and Intervene

How well can students determine if solving a word problem requires multiplication or division? Can students write a complete sentence and follow steps to decide if they will multiply or divide to solve a word problem? Use the rubric to identify students who need extra support through additional help and the Intervention activity.

Intermediate

☐ Correctly determines in 2 out of 3 word problems whether to multiply or to divide and solves them.

☐ Writes out the steps with a few errors to explain how problem was solved.

Example of a sentence a student might write: *Need multiply.*

Advanced

☐ Correctly determines in 3 out of 3 word problems whether to multiply or to divide and solves them.

☐ Writes out the steps in complete sentences with few errors to explain how problem was solved.

Example of a sentence a student might write: *He need to multiply to find answer.*

> **INTERVENTION** 5 minutes
>
> If students are having difficulty reading word problems and deciding whether to multiply or to divide in order to solve them, remind students that when they multiply, they combine equal groups; when they divide, they share equally. As students solve problems, have them ask: *Am I adding together equal groups of things? Am I trying to share something equally? Do I need to find out how many groups?* Make available to students counters and other manipulatives to help them make groups.

Lesson

1

Prerequisite Background Knowledge
• Basic concepts of place value
• Basic multiplication facts
• Addition of 1- and 2-digit numbers

Understand the Main Idea

Objective Break apart numbers to make them easier to multiply.

30 minutes

Teach this lesson:
• **Before** introducing material on multi-digit multiplication in students' grade-level math textbooks
• **Before** students complete the activities on page 37 of the student worktext

You need these materials:
• scored crackers
• 4 small boxes
• Transparency 19
• base-ten blocks

BP 5 ELL BEST PRACTICE #5:
Higher-Order Thinking

English language learners are just as capable as other students of using higher-order thinking. However, they are hampered by their inability to express their thinking in English. As you teach this module, help students make connections between numbers, analyze products, and ask questions to solve problems with unknown words.

Throughout this module, when you see **BP 5**, you will find an example of how you can activate higher-order thinking.

Module 10: Model Multiplication by 1- and 2-Digit Numbers

Understand the Main Idea

Objective Break apart numbers to make them easier to multiply.

LESSON 1

Learn the Main Idea

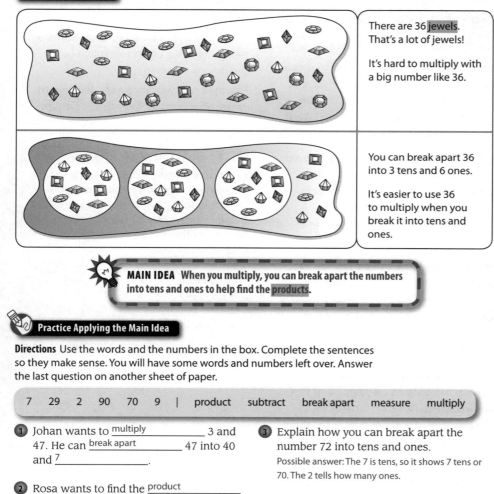

There are 36 jewels. That's a lot of jewels!

It's hard to multiply with a big number like 36.

You can break apart 36 into 3 tens and 6 ones.

It's easier to use 36 to multiply when you break it into tens and ones.

  MAIN IDEA When you multiply, you can break apart the numbers into tens and ones to help find the products.

Practice Applying the Main Idea

Directions Use the words and the numbers in the box. Complete the sentences so they make sense. You will have some words and numbers left over. Answer the last question on another sheet of paper.

| 7 29 2 90 70 9 | product subtract break apart measure multiply |

❶ Johan wants to <u>multiply</u> 3 and 47. He can <u>break apart</u> 47 into 40 and <u>7</u>.

❷ Rosa wants to find the <u>product</u> of 8 × 29. She can break apart <u>29</u> into 20 and <u>9</u>.

❸ Explain how you can break apart the number 72 into tens and ones.
Possible answer: The 7 is tens, so it shows 7 tens or 70. The 2 tells how many ones.

A Introduce

Hold up a cracker that is scored so it easy to break. Say: *You can break apart this cracker. You can break it into parts.* Demonstrate how to break the cracker. Then say: *I broke apart the cracker into parts.*

Hand out a large scored cracker to each pair of students. Say: *You can break apart crackers, too.* Invite students to break their crackers into small bits and to eat them.

Say: *You can break apart numbers, too. You can break numbers into smaller numbers.*

Write the number 12 on the board. Draw 12 Xs or circles beneath it. Ask students how they could break apart 12 into smaller numbers. Accept reasonable responses, and write them on the board. Say: *[Kimiko] says we can break 12 into 9 + 3. Is she right? Let's see . . . Here are 9 Xs, and that leaves 3 Xs. Yes! We can break apart 12 into 9 + 3.* Repeat till there are 3–4 possible solutions on the board, including 10 + 2.

BP 5 Point to 10 + 2. Say: *It can be very useful to break apart 12 into 10 + 2. Who knows why?* Have students discuss with a partner why 10 + 2 might be an especially good way to break 12 apart.

Highlighted words and phrases may affect student comprehension.

Elicit that when you break 12 into 10 + 2, you are splitting 12 into tens and ones. Point out that tens and ones are important in math. Say: *Sometimes it's good to break 12 into 6 + 6, or 9 + 3. But it often makes more sense to split a number into tens and ones.*

Repeat with 25, drawing out that it is helpful to break 25 apart into 20 + 5.

Read aloud the Lesson Objective with students. Highlight the fact that this module will be about multiplication.

Have students study the illustrations in the Learn the Main Idea section on page 37. Ask if anyone is wearing jewels or knows someone who wears them. Have volunteers read the text aloud. Emphasize that the second panel shows the same number of jewels as the first panel, but they are grouped into tens and ones.

Read aloud the Main Idea. Remind students that a product is the answer to a multiplication problem. Tell students that when they break numbers into tens and ones, multiplying them will be easier.

B Teach and Learn

Focus students' attention on the first illustration, on the top. Ask: *How many jewels are in the picture?* (36) *Are they easy to count?* (no) Explain that the jewels are not organized, so they're hard to count.

Have four students come to the front of the room. Hand each one a small box. Say: *Let's say that each of these boxes has 36 jewels inside, just like in the picture. So four people each have 36 jewels. What multiplication expression tells how many jewels in all?* Draw out that 4 × 36 gives the total number of jewels. Write this expression on the board.

Then touch the number *4* on the board and say: *Many of you know the fours facts.* Then touch *36.* Say: *But you probably don't know the 36 facts! Most people, even teachers, do not learn the facts for 36. You don't multiply numbers like 36 very often. So it doesn't make sense to memorize facts with 36.*

Call students' attention to the second illustration, on the bottom. Ask: *How did they break apart 36 in this picture?* (3 tens and 6 ones) *Why?* Elicit that tens and ones are useful for many reasons. Point out also the part

of the text that says that breaking the number into tens and ones will help if students try to multiply the number.

Say: *The page tells you that it is easier to multiply 36 if you break it apart into 30 + 6. But it does not tell you why that will make it easier!* Explain that students will learn more about how to multiply large numbers when they do the lessons in their math textbooks.

BP 5 **Have students work with a partner.** Ask them to discuss and then write why they think it is easier to multiply a number like 36 if it is broken into tens and ones.

- **Ask guiding questions such as:** *What can you do if you have tens and ones? If you know 4 × 3, does that help you solve any other multiplication problems? Which ones?* Encourage students to include diagrams or pictures with their work. Circulate through the room, offering assistance as needed.

- **Have students share their thinking with other pairs.** Then collect students' work. Explain that you will keep the papers and have them compare their ideas now to what they will learn in the grade-level lessons.

C Review and Practice

Review breaking apart numbers by asking the class how they would find the product of 54 × 3. Lead them into breaking 54 into 5 tens and 4 ones.

Display Transparency 19. Walk students through the example problem, and have them write down their work. Stress that they break the numbers into tens and ones. Remind students that they have done this in earlier work.

Once students seem comfortable with this process, have them work in pairs to copy and complete the remaining problems on the transparency. Go over all the problems as a class to make sure students understand.

Call students' attention to the directions for Practice Applying the Main Idea. Point out that they will find all the numbers and words they need in the word box. Emphasize that some of the words and numbers will not be used.

Have students solve the problems on their own. Discuss answers as a class when everyone has completed the assignment.

D Assess and Intervene

Do students understand the concept of breaking numbers into tens and ones to make multiplication easier, based on Practice Applying the Main Idea on page 37? Use the rubric to identify students who need extra support through additional help and the Intervention activity.

Intermediate

☐ Successfully fills in at least five of the six missing words and numbers.

☐ Writes a phrase or sentence, with some errors, mentioning both tens and ones in the response.

Example of a sentence a student might write: *The 7 come first so tens the ones coming last so ones is 2.*

Advanced

☐ Successfully fills in all six of the missing words and numbers.

☐ Writes a sentence, with few errors, that tells how to obtain both the tens and the ones.

Example of a sentence a student might write: *There are 7 tens which make 70, and there is 2 left over so it is 72.*

INTERVENTION   5 minutes

If students struggle with the problems at the bottom of page 37, they may not recall place value concepts clearly. Have them work with base-ten blocks to model various numbers. Demonstrate how to use these blocks to model and count 53 (5 tens 3 ones). Next, have them read and write the number 53 based on the information in the model. Show how placing the digit 5 in the tens column means that it stands for 5 tens, or 50. Repeat with other examples. Then have students model, read, and write other numbers with a partner.

Lesson

2

Learn the Vocabulary

Objective Talk and write about multiplying 1- and 2-digit numbers using the vocabulary words.

⏱ **30 minutes**

Teach this lesson:
- **Before** students complete work on multiplication of 1- and 2-digit numbers in their grade-level textbooks
- **Before** students complete the activities on page 38 of the student worktext

You need these materials:
- Transparency 20
- Vocabulary Cards
- manipulatives: ones, tens, and hundreds

Lesson Vocabulary

Essential Vocabulary

Distributive Property   to regroup _____ as _____   partial product

Additional Vocabulary

array*   row   column
factor   product   to break apart*

* - Terms that have Vocabulary Cards.

LESSON

2

Learn the Vocabulary

Objective Talk and write about multiplying 1- and 2-digit numbers using the vocabulary words.

Learn the Words

Directions Fill in the missing words and numbers.

You can use the **Distributive Property** to multiply a sum by a number.

4 × (5 + 2) = ?	3 × (5 + 4) = ?
First, find 4 groups of 5. Multiply 4 × 5 (one addend): 4 × 5 = 20	First, find 3 groups of 5. Multiply 3 × 5 (one addend): 3 × 5 = 15
Next, multiply 4 × 2, the other addend: 4 × 2 = 8	Next, multiply 3 × 4, the other addend: 3 × 4 = 12
Finally, add the **partial products**: 20 + 8 = 28	Finally, add the partial products: 15 + 12 = 27
4 × (5 + 2) = 28	3 × (5 + 4) = 27

Sometimes you might need to **regroup** one amount as another amount.

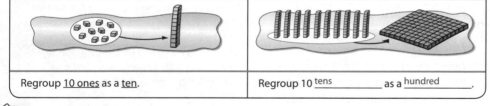

Regroup 10 ones as a ten.	Regroup 10 tens as a hundred.

Practice the Words

Directions Use the vocabulary words in **dark print** above to fill in the missing letters in the sentences below. The r's will help you find the words. Answer the last question on a separate sheet of paper.

1. You can use the _ _ _ _ _ r _ _ _ _ _ _ _ _ _ _ _ r _ _ _ _ r _ _ to multiply a sum by a number. Distributive Property

2. When you use the Distributive Property, you need to add the _ _ r _ _ _ _ _ r _ _ _ _ _ _ _. partial products

3. You may need to r _ _ r _ _ _ one amount as another amount. regroup

4. Bo Yeon has 2 rows of cars with 29 cars in each row. How many cars does he have? What can he do to find out how many cars he has? 58; answers will vary

---

A Introduce

Ask students to recall what they learned about breaking numbers apart. Encourage students to look back in their student worktexts to help with vocabulary. Help students use complete sentences.

As students speak, write important words they use on the board. These words might include *product*, *multiply*, and *break apart*. Read the list aloud.

Add the three Essential Vocabulary terms to the list. Read each in turn, and have students repeat. Add words from the Additional Vocabulary list as well, if you think they will be helpful.

Read aloud the Lesson Objective with students. Explain that students will learn more about the words on the board in this lesson.

B Teach and Learn

Circle the phrase *Distributive Property* on the board. Point out that *distributive* is related to *distribute*.

Explain that when you *distribute* something, you give some of it to each person. When you gave students crackers in the previous lesson, you distributed them to the students. Tell students that the Distributive Property lets you *distribute* one number in a multiplication problem. Inform students they

Highlighted words and phrases may affect student comprehension.

can distribute one number in a multiplication problem and multiply it by the other numbers to find the product.

Draw students' attention to the Learn the Words box on page 38 of the student worktext. Read aloud the introductory text about the Distributive Property. Be sure that students know the word *sum*.

⬚ Display Transparency 20. Point to the top array. Say: *This is an array. There are 4 rows. There are 5 columns, and then 2 columns. So there are 5 + 2 columns in all.* Touch the numbers and columns as you say them.

- **Next, touch the left section and then the right section of the array.** Say: *I can use the Distributive Property to find out how many flowers are over here* (the left) *and how many are over here* (the right).

Walk students through the following Think Aloud:

☁ **Think Aloud**

Point to the example *4 × (5 + 2) = ?* on page 38 of the student worktext. Say that this problem matches the picture on the transparency.

Read aloud the first step. Remind students what an addend is. Say: *The addends in this problem are 5 and 2. First, I multiply 4 times 5. What do I get?* Elicit that you get 20.

Then refer to the transparency. Outline the 4 × 5 rectangle on the left of the array. Say: *This part of the array shows 4 × 5. It has 4 rows and 5 columns. So there are 4 × 5 = 20 squares in it.* Write *20* on the left section of the array.

Continue with the second step. Say: *Now I multiply 4 times the other addend.* Establish that 4 × 2 = 8. Relate the number 8 to the space on the right section of the transparency. Point out that this space is 4 rows by 2 columns, or 4 × 2, which equals 8. Then write the number *8* on the right section of the transparency.

Say: *The products 20 and 8 are called* partial products. *Now, I have to add the partial products.* Elicit that 20 + 8 = 28.

Sum up by saying: *The distributive property can help you solve hard multiplication problems with big numbers.*

Indicate the problem 3 × (5 + 4) = ? in the second column of page 38. Link this problem to the second array on the transparency. Point out that there are 3 rows and 5 + 4 columns in this array.

Have student pairs fill in the missing words and numbers in the second column of page 38. Encourage them to use the problem in the left column, as well as the picture on the transparency, to help them. Go over the answers with the class when all students are finished.

BP 5 Ask students how the arrays helped them understand the Distributive Property. Write their ideas on the board.

Move ahead to the information on regrouping. Read aloud the introductory text. Remind students that they have learned about regrouping before.

Ask students to work with partners. Have them tell each other what they already know about regrouping. Then have them write or draw to communicate their ideas. Have volunteers share their work with the whole class.

Stress that *regroup* often goes with the word *as*. Have students study the picture of 15 ones. Ask: *How many ones do you see?* (15) *How many are circled?* (10) *What is happening to those 10 ones?* (they are being traded for a ten) *What happens to the other 5 ones?* (they are left as ones) Read aloud the text below the picture, stressing the word *as*.

⬚ Have students complete the second example on their own or with a partner. Then have them complete the Vocabulary Cards for these terms.

⒞ Review and Practice

BP 5 Write the three Essential Vocabulary terms on the board. Review the meaning of each term with students. Be sure the students understand the words. Then have students choose two of the terms and tell a partner how the two terms are related.

⬚ Have students play a game with their Vocabulary Cards. Have them work in pairs. Ask one student to shuffle the three cards and then choose one at random. Have the student use words or pictures to describe the term to his or her partner without naming it. The object is to guess the term. Continue, with partners taking turns.

Direct students' attention to Practice the Words. Read the directions aloud. Have students solve the problems independently. Circulate and assess.

⒟ Assess and Intervene

Can students use the vocabulary terms, based on Practice the Words on page 38? Use the rubric to identify students who need extra support through additional help and the Intervention activity.

Intermediate

☐ Identifies all three vocabulary terms.
☐ Writes a sentence that may contain several errors but uses the term *regroup*.

Example of a sentence a student might write: *He can regroup, count tens and ones.*

Advanced

☐ Identifies all three vocabulary terms.
☐ Writes a sentence with few if any errors that uses the phrase *regroup ones as tens* or a variant.

Example of a sentence a student might write: *He can regroup 29 ones as tens and ones, then add.*

INTERVENTION 10 minutes ⏱

If students cannot explain how to regroup, they may need more practice regrouping with concrete materials. Give students about 15 manipulatives and have them group them into a pile of 10 and a pile of 5. Then show them how to trade the pile of 10 for a tens rod. Say: *We regrouped 10 ones as a ten.* Have students repeat your words. Explain that the amount is the same, but that instead of 15 ones, they now have 1 ten and 5 ones. Repeat with other numbers. Then repeat, regrouping 15 tens as 1 hundred with 5 tens left over, and say: *We regrouped 10 tens as a hundred.*

Use More Language

Objective Use *by* _____ *-ing* to explain how to find products using the Distributive Property.

---

30 minutes

Teach this lesson:
- **After** students complete the lessons on multiplication of multi-digit numbers in their grade-level math textbooks
- **Before** students complete the activities on page 39 of their student worktexts

You need these materials:
- envelope and "letter"
- deck of cards
- chart paper

Use More Language

Objective Use *by* _____ *-ing* to explain how to find products using the Distributive Property.

LESSON

3

Learn the Language

Directions Fill in the missing words and numbers.

> There are 52 cards in a deck of cards. how many cards are there in 3 decks?

> I need to multiply 3 x 52 to solve this problem.

First, break apart 52 into 50 + 2. Next, multiply the tens. Then multiply the ones. Last, add the partial products.

You can multiply 3 × 52 **by breaking apart** 52 into 50 + 2, **multiplying** the tens, **multiplying** the ones, and **adding** the partial products.

> There are 12 eggs in a carton. How many eggs are there in 4 cartons?

> I need to multiply 4 x 12 to solve this problem.

First, break apart 4 and 12 into tens and ones. Next, multiply to find all the partial products. Last, add the partial products.

You can multiply 12 × 4 **by** breaking apart 12 and 4 into tens and ones, multiplying to find all the partial products, and adding the partial products.

Practice the Language

Directions Write the missing words and numbers. Answer the last question in a complete sentence.

1 You can multiply 6 × 14 by breaking apart 14 into 10 + 4, multiplying the tens, multiplying the ones, and adding the partial products.

2 You can multiply 5 × 13 by breaking apart 13 into tens and ones, multiplying each number by 5 to find all the partial products, and adding the partial products.

3 Write a sentence to explain how you can multiply 9 × 24.

Possible answer: You can multiply 9 × 24 by breaking apart 24 into 20 + 4, multiplying the tens by 4, multiplying the ones by 4, and adding the partial products.

A Introduce

Display an envelope. Ask students to name it and to tell what it is used for. Elicit that envelopes can hold *letters* or *mail*.

Hold up a typed or handwritten sheet of paper. Say: *I wrote a letter to my friend. My friend lives in ____. What do I have to do to make sure my friend gets the letter?* Draw out that the envelope needs an address and a stamp, and that it needs to be sent through the mail.

Say: *I can send a letter by mailing it.* Write this sentence on the board, and have students read it aloud. Underline the words *by* and *mailing,* and call students' attention to these two words. Point out that we say *by mailing it,* not *by mail it;* the verb *mail* takes the ending *-ing* when it goes with the word *by.*

Write the sentence frame *I can ____ by ____ing ____.* on the board. Read it aloud with students. Point out that the first blank tells a thing you can do, and that the part after the word *by* tells how you can do it.

Write the following sentence starters on the board: *I can earn money by ____; I can clean the floor by ____;* and *I can make a calculator work by _____.* Have students work in partners to complete the sentences. (Possible answers: doing chores/walking my neighbor's dog; scrubbing it/sweeping it; pushing the keys) Go over students' answers when they are finished. Write their suggestions on the board and underline the *by ____ing* construction in each.

> Highlighted words and phrases may affect student comprehension.

Explain that this lesson asks students to practice using the phrase *by _____ing* with math ideas. Read the Lesson Objective aloud. Remind students that products are answers to multiplication problems.

B | Teach and Learn

Call students' attention to the phrase *the Distributive Property* in the Lesson Objective. Remind students that they used this property while working on the lessons they just completed.

BP 5 **Divide students into groups of four or five.** Have students take turns explaining something they know about the Distributive Property. Possible answers include: *It helps you multiply, You use partial products,* or *It's good when you have big numbers.* Have one student in each group record the group's answers. Then ask each group to share 1–2 of their ideas with the rest of the class.

Have students read the problem on the upper left of page 39 of the student worktext. Display a deck of cards; be certain they know that a *deck* of cards means a complete set of cards. Explain that they have seen problems like this in their math books.

- **Ask several comprehension questions, including** *What is this problem about?* (decks of cards) *How many cards are in a deck?* (52) *How many decks are there?* (3)

BP 5 **Read aloud the speech bubble on the right of the page.** Ask students how they know this is an example of a multiplication problem.

Remind students that they can use the Distributive Property to solve this problem. Ask them to close their worktexts. Say: *Suppose you have to solve 3 × 52. What do you do first? Next? Last?*

Have students help you create a list on the board of the steps for solving 3 × 52 using the Distributive Property. Use this exercise as a review of the math needed to solve the problem, but focus students' attention on the steps as well. As students describe what to do, guide them to say: *First, break apart 52 into 50 + 2 . . . Next, multiply 3 × 50 . . .* Try to write the list on the board so it matches the list in the student worktext as closely as possible.

Read the steps on the board with students once they have solved the problem. Then have students look at the list of steps in the left column of their worktexts. Have them compare the two lists. Elicit that they are the same, with minor differences in wording.

Say: *You can use these steps to describe how to solve this problem. Or you can write one sentence. You can use* by _____ ing *to write it.*

Call students' attention to the sentence to the right of the steps. Have students read it aloud slowly, pausing at each comma. Explain that this sentence includes all the steps. Show students how *break apart, multiply,* and *add* become *breaking apart, multiplying,* and *adding* when *by* is used.

Have students study the second example with a partner. Explain that eggs usually come in a carton, or box, of 12.

BP 5 **Have students explain to their partners how this problem is like the previous problem.**

Go through the steps on the left of the page with students. Point out that this series of steps is very similar to those for the problem above.

Have students work with a partner to fill in the missing words on the lower right of the Learn the Language box. Check that students are using the proper verbs and adding *-ing*. Discuss answers with the class when all pairs are finished. If time permits, have students solve the problem using the series of steps given in the sentence they wrote.

C | Review and Practice

Review using the Distributive Property to find products by referring students to the sentence in the first example at the top of page 39. Choose four students at random. Say: *I can multiply 3 × 52 by _____.* Have one student stand up and say the next part of the sentence (*breaking apart 52 into 50 + 2*), followed by the other students saying the next clauses in turn. Repeat with other students.

Then repeat with the second example. Emphasize that while the clauses are slightly different, each clause in each sentence uses *by _____ ing.*

Have students read the directions for Practice the Language activity at the bottom of page 39. Point out that the first two items ask students to fill in missing information, while the third requires them to write a sentence on their own. Have students solve these problems independently. Check their work.

D | Assess and Intervene

Can students use the *by + -ing* construction to explain the Distributive Property, based on Practice the Language on page 39? Use the rubric to identify students who need extra support through additional help and the Intervention activity.

Intermediate

- ☐ Fills in at least seven words or numbers correctly.
- ☐ Writes a sentence using prompts or the sentence frames given in the lesson.

Advanced

- ☐ Fills in all words and numbers correctly.
- ☐ Writes a sentence without the need for prompts or the sentence frames given in the lesson.

INTERVENTION 10 minutes

If students struggle with this assignment, they may have trouble using *-ing.* Help them write the example sentences with *by _____ -ing* on chart paper, circling the word *by* and underlining the words with *-ing.* Help them number the clauses as well. Then have them compare sentences 1 and 2 in Practice the Language to the example they copied. Have them number the clauses in these sentences as well. Help them identify which clause in the problems goes with which clause in the example. Finally, show them how to transfer an existing word in the example to the blank space in the problems.

Lesson

4

Solve Math Problems

Objective Solve problems that use words you don't know.

30 minutes

Teach this lesson:
- **After** students complete work in their grade-level texts on modeling multi-digit multiplication
- **Before** students complete the assignments on page 40 of the student worktext

You need these materials:
- Worksheet 10
- keys or key ring
- roll of tape

LESSON

4

Solve Math Problems

Objective Solve problems that use words you don't know.

Learn to Solve Problems

Problem	Najwa made 5 (yabs) of (dutiles). She used 13 (dutiles) to make each (yab). How many *dutiles* did Najwa use in all?

	Think	Write
Step 1:	Read the problem. Underline the question. Circle the words you don't know.	I don't know the words "yabs" and "dutiles."
Step 2:	Read the problem again. Write what you know about the unknown words.	A "yab" is a thing you can make. You use "dutiles" to make them.
Step 3:	Think of words you know that might help you understand the unknown words. Use those words to draw a picture.	It's a little like beads and bracelets. You can use beads to make bracelets, just like you can use "dutiles" to make "yabs."
Step 4:	Write a number sentence to solve the problem.	5 × 13 = 65

Practice Solving Math Problems

Directions Follow the steps above to solve the problems below. For problem 1, write down all the steps above to solve the problem. Then write a number sentence for the other three problems and solve them. Draw a picture to illustrate each. Use a separate sheet of paper.

1. Magda has 15 parcats. Each parcat has 6 fintors. How many fintors are there on all the parcats? 15 × 6 = 90

2. It takes Gia 7 minutes to run one zepple. If she keeps running at the same speed, how long will it take her to run 25 zepples? 25 × 7 = 175 minutes

3. There are 8 rows of lumleys in the gruppet. Each row has 31 lumleys. How many lumleys are in the gruppet in all? 8 × 31 = 248

4. Enongo has 5 wibbs. She puts 12 tipallies in each wibb. Then she gets 7 more wibbs and puts 12 tipallies in each. How many tipallies does she use in all? (5 × 12) + (7 × 12) = 144

40 • Model Multiplication by 1- and 2-Digit Numbers

Highlighted words and phrases may affect student comprehension.

EXTENSION AND ENRICHMENT 10 minutes

Have students write word problems of their own that involve multiplication. Then have them write the problems again, this time replacing one or two of the English nouns and verbs they used with equivalent words from their first languages (if your ELLs come from a variety of language backgrounds) or with words of their own invention (if your students share a first language). Combine the problems into a booklet and challenge students to solve each other's work.

A Introduce

Ask students to talk about a time when they had to solve a word problem, but the problem included words they did not know. Have students offer examples from their grade-level math textbooks if possible. Explain that words that students don't know are called *unknown words* or *unfamiliar words*.

Say: *It can be hard to solve a problem when there are unknown words. What can you do when you don't recognize a word?* Accept all reasonable answers, and write them on the board. Say: *[Pao] says you can ask someone . . . [Leila] thinks you should look it up in the dictionary . . . [Perla] says you don't need to know every single word.*

Read the Lesson Objective aloud. Explain that this lesson will give students a strategy that sometimes works for solving problems when they can't look up unfamiliar words or ask what they mean. Tell students that it only works when the words are not necessary for solving the problem, but that sometimes unknown words are necessary.

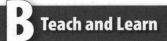

Read aloud the problem on the top of page 40 of the student worktext. Then read the problem aloud.

Say: *There are at least two words in this problem that are unfamiliar to all of you. What is a* yab? *What is a* dutile? Shrug your shoulders and explain that you don't know what these words mean, either. Tell students that these are nonsense words made up for this problem.

Use the following Think Aloud to help students solve the problem.

Think Aloud

Read Step 1 aloud as students follow along. Point out that the question has been underlined in students' worktexts, and that the unfamiliar words have been circled. (Explain that Najwa is a name.) Then read aloud the sentence to the right of Step 1: *I don't know the words* yabs *and* dutiles.

Proceed to Step 2. Read it aloud. Say: *I know that Najwa made 5 yabs. So a yab is a thing you can make.* Point out the first sentence to the right of Step 2.

Ask students what Najwa used to make the yabs. Elicit that she made them out of dutiles. Say: *I still don't know what a yab is. And I don't know what a dutile is. But I know that you can make yabs. And I know that you can use dutiles to make them.* Draw students' attention to the second sentence on the right of Step 2.

BP 5 **Write the sentence frame *You can use ____ to make ____* on the board.** Read it aloud. Say: *You can use dutiles to make yabs. What other words could go in this sentence?* Hold up a key ring and a roll of tape. *Does it make sense to say: You can use metal to make keys?* (yes) *Does it make sense to say: You can use a roll of tape to make cookies?* (no)

Have students work with a partner to think of things that can be used to make other things. List students' ideas on the board. Help them use the sentence frame to express their ideas.

Read students' ideas aloud. Say: *[Ajit] and [Mari] say you can use bread to make sandwiches. [Warad] and [Suun] say you can use wood to make boxes.* Then read aloud Step 3

and the sentence to its right. Say: *Your ideas were great! The book uses a different idea. It says that yabs and dutiles are a little like bracelets and beads. Let's check. Can you use beads to make a bracelet? Yes, you can.* Read aloud the sentences about beads and bracelets.

Go back to the top of the page. Say: *There are 5 yabs. It takes 13 dutiles to make each yab. Let's pretend that there are 5 bracelets, and it takes 13 beads to make each bracelet.* Point out that the picture in the text shows the bracelets. Tell students that yabs might or might not look like bracelets; but the words are used in the same way.

BP 5 **Ask students how they can use the picture to solve the problem.** Have them work with a partner and write an answer in words. Then have pairs share their ideas. Elicit that this is an example of a multiplication problem, because each bracelet (or yab) has 13 beads (or dutiles).

Complete the problem by reading Step 4 and the corresponding text with students. Wrap up the Think Aloud by pointing out that students never did find out what yabs and dutiles were—and that it made no difference.

Distribute copies of Worksheet 10 to pairs of students. Explain that the circled words on this worksheet are nonsense words, just like *yab* and *dutile*. Have students work together to complete the assignment. Check students' work and encourage them to share their sentences with other classmates.

C Review and Practice

Remind students that they can solve some word problems even when they don't know all the words in the problems. Have students review the steps they learned in the Learn to Solve Problems section of this lesson. Emphasize the third step, in which students find real words that fit the unknown words in the sentence.

Write the following problem on the board: *Three friends each have 14 pilmas in a chorper. How many pilmas do they have in all?* Read the problem aloud. Point out that *pilmas* and *corper* are made-up words. Have students work with a partner to follow the steps and

solve the problem. Remind them to write in complete sentences. Go over the possible scenarios and the solution to the problem when students are finished working. ($3 \times 14 = 42$)

Call students' attention to the four questions in Practice Solving Word Problems. Read the directions aloud. Remind students that they should follow the steps listed on the page, draw pictures, and write a complete sentence for number 1 and then number sentences for the other problems. Have students solve the problems independently. Assess their work.

D Assess and Intervene

Can students solve problems with unknown words by relating the sentences to words and situations they already know, based on Practice Solving Math Problems on page 40? Use the rubric to identify students who need extra support through additional help and the Intervention activity.

Intermediate

☐ At least three pictures and statements accurately represent the scenario in the problem.

☐ Answers are written in complete sentences with several errors that do not interfere with meaning.

Advanced

☐ All pictures and statements accurately represent the scenario in the problem.

☐ Answers are written in complete sentences with few or no errors.

INTERVENTION 5 minutes

If students have trouble answering the last question, they may not realize that there are two separate groups of wibbs in the problem. Check students' pictures carefully, and help them see that they have two separate pictures that can be combined into one. Show students that they may need to regroup the 5 and 7 into 10 and 2 in order to solve the problem using the Distributive Property.

Understand the Main Idea

Objective Show how to form equal groups, and tell what is left over.

40 minutes

Teach this lesson:
- **Before** introducing lessons on division in students' grade-level math textbooks
- **Before** students complete the activities on page 41 of the student worktext

You need these materials:
- countable objects (paper clips, math manipulatives, or elastic bands)
- Transparency 21
- 11 collectible cards (sports, action figures, etc.)
- 2 boxes to hold the cards
- lined paper

Prerequisite Background Knowledge
- Basic concepts and vocabulary of division

BP 6 *ELL BEST PRACTICE #6:*
Hands-On Activities

For English language learners, hands-on activities are a way to learn academic concepts and language in ways that are not affected by how much English they understand. As students are learning to find quotients and remainders, allow them to manipulate objects such as base-ten blocks, coins, and other countable objects. Students will associate these activities with the language they hear, thus gaining proficiency in English as well as understanding how to find division facts.

Throughout this module, when you see **BP 6**, you will find an example of using hands-on activities with students.

Module 11: Model Division by 1-Digit and 2-Digit Numbers

Understand the Main Idea

LESSON 1

Objective Show how to form equal groups, and tell what is left over.

Learn the Main Idea

MAIN IDEA When you divide things into equal groups, sometimes you have something left over.

Practice Applying the Main Idea

Directions Answer the questions in complete sentences. On a separate sheet of paper, draw pictures to show how many of each object goes in each group.

1. When you divide 14 pencils into 3 equal groups, how many pencils are in each group? How many are left over?

   4 pencils are in each group. 2 pencils are left over.

2. When you divide 6 grapes into 4 equal groups, how many grapes are in each group? How many are left over?

   1 grape is in each group. 2 grapes are left over.

3. When you divide 14 stickers into 6 equal groups, how many stickers are in each group? How many are left over?

   2 stickers are in each group. 2 stickers are left over.

4. Explain *equal groups* and *left over* in your own words. Possible response: Equal groups have the same number of things in them. Left over is the number of things that don't fit into the equal groups.

A Introduce

Read aloud the Lesson Objective with students.

Help students activate their prior knowledge. Ask: *Do you collect things like cards, stamps, or action figures? Have you ever put your collection into groups?*

Use the pictures on page 41 of the student worktext as a visual presentation of the concepts of equal groups and left over. Point to Panel 1, on the left. Ask: *What does this boy collect? What is he doing with his collection?* Read the thought bubbles aloud with students.

- **Focus on Panel 2, on the right.** Ask: *How many cards are in each box? Is there an equal number of cards in each box?* Show students that there are five cards in each box. Ask: *Are all the cards in boxes? How many cards are not in the boxes?* Point to the one card left out of the box.

Have students form pairs. Have them talk about the pictures and then share with the class. Encourage the pairs to describe how the boy divided the cards. For example, ask: *How did the boy divide the cards? Was he able to put all the cards in the boxes?*

Highlighted words and phrases may affect student comprehension.

Elicit responses, and tell students that sometimes when you form equal groups, you have some things that don't fit in the groups.

Read aloud the Main Idea with students. Say: *The boy put the same number of cards in each box. He divided his cards into equal groups. One card was not in the boxes. One card was left over.*

Teach and Learn

Introduce the concepts of *equal groups* and *left over*. Write *equal groups* and *left over* on the board. Point to and pronounce the words, and have students repeat them. Say: *When I put the same number of things in different groups, I make equal groups. If some things are extra, and they don't fit in the equal groups, they are left over.* Tell students that the boy made two equal groups of cards. One card was left over.

BP 6 Use paper clips to model *equal groups* and *left over*. Take a handful of paper clips and say: *I want to put these paper clips in 3 equal groups.* Divide the paper clips into three groups. Say: *When I put the same number of paper clips in three groups, some paper clips might not fit equally in the groups.* Hold up the leftover paper clips and say: *There are (2) paper clips left over.* Write *3* under the phrase *equal groups* on the board, number each group from 1 to 3, and write the number of the remainder under the phrase *left over*.

- **Write the following sentence frames on the board:** *There are _____ equal groups of paper clips. There is/are _____ left over.*

- **Ask groups of three students to take a handful of paper clips and repeat what you just modeled.** Encourage them to try the activity several times with the same number of paper clips but different numbers of equal groups. Students should use the sentence frames you wrote on the board to talk about each try. Then have each group write one of their sentences on the board and read it for the class.

Review and Practice

Use Transparency 21 to show how to form equal groups and tell what is left over. Have students work in pairs. Have the pairs work together to fill in the blanks in the sentence frames based on the pictures in Learn the Main Idea on page 41. Ask pairs of volunteers to read the problem.

- **BP 6 Show students 11 collectable cards and two boxes.** Ask the class to count the cards and boxes with you. Then say: I *want to put the same number of cards in each box. I want to divide the cards into two equal groups.* Divide the cards, and set aside the leftover. Read the sentence on Transparency 21 as you fill in the blanks. Chorally read the problem and solution aloud with students.

- **Repeat this type of modeling with other countable objects.** Vary the number of objects, equal groups, and leftovers. Use Transparency 21 to model how to frame the word problem questions. Have students suggest the number of objects, number of groups, and number left over. They should use the sentence frame to answer.

- **Challenge pairs to write a word problem using the sentence frames on Transparency 21.** Encourage them to ask about countable objects in the room. Circulate around the room, making sure students' language and math is correct. Have students exchange their problems with another pair and solve them. Then ask them to check the language and math of the other pair's answers. Invite volunteers to read their problems and answers aloud in complete sentences.

Read the directions for the Practice Applying the Main Idea activity in the student worktext. Tell students that these problems are like what they did on the transparency. Circulate to check each student's comprehension and completion of the activity. When students are done, ask individuals to read and explain their answers.

Assess and Intervene

Can every student show how to form equal groups and say what is left over based on Practice Applying the Main Idea on page 41? Use the rubric to identify students who need extra support through additional help and the Intervention activity.

Intermediate

- ☐ Correctly answers at least 2 of the word problems in complete sentences, using the sentence frames.
- ☐ Writes simple definitions that may include some errors. Uses simple clauses and phrases that have been explicitly taught.

  Example of sentences students might write: *Equal groups are same things. Left over is things no fit in groups.*

Advanced

- ☐ Correctly answers all 3 of the word problems in complete sentences without the need for sentence frames.
- ☐ Writes more complex definitions, using forms of sentences with a variety of lengths and complexities.

  Example of sentences students might write: *Equal groups have same number of things. Left over is number of things that doesn't fit in equal groups.*

INTERVENTION   10 minutes

BP 6 If students cannot show equal groups or what is left over, tap their kinesthetic, visual, and auditory modalities by drawing 14 stars on a sheet of paper and counting them aloud. Then have students draw the same number of stars in three circles, crossing out the ones you drew as they do so, and leaving out two stars. Point to the drawings and have students repeat: *When we divide 14 stars into 3 equal groups, 4 stars are in each group and 2 stars are left over.* Continue this activity using countable objects and forming equal groups.

Lesson

Learn the Vocabulary

Objective Talk and write about the steps of division using the vocabulary words.

45 minutes

Teach this lesson:
- **Before** introducing lessons on division in students' grade-level math textbooks
- **Before** students complete the activities on page 42 of the student worktext

You need these materials:
- chart paper for word web to keep throughout module
- colored markers
- base-ten blocks or snap cubes
- Vocabulary Cards

Lesson Vocabulary

Essential Vocabulary		
remainder	to bring down	left/left over

Additional Vocabulary		
quotient	dividend	divisor
to regroup*	to divide evenly	equal groups*
an equal number		

* - Terms that have Vocabulary Cards

A Introduce

Read aloud the Lesson Objective with students. Have students look at page 41 in the student worktext. Ask them to tell a partner what they remember about division, and then share with the class.

As a class, brainstorm vocabulary words that will be important to know. On chart paper, draw a word web with the word *division* in the center. Write all words suggested by students. Leave extra space to add the definitions of the Essential Vocabulary words. Display the word web throughout the module for reference.

Write words from the Additional Vocabulary box on the board. Elicit or provide examples or definitions.

Learn the Vocabulary

Objective Talk and write about the steps of division using the vocabulary words.

Learn the Words

remainder: the number that is left after you finish dividing
left/left over: extra
to bring down: a step in writing a long division problem that shows regrouping

Practice the Words

Directions Label the following problem with the words below. Then answer the last question in a complete sentence.

> **Problem** Mr. Diaz has 55 books and 4 shelves. He wants to put an equal number of books on each shelf. How many books should he put on each shelf? How many are left over?

remainder   bring down   left over

```
 13 R3 ← ①  remainder or left over
4)55
 -4
 ──
 15 ← ②  bring down
 12
 ──
  3 ← ③  remainder or left over
```

④ Explain *to bring down* and *remainder* in your own words. Answers will vary. To bring down is a way of showing regrouping in long division. Remainder is the number of things left over after dividing into equal groups.

B Teach and Learn

Orally and visually introduce the Essential Vocabulary. Direct students to open the student worktext to page 42. Have them look at the first picture and describe to a partner what the boy in the picture did. Call on volunteers to share. Read aloud the speech bubble. Say the words *left over* and *remainder,* and write them on the web. Have students repeat. Tell students that these are two of the important terms that they are going to learn so they can talk and write about long division. Explain that they will learn to do long division in their math textbooks later on.

Highlighted words and phrases may affect student comprehension.

Use the second picture on page 42 of the student worktext to demonstrate the three Essential Vocabulary terms. Say: *The teacher in the picture is showing the class how to do long division.* Chorally read the speech bubble with students. Do not read the definitions yet.

Demonstrate the definitions of the Essential Vocabulary using base-ten blocks or snap cubes and the following Think Aloud.

Think Aloud

Write *41 ÷ 3* and the partial division from the student worktext on the board. Show 4 tens blocks and 1 ones block. Divide three of the tens blocks into three groups. Point to the divisor 3 in the partial division on the board and to the 1 in the quotient as you say: *When I divide 4 tens into 3 equal groups, I put 1 tens block in each group. I have 1 tens block left.*

Demonstrate regrouping the remaining tens block into 10 ones blocks. Say: *When I regroup, I exchange the tens block I have left for 10 ones blocks. Then I add them to the other ones block.* Point to appropriate numbers in the partial division problem on the board as you say: *I have 1 ten left after I divided 4 tens. I exchange the 1 ten for 10 ones. I have 1 one in the divisor that I didn't divide yet. So I have 11 ones. I have to show this when I write a long division problem, so I bring down the 1 one from the dividend and add it to the 1 ten. This makes 11 ones. I see an arrow that shows me how to bring down the one. Now I can divide the 11 ones into 3 equal groups.* Demonstrate dividing the 11 ones blocks.

Hold up the two remaining blocks. Say: *Two blocks are left over. The remainder is 2. I write the answer: 13 R2. The R stands for remainder. I know that the remainder has to be less than the divisor. If it is larger, I can divide again.* Point to the answer in the student worktext.

With a different colored marker, complete the web with the Essential Vocabulary words. Then say the words and have students repeat.

Chorally read the definitions at the bottom of the panel with students. Have small groups discuss the definitions and come up with a definition in their own words that they will share with the class.

Have three groups of students each dictate the definitions for one Essential Vocabulary word. Write the definitions on the web as students dictate. Read them, and have students repeat. Ask groups to give examples for each word.

📇 **Have students complete Vocabulary Cards for the words in this module.**

C ▸ Review and Practice

Write these sentence frames on the board: ____ *block(s) is/are left over. The remainder is ____. I did / did not bring down a one to solve this problem.*

BP 6 ▸ Write four simple division problems on the board: two that require students to regroup, and two that do not. Divide students into pairs, and distribute manipulatives so they can follow along with you and then work independently.

Model how to solve 53 ÷ 4 using manipulatives and a Think Aloud.

Think Aloud

Say: *First, I use the base-ten blocks to show the dividend. Then I divide the blocks into 4 equal groups. I have 1 tens block and 3 ones left over. I regroup the tens block as 10 ones. Now I bring down the 3 ones from the dividend and regroup. I have 13 ones. I divide the 13 ones into the 4 equal groups. One block is left over. The remainder is 1.*

Write the same problem in long division on the board. Model how to bring down the 3 ones and combine or regroup with the tens. Circle the ones as you say: *I bring down the 3 ones from the dividend to regroup and solve the problem.*

Have pairs solve the rest of the problems on the board. Then ask each pair to use the sentence frames to explain their answer and the steps they used to find it.

Together, read the Practice the Words directions aloud. Model how to complete the first item as an example.

Have students work individually to complete the Practice the Words activity. Circulate and assess their progress using the rubric.

D ▸ Assess and Intervene

Is every student able to use the Essential Vocabulary to write about the steps of division based on Practice the Words on page 42? Use the rubric to identify students who need extra support through additional help and the Intervention activity.

Intermediate

☐ Writes all 3 labels correctly.

☐ Writes phrases or sentences that show a general understanding of *bring down* and *remainder*; errors may impede communication somewhat.

Example of sentences a student might write: *Bring down for regroup in division. Remainder left after divide.*

Advanced

☐ Writes all 3 labels correctly.

☐ Writes complete sentences that clearly and correctly explain *bring down* and *remainder*; errors do not impede meaning.

Example of sentences a student might write: *Bring down show regroup in long division. Remainder is left over after I divide.*

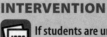

INTERVENTION 10 minutes

📇 **If students are unable to use the Essential Vocabulary to talk about the steps of division, encourage them to use the Vocabulary Cards.** Allow time for each student to place his or her cards in order according to the steps of division. Ask students to use complete sentences to explain the order they chose. Provide sentence frames if necessary. Model a correct response: *First I divide the tens. Then I see if I have tens left over. Then I bring down the ones and regroup them with the tens. I divide again. If I have something left over, that is the remainder.*

Use More Language

Objective Read and write division problems in number sentence form and long division form.

45 minutes

Teach this lesson:
- **After** lessons on division in students' grade-level math textbooks
- **Before** students complete the activities on page 43 of the student worktext

You need these materials:
- scrap paper
- Worksheet 11 (1 copy for each student)
- grade-level math textbook

Use More Language

Objective Read and write division problems in number sentence form and long division form.

LESSON **3**

Learn the Language

12 divided by 6 equals 2.

$12 \div 6 = 2$

Read left to right.

12 divided by 6 equals 2.

$$6\overline{)12} \quad \begin{array}{c} 2 \end{array}$$

Read right to left, then up and right.

 Practice the Language

Directions: For questions 1 to 3, solve each problem and write the number sentence as a word sentence. For questions 4 and 5, write a number sentence, and solve it, and then write the problem in long division form. Answer question 6 in a complete sentence on a separate sheet of paper.

1 $30 \div 3 = \underline{10}$

30 divided by 3 equals 10.

2 $7\overline{)14} \quad {}^{2}$

14 divided by 7 equals 2.

3 $48 \div 12 = \underline{4}$

48 divided by 12 equals 4.

4 72 photos in 6 folders

$72 \div 6 = 12$

$6\overline{)72} \quad {}^{12}$

5 18 CDs on 2 shelves

$18 \div 2 = 9$

$2\overline{)18} \quad {}^{9}$

6 When do you use the number sentence form and when do you use the long division form? Answer in a complete sentence. Possible answer: I use number sentences for simple problems and long division for longer problems.

Model Division by 1-Digit and 2-Digit Numbers • 43

A Introduce

Review division and the vocabulary used to talk about division using the word web from Lesson 2.

Read aloud the Lesson Objective with students. Ask: *Why is it important to be able to read and write division problems in number sentence form and in long division form?* Encourage students to use the words on the word web. List students' responses on the board.

Ask students to demonstrate how they can write division problems. Distribute blank paper, and ask students to fold it in half. Dictate the division problem *12 divided by 4 is 3*. In large numbers, ask students to write the division problem on the top half of the paper. Then ask them to write the same division problem in a different way on the bottom half of the sheet of paper. Finally, ask the students to hold up their papers. Note which students know both forms, which only know number sentences, which know how to divide two-digit numbers using a form that is not long division form, and which know long division. Differentiate instruction accordingly throughout the lesson.

Highlighted words and phrases may affect student comprehension.

B Teach and Learn

Have students open the student worktext to page 43. Say: *Knowing how to read and write division problems is important so you can divide the correct number into the correct number of groups. This lesson will show you how to read and write division problems in number sentences and in long division. You can make sure that you understand how it is done in your textbooks. If you have learned how to divide in a different way, you can see the difference between your way and long division.*

Allow time for students to look at the illustrations on page 43. On the board, write *12 ÷ 6 = 2*. Ask a volunteer to read the problem. Draw an arrow below the problem, from left to right. Say: *You read this number sentence from left to right.*

Write 6)12 on the board. Ask a volunteer to come to the board. Have him or her use gestures to show right to left and up as he or she reads the number sentence. Ask the student to draw an arrow below the problem from right to left and then up and to the right. Say: *You read this problem from right to left and then up and right.* Invite the volunteer to write the sentence that describes both problems: *12 divided by 6 equals 2.*

 Distribute a copy of Worksheet 11 to each student.

- **Model reading the first problem.** Then model how to write the problem in the other two forms.

- **Have groups of three students work together to complete Worksheet 11.** Tell them that they do not need to solve the problems unless they want to. The objective is to learn to write them in different ways, not to solve them. If necessary, provide a sentence frame: _____ *divided by* _____ *equals* _____.

- **Review the worksheet as a class.** Model drawing the arrow under problem 1 from left to right. Then read the problem, solve it, and reread it. Next, write the long division form, and model drawing the arrow from right to left and then up and right before reading it. Encourage students to draw the arrows before they share their responses. Circulate to make sure students are drawing the arrows correctly.

Give pairs of students a grade-level math textbook and blank paper. Have one partner open to a page of division problems and read one problem at a time, waiting for his or her partner to write the problem in the two forms shown in this lesson. After each problem, ask partners to switch roles.

Ask individual students to write four division problems, two as number sentences and two in long division form. Have them leave the problems unsolved. Circulate around the room to ensure that students are writing level-appropriate problems.

Have students exchange their papers with a partner and solve each other's problems. Ask partners to review the problems, reading the problems and quotients aloud and correcting each other when necessary. Circulate around the room, assisting as needed.

C Review and Practice

Play a dictation game. Ask students to form groups of three. Give each group a piece of scrap paper and a pencil. Dictate a division problem. The first student writes the problem in number form and passes it to the second student, who writes it in word form and then passes it to the third student, who writes it in long division form. Students are not required to solve the problem, just to write the forms.

To vary the game, students can work in groups of three to solve each division problem you dictate. Once they have solved it, they raise their hands. One student presents the solution to the problem. The other groups can then check to see if it is correct. You may choose to score the game according to the personalities and abilities of your class. If you score the game, consider rewarding the team that finishes first and is completely correct. If no one answers correctly, circulate around the room, indicate which parts are wrong, and allow time for students to correct their work.

Together, read the directions for the Practice the Language activity on page 43 of the student worktext. Ask a volunteer to come to the board to model completing the first problem as an example.

Have students work individually on the Practice the Language activity. Circulate and assess students as they complete the activity.

D Assess and Intervene

Can students read and write different forms of division problems correctly based on Practice the Language on page 43? Use the rubric to identify students who need extra support through additional help and the Intervention activity.

Intermediate

- ☐ Correctly converts at least 2 division forms to word forms.
- ☐ Correctly converts at least 1 word form to both division forms.
- ☐ Uses phrases to write a logical explanation for when to use each form, although it may lack detail and errors may affect meaning.

Example of sentences a student might write: *Use number sentence for problem simple. Use long division for problem long.*

Advanced

- ☐ Correctly converts all 3 division forms to word forms.
- ☐ Correctly converts 2 word forms to both division forms.
- ☐ Uses complete sentences to write a logical explanation that clearly and completely tells when to use each form.

Example of sentences a student might write: *I would use number sentence when do problem in my head. I would use long division when need to write the problem.*

INTERVENTION 10 minutes

If students have trouble reading and writing the two different forms of division, tell students that we always read the dividend first, then the divisor, and finally the quotient. Give students a division problem, such as *15 divided by 5 equals 3*. Make a chart that shows the number in the three parts of the problem using both forms. Teach students to chant: *I read the dividend first.* (clap hands) *Then "divided by."* (clap hands) *I read the divisor next.* (clap hands) *I read the quotient last!* (clap hands). Have them start over again. Have students point to each part of the problem as they chant. Ask one student to be the divisor, another the dividend, another the quotient. As they chant, the one whose part is chanted stands up.

Solve Math Problems

Objective Explain why a remainder is reasonable or unreasonable.

40 minutes

Teach this lesson:
- **After** lessons on division in students' grade-level math textbooks
- **Before** students complete the activities on page 44 of the student worktext

You need these materials:
- paper clips or other countable objects
- Transparency 22
- grade-level math textbook
- elastics and bags

EXTENSION AND ENRICHMENT   15 minutes

Ask students to develop a Steps of Division poster. As a class, develop a sample division problem. Brainstorm the steps required to solve it. Record students' responses on the board or on chart paper. Ask students to form small groups. Have each group make a Steps of Division poster that clearly shows (with illustrations, vocabulary, and examples) how to solve the division problem. Have students use the words in the word web to label the parts of the problem. Display the posters in the classroom throughout the division lessons.

Solve Math Problems

Objective Explain why a remainder is reasonable or unreasonable.

Learn to Solve Problems

Problem Ming has 38 elastics. She wants to put them in 4 bags. She says she will put 8 elastics in each bag and have 6 elastics left over. Is this reasonable? Explain why or why not.

	Think	Write
Step 1:	Read the problem. Underline the question. What do you have to do?	Tell if the answer to the problem is reasonable or unreasonable, and explain why.
Step 2:	Identify the dividend, divisor, quotient, and remainder.	dividend: 38, divisor: 4, quotient: 8, remainder: 6
Step 3:	Compare the remainder and the divisor. If the divisor is greater than the remainder, the answer is reasonable. If the remainder is greater or the same as the remainder, the answer is unreasonable.	6 > 4 The remainder is greater than the divisor. The answer is unreasonable.
Step 4:	Explain why the answer is reasonable or unreasonable.	The remainder is unreasonable because Ming can put one more elastic in each bag.

Practice Solving Math Problems

Directions Explain why the following answers are reasonable or unreasonable. Write your answers in complete sentences on a separate sheet of paper.

1. If 39 students are divided into teams of 9 students each, there will be 4 teams, with 3 students left over. The remainder is less than the divisor. The answer is reasonable because the students cannot make one more team.

2. Samir has 24 photos. He can put 6 photos on each page of his album. He will need 3 pages. He will have 6 photos left over. The remainder is the same as the divisor. The answer is unreasonable because Samir can make one more group (page) of 6 photos.

3. Mr. Lee's art class made 28 sculptures to display equally on 6 tables. The class thinks they will display 3 sculptures on each table and have 10 left over. The remainder is greater than the divisor. The answer is unreasonable because the class can put one more sculpture on each table.

A Introduce

BP 6 Read aloud the Lesson Objective with the class. Ask: *What's a remainder?* (The number of items left over after dividing into equal groups.) Then ask volunteers to define *reasonable* and *unreasonable*. If no one can, say: *Reasonable means that something makes sense or seems right. Unreasonable means that something doesn't make sense or seem right.* Demonstrate an example. Hold up a handful of 42 paper clips (or other countable objects). Then model using a Think Aloud as you write the problem on the board.

Think Aloud

Say: *I have 42 paper clips, and I want to give an equal amount to my 20 students. I think I can give each student 1 paper clip and the remainder will be 22. Is that reasonable? Does that seem right? No, because I have 22 paper clips left over. That means I can give another paper clip to each student. So, if I give 2 paper clips to each student and have a remainder of 2, is that reasonable? Yes, that is reasonable because I don't have enough paper clips left to give everybody one more.*

Tell students that they will learn how to explain if a remainder is reasonable or unreasonable in this lesson.

Highlighted words and phrases may affect student comprehension.

B Teach and Learn

Write the following definitions on the board: *reasonable: makes sense or seems right,* and *unreasonable: doesn't make sense or seem right.* Point out that the prefix *un-* at the beginning of a word means *not.* Ask volunteers to read the definitions aloud and explain the terms in their own words.

Ask students to open their student worktexts to page 44. Copy the problem on the board, and have a volunteer read it aloud. Use a Think Aloud to model how to explain if the remainder is reasonable or unreasonable.

> **Think Aloud**
>
> **Read Step 1 aloud and say:** *What do I have to do? I'll read the problem aloud and look for the question mark. I'll underline the sentence with the question mark.* Underline the question. *I know now that I have to tell if the remainder is reasonable or unreasonable. Then I have to explain why.*
>
> **Read Step 2 aloud and say:** *Now I will identify the facts. I will circle the dividend, divisor, quotient, and remainder.* Then label each, so students are sure which is the divisor and which is the remainder.
>
> **Read Step 3 aloud and say:** *Now I will compare the divisor and remainder.* Point to each one. Say: *Which is greater? I see that the remainder 6 is greater than the divisor 4.* Write *6 (remainder) > 4 (divisor)* on the board.
>
> **Read Step 4 aloud and say:** *If the remainder is greater than the divisor or the same, then the remainder is unreasonable. The remainder 6 is unreasonable here because Ming can put one more elastic in each bag.*

BP 6 **Model how to solve the above problem using elastics and bags.** Read and solve the problem as it is written, leaving six elastics left over. Show that the remainder is unreasonable as you put one more elastic into each bag.

Display Transparency 22. Have volunteers read each step for determining if a remainder is reasonable or unreasonable.

BP 6 **Distribute elastics or paper clips to groups of three or four students.** Have them model how to solve the problem using the objects and following the steps on the transparency.

- **Find two division word problems that have remainders in the grade-level textbook.** Ask the students to remain in their groups, but to solve the problems individually. Then they should follow the steps to determine and explain if the remainder is reasonable or unreasonable. Have students compare their solutions with others in the group and correct their work.

- **Monitor, and provide assistance as needed.** Circulate around the room, and answer questions as students work. Then ask groups to share their explanations. Correct as necessary.

C Review and Practice

Ask volunteers to retell the steps to determine and explain if a remainder is reasonable or unreasonable. As students retell the steps, ask them prompting questions. For example, say: (Step 1) *How do you know what a problem is asking you to do? How do you identify the question?* (Step 2) *What are the different parts of a division problem? How can you identify these parts?* (Step 3) *What two numbers should you compare? Why? What are you looking for?* (Step 4) *What does* reasonable *and* unreasonable *mean? How can you tell if a remainder is reasonable?*

Read aloud the directions for Practice Solving Math Problems on page 44. Remind students to circle all the important numbers in the problem before they decide if the remainder is reasonable or unreasonable.

Display Transparency 22, and highlight the responses to Step 4, showing how they can be used as sentence frames. Write the following sentence frames on the board: *The remainder is _____ the divisor. My answer is _____ because I can/cannot put one more into each group or make any more equal groups.*

As students work on problems individually, circulate and assess how well they are using the steps taught in this lesson.

D Assess and Intervene

How well can students explain why a remainder is reasonable or unreasonable based on Practice Solving Math Problems on page 44? Use the rubric to identify students who need extra support through additional help and the Intervention activity

Intermediate

☐ Correctly identifies and explains whether a remainder is reasonable in at least 2 problems.

☐ Uses the sentence frames to write explanations, with only minor errors.

Advanced

☐ Correctly identifies and explains whether a remainder is reasonable in all 3 problems.

☐ Writes explanations without using the sentence frames; may have several errors, but they do not impede comprehension.

INTERVENTION   5–15 minutes

BP 6 **If students are unable to determine whether a remainder is reasonable,** write examples of problems that have remainders that are too large. Have students model the problems with countable objects. Show students how the too-large remainders can be distributed among the groups. As students manipulate the countable objects, encourage them to verbalize what they are doing: *I can put 1 more block in each group. So the remainder was too large. It was unreasonable.*

Prerequisite Background Knowledge
• Rounding
• Estimation
• Basic concepts and vocabulary of multiplication and division

Understand the Main Idea

Objective When you want to estimate, choose numbers that are easy to multiply and divide in your head.

45 minutes

Teach this lesson:
• **Before** introducing lessons on mental math and estimation with multiplication and division in the grade-level math textbook
• **Before** students complete the activities on page 45 of the student worktext

You need these materials:
• Transparency 23
• chart paper

BP 1 ELL BEST PRACTICE #1:
Comprehensible Language

ELLs are not able to understand everything that is said in the classroom. Teachers can modify their language in many different ways to help ELLs understand more of the language and concepts presented. For example, when you explain mental math and estimation with multiplication and division, use simple vocabulary and sentence structure and provide examples that students are familiar with.

Throughout this module, when you see **BP 1**, you will find an example of using comprehensible language with students.

Module 12: Mental Math and Estimation with Multiplication and Division

LESSON
1

Understand the Main Idea

Objective When you want to estimate, choose numbers that are easy to multiply and divide in your head.

Learn the Main Idea

About how many toys did we collect in all?

Toy Drive
Class A = 28
Class B = 27
Class C = 28
Class D = 29

Each class collected about 28 toys. $28 \times 4 = ?$ I can do the math in my head.

I think: I change 28 to 30 because it is close to 28 and easy to multiply by 4.
$$3 \times 4 = 12$$
$$30 \times 4 = 120$$
So, 28×4 is about 120.
We collected about 120 toys.

There are about 440 bottles of juice. There are 5 schools in our town. How many bottles should we give to each school?

$440 \div 5 = ?$ I can do the math in my head.

I think: I change 440 to 450 because it is close to 440 and is easy to divide by 5.
$$45 \div 5 = 9$$
$$450 \div 5 = 90$$
That's about 90 bottles for each school.
So, $440 \div 4$ is about 90.

MAIN IDEA You can use patterns of zeros, or estimation, or both to multiply and divide in your head.

Practice Applying the Main Idea

Directions Find an estimated answer. Do the math in your head. Then explain how you got your answer. Answer the last question in a complete sentence.

Example
$63 \times 8 =$ about 480. Change 63 to 60. Multiply $6 \times 8 = 48$. So, $6 \times 80 = 480$.

1. $41 \times 6 =$ about 240. Change 41 to 40. Multiply $4 \times 6 = 24$. So, $40 \times 6 = 240$.

2. $78 \times 2 =$ about 160. Change 78 to 80. Multiply $8 \times 2 = 16$. So, $80 \times 2 = 160$.

3. $410 \div 8 =$ about 50. Change 410 to 400. Divide $40 \div 8 = 5$. So, $400 \div 8 = 50$.

4. $310 \div 5 =$ about 60. Change 310 to 300. Divide $30 \div 6 = 5$. So, $300 \div 5 = 60$.

5. Why do you change numbers when you multiply and divide in your head? Answer in a complete sentence. Answers will vary. Sometimes I only need an estimate. I can use easier numbers that are close to the numbers in the problem.

Mental Math and Estimation with Multiplication and Division • 45

A Introduce

Read aloud the Lesson Objective with students. Ask: *Why do you think it is a good idea to choose numbers that are easy to multiply or divide in your head?* (It is simpler, faster; sometimes I don't need an exact answer) Have students discuss their responses with a partner.

On chart paper, make a two-column chart. Write students' responses in the first column as you activate prior knowledge. Label the first column *What We Know.*

• **Help students activate prior knowledge.** Ask: *When you have to multiply or divide and you do not have paper and pencil, what do you do? How do you get your answer?* Elicit several responses from students and write them in the chart. Keep the chart up to use throughout the module.

Use the artwork on page 45 of the student worktext as a visual introduction to the concept of choosing numbers that are easy to multiply and divide in your head.

• **Give pairs of students time to look at the visuals on page 45.** Have them describe to each other what they see.

• **Point to the picture on the left.** Ask: *What is the boy asking? What does the girl do so it is easier to multiply in her head?*

Highlighted words and phrases may affect student comprehension.

- **Point to picture on the right** Ask: *What is the girl asking? What does the boy do so it is easier to divide in his head?*

-  **Chorally read aloud the text in each frame with students.** Summarize what happened in each picture: *The girl needed to multiply 28 × 4 in her head, but it was too difficult. She changed 28 to a close number, 30. This is an easier number to multiply by 4. Then she got an estimate for an answer. The boy needed to divide 440 ÷ 5 in his head. Point to the second picture. He knows 45 ÷ 5, so he changed 440 to 450 because it is easier to divide 450 ÷ 5. Then he got an estimate for an answer. The girl and the boy looked at the patterns of zeros to help them multiply and divide. When we change numbers to easier numbers so we can divide or multiply in our heads, we don't get an exact answer, we get an estimate. An* estimate *is an answer that is close to the exact answer.*

Read aloud the Main Idea with students. Ask students what they already know about estimating—choosing numbers that are easy to compute in their heads—from their own lives or from previous lessons. Add their responses to the first column on the chart. Point out that the students in the pictures used estimation and patterns of zeros. Tell students that they will learn more about patterns of zeros later.

B Teach and Learn

The following multiplication problem is not easy to multiply mentally. Write it on the board: *33 × 4 = ?* Read it chorally aloud. Ask: *Is this easy or hard to multiply in your head?* Elicit students' responses.

Then model solving the problem with a Think Aloud.

Think Aloud

Say: *What will make it easier for me to multiply 33 × 4 in my head? I can change 33 to 30. But this is still a little hard. So I will multiply 3 × 4 = 12. Now, 30 × 4 is the same, except for the zero. So, the answer to 30 × 4 will also have a zero. 30 × 4 = 120. So, 33 × 4 is about 120.*

The following division problem is not easy to divide mentally. Write it on the board:

185 ÷ 6 = ? Read it chorally aloud. Ask: *Is this easy to divide in your head?* Elicit students' responses and allow them to discuss with a partner how they would solve the problem. Then model how to solve it with a Think Aloud:

Think Aloud

Say: *I see 185 ÷ 6 = ? What will make it easier for me to divide in my head? I know that 18 is easy to divide by 6. So, I will change 185 to 180. I will divide without the zeros first: 18 ÷ 6 = 3. I know that 180 ÷ 6 is the same, except for the zero. So, the answer to 180 ÷ 6 will also have a zero. 180 ÷ 6 = 30. So, 185 ÷ 6 is about 30.*

Write the following problems on the board. Have students work in small groups to find estimated numbers, using numbers that are easier to multiply and divide: *61 × 4 = ? 87 × 7 = ? 61 ÷ 7 = ? 79 ÷ 8 = ?*

C Review and Practice

Review the Lesson Objective by asking: *Why do you change numbers to multiply or divide? How can you change numbers? Is your answer exact or an estimate?* Write students' responses in the second column of the chart labeled *What We Learned*.

Use Transparency 23 to practice choosing numbers that are easy to multiply or divide mentally. Cover the second column on the transparency.

 **Have students work in pairs.** Read Problem 1 aloud. Say: *We need to multiply in our heads.* Then prompt students with questions, such as: *Is 19 × 12 easy to multiply in my head? How can we change the number 19 to make it easy to multiply by 12?* (use rounding) *What number will that change to?* (20) *Why is it easier to multiply 20 × 12?* (because it's easy to multiply 2 × 12) *So, 2 × 12 = 24. What happens with the zero?* (20 × 12 is the same, except for the zero) *The answer to 20 × 12 will also have a zero. 20 × 12 = 240. So, 19 × 12 is about 240. That's about 240 paper clips.*

Have pairs complete the remaining problems. Make sure to cover the second column on the transparency. Allow students to use the Learn the Main Idea section for reference. Ask them to write only the number sentences to solve each problem. Circulate and assist as

necessary. When they have finished, uncover the answers from Transparency 23 and read them aloud.

Read aloud the directions for the Practice Applying the Main Idea Activity in the student worktext. Go over the example. Have students complete the activity independently. Use the rubric to assess their work.

D Assess and Intervene

Does everyone understand how to choose numbers that are easy to multiply and divide in their heads, based on Practice Applying the Main Idea on page 45? Use the rubric below to identify students who need extra support through additional help and the Intervention Activity.

Intermediate

☐ Correctly changes numbers to numbers that are easier to compute mentally in at least 3 of questions 1–4, and solves the problems correctly.

☐ Answers question 5 with a simple phrase, with some errors that do not impede comprehension.

Example of a sentence a student might write: *Change numbers make easy in my head.*

Advanced

☐ Correctly changes numbers to numbers that are easier to compute mentally in questions 1–4, and solves the problems correctly.

☐ Answers question 5 using a sentence, with few errors and a clear explanation.

Example of a sentence a student might write: *I change numbers because I want numbers easy in my head.*

INTERVENTION 10 minutes

If students are having trouble changing numbers to simpler numbers they can compute mentally, write number sentences on the board, such as: *33 × 4 = ?* Point to the larger factor. Have students suggest close numbers that are easier to compute mentally. Help them explain why. Then have students solve the problems.

Learn the Vocabulary

Objective Talk and write about how to use estimation to multiply and divide in your head using the vocabulary words.

45 minutes

Teach this lesson:
- **Before** introducing lessons on mental math and estimation with multiplication and division in the grade-level math textbooks
- **Before** students complete the activities on page 46 of the student worktext

You need these materials:
- magnetic numbers and the symbols: $\times$, $=$, ?
- index cards
- What We Know/What We Learned chart from Lesson 1

Lesson Vocabulary

Essential Vocabulary

divisible	compatible numbers
underestimate	overestimate

Additional Vocabulary

to adjust	to substitute	
multiple*	pattern*	basic facts

* - Terms that have Vocabulary Cards.

LESSON 2

Learn the Vocabulary

Objective Talk and write about how to use estimation to multiply and divide in your head using the vocabulary words.

Learn the Words

Word/Phrase	Definition	Example
compatible numbers	two numbers that work well together; they are easy to add, subtract, multiply, or divide in your head	$8 \times 387 = ?$ I can use **compatible numbers** to estimate the answer. 8 and 400 are compatible numbers. They are easy to multiply in my head.
underestimate	a number that is less than the exact amount	$220 \div 4 = ?$ I estimate. I change 220 to a smaller number, 200. I divide and my answer is 50. My answer is an **underestimate** because it is less than the exact amount.
overestimate	a number that is greater than the exact amount	$356 \div 2 = ?$ I estimate. I change 356 to 400 because it is easier to divide in my head. I divide and my answer is 200. My answer is an **overestimate** because it is greater than the exact amount.
divisible	a number that, when divided by another number, has a quotient that is a whole number and a remainder of zero	$32 \div 4 = 8$ 32 is **divisible** by 4 because the answer is a whole number and the remainder is zero.

Practice the Words

Directions Fill in the blanks by using the vocabulary words and solving the problems.

1 Estimate 461×2. Change 461 to 500. My estimate is <u>1,000</u>. It is an <u>over-estimate</u> because <u>it is greater than the exact amount.</u>

2 Estimate $276 \div 6$. Change 276 to 240. My estimate is <u>40</u>. It is an <u>under-estimate</u> because <u>it is less than the exact amount.</u>

3 $150 \div 2 = 75$. The quotient is a whole number and the remainder is zero. So 150 is <u>divisible by 2.</u>

4 Estimate $342 \div 5$. When you change 342 to 350, you use <u>compatible numbers.</u>

A Introduce

Read aloud the Lesson Objective with students. Point to the Learn the Main Idea section on page 45 of the student worktext. Have students refer to it as you ask: *What do you remember about changing numbers so they are easier to multiply or divide in your head?* Have students share their answers with a partner.

As a class, brainstorm ideas for vocabulary words that will be important for doing multiplication and division as mental math. Write suggested words on the board and add Essential Vocabulary to the list.

Choose words from the Additional Vocabulary box that you think will be useful. Add them to the list of words on the board. Elicit or provide examples for all the words on the list.

B Teach and Learn

Orally introduce the Essential Vocabulary as explained below. As you do so, refer to the Learn the Words section on page 46.

Explain and demonstrate the Essential Vocabulary using magnetic numbers and symbols. Have students work along with you to create different number sentences.

Write each word and model its pronunciation. Read each definition and example aloud. Then have students read each word, definition, and example with you.

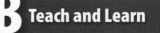

Highlighted words and phrases may affect student comprehension.

BP 1 **Write *compatible numbers* on the board.** Say: *When we multiply or divide in our heads we can use rounding or we can use compatible numbers. Compatible numbers are two numbers that are easy to add, subtract, multiply, or divide in your head. Compatible numbers are not always the closest numbers, like the numbers you use when you round. They are "friendly numbers" because they are easy to multiply or divide.*

- **Divide the class into small groups.** Distribute magnetic numbers and symbols. Model how to write $8 \times 387 = ?$ Ask: *Is 8×387 easy to multiply in your head? I can round 387 to the nearest ten and get 390, but 390 is not easy to multiply by 8. 400 is easy because 4×8 is easy to multiply. I also know 4×8 is a basic fact and they are compatible numbers. Let's multiply 8×400. Notice what happens with the number of zeros in the factors and in the product.* Change 387 to 400. Use the magnetic numbers and symbols to model $8 \times 4 = 32$; $8 \times 40 = 320$; $8 \times 400 = 3,200$. Place the number sentences underneath each other, line them up, and have students point out the patterns of zeros.

- **Write on the board: *387 × 8 = about 3,200*.** Say: *387 × 8 is about 3,200. Why did I change 387 to 400?* (because they are compatible numbers and they are easy to multiply in my head) Say: *Sometimes when you use compatible numbers or rounding, the number that you change to is the same.*

Point out the words *underestimate* and *overestimate*. Ask: *Can you find the two smaller words in these words?* (under, over, and estimate) Say: Under *means less than a number and* over *means more than a number.* Under *and* over *are opposites.*

- **BP 1** **Write *underestimate* on the board.** Use magnetic numbers and symbols to model $220 \div 4 = ?$ Say: *I can use compatible numbers to estimate. What number is easy to divide by 4 in my head, 200 or 220?* Prompt students to say: *200 because $220 \div 4$ is easy to divide in my head.* Replace 220 with 200 and divide.

- **Have the groups follow along with you as they make their own number sentences:** $20 \div 4 = 5$, $200 \div 4 = 50$. Say, *$220 \div 4$ is about 50. This is an estimate.* Write: $220 \div 4 = 55$. Say: *The exact answer is 55. Our estimate is an* underestimate *because the estimate of 50 is less than the*

exact answer. Provide additional multiplication/division examples. Then ask: *What is an underestimate?*

BP 1 **Write *overestimate* on the board.** Model $356 \div 2 = ?$ Ask: *Is this easy to divide in your head? Is 300 or 400 divided by 2 easier to divide in your head?* (400 is easier because it is easy to divide $4 \div 2$) Change the number 356 to 400 and divide. Repeat the same process as groups follow along with their own numbers. Say: *$356 \div 2$ is about 200. This is an estimate, not an exact answer.* Write $356 \div 2 = 178$ on the board. Say: *The exact answer is 178. Our estimate is an* overestimate *because the estimate of 200 is more than the exact answer.* Provide additional multiplication/division examples. Ask: *What is an overestimate?*

Write *divisible* on the board. Use magnetic numbers and symbols to write: $32 \div 4 = 8$. Say: *I can divide $32 \div 4$. 32 is divisible by 4 because the quotient, the answer, is a whole number, and the remainder is zero. There is nothing left over when we divide.* Write three more examples of divisible numbers on the board: $25 \div 5$; $90 \div 10$; $600 \div 6$. Then ask: *Is 25 divisible by 5? Is 90 divisible by 10? Is 600 divisible by 6? What does divisible mean?*

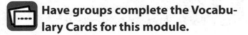 **Have groups complete the Vocabulary Cards for this module.**

C Review and Practice

Review the meaning of the Essential Vocabulary by asking: *What are compatible numbers? What is an underestimate? An overestimate? A number that is divisible by another number?* Write students' responses in the *What We Learned* column.

Divide the class into pairs. Distribute index cards with number sentences on one side and the vocabulary word on the other. Have pairs solve the problems and use the vocabulary word to explain why they are compatible numbers, an underestimate, an overestimate, or a number that is divisible by another number. Have pairs share their work with the class.

Have students work independently to complete the Practice the Words Activity. Circulate and assess their progress. Use the rubric to assess their work.

D Assess and Intervene

Does every student understand the Essential Vocabulary in Practice the Words on page 46? Use the rubric to identify students who need extra support through additional help and the Intervention activity.

Intermediate

☐ Completes 3 of the 4 questions with the correct vocabulary term.

☐ Explains answers in questions 1 and 2 using the idea of an estimate being more or less than the exact answer; errors do not impede comprehensions.

Example of a phrase a student might write: *1,000, bigger exact answer.*

Advanced

☐ Completes all 4 of the questions with the correct vocabulary term.

☐ Explains answers in questions 1 and 2 using the idea of an estimate being more or less than an exact answer, with minimal errors.

Example of a sentence a student might write: *40 is less than exact number.*

INTERVENTION 10 minutes

If students are having trouble understanding word meanings, help them make visual connections. Write: *Compatible numbers are like two good friends working together.* Draw two numbers holding hands, such as 4 and 2. Have students do the same with other compatible numbers. Explain that *under* also means *too low* or *less than.* Write *under* with an arrow pointing down to show that the number goes down, is too low, or is less than the exact amount. Say: *That is why* underestimate *means that our answer is less than the exact amount.* Explain that *over* is the opposite of *under;* it can mean *too much* or *more than the exact amount.* Say: *That is why* overestimate *means that our answer is too much, or over the exact amount.*

Use More Language

Objective Describe patterns for multiplying and dividing with zeros using synonyms of *because*.

---

45 minutes

Teach this lesson:
- **After** lessons on mental math and estimation with multiplication and division in the grade-level math textbook
- **Before** students complete the activities on page 47 of the student worktext

You need these materials:
- magnetic numbers and the symbols: $\times$, =, ?
- What We Know/What We Learned chart from Lesson 1
- Transparency 24
- paper strips

Use More Language

Objective Describe patterns for multiplying and dividing with zeros using synonyms of *because*.

LESSON
3

Learn the Language

Multiplication Problem
Our school recycles about 2,000 milk cartons each week. About how many milk cartons will we recycle in 4 weeks?

Solve the problem: $2,000 \times 4 = ?$

Multiply in steps to see the patterns of zeros:
$2 \times 4 = 8$
$20 \times 4 = 80$
$200 \times 4 = 800$
$2,000 \times 4 = 8,000$

Our school recycles about 8,000 milk cartons in 4 weeks.

Explain your answer: <u>Because</u> the number of zeros in one factor increases, the number of zeros in the product also increases.

Division Problem
Nine schools collected about 4,500 books to donate to the new town library. They each collected about the same number. About how many books did each school collect?

Solve the problem: $4,500 \div 9 = ?$

Divide in steps to see the patterns of zeros:
$45 \div 9 = 5$
$450 \div 9 = 50$
$4,500 \div 9 = 500$

Each school collected about 500 books.

Explain your answer: <u>As</u> the number of zeros in the dividend increases, the number of zeros in the quotient also increases.

Practice the Language

Directions Show the patterns of zeros. Then write a complete sentence with *because, since,* or *as* to explain the patterns of zeros on a separate sheet of paper. Solve each problem on a separate sheet of paper.

Example Manny's dog eats about 3,000 pieces of pet food a week. About how many pieces of pet food does Manny's dog eat in eight weeks? $3 \times 8 = 24$, $30 \times 8 = 240$, $300 \times 8 = 2,400$, $3,000 \times 8 = 24,000$. As the number of zeros in one factor increases, the number of zeros in the product also increases.

1 The bus driver drives about 2,000 miles in 5 days. He drives about the same number of miles each day. About how many miles does he drive in 1 day? $20 \div 5 = 4$. $200 \div 5 = 40$. $2,000 \div 5 = 400$. The bus driver drives about 400 miles in 1 day. Because the number of zeros in the dividend increases, the number of zeros in the quotient also increases.

2 There are 9 students in our art class making kites. Each kite needs about 300 inches of string. About how much string do we need altogether? $9 \times 3 = 27$. $9 \times 30 = 270$. $9 \times 300 = 2,700$. We need about 2,700 inches of string. Since the number of zeros in one factor increases, the number of zeros in the product also increases.

A Introduce

Remind students what they learned in Lessons 1 and 2. Refer them to the *What We Know/What We Learned* chart and have them read the second column chorally. Have students find examples of compatible numbers, underestimate, overestimate, and divisible numbers in their textbooks. Have them use the sentence frame: *This is an example of _____ because _____.* to explain the examples they find to a partner.

Read aloud the Lesson Objective with students. Remind them of how they changed numbers so they could multiply in their heads and what happened with the patterns of zeros.

Write the word *synonym* on the board. Say: *A synonym is a word that means the same, or nearly the same, as another word.* Write *big/large* on the board. Use each word in a sentence. Write *small, change,* and *great* on the board. Have students help you write synonyms for each word. Invite them to use each pair of synonyms in sentences.

Say: *Some words have many meanings, such as* bat, *a baseball bat and* bat, *the animal. The word* since *means for how long. For example, I have been in the 4th grade since September. The word* as *means while. For example, I listened carefully while the teacher read the book. The words* since *and* as *are also synonyms of* because.

Write the words *because, as,* and *since* on the board. *When we use* because, since, *and* as *to explain why something happens, we understand that these words are synonyms.*

Highlighted words and phrases may affect student comprehension.

Write, read, and underline *because, since,* **and** *as* **in each sentence:** <u>Because</u> *the temperature gets warmer, we know summer is near.* <u>Since</u> *the temperature gets warmer, we know summer is near.* <u>As</u> *the temperature gets warmer, we know summer is near.* Write and read additional examples. Say: *We are going to use* because, as, *and* since *to describe patterns for multiplying and dividing with zeros.*

B | Teach and Learn

Have students open the student worktext to page 47. Read the multiplication problem aloud. Write *2,000 × 4 = ?* on the board and read it aloud. Say: *We are going to multiply in steps. Look at the pattern of zeros and describe what you notice.* Use the magnetic numbers and symbols. With students, create these number sentences and read them aloud: *2,000 × 4 = ? 2 x 4 = 8; 20 × 4 = 80; 200 × 4 = 800; 2,000 × 4 = 8,000.* Make sure the zeros are lined up.

Model how to look for patterns of zeros with a Think Aloud.

> **Think Aloud**
>
> **Ask:** *What happens to the zeros in the factor and product when I multiply? Let me count the zeros in the factors and in the product.* Point to the zeros as you count them. *I see that when the number of zeros in one factor increases, the number of zeros in the product also increases.*

Say: *The word* increases *means grows in numbers. We will use* increases *in our sentences to describe what happens with the zeros when we multiply and divide.*

Write the sentence on the board: <u>Because</u> *the number of zeros in one factor increases, the number of zeros in the product also increases.* Underline *Because.*

Say: *We can use the synonyms* as *and* since *to say the same explanation for patterns of zeros.* Say, read, and write: <u>As</u> *the number of zeros in one factor increases, the number of zeros in the product also increases.* Underline *As.*

Write: <u>Since</u> *the number of zeros in one factor increases, the number of zeros in the product also increases.* Underline *Since.* Read all the sentences chorally.

Ask: *What happens to the zeros in the factor and the product when we multiply with multiples of 10, 100, and 1,000?* Have students point to or count the zeros in number sentences and use the sentences on the board to answer.

Leave the sentences on the board for students to use as a reference.

Read aloud the division problem on page 47. Write *4,500 ÷ 9 = ?* on the board and read it aloud. Say: *We are going to divide in steps. Look at the pattern of zeros and describe what you notice.* Use magnetic numbers and symbols. Create these number sentences and read them aloud: *4,500 ÷ 9 = ?, 45 ÷ 9 = 5; 450 ÷ 9 = 50; 4,500 ÷ 9 = 500.* Make sure the zeros are lined up.

Ask: *What happens to the zeros in the dividend and the quotient when we divide?* Elicit responses by having students count zeros in the dividend and quotient to show they have the same number of zeros. Say, write, and read aloud: <u>Because</u> *the number of zeros in the dividend increases, the number of zeros in the quotient also increases.* Have students repeat. Underline *Because.*

Say: *We used the synonyms* because, as, *and* since *to describe patterns of zeros in multiplication. We can use these synonyms to describe patterns of zeros in division, too.* Say, write, and read aloud: <u>As</u> *the number of zeros in the dividend increases, the number of zeros in the quotient also increases.* Underline the word *As.* Say, write, and read aloud: <u>Since</u> *the number of zeros in the dividend increases, the number of zeros in the quotient also increases.* Underline *Since.* Have students repeat each sentence.

Say: *All three sentences mean the same thing. The words* because, as, *and* since, *used in this way are synonyms.*

C | Review and Practice

Review patterns of zeros by asking students: *What happens when the number of zeros in one factor increases? What happens when the number of zeros in the dividend increases?* Have students use the sentences on the board to answer.

 Present Transparency 24. Read aloud the directions and the number sentences. Have students write the number sentences on a separate sheet of paper. As you work together, ask: *How many zeros do*

we need now? What can you tell me about the patterns of zeros in these number sentences? What can you tell me about the words because, as, and since in these sentences?

Have students complete the Practice the Language activity on page 47 independently. Circulate and assess their progress. Use the rubric to assess their work.

D | Assess and Intervene

Can every student use the synonyms to explain what happens when we divide and multiply with zeros? Use the rubric to identify students who need extra support through additional help and the Intervention activity.

Intermediate

☐ Writes 2 sentences with the help of the sentence frame, using the synonyms to explain dividing/multiplying with zeros, with some errors that do not impede comprehension.

Example of a sentence a student might write: *Because the number of zeros increase in one factor, number of zeros also increase in product.*

Advanced

☐ Writes 2 sentences without the sentence frame, using the synonyms to explain dividing/multiplying with zeros, with minor errors that do not impede comprehension.

Example of a sentence a student might write: *As number of zeros grow in dividend, number of zeros grow in quotient.*

INTERVENTION   10 minutes

If students are having trouble understanding the language in the lesson, write each word of the sentence frames on Transparency 24 on a paper strip. Then have students arrange the strips in order to form the sentences. Have them substitute the synonyms: *as, since,* and *because* and read the sentence each time. Make sure to have them match *one factor* with the product and *dividend* with the quotient.

Solve Math Problems

Objective Explain why you chose rounding or compatible numbers to estimate the answer in multiplication and division problems.

45 minutes

Teach this lesson:
- **After** lessons on estimation in their grade-level math textbook
- **Before** students complete the activities on page 48 of the student worktext

You need these materials:
- Worksheet 12
- What We Know/What We Learned chart from Lesson 1

Solve Math Problems

Objective Explain why you chose rounding or compatible numbers to estimate the answer in multiplication and division problems.

Learn to Solve Problems

Rounding	Compatible Numbers
Problem The school cafeteria sells 290 cartons of milk each day. About how many cartons do they sell in 6 days?	**Problem** Tommy's family drove 1,298 miles on their 7-day vacation. If they drove the same distance each day, about how far did they drive in 1 day?
Read/Write: • Underline the question. • Circle the important information.	**Read/Write:** • Underline the question. • Circle the important information.
Think: I will use <u>rounding</u> to multiply. 300 is close to 290. And it is easy to multiply 300 by 6. $$300 \times 6 = ?$$ $$3 \times 6 = 18$$ $$30 \times 6 = 180$$ $$300 \times 6 = 1,800$$ We sell about 1,800 milk cartons in 6 days.	**Think:** I will use <u>compatible numbers</u> to divide. I adjust 1,298 to 1,400. Then it is easier to divide by 7. The rounded number 1,300 is more difficult to divide by 7 in my head. $$14 \div 7 = 2$$ $$140 \div 7 = 20$$ $$1,400 \div 7 = 200$$ They drove about 200 miles in 1 day.
Explain: I used rounding because I can multiply 300 times 8 in my head.	**Explain:** I used compatible numbers because I can divide 1,400 by 7 in my head.

Practice Solving Math Problems

Directions Follow the steps above to solve the word problems below. Solve the problems on a separate sheet of paper. Answer each problem using *because* and a complete sentence.

1. The 12 students in my class are sharing 256 stickers. About how many stickers will each student get?
   Each student will get about 20 stickers.

2. At the school Science Fair, students presented 123 projects each day for 4 days. About how many projects did they present in all? They presented about 400 projects in all.

3. We collected 1,548 bottles for our bottle drive in 8 days. We collected about the same number of bottles each day. About how many bottles did we collect each day?
   We collected about 200 bottles each day.

4. Four giraffes weigh about 17,432 pounds. About how many pounds does one giraffe weigh? One giraffe weighs about 4,000 pounds.

Highlighted words and phrases may affect student comprehension.

48 • Mental Math and Estimation with Multiplication and Division

EXTENSION AND ENRICHMENT 10 minutes

Write a word from the list below on the board, writing the first and last letters only, with lines for each letter in between. Divide students into small groups. Give each group a piece of paper. Tell them that they will have to fill in the spaces between the first and last letter to guess the word. The group that calls out the word has to make a sentence with it. Continue as time permits, using the words from the list. Remind students not to call out the word and to work on the paper. Word list: *estimate, multiplication, divide, factor, product, dividend, quotient, rounding, patterns, zero, because, as, since, compatible, underestimate, overestimate, divisible, basic, fact, adjust, substitute.*

A Introduce

Read aloud the Lesson Objective with students. Display the chart from Lesson 1 and have students read it chorally. Ask: *What other words or ideas have we learned about mental math that we should add to the chart?* Have students discuss with a partner what is on the chart. Invite volunteers to write any additional information.

Make sure students understand how to use rounding, patterns of zero, and compatible numbers to estimate when solving word problems. Review this with students, using examples from these lessons or their math textbook.

Tell students that they will learn how to explain why they chose rounding or compatible numbers to estimate when solving multiplication and division problems.

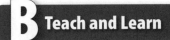 **Teach and Learn**

Write *rounding* **on the board**. Have students open their worktexts to page 48 and look at Learn to Solve Problems.

Model how to solve the problem on the left by using the following Think Aloud.

Think Aloud

Underline "About how many cartons do they sell in 6 days?" and say: *I need to underline the question. About tells me it is an estimate, not an exact answer. The number sentence is 290 × 6 = ?* Write the number sentence on the board. Say: *That's difficult to multiply using mental math. I will use rounding.*

Say: *I need to read the problem and circle the important information.* Write the rounding problem on the board and read it aloud. Circle "290 cartons" and "in 6 days." Say: *It says "in 6 days," so I have to multiply by 6. Cross out 290 and write 300. I round to 300 because 300 × 6 is easy to multiply mentally: 3 × 6 = 18. So, 300 × 6 = 1,800. That's about 1,800 cartons of milk in 6 days.*

Write *compatible numbers* **on the board**. Write the compatible numbers problem from page 48 on the board and read it aloud.

Model how to solve the on the right problem by thinking aloud.

Think Aloud

Read and underline the question: *If they drove the same distance each day, about how far did they drive in 1 day?*

Say: *I read the problem and circle the important information. I circle "1,298 miles" and "7-day vacation."* Circle this information.

Say: *The word* each *tells me I have to divide, and the word* about *tells me it is an estimate, not an exact answer. That means I have to find out how many miles they drove each day. So I'll divide. The number sentence is 1,298 ÷ 7 = ? If I use rounding, 1,300 is not easy to divide by 7. I know the basic facts for 14 ÷ 7. They are* compatible numbers: *14 ÷ 7 = 2; 140 ÷ 7 = 20; 1,400 ÷ 7 = 200. That's about 200 miles each day.*

Write the sentence frame on the board: *I used ____ because ____.* Tell students to use the sentence frame to explain why they chose rounding or compatible numbers to estimate their answer.

Choose two word problems from the grade-level math textbook. Choose problems that involve estimation, using rounding and compatible numbers to multiply and divide. Write these problems on the board or have students keep their textbooks open.

- **Divide the class into groups of four.** Give each group copies of Worksheet 12. Groups should solve problems using one worksheet for each problem. All answers should incorporate the sentence frame.

- **As students work, circulate, helping as necessary.** Remind them how to use the patterns of zeros for multiplication and division. Help them understand when to multiply and divide by asking them if they are finding a total (multiplication) or finding how many in each group (division). Allow students to use their worktexts as a reference.

C **Review and Practice**

Ask for volunteers. Have them tell how they choose to use rounding or compatible numbers to solve multiplication or division problems. Summarize: *When we estimate, we substitute a number that is close to the original number. Sometimes we use a number that is not very close because it is easy to multiply or divide.* Guide them to look at the What We Know/What We Learned chart to use the vocabulary in this module to explain their choices.

Write multiplication and division word problems on the board. Problem 1: *Our school has 325 students. Everyone is going on a field trip. There are 8 buses. About how many students should go on each bus?* Problem 2: *Our town art museum has 133 paintings. The town wants to show 6 paintings at the library each month. About how long will it take for the town to show all the paintings?*

Divide the class into pairs. Read aloud each problem on the board. Have pairs follow the steps on their worksheet to solve each problem. Then have them use the sentence frame to explain their work.

Read aloud the directions for Practice Solving Math Problems in the student worktext. Circulate and assess how well students are using rounding and compatible numbers and explaining how they solved each problem. Use the rubric to assess their work.

D **Assess and Intervene**

How accurately can students choose rounding or compatible numbers to solve the problem and explain their choice, based on Practice Solving Math Problems on page 48? Use the rubric to identify students who need extra support through additional help or the Intervention activity.

Intermediate

☐ Chooses the appropriate strategy to solve at least 2 word problems.

☐ Answers are written using the sentence frame and *because,* with errors that do not impede comprehension.

Example of a sentence a student might write: *I used compatible number because easy multiply 4 × 8 in my head.*

Advanced

☐ Chooses the appropriate strategy to solve at least 3 word problems.

☐ Answers are written without the sentence frame, with minimal errors, that do not impede comprehension.

Example of a sentence a student might write: *I use rounding because in my head is easy to divide 20 by 5.*

INTERVENTION 10 minutes

Are students having trouble explaining why they chose a strategy to solve the problems? If so, have them write the number sentence on a piece of paper. Then draw two columns titled *compatible numbers* and *rounding*. Help students list the rounded numbers and compatible numbers they might use for each number sentence. Then help them decide which numbers are closer to the actual numbers and which numbers are easier to multiply/divide in their heads. Have students complete the sentence frame: *I will use ____ because it is ____.*

Algebraic Expressions

Lesson

1

Understand the Main Idea

Objective Describe what an expression is.

---

30 minutes 🕐

Teach this lesson:
- **Before** introducing material on expressions in students' grade-level math textbooks
- **Before** students complete the activities on page 49 of the student worktext

You need these materials:
- index cards
- butcher paper

Prerequisite Background Knowledge
- Basic concepts of addition, subtraction, multiplication, and division

---

BP 2 *ELL BEST PRACTICE #2:*
Assessing, Activating, and Building Background Knowledge

English language learners often have difficulty connecting what they have learned at home or in previous schooling with what they are learning in school. Teachers can help make ELLs aware of what they already know about a topic. As you introduce expressions, relate this work to students' understanding of the basic operations. At the same time, help students fill in any gaps they may have in these skills.

Throughout this module, when you see **BP 2** you will find an example of how you can assess, activate, and build background knowledge.

Module 13: Algebraic Expressions

Understand the Main Idea

Objective Describe what an expression is.

Learn the Main Idea

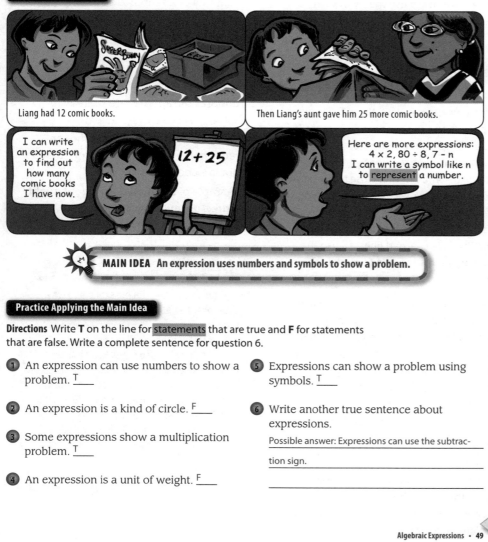

Liang had 12 comic books.

Then Liang's aunt gave him 25 more comic books.

I can write an expression to find out how many comic books I have now.

12 + 25

Here are more expressions: 4 x 2, 80 ÷ 8, 7 - n I can write a symbol like n to represent a number.

MAIN IDEA An expression uses numbers and symbols to show a problem.

Practice Applying the Main Idea

Directions Write **T** on the line for statements that are true and **F** for statements that are false. Write a complete sentence for question 6.

1. An expression can use numbers to show a problem. <u>T</u>

2. An expression is a kind of circle. <u>F</u>

3. Some expressions show a multiplication problem. <u>T</u>

4. An expression is a unit of weight. <u>F</u>

5. Expressions can show a problem using symbols. <u>T</u>

6. Write another true sentence about expressions.
   Possible answer: Expressions can use the subtraction sign.
   _____

Highlighted words and phrases may affect student comprehension.

Algebraic Expressions • 49

LESSON **1**

A **Introduce**

Read aloud the Lesson Objective with students.

Write the word *expression* on the board and read it aloud. Ask students if they have heard of or read this word before. Tell students the word is sometimes used to describe the look on a person's face. (She is sad. He looks happy.) Say that expression can also mean feeling. (She read that story with great expression.)

Tell students the word *expression* has a math meaning, too. Have students talk with a partner about possible math meanings of the word. Then ask students to report to the class.

Focus students' attention on the first picture in the box under Learn the Main Idea. Read aloud the text below it. Point out that they can see just some of the comic books.

Have students look at the second box. Have a volunteer read aloud the text under it. Point out again that not all the comic books can be seen.

Have students mark their places and close their books. Help students restate the problem. Ask: *What happened first?* (Liang had some comic books.) Ask: *How many did he have?* (12) Write *12* on the board. Ask: *Then what happened?* (he got more) *Who gave him the new comics?* (his aunt) *How many did she give him?* (25) Write *25* on the board, too.

- **Remind students that drawing a mental picture is a good way to help them understand a problem.** Have them picture the comic books in their heads. Encourage them to use an original picture or the picture in the worktext. Ask students to describe their mental images to a partner.

BP 2 **Build background knowledge.** Say: *We know how many comics Liang had. We know how many new comics he got. We can write a question about these numbers. What question can we write?* Give small groups of students index cards and have them brainstorm possible questions. Then have students share their questions with the whole class. Write students' questions on the board.

- **Point out that there are several good questions that students could ask.** Point to the question: *How many comic books does Liang have now?*

BP 2 **Write the four operations symbols on the board.** Ask students to tell you which symbol they would use to find the total number of comic books. (the plus sign) Say: *Yes, you can add to find out how many comics Liang has now.*

Have students open their books. Read the third panel aloud. Say: *12 + 25 is an expression. It uses numbers and a plus sign to show the problem. The 12 represents ____.* Pause and let students fill in: *the number of comic books Liang started with.* Then say: *The 25 represents ____.* Pause again so students can say: *the number of comic books his aunt gave him.* Then say: *This expression can help us find how many comic books Liang has now.*

Move on to the fourth panel. Have a volunteer read the speech bubble aloud. Point out the use of the *n.* Say: *The* n *is a symbol. It stands for a number. That means it takes the place of a number. You can use a symbol if you don't know what a number is.* Tell students they'll learn more about symbols.

Read the Main Idea aloud with students. Point out that expressions do not contain equals signs or greater and less than symbols.

Teach and Learn

Write the expression *5 × 4* on the board. Say: *An expression uses numbers and/or symbols to show a math problem. 5 and 4 are numbers, and × is an operation symbol that means* times. *So 5 × 4 is an expression.*

BP 2 **Ask students to suggest a real-life scenario that fits the expression *5 × 4.*** Possible suggestions include: *There are 5 dogs and each dog has 4 legs* or *I drew 5 pictures and used 4 tacks to hang each one up on the wall.*

Write the expression *9 ÷ 3* on the board. Ask students if this is an expression and why. (Yes, because it uses numbers to describe a math problem.) Write on the board and say: *An expression uses ____ and symbols to show a math ____.* Have students fill in the missing words orally.

- **Repeat with the expressions *10 × 3 + 1* and *45 − 2.*** Leave out different words in the sentence above each time. Sum up by saying that both are expressions.

Write the expression *9 + n* on the board. Tell students that *n* stands for a number. Ask students if this is an expression. Have them share their ideas with a partner. Encourage them to consult the wording of the Main Idea as they decide.

- **Elicit that *9 + n* is an expression because it describes a math problem in numbers and symbols.** Explain that + is a symbol meaning *plus* and that *n* is a symbol that stands for a number. Say: *An expression uses ____ and ____ to show a math problem.* Have students orally fill in the words *numbers* and *symbols.*

- **Repeat a similar procedure with *b − 10* and *t + 25.*** Have partners decide if they are expressions and why.

Review and Practice

Remind students that expressions require numbers and symbols.

Have students work with a partner. Give each pair a sheet of butcher paper. Have students write expressions with numbers and symbols. Circulate through the room, checking that students are writing correct expressions.

Direct students' attention to the questions at the bottom of page 49. Read the directions aloud. Say that students will need to write a sentence of their own to answer number 6.

Have students answer the questions on page 49 on their own. Go over the answers when everyone is finished.

Assess and Intervene

Can students identify true statements about expressions, based on Practice Applying the Main Idea on page 49? Use the rubric to identify students who need extra support through additional help and the Intervention activity.

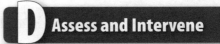

Intermediate

- ☐ Correctly determines whether at least 3 of the statements are true.
- ☐ Writes a true sentence about expressions, with a few errors.

  Example of a sentence a student might write: *Expression use number and letter.*

Advanced

- ☐ Correctly determines whether all 5 statements are true.
- ☐ Writes a true sentence about expressions, making only minor errors.

  Example of a sentence a student might write: *Expressions use different symbol and number.*

INTERVENTION 5 minutes

If students have difficulty completing the activity, teach them the following statements in chant form:
- An expression can use numbers.
- An expression can use symbols.
- An expression can show a problem.

Have students repeat the chant and clap as often as needed to memorize the statements.

Learn the Vocabulary

Objective Talk and write about expressions using the vocabulary words.

30 minutes

Teach this lesson:
- **Before** students begin work on expressions in their grade-level math textbooks
- **Before** students complete the activities on page 50 of the student worktext

You need these materials:
- Vocabulary Cards
- Transparency 25

Lesson Vocabulary		
Essential Vocabulary		
unknown	algebra	expression
symbol	to simplify	to evaluate
variable		
Additional Vocabulary		
value *	parentheses	order of operations

* – Term that has a Vocabulary Card.

LESSON
2

Learn the Vocabulary

Objective Talk and write about expressions using the vocabulary words.

Learn the Words

Directions Fill in the missing words and numbers.

Expressions use numbers and symbols to show problems. A **symbol** is a sign that represents something else. To **simplify** or to **evaluate** an expression means to find the value of the expression.

These expressions use only numbers and operation symbols: + − × ÷			Write an expression. Use only numbers and operation symbols.
4×3	$16 - 2$	$8 \times 3 - 1$	Possible response: $3 + 21$

Expressions can use other symbols, too, like n or x. These symbols stand for numbers.			Symbols that stand for numbers are called **variables.** The numbers that variables stand for are unknown. Sometimes a variable is called an **unknown.**
These expressions use numbers and variables:			Write an expression. Use numbers and variables.
$2 \times n$	$x + 30$	$15 \div m$	Possible response: $5 - t$

The kind of math that uses variables is called **algebra**.

Practice the Words

Directions Write the missing words, one letter at a time, on each short line. Then read the letters in the boxes to spell out a mystery word for number 7. Write a sentence to answer number 8 on a separate sheet of paper.

1. An e x p r e s s i o **n** uses numbers or symbols to show problems.

2. You can use a symbol to stand for an **u** n k n o w n number.

3. When you s i **m** p l i f y an expression, you find its value.

4. Some expressions use a s y m **b** o l such as m, k, or n.

5. A symbol in an expression is often called a v a r i a b l **e** .

6. A l g e b **r** a is the kind of math that uses variables.

7. Write the mystery word. n u m b e r

8. Write a sentence that uses at least two of the words you wrote. Underline the words you used. Possible answer: You can <u>simplify</u> an <u>expression</u> by finding its value.

A Introduce

Read aloud the Lesson Objective with students.

Ask students to think back to the previous lesson. Give an index card to each student. Have students choose one word that they thought was especially important in Lesson 1 and write it on their card.

Have students move through the room. Ask each student to find a student who has chosen a different word. Instruct the two students to take turns teaching each other their words, describing the meaning of the word or giving an example of its use. When pairs are finished, have them find another classmate who has chosen yet a different word.

Have students share their words with the rest of the class. Write these words on the board. Read the list of words aloud.

Add any words from the Essential Vocabulary list that are not mentioned by students, such as *algebra* or *simplify*. Also choose words from the Additional Vocabulary list that you think will be useful. Elicit or provide examples for all the words on the list.

B Teach and Learn

Read aloud the first statement on page 50 of the student worktext. Point out that students have already learned about expressions in the previous lesson.

Highlighted words and phrases may affect student comprehension.

BP 2 Read aloud the second sentence.
Point out that the word *simplify* is related to another word that students probably know. (If they need a hint, explain that it is related to a *simple* word they may know.) Remind students that *simple* means *basic* or *easy*. Explain that to *simplify* means *to make something easy or simple or simpler*. Say that sometimes we use the word *evaluate* in place of *simplify*.

- **BP 2 Demonstrate what it means to simplify an expression.** Write *19 − 2* on the board and establish that it is an expression. Then say: *It's easy to find the value of 19 − 2. I know that 19 − 2 is 17. So, the value of this expression is 17.* Point out that the number 17 is simpler to write and to read than the longer expression 19 − 2. Repeat with 8 × 4 if necessary.

Have students in groups of four read the next section of the Learn the Words box. Point out that they have written and seen expressions in the previous lesson. Encourage them to work with their groups to simplify each of the given expressions. (12, 14, and 23) Then have them follow the worktext directions by each writing an expression of their own and sharing it.

Move on to the next section. Read aloud the information on symbols. Pay particular attention to the section beginning: *Symbols that stand for numbers are called variables.*

- **BP 2 Say:** *We learned about these symbols in the last lesson. What do you remember about symbols?* Have students tell what they recall about symbols that stand for numbers.

- **Say:** *Symbols that stand for numbers are called variables.* Write *s + 15* on the board. Ask students which is the variable. Elicit that the variable is *s*. Repeat with *y ÷ 5* and *2 − m*.

- **Read aloud the sentence:** *The numbers that variables stand for are unknown.* Write *unknown* on the board and circle the root word *know*. Say: *If you know something, it is known.* Underline the final *n* in *unknown*. Then say: *If you do not know something, it is unknown.* Explain that *un-* is a prefix that often means *not*, so *unknown* means *not known*.

- **Ask:** *How many students are in the class?* Have students say whether this number is known or unknown. (known) Repeat with: *How many stars are in the universe?* (unknown) Sum up by saying: *The numbers that variables stand for are unknown. You do not know what the numbers are. They are unknown.*

- **Touch the expression *s + 15* on the board again.** Say: *Which is the unknown?* (*s*) Remind students that *s* is a symbol, a variable, and an unknown, all at the same time.

Have students study the examples of expressions with variables. Then have them write an expression with a variable and share it with a partner. Check students' work.

Read aloud the last statement in the Learn the Words box. Explain that algebra is a kind of mathematics, like geometry. Add that algebra is one of many words that comes to English from Arabic.

Have students complete the Vocabulary Cards for the words in this module.

Review and Practice

To review the vocabulary, display Transparency 25. Read aloud each word or phrase and example, one by one. Then quiz students by saying the word and having them give the example. Then give the example; they say the word.

- **Have students work with a partner.** Have them choose a word from the transparency and explain why the corresponding example fits with the word, using the sentence frame: _____ *is an example of* _____ *because* _____. If necessary, go over the example on the transparency. Have students write their sentence on a piece of paper and then practice saying it. Walk around the room, listening to sentences and making sure students are using the words correctly. Invite students to write a sentence for each word.

- **Call the class back together.** Have students share especially interesting sentences with the class. Then write some of their sentences on a blank transparency for all to read.

Call students' attention to the directions at the bottom of page 50. Point out that students will need to read the definitions and find words from the box above that fit. Then they will write the words, one letter per line. Remind students that they will need to write a sentence for number 8.

Emphasize that the highlighted letters will spell out a word that students know. You can tell them that the word appears somewhere else on page 50.

Have students solve numbers 1–8 independently.

D Assess and Intervene

Do students understand the vocabulary words, based on their work in Practice the Words on page 50? Use the rubric to identify students who need extra support through additional help and the Intervention activity.

Intermediate

- ☐ Identifies at least 4 or more of the first 6 words.
- ☐ Writes a sentence with a few errors using 2 of the vocabulary words.

  Example of a sentence a student might write: *You use symbol in expression.*

Advanced

- ☐ Identifies all of the first 6 words.
- ☐ Writes an original sentence with few errors using 2 of the vocabulary words.

  Example of a sentence a student might write: *In algebra you use a symbol for unknown.*

INTERVENTION 5 minutes

If students have difficulty completing numbers 1–6 in Practice the Words, give them the following word group: *unknown, symbol, variable, square*. Have them work together to pick out the word that doesn't fit. (square) Repeat with *circle, rectangle, triangle, algebra* (algebra) and *expression, simplify, meter, variable* (meter). For each group, go through the words one by one and help students describe how three of the words are related.

Lesson 3

Use More Language

Objective Use words and phrases that unknown variables may represent.

30 minutes

Teach this lesson:
- **After** students complete the activities on expressions in their grade-level math textbooks
- **Before** students complete the activities on page 51 of their student worktexts

You need these materials:
- poster board
- counters
- Worksheet 13

EXTENSION AND ENRICHMENT   10 minutes

Have students write simple word problems of their own with and without variables. Ask them to draw pictures to go with the problems and to write expressions that fit the problems. Encourage students to present their work to the class orally. Then distribute poster board and have students display their work in poster form for others to view.

Use More Language

Objective Use words and phrases that unknown variables may represent.

Learn the Language

Directions Fill in the missing words.

Enongo had some grapes. She ate 10. We don't know how many grapes Enongo had at first.

The word *some* tells us to use a variable. Enongo had *g* grapes at first. Now she has *g* — 10 grapes.

César bought a number of model cars. Each car cost $2.00. How much money did he spend on model cars? We don't know how many <u>cars</u> César bought.

The phrase *a number of* tells us to use a <u>variable</u>.

César bought *c* cars. He spent *c* × $2.

Practice the Language

Directions Draw lines to match the word problems on the left with the correct expressions on the right. In numbers 2 and 4, underline the phrase in the problem that the variable represents. Answer number 5 on a separate sheet of paper.

1. There were 6 dogs in the yard. Each dog had 2 ears. Write an expression to show the total number of ears.

2. Gerome bought 3 wooden ducks at a fair. His sister bought <u>the rest of the ducks that were for sale</u>. Write an expression to show how many ducks Gerome and his sister bought in all.

3. The school has 18 doors. Half the doors are painted blue. The rest of the doors are painted white. Write an expression to show the number of doors that are painted white.

4. Vevi saw <u>a number of deer</u>. Each deer had 4 feet. Write an expression to show how many feet the deer had in all.

d × 4

6 × 2

3 + *d*

18 ÷ 2

5. Write a word problem that goes with the expression 10 − *d*.
   Possible answer: Ted had $10.00. Then he spent some of the dollars. How many dollars did he have left?

Algebraic Expressions · 51

A Introduce

Read aloud the Lesson Objective with students.

Explain that word problems can usually be solved by writing expressions. Say: *Some word problems use numbers. Then you can use ordinary numbers in your expressions.* Give the example: *I had 7 cans of soup. Then I bought 2 more. How many cans of soup do I have now?* Elicit that the expression *7 + 2* goes with this problem.

- **Then say:** *Some word problems use words like* some *or* an amount. *These problems don't tell us exactly how much.* Give the example: *I had some boxes of cereal. Then I bought 3 more boxes. How many boxes of cereal do I have now?* Point out that students don't know how many cereal boxes there were at first. Explain that this problem needs a variable to stand for that number.

B Teach and Learn

Draw students' attention to the drawing on the left at the top of page 51 of the student worktext. Tell students that this girl's name is Enongo. Ask what she has in the bag. (grapes) Then ask: *Can we see how many grapes she has in the bag?* Elicit that the grapes are not visible.

Highlighted words and phrases may affect student comprehension.

BP 2 **Read the first two sentences under the picture.** Then have students work in groups of four to access their background knowledge. Have the groups answer questions to help them understand the situation described in the problem.

- **Begin by asking:** *How many grapes did Enongo eat? How do you know?* Establish that she ate 10 grapes and that this information comes directly from the problem.

- **Next, ask:** *After Enongo ate the grapes, did she have more or fewer grapes than when she started?* Allow groups time to discuss the answer to this question. Encourage them to sketch a drawing or act out the problem, using counters, if they are uncertain. Elicit that she had fewer grapes.

- **Then, ask what operation students should use in an expression.** On the board, write *addition, subtraction, multiplication,* and *division* to remind them of the names. Elicit that subtraction is the operation that should be used.

- **Ask:** *Could Enongo have started with 5 grapes? Why or why not?* Again, allow groups to discuss the question. Draw out that she could not have started with 5 grapes, because she ate 10; therefore, she must have started with at least 10 grapes.

- **Finally, ask students whether they know how many grapes Enongo had to start.** Draw out that this information is not given in the problem. Say: *This number is unknown.*

Read aloud the next sentence in the left column, beginning *We don't know . . .* Point out that the problem does not give a number, only the word *some.*

Continue to the next sentence. Write the word *some* on the board. Say: *We use words like* some *when we don't know exactly how many. Maybe Enongo started with 100 grapes. Maybe she started with 25. Maybe she had 4,000!* Explain that students cannot use a number to stand for this unknown quantity. Instead, they will have to use a variable.

Call students' attention to the last two sentences in the left column. Read them aloud. Point out that *g* is used as the variable here. Ask students to tell each other what *g − 10* means. (the number of grapes Enongo had to begin with, less the 10 that she ate)

Repeat with the problem in the right column. Note that students will need to fill in two missing words. Add the phrase *a number of* to the board, below where you wrote *some.* Say: *The phrase* a number of *is like* some. *You use it when you don't know exactly how many. When you see these phrases, you need to use a variable to stand for that number.* Add other phrases to the list, such as *the others* and *the amount.*

C Review and Practice

Hold up a handful of counters. Say: *I have some counters. Next, I'm going to take 2 more counters. I wonder how many I'll have then.*

- **Say:** *I can write an expression to show how many. What should I write to show how many counters I have right now?* Have a volunteer come to the board and write a variable, such as *c,* to stand for this number. Say: *That's right; I need to use a variable because I have some counters. I don't know how many.*

- **Continue, extending the expression to read** *c + 2.* Touch each element as you say: *The c is for the word* some. *The plus symbol and 2 are there because I am getting 2 more counters.*

Repeat the scenario. Start with some counters and give away 3. Say this goes with the expression *c − 3.*

Have students work with a partner. Distribute a copy of Worksheet 13 to each pair. Have them work together to determine whether the scenario should be represented by a number or by a variable. Then have them compare answers with another pair. Encourage them to discuss any points of conflict before asking you to resolve them. Go over the answers when they finish.

Read aloud the directions for Practice the Language at the bottom of page 51. Point out that the word problems appear on the left and the expressions appear on the right. Explain that some of the expressions use variables and that others do not. Tell students that they can figure out which ones use variables by looking for words, such as: *a number of* and *the rest of.* Point out that students will have to write complete sentences for number 5.

Have students complete the activity on their own. Note where students are having difficulty.

D Assess and Intervene

Can students identify words and phrases that require them to use variables when writing expressions, based on their work in Learn the Language on page 51? Use the rubric to identify students who need extra support through additional help and the Intervention activity.

Intermediate

☐ Matches at least 2 of the problems with the correct expressions.

☐ Writes a word problem that fits the expression and may contain a few language errors that do not interfere with communication.

Example of a problem a student might write: *Ted have 10 dollar. Spend some. How many dollar Ted have?*

Advanced

☐ Matches all 4 of the problems with the correct expressions.

☐ Writes a word problem that fits the expression and may contain only minor language errors.

Example of a problem a student might write: *Ted had 10 dollars. He spend some dollar. How many dollars Ted have left?*

INTERVENTION 5 minutes

Help students create a web to show the important ideas of this lesson. Make a web design on the board and have students dictate the most important idea of the lesson to you (that some words go with variables in expressions). Then have students brainstorm other ideas about the lesson, such as: *The word* some *tells you to use a variable* and *Sometimes you don't know exactly what a number is.* Write these words on the strands of the web and read them aloud.

Lesson

4

Solve Math Problems

Objective Act or draw out a problem to help you write an expression.

30 minutes 🕐

Teach this lesson:
- **After** students complete the lessons on expressions in their grade-level math textbooks
- **Before** students complete the activities on page 52 of the student worktext

You need these materials:
- play money
- three boxes
- counters or other small objects
- Transparency 26

LESSON

4

Solve Math Problems

Objective Act out or draw a problem to help you write an expression.

Learn to Solve Problems

Problem
Olga had $25.00. She bought gifts for 3 friends. Each gift cost $5.00. Write and simplify an expression to show how much money she had left.

Problem
Lucas has twice as many yo-yos as model trucks. Then he gets 4 more yo-yos. Write and simplify an expression to show how many yo-yos Lucas has now. Use *t* to stand for the number of model trucks.

Step 1:	Read the problem. Act out or draw what happened.	
Step 2:	Write the expression. Use numbers and symbols.	
	$25 − (3 × $5)	(2 × t) + 4
Step 3:	Simplify the expression.	
	3 × $5 = $15	We don't know how many model trucks Lucas has.
	$25 − $15 = $10	Suppose he has 4. Use 4 for the value of t.
	Olga had $10.00 left.	2 × 4 = 8
		8 + 4 = 12 Luca has 12 yo-yos.

Practice Solving Math Problems

Directions Follow the steps above to solve the word problems below. Then write a complete sentence to simplify each expression. Solve each problem on a separate sheet of paper.

① There are 8 people at lunch. Each one eats 2 bananas. Write an expression to show how many bananas they eat in all.
8 × 2; 16; The people eat 16 bananas in all.

② Some boys are in the swimming pool. Then 6 more boys get in. Write an expression to show how many boys are in the pool now. Use *n* to show how many boys are in the pool at first. Then simplify the expression if *n* = 15. n + 6; 21; There are 21 boys in the pool now.

③ Vidze has $30.00. He buys a notebook for $3.00 and a T-shirt for $15.00. Write an expression to show how much money he has left. $30 − $3 − $15; $12; Vidze has $12.00 left.

④ Alicia has 20 red beads and 36 blue beads. The rest of her beads are green. Write an expression to show how many green beads she has. Use *b* to show how many beads she has in all. Then simplify the expression if *b* = 100.
b − 20 − 36; 44; Alicia has 44 green beads.

52 · Algebraic Expressions

A Introduce

Read the Lesson Objective aloud with students. Ask students what it means to act something out. Write students' answers on the board and read them aloud.

Tell students that the word *act* is often connected with plays. Ask if students have ever been in a play. Say: *When you are in a play, you* act.

Explain that students can also act out math problems. Say: *When you act out a math problem, you show what is happening.* Explain that students can act out problems with materials, such as counters or play money. Add that it also can help to draw a picture.

- **BP 2** Ask if students have used the strategy *act it out* to solve math problems before. Invite volunteers to describe the problems they solved, using this method, and to tell how they used the strategy.

B Teach and Learn

Read aloud the problem at the top left hand side of page 52. Ask comprehension questions to make sure students understand the scenario. Sample questions include: *How much money did Olga have?* ($25.00) and *What did she buy?* (gifts for friends) Be sure students understand that they need to write an expression and then simplify it.

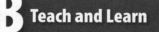
Highlighted words and phrases may affect student comprehension.

Have students practice retelling the problem, using time order words. Have them tell a partner what happened first, next, and last. Ask them to write their ideas, using these words. Have volunteers share their discussions with the class.

Read aloud Step 1 or have a volunteer do so.

Say: *We can use materials to act out this problem. What materials can we use?* Have students consult with a partner and suggest appropriate materials to help model the problem. Write these ideas on the board.

Highlight any suggestions that involve the use of play money. If no suggestions mention this material, add it to the list. Say: *I like [Badhri's] suggestion that we use play money. I like it because this problem has to do with money. The problem tells how Olga spent some money. So it makes sense to use money to act it out.* Then involve the whole group in a drama about Olga.

Choose one student to act the part of Olga. Provide this student with $25.00 in five-dollar bills. Have the student count the money while the rest of the class watches to make sure the total is $25.00.

- **Ask another student to play the part of a store clerk.** Give this student three boxes. Explain that these boxes represent the gifts Olga will buy.

- **Have both students come to the front of the room.** Have the student playing Olga explain what she needs. Have the student playing the clerk give her the boxes in exchange for three of the five-dollar bills. Encourage them to talk throughout the transaction. For example, have "Olga" say *I need 3 gifts for my sisters,* and have the cashier explain that the gifts each cost $5.00.

- **Repeat.** Use other students to play the parts of Olga and the clerk.

Call students' attention to the picture at the top of the left column in the student worktext. Explain that the picture also shows what happened. Say: *If you don't have enough people or materials to act out a problem, you can draw what is happening.*

Move to the second row and read aloud Step 2. Ask: *How much money did Olga have to start?* Elicit that she had $25.00. Write $25.00 on the board. Then ask: *How much did each gift cost?* ($5.00) *How many gifts did she buy?* (3) Have students help you record this

information on the board as *3 × $5;* write this to the right of where it says *$25.00.* Place parentheses around this expression.

- **BP 2** Be sure students can explain what parentheses are used for. (to signal that the operations inside them are to be done first)

- **Then write a minus sign between *$25.00* and the expression *(3 × $5)* on the board.** Point out that this is the expression written in the student work text on page 52. Instruct students to talk with a partner about why the operation should be subtraction. (to model how she spent the money) If needed, have students act out the problem again.

Draw students' attention to the third row. Read the third step aloud.

- **Have groups of four study the third row with a partner.** Encourage them to take turns explaining what they see and how the problem is being simplified. Walk around the room, listening to conversations and helping students form ideas.

Summarize the process. Hold up the original five-dollar bills. Say: *Olga spent 3 of these bills to buy gifts.* Put 3 of the bills down and say: *Now she has $10.00 left.*

Repeat with the second example. Use counters to stand for the three extra yo-yos and use boxes to represent the boxes of trucks and yo-yos. Point out that this problem includes a variable. Summarize by saying: *You can use this strategy even if there are variables.*

C Review and Practice

Briefly review the steps in the student worktext for solving problems by using the strategy *act it out.* Ask students to name the steps in order several times. Encourage them not to use their worktexts for reference after a couple of times, but rather to use their memory.

- **Then reverse the activity.** Read the steps aloud and have students identify whether the steps are 1, 2, or 3.

Divide students into pairs and display Transparency 26. Have students use a piece of paper as they solve each problem. Ask students to act out these

problems, using whatever materials they need. Then have them use the steps to write and simplify an expression. Move around the room, checking students' work and offering assistance as needed.

Read aloud the directions for Practice Solving Math Problems at the bottom of page 52. Explain that students will need to act out the problems on their own, but that they may use materials if they will help; they may also draw pictures. Remind students to write their final answer in a complete sentence. Have students solve these problems independently.

D Assess and Intervene

Can students use the strategies and steps given to solve word problems, based on their work in Practice Solving Math Problems on page 52? Use the rubric to identify students who need extra support through additional help and the Intervention activity.

Intermediate

☐ Solves at least 3 problems successfully.

☐ Writes a sentence with a few errors to give the final answer.

  Example of a sentence a student might write: *The people eat 16 bananas.*

Advanced

☐ Solves all problems successfully.

☐ Writes a complete sentence with few errors to give the final answer.

  Example of a sentence a student might write: *He has got left $12.00.*

INTERVENTION 5 minutes

If students cannot answer the questions correctly, they may be using the wrong operations for the problem. Help them look for key words, such as *each* in problem 1 and *more* in problem 2, that suggest an operation (*each*—multiplication; *more*—addition). Tell students these words do not always indicate the particular operation, but that they provide a good starting point. Help students draw up a list of key words and remind them to use these words to assist them in writing expressions.

Understand the Main Idea

Objective Explain how you can solve equations with variables.

Prerequisite Background Knowledge
- Concepts of expressions and variables
- Order of operations

30 minutes

Teach this lesson:
- **Before** introducing material on equations in grade-level math textbooks
- **Before** students complete the activities on page 53 of the student worktext

You need these materials:
- Transparency 27

BP 3 ELL BEST PRACTICE #3:
Performance Assessment

English language learners often know more than they can demonstrate on standard reading- and writing-based assessments. As a result, it can be more effective to evaluate their learning based on observations of their performance on ordinary classroom tasks. Use rubrics, checklists, and similar tools to check students' work on authentic tasks requiring them to work with equations.

Throughout this module, when you see **BP 3**, you will find an example of how you can use performance assessment to evaluate students' progress.

Module 14: Algebraic Equations

Understand the Main Idea

Objective Explain how you can solve equations with variables.

Learn the Main Idea

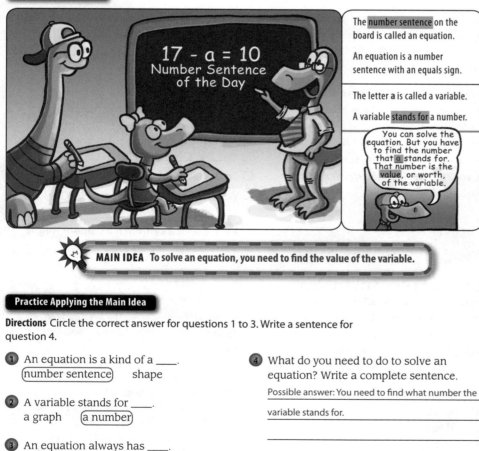

The number sentence on the board is called an equation.

An equation is a number sentence with an equals sign.

The letter *a* is called a variable.

A variable stands for a number.

You can solve the equation. But you have to find the number that *a* stands for. That number is the value, or worth, of the variable.

MAIN IDEA To solve an equation, you need to find the value of the variable.

Practice Applying the Main Idea

Directions Circle the correct answer for questions 1 to 3. Write a sentence for question 4.

1. An equation is a kind of a ____.
   (number sentence)   shape

2. A variable stands for ____.
   a graph   (a number)

3. An equation always has ____.
   (an equals sign)   a square

4. What do you need to do to solve an equation? Write a complete sentence.
   Possible answer: You need to find what number the variable stands for.

A Introduce

Read aloud the Lesson Objective with students on page 53 of the student worktext. Tell students they will be learning about solving equations.

Have students study the picture at the top left of the page. Ask: *What do you see? What is happening in the picture?* (a school for dinosaurs) Have students discuss in pairs and then share with the class.

Call students' attention to the teacher in the picture. Ask: *What is the teacher writing?* (a number sentence)

- **Then ask:** *What symbols do you see in the number sentence?* (− and =, possibly *a*) *What numbers do you see?* (17 and 10) *What else do you see?* Say that the number sentence includes the letter *a*.

Ask students why they think the letter *a* is in this number sentence. Say: *The letter* a *is usually part of a word, not part of a number sentence. Why do you think it is here? What do you think it means?*

- **Have students discuss the questions with a partner.** Have them write words or phrases to summarize their discussions.

Highlighted words and phrases may affect student comprehension.

- **Invite pairs to share their ideas with the rest of the class.** Write suggestions on the board. If the word *variable* comes up, highlight it. Otherwise, explain that the letter *a* is called a *variable*.

Read aloud the sentences to the right of the picture. Emphasize the words *equation* and *variable*. Explain that an equation is a kind of number sentence. Then say: *The letter* a *is a variable. We don't know what number* a *stands for. Later, you'll learn how to figure it out!*

Call students' attention to the speech bubble at the bottom right of the Learn the Main Idea box. Have a volunteer read the text aloud. Explain that solving the equation means finding the number that *a* stands for.

BP 3 **Read aloud the Main Idea with students.** Ask students if they understand the Main Idea. Have them hold their thumbs straight up if they think they completely understand the concept, hold their thumbs straight down if they feel completely confused, and point their thumbs to the side if they think they understand some, but not all. Use this information to help you determine how quickly or slowly to proceed through the lesson.

B Teach and Learn

Display Transparency 27 to help students understand number sentences. Ask students to identify the number sentences. (They have numbers, operation symbols [like +, −, etc.], and a greater than or less than or equal to symbol.) Then have students say which expressions are not number sentences. Cross those out on the transparency.

Say: *Some number sentences are called* equations. Write *equation* on the board and ask students what English word it reminds them of. Elicit that the start of *equation* is similar to *equal.*

Ask students to tell a partner what they think an equation is. Then have each pair copy all the equations from the transparency to a sheet of paper. When they are finished, have them compare their answers with another pair. Then have volunteers read the equations aloud. Circle them on the transparency. Chant and clap together: *An e-QUA-tion has an E-quals sign.*

Write the word *variable* on the board. Read it aloud. Next to it, write the word *vary.* Say: *This word means* to change. Point out that it is not the same as the word *very,* meaning *a lot.* Draw a line from *vary* to *variable.* Say: *The word* variable *is related to the word* vary. Variable *is a word you may have learned before. When we don't know what a number is, we can use a variable to stand for or to represent that number.*

Play Find That Variable to help students explore variables. Write the letter *s* on the board. Then secretly write the number 8 on a sheet of paper. Say: *This variable stands for a number between 0 and 10. I have written the value of the variable on this sheet of paper.* Then have students guess the value of the variable, using the sentence form: *Is the value of the variable greater than/less than/equal to _____?* Help them build on the data from each guess to find the value of the variable. Repeat with other numbers, or have students play in small groups.

Focus students' attention again on the speech bubble at the bottom right of the Learn the Main Idea box. Read these sentences aloud slowly. Emphasize the words *solve* and *value* and explain their meanings. Say: *When we played Find That Variable for the first time, the value of the variable was 8. You solve an equation by finding the value of the variable.*

Have a volunteer read aloud the Main Idea again. Repeat having students use their thumbs to show you comprehension of the Main Idea. Note who understands more during this part of the lesson and who still seems confused.

C Review and Practice

BP 3 **Help students review the concepts in this lesson by asking them questions, such as:** *What is an equation? How can you solve an equation?* Model some of these questions and write them on the board, but encourage students to develop questions of their own, too. Circulate, observing how well students ask and answer the questions.

Call students' attention to the questions at the bottom of page 53. Read the directions aloud. Emphasize that the fourth question asks students to write a sentence. Have students complete the four items independently. Note difficulties with vocabulary or concepts.

D Assess and Intervene

How well can students use the words *equation, solve,* and *variable,* based on Practice Applying the Main Idea on page 53? Use the rubric to identify students who need extra support through additional help and the Intervention activity.

Intermediate

☐ Circles all 3 correct answers.
☐ Uses the words of the Main Idea to write a sentence.

Example of a sentence a student might write: *You need to find the value of the variable.*

Advanced

☐ Circles all 3 correct answers.
☐ Writes an original sentence, with only minor errors, that explains how to solve an equation.

Example of a sentence a student might write: *You find out what the number is the variable stands for.*

INTERVENTION 10 minutes

Help students create a web to show what they know about equations and variables. Draw a web on the board. In the center circle, write EQUATION. Draw strands going out from the center circle in all directions. Go through the Learn the Main Idea box with students. Have them tell you what they know about equations as you write the information on the strands of the web. Have them copy the web onto paper. Repeat with a web for variables. Have students keep the webs and use them for reference.

Learn the Vocabulary

Objective Talk and write about equations and inequalities using the vocabulary words.

45 minutes

Teach this lesson:
- **Before** students begin work on algebraic equations in their math grade-level textbooks
- **Before** students complete the activities on page 54 of their student worktexts

You need these materials:
- pan balances and weights
- Vocabulary Cards
- Worksheet 14

Lesson Vocabulary

Essential Vocabulary

| equation | inequality | to solve/solution |

Additional Vocabulary

| equal* | to substitute _____ for _____ |
| variable* | to replace _____ with _____ |

* - Terms that have Vocabulary Cards.

LESSON
2

Learn the Vocabulary

Objective Talk and write about equations and inequalities using the vocabulary words.

Learn the Words

An **equation** is a number sentence that uses =. 2 + 1 = 3 is an equation.	An **inequality** is a number sentence that uses < or >. 2 + 1 < 4 is an inequality.

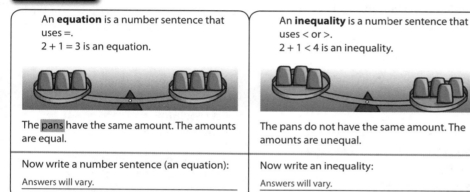

The pans have the same amount. The amounts are equal.	The pans do not have the same amount. The amounts are unequal.
Now write a number sentence (an equation): Answers will vary.	Now write an inequality: Answers will vary.

When you **solve** an equation, you find the value of the variable. The value is called the **solution.**

$a + 5 = 8$ I can solve the equation by finding the value of a. $3 + 5 = 8$ So the solution is $a = 3$.	$9 - b = 2$ I can <u>solve</u> the equation by finding <u>the value of b</u>. $9 - 7 = 2$. So the <u>solution</u> is $b = $ <u>7</u>.

Practice the Words

Directions Write *equation* or *inequality* on the line for problems 1 to 4. Also solve problems 3 and 4. Write a sentence for problem 5 on a separate sheet of paper.

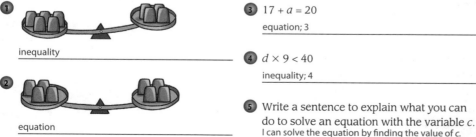

① inequality

② equation

③ $17 + a = 20$

equation; 3

④ $d \times 9 < 40$

inequality; 4

⑤ Write a sentence to explain what you can do to solve an equation with the variable c.
I can solve the equation by finding the value of c.

A Introduce

Read the Lesson Objective aloud with students.

Have students look back over Lesson 1 on page 53 of the student worktext. Instruct them to discuss with a partner what the lesson was about.

- **BP 3** Ask students to share their conversations with the rest of the class. Have them use sentences, if possible, to explain their thinking. Take notes on how well they summarize and appear to understand the ideas in Lesson 1.

Listen for the words students use. When each student finishes speaking, write important math words on the board. Say: *[Anitra] was talking about equations. So I'll write equation on the board. It's a good word to use when you're talking about variables.*

Add the Essential Vocabulary words *inequality, to solve,* and *solution*. Then circle the Essential Vocabulary words on the board. Say: *These words are very important words.* Choose words from the Additional Vocabulary box that you think will be useful. Elicit or provide examples or definitions for all the words on the list.

- **Read each word in turn and have students say them back to you.** Pay particular attention to the word *inequality*. Have students say the word after you, clapping together as they say each syllable *in-e-qual-i-ty*. Be sure they put stress on *-qual*.

Highlighted words and phrases may affect student comprehension.

B | Teach and Learn

Draw students' attention to the box on the top left. Have a volunteer read aloud the first sentence. Remind students that they learned about equations before. Access their knowledge from Lesson 1 by asking students what word is related to *equation* (equal) and how that helps them remember the meaning of *equation*. (An equation has an equals sign.)

- **Help students practice the definition of *equation.*** Read aloud the first sentence several times with students. Then have them read it chorally while you listen. Write the sentence frame *An equation is a ____ that uses =.* on the board and have students identify the missing words (number sentence). Erase the sentence and write two more incomplete sentences: *An ____ is a number sentence that uses =.* and *An equation is a number sentence ____.*

- **Read aloud the sample equation above the picture.** Then have students study the picture. Have them explain to a partner what they see. Call on volunteers to describe the picture. Elicit that the picture in Box 1 shows a balance with two pans and that the pans are in balance. Read aloud the text below the picture.

- **Point out that the picture models the equation 2 + 1 = 3.** Use an actual balance and weights to show what is happening. Say: *The pan on the left has 2 weights and 1 more weight. That is 2 + 1. What does the pan on the right have?* (3 weights) *Are the pans balanced?* (yes) *Are the amounts equal?* (yes) *So this picture shows the number sentence, or equation, 2 + 1 = 3.*

- **Read aloud the direction line.** Encourage students to use a variable in their equation if they want to. Ask them to share their equations with a partner and then with another pair.

Call students' attention to the definition of *inequality* in the box on the right. Point out that *in* is a prefix that means *not.* Say: *The word* equality *means being equal. You can hear the word* equal *in* equality. *So the word* inequality *means being unequal. It means that the two amounts are not the same.*

- **Review the use and meaning of the symbols < and >.** Point out the use of the symbol < in the sample inequality.

- **Walk students through the explanation of inequalities as you did for equations.** Emphasize that the pans in the picture are not balanced, so the picture shows an inequality. Have students write their own inequalities and share them with a partner.

Have students form groups of four. Give each group a pan balance, up to 20 weights, and a copy of Worksheet 14. Have students model, sketch, and write equations and inequalities, using the balance and the weights. Ask the group to work together to set the weights for each number sentence and record the results on their worksheets.

Read aloud the sentences that introduce the words *solve* and *solution* in the middle of the Learn the Words box. Remind students that they have heard the word *solve* used many times to mean *find the answer.* Explain that when you solve an equation, you find the number the variable stands for.

- **Read aloud the information in Box 3 on the left.** Be certain students understand that the *value* of the variable simply means *the number that the variable stands for.* It is not necessary yet to explain how students can find the value of *a* in this equation. They should understand, however, that the value *3* makes the sentence true and is the correct solution. Ask: *Could the value of* a *be 6? Why or why not?* Elicit that 6 is not the value of *a* because 6 + 5 does not equal 8.

- **Have students read the information in Box 4 in the right box.** Then have them fill in the missing words. Ask them to check their answers with a partner.

C | Review and Practice

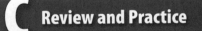

Have students complete the Vocabulary Cards for the words in this module. Have them work with a partner. Ask them to take turns flipping over a card and using the word in a sentence. Encourage them to vary their sentences.

Call students' attention to Practice the Words at the bottom of the page. Have them solve the problems on their own. Observe and assess how students approach the problems.

D | Assess and Intervene

Can students use vocabulary words, based on their work in Practice the Words on page 54? Use the rubric to identify students who need extra support through additional help and the Intervention activity.

☐ Identifies all 4 items as showing equations or inequalities.

☐ Writes a complete sentence, with a few errors, that explains how to solve the equation.

Example of a sentence a student might write: *I solve the equation when find what is real number for* c.

Advanced

☐ Identifies all 4 items as showing equations or inequalities.

☐ Writes a clear sentence with few, if any, errors that describes how to solve the equation.

Example of a sentence a student might write: *I can solve the equation if I find what number* c *stand for.*

INTERVENTION 5 minutes

Students who have trouble with this assessment are likely confused about what equations are and aren't. Have students sketch a horizontal line and write *equation* on it. Say: *An equation is balanced. Everything is equal.* Then sketch a diagonal line that rises and another that falls. Write *inequality* on both. Say: *An inequality is unbalanced. It is not equal.* Give students additional examples of equations (number sentences) and inequalities and use these drawings as they work.

Use More Language

Objective Use *let* n *equal* _____ and other phrases to write, solve, and check equations.

---

30 minutes

Teach this lesson:
- **After** students complete the work on equations in their grade-level math textbooks
- **Before** students complete the activities on page 55 of the student worktext

You need these materials:
- Transparency 28
- chart paper

EXTENSION AND ENRICHMENT 15 minutes

Have students work in small groups. Ask them to write a skit that describes how to solve the equation $5 \times t = 40$. Encourage them to make the skit fun as well as informative. Have groups act out their skits for the class. If possible, record the skits on a camcorder and play them later for the class.

Use More Language

LESSON **3**

Objective Use *let* n *equal* _____ and other phrases to write, solve, and check equations.

Learn the Language

Ramón had 12 pencils. Then he gave some pencils away.

Now he has 4 pencils. How many pencils did he give away?

Let *n* equal the number of pencils Ramón gave away.

I can write an equation. 12 − n = 4

I think the solution is 8.

To check the solution, replace *n* with 8. Then subtract. 12 minus 8 *does* equal 4. So the solution is *n* = 8.

Practice the Language

Directions In problems 1 to 4, draw a line to connect the sentence with the correct word problem. Then write a sentence for problem 5.

1. Let *n* equal the number of red birds Jorge saw.

2. Let *n* equal the number of blue birds Jorge saw.

3. Check your answer by replacing *n* with 12.

4. Check your answer by substituting 20 for *n*.

Jorge saw 13 red birds and some blue birds. He saw 25 birds in all. How many blue birds did he see?

Jorge saw some red birds. He saw 12 blue birds. He saw 32 birds in all. How many red birds did he see?

5. Write a sentence that begins *Let* n *equal* . . . for this word problem: Chizuko ate 16 grapes. She ate twice as many grapes as Lana. How many grapes did Lana eat?

Let *n* equal the number of grapes Lana ate. _____

_____

Highlighted words and phrases may affect student comprehension.

A | Introduce

Write the expression *let* n *equal* ____ on the board and read it aloud. Explain that the blank refers to an amount. Say: *This sentence could be* Let *n* equal the number of wheels on a car, *or* Let *n* equal the number of students in our school, *or any other amount.*

- **Ask if students remember seeing this phrase in their math textbooks.** If students do, have them tell what they know about it. Then explain that the phrase is often used when people are talking about variables.

Read aloud the Lesson Objective with students. Point out the phrase *let* n *equal* ____. Explain that students will learn how to use this phrase and others like it as they work through the lesson.

B | Teach and Learn

Call students' attention to the Learn the Language box on page 55 of the student worktext. Point out the picture of the boy on the left. Ask students what the boy is holding (pencils) and how many pencils he has. (12) Have a volunteer read aloud the text next to the picture.

Move on to the box on the right. Ask how many pencils Ramon is holding. (4) Read aloud the text next to the picture. Emphasize the question: *How many pencils did he give away?*

BP 3 Have students practice describing the scenario. Have them tell a partner what happened first, next, and last. (First, Ramon had 12 pencils; next, he gave some away; last, he had 4 pencils.) Circulate through the room, listening carefully to students' descriptions and offering help as needed.

Use the following Think Aloud to guide students through the steps they will use to solve the problem.

Think Aloud

Say: *I know how many pencils Ramon had at the beginning. He had 12 pencils at the beginning. And I know how many he has now. What do I need to know?* Elicit that you need to know how many pencils he gave away.

Call students' attention to the statement under the first two pictures in the student worktext. Write on the board: *Let* n *equal the number of pencils.* Next to it, write: *I need to know how many pencils Ramon gave away. I'll call this number* n *until I figure out what it is.*

Read both sentences aloud. Place an equals sign between them. Say: *These say the same thing. When you say, "Let* n *equal the number of pencils," you are saying, "I need to know how many pencils. I don't know that number yet. So I'll call it* n *for now."*

Say: *Next, I'll write an equation.* Have students together read aloud the thought bubble on the bottom left of the Learn the Language box.

Walk students through the equation by saying: *The number 12 tells how many pencils there were at first. Next comes a minus sign because Ramon gave some pencils away. Then I write* n *to show that I don't know how many he gave away. Last comes an equals sign and the number he has left, which is 4.* Review the parts of the equation piece by piece, this time having students explain the meaning of each term.

Say: *Next, I have to decide what* n *is. Let's see . . . The girl in the picture thinks it's 8. She thinks the value of the variable is _____.* Pause and let students complete the sentence with 8. Explain that 8 makes sense because it is less than 12.

Explain that you can now check your answer. Read aloud the sentence beginning *To check the solution* in the student

worktext. Emphasize the expression *replace* n *with 8.* Say: *This means try using 8 instead of* n. Write 12 − n = 8 on the board; erase n and write 8 instead. Say: *I took* n *away, and I wrote 8 instead. I replaced* n *with 8.* Tell students that they can also use the expression *substitute _____ for* n. Note that the position of n changes in these two expressions: you replace n with 8, or you substitute 8 for n.

Ask students if 12 − 8 is equal to 4. Elicit that it is. Explain that you checked your answer and found that it was correct. Wrap up by explaining that the phrases *let* n *equal _____* and *replace* n *with _____* are very useful and very common in this kind of math.

Have students look back at the example in their student worktexts. Ask them if they should use the expression *let* n *equal _____* for an amount they know or for an amount they do not know. Draw out that they should use this expression for an unknown amount.

BP 3 **Display Transparency 28.** Read the problem aloud. Then guide the whole group through the steps that follow, asking them to fill in the blanks and solve the problem. Emphasize the correct use of the phrases *let* n *equal _____, substitute _____ for* n, *and replace* n *with _____.*

C Review and Practice

Write the following problem on the board: *Jeff has 16 thick markers and some thin markers. He has 20 markers in all.* Ask pairs to discuss what information they know and what information the problem does not tell them. Elicit that the problem does not tell how many thin markers Jeff has. Explain that students could start solving this problem by writing: *Let* n *equal the number of thin markers Jeff has.* Repeat with other problems if needed.

Read aloud the directions for Practice the Language at the bottom of page 55. Explain that some of the statements go with the first problem and that others go with the second problem. Have students solve the problems independently. Go over the answers when all students are finished.

D Assess and Intervene

Can students use phrases such as *let* n *equal _____* appropriately, judging by their work in Practice the Language on page 55? Use the rubric to identify students who need extra support through additional help and the Intervention activity.

Intermediate

☐ Correctly associates at least 3 statements with the correct problem.

☐ Writes a sentence, which may contain some errors, associating n with the number of grapes Lana ate.

Example of a sentence a student might write: *Let* n *equal how many grape Lana eating.*

Advanced

☐ Correctly associates all statements with the correct problem.

☐ Writes a sentence, with few or no errors, associating n with the number of grapes Lana ate.

Example of a sentence a student might write: *Let* n *equal the number of grapes Lana eat.*

INTERVENTION 5 minutes

Help students identify which amounts in problems are known and which are not known. Write a simple problem on chart paper, such as *There are 7 boys playing ball. There are some girls playing ball, too. 18 children in all are playing ball.* Have students locate amounts that they know and circle them in green (7 boys; 18 children). Have them find amounts they do not know and circle them in red (some girls). Write *let* n *equal _____* in red and draw a line from that to the unknown information—the number of girls who are playing ball. Repeat with other problems if needed.

Solve Math Problems

Objective Write equations to help solve word problems.

---

30 minutes

Teach this lesson:
- **After** students complete the material on equations and variables in their grade-level math texts
- **Before** students complete the activities on page 56 of the student worktext

You need these materials:
- sticky notes
- beanbag
- counters or strips of paper

LESSON
4

Solve Math Problems

Objective Write equations to help solve word problems.

Learn to Solve Problems

> **Problem** Asok won 20 ribbons for running races. He has 4 walls in his room. He put an equal number of ribbons on each wall. How many ribbons did Asok hang on each wall?

	Think	Write
Step 1:	Read the problem. Underline the question. Circle the facts.	The question is: How many ribbons did Asok hang on each wall?
Step 2:	Find the information you need to know. Let *n* stand for this number.	I don't know how many ribbons are on each wall. So I'll let n equal the number of ribbons on each wall.
Step 3:	Write an equation using *n*.	There are 4 walls. Each wall has n ribbons. There are 20 ribbons in all. My equation is $4 \times n = 20$.
Step 4:	Solve the equation. Write a sentence to show the answer.	$20 \div 4 = 5$. So n = 5. Asok hung 5 ribbons on each wall.

Practice Solving Math Problems

Directions Follow the steps above to solve problems 1 to 3 below. Write an equation to solve each problem. Then write the answer to problem 4 in a complete sentence. Use a separate sheet of paper.

1. Marta had 38 CDs on her shelf. She put some of them in a box. There were still 24 CDs left on the shelf. How many CDs did Marta put in the box? Possible equation: $38 - c = 24; c = 14$

2. Nico played 12 games at the fair. That was three times as many games as Nico's brother played. How many games did Nico's brother play at the fair? Possible equation: $g \times 3 = 12; g = 4$

3. Won Li is 6 inches taller than Saari. Saari is 54 inches tall. How tall is Won Li? Possible equation: $t - 6 = 54; t = 60$

4. How did you write the equation for problem 3? Explain in a complete sentence. Answers will vary.

A Introduce

Read aloud the Lesson Objective with students. Briefly review the meaning of the word *equation*. Point out again the *equa-* beginning to the word and remind students that *equa-* and *equi-* come from the same root as *equal*.

- **Write the word *equilateral* on the board.** Read it aloud and underline the *equi-* prefix. Say: *If a shape is equilateral, all the sides are _____.* Pause and allow students to complete the sentence with *equal* or *the same*. Continue with *equator* (an imaginary line dividing the world into two parts that are equal), *inequality* (a number sentence where the two sides are not equal), and *equinox* (a time of year when day and night are of equal length).

Explain that this lesson will give students more practice in writing and solving equations.

B Teach and Learn

Read aloud the problem at the top of the Learn to Solve Problems box on page 56 of the student worktext.

Ask a series of basic comprehension questions to check students' understanding. *What did Asok win?* (ribbons) *How many did he win?* (20) *What did he want to do with them?* (hang them on his walls) *How many walls*

Highlighted words and phrases may affect student comprehension.

did he have? (4) Did he want to put an equal number of ribbons on each wall or a different number on each wall? (an equal number)

Invite students to visualize Asok's room and his ribbons. Ask them to consider what color the ribbons are, if the walls are high or low, what else might already be on the walls, and other similar questions. Have students share their ideas with a partner. Explain that visualizing a word problem can often help students solve it.

Call students' attention to the four steps in the Learn to Solve Problems box.

Have a student read the first step aloud. Point out that the question has been underlined and that the facts have been circled. Emphasize that the part about equal numbers on each wall counts as a fact. Say: *To solve this problem, you need to know that each wall has an equal number of ribbons. So you need to circle that fact.*

Continue to the second step. Have a volunteer read it aloud. Say: *This problem uses an amount that I don't know. I don't know how many ribbons Asok will put on each wall.* Point out that you can use a variable to stand for the amount you don't know. Explain that you can use any letter to stand for a variable, but that *n* is often used by mathematicians and by math textbooks.

- **Draw students' attention to the right side of the page and the responses to the second step.** Have students read that information aloud. Emphasize the *let* n *equal* ____ construction and remind students that they have already learned this phrase.

Move on to the third step and read it aloud. Then ask students to close their student worktexts. Have them discuss with a partner if the equation should use addition, subtraction, multiplication, or division. Write the original problem on the board to assist students. Remind them that they may find it helpful to think of the visual picture they discussed earlier in the lesson.

Have pairs write the operation sign they choose on a sticky note (+ for addition, and so on). Ask them to post the notes on the board and stand by them.

- **Review the sticky notes with students.** Ask which operation they chose most/least frequently. Then ask volunteers to explain their choices. Encourage them to use complete sentences.

Have students return to Step 3 in their student worktexts. Read aloud the corresponding statements on the right side of the page. Stress that each wall has *n* ribbons. Say: *The word* each *tells me there are equal groups, so I either multiply or divide. I can use inverse operations to write either a multiplication or a division sentence. Point out that each wall has the same number of ribbons, so it makes sense to use multiplication.*

- **Break down the equation with students as you did with the pencils problem in Lesson 3.** Say: *The 4 tells you* ____ . Have students complete the sentence with *the number of walls in Asok's room*. Continue with the multiplication sign, the variable *n*, the equals sign, and the number *20*. Be sure students understand each piece of the equation.

Continue with the last step. Read it aloud and have volunteers read the responses in the right column. Review why students should use division to find the value of *n* (because it is the inverse operation for multiplication). Point out that the answer to the question, like other responses in carrying out the steps, is a complete sentence.

BP 3 Ask what questions students have about the steps. Help them try to answer each other's questions.

Review and Practice

Give students a chance to read through the steps in the Learn to Solve Problems box by themselves. Say that they will play a game that will give them a chance to practice these steps and explain them to their classmates.

Call out the name of a student. Then toss a beanbag to that student and say: *First step!* Have the student describe the first step listed in the Learn to Solve Problems box. Have the student try to summarize as much of the step as possible in his or her own words, but permit the student to ask a partner, if needed. Say: *[Jean-Claude] remembered that the first step was to read the problem, underline the question, and circle the facts.*

Have the student with the beanbag choose another student and toss the beanbag to that student. Ask that student to explain the second step. Continue until all four steps have been described. Then

challenge the class to try it again, this time relying less on the worktext. Repeat until each student has had at least one turn with the beanbag.

Read aloud the directions to Practice Solving Math Problems on page 56. Have students solve these problems on their own. Remind them to use complete sentences for the answers to each step.

D Assess and Intervene

Can students write equations to solve word problems, based on Practice Solving Math Problems on page 56? Use the rubric to identify students who need extra support through additional help and the intervention activity.

Intermediate

- ☐ Successfully writes and solves at least 2 equations.
- ☐ Writes answers to steps in complete sentences with a few errors that do not interfere with meaning.

Advanced

- ☐ Successfully writes and solves all 4 equations.
- ☐ Writes answers to steps in complete sentences with no more than one or two errors to explain how the equation was written.

INTERVENTION 5 minutes

If students have trouble solving these word problems, they may be helped by drawing pictures. Have students draw a picture of the scenario described in the sample problem, which they visualized earlier in the lesson. Ask them to draw Asok's room, sketching each of the four walls. Then ask them to use counters or strips of paper to represent each of the 20 ribbons. Have them distribute the objects one by one to demonstrate that there will be 5 ribbons on each wall. Then show how this process is equivalent to writing the algebraic equation $4 \times n = 5$. Repeat with other examples from students' grade-level textbooks, if necessary.

Understand the Main Idea

Objective Write a rule and an equation to show a pattern.

30 minutes

Teach this lesson:
- **Before** introducing the lessons on patterns and functions in students' grade-level math textbooks
- **Before** students complete the activities on page 57 of the student worktext

You need these materials:
- food packages that contain multiple items, such as a box of cereal bars or a pack of juice boxes
- calculators
- centimeter cubes

Prerequisite Background Knowledge
- Concepts of pattern, equation, and variable

BP 6 ELL BEST PRACTICE #6:
Hands-On Actvities

For English language learners hands-on activities are a way to learn academic concepts and language in ways that are not affected by how much English they understand. As students are trying to grasp the number relationships demonstrated by functions, provide pictures and objects that are examples of daily life. Have students count to find that each toy car has four wheels, each person has two eyes, each chair has four legs, and so on.

Throughout this module, when you see **BP 6**, this is an example of a hands-on activity.

Module 15: Patterns and Functions

Understand the Main Idea

Objective Write a rule and an equation to show a pattern.

LESSON
1

Learn the Main Idea

My name is Roberto. I am 3 years older than my sister Elena.

Each package has six stickers. Two packages have 12 stickers. Show the pattern in a table.
p = package, s = stickers

Input (p)	1	2	3
Output (s)	6	12	18

Rule: Multiply the number in the Input row by 6.
What is the Output number?
Words: packages × 6 = stickers
Equation: $p \times 6 = s$

Show the pattern of ages in a table.
e = Elena's age, r = Roberto's age

Input (e)	2	4	6	10	12
Output (r)	5	7	9	13	15

Rule: Add 3 to the number in the Input row.
What is the Output number?
Words: Elena's age + 3 = Roberto's age
Equation: $e + 3 = r$

MAIN IDEA You can write rules for patterns and write equations to show the rules.

Practice Applying the Main Idea

Directions For each table below, fill in the rule and write an equation that shows the rule. Answer the last question using complete sentences.

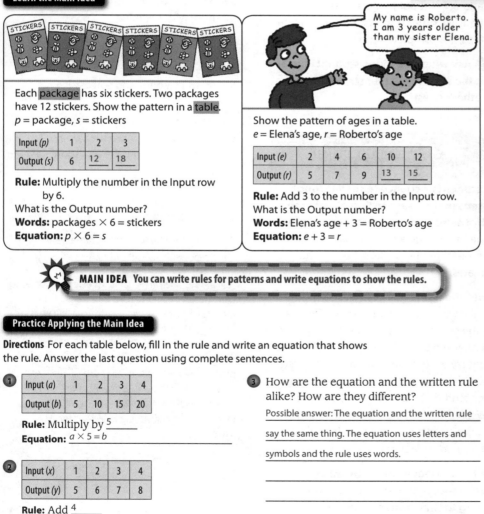

①
Input (a)	1	2	3	4
Output (b)	5	10	15	20

Rule: Multiply by 5
Equation: $a \times 5 = b$

②
Input (x)	1	2	3	4
Output (y)	5	6	7	8

Rule: Add 4
Equation: $x + 4 = y$

③ How are the equation and the written rule alike? How are they different?
Possible answer: The equation and the written rule say the same thing. The equation uses letters and symbols and the rule uses words.

Patterns and Functions • 57

A Introduce

Read aloud the Lesson Objective with students.

Help students activate their background knowledge. Ask: *What kinds of food have you seen at the grocery store that comes in packages? How many items are in a package? When each package has the same number of items, we can find out how many are in 2 packages, 5 packages, or even 10 packages.*

BP 6 Show students examples of multi-pack products from the grocery store. Hold up one package, and tell students the number of items that it holds. Then say: *Suppose that I buy 2 packages. How many items are in 2 packages? How many items are in 3 packages?* Ask students to explain to a partner how they found out the number of items in more than one package.

Ask students to look at the first illustration on page 57. Have them discuss with their partners what is in the package, how many are in each package, and how many packages there are.

Review with the class the concepts of equations and patterns. Ask students for examples of equations, and list a few responses on the board. Then write *2, 8, 14, 20, . . .* on the board. Say: *These numbers follow a pattern.*

Highlighted words and phrases may affect student comprehension.

Ask: *What is the rule for the pattern?* (add 6) Elicit other examples of patterns and rules.

Read aloud the Main Idea with students. Explain that they will learn how to write an equation to go with a pattern.

B Teach and Learn

Make a five-column, two-row table on the board, and label the rows *Input* and *Output*. Above the table, write: *Rule: Multiply by 5.* Have students work in groups of four. Have one student in each group copy the table on a sheet of paper. Give each small group of students a calculator.

Write *2* as the first input number in the table. Say: *We are going to make a pattern using the rule "Multiply by 5."* Model how to multiply by 5 on the calculator. Have the groups work along with you. Say: *We put a number in the calculator, applied a rule, and a different number came out. What was the rule?* (multiply by 5)

Explain that a table can be used to record the numbers that go in the calculator and the numbers that come out. If necessary, review the words *column* and *row* and show students that the related input and output numbers are in the same column.

BP 6 Have small groups continue with other input numbers until the table is filled in. Ask for volunteers to come to the board and fill in the table.

Direct students' attention to the first example on page 57, on the left. Ask them to look at the illustration. Chorally read the first two sentences with students. Have them look at the table to see how many stickers are in the different packages. Ask: *How do we find out what the rule is?* Give groups time to think and come up with an answer. Say: *Because there are 6 stickers in each package, the rule is to multiply by 6. First, choose a number in the Input row. Then, multiply that number by 6. Finally, write the result in the Output row.* Have volunteers describe the remaining input and output numbers in the table.

Discuss the relationship between the written rule and the equation. Write *packages* $\times$ *6 = stickers* and *p* $\times$ *6 = s* on the board. As you point to each element in the equation say: *The number of packages,* p, *times 6 equals the number of stickers,* s. Explain that

the equation is a way to express this idea in a math sentence.

Read the text below the first picture on page 57. Point out that the words and the rule are the same as what you just wrote on the board.

C Review and Practice

Tell students that patterns can use any operations. Read the text in the speech bubble on page 57, on the right. Explain that as the brother and sister get older, both their ages will change, but Roberto will always be three years older than Elena.

Refer students to the table. Point out that the numbers in the input row show Elena's age and the numbers in the output row show Roberto's age. Say: *To find Roberto's age, add 3 years to Elena's age. The rule used to make the pattern is add 3.*

Write the words *Elena's age + 3 = Roberto's age* on the board. Ask students to think of a way to write it as an equation. Then write *e + 3 = r.* Ask students to substitute the *e* and *r* number pairs from the table into the equation to show how the equation is used to make the chart. (2 + 3 = 5, etc.)

Divide the class into pairs. Ask pairs to find Roberto's age when Elena is 10 and 12. Then have partners discuss the relationship in their ages using the following language: *When Elena is _____ years old, Roberto is _____ years old.*

Write the following table on the board:

Rule:

Equation:

Input (*d*)	4	5	6	7
Output (*c*)	8	10	?	?

BP 6 Have pairs decide what the rule is, write an equation for the rule, and complete the table. Ask volunteers to share the rule and the equation with the class and write them on the board. (multiply by 2; *d* $\times$ 2 = *c*)

Read the directions for Practice Applying the Main Idea. Point out that this activity is similar to what they just did. Have students complete the activity individually.

Check students' work. Share and discuss students' answers, and assist with the last question as necessary.

D Assess and Intervene

Do all students understand how to write equations and rules to show patterns based on Practice Applying the Main Idea on page 57? Use the rubric to identify students who need extra support through additional help and the Intervention activity.

Intermediate

☐ Correctly completes one table, one rule, and one equation.

☐ Comparison of rule and equation may be vague, but the idea that both mean the same is evident.

Example of a sentence a student might write: *Rule has words, equation letters, same thing.*

Advanced

☐ Correctly completes both tables, both rules, and both equations.

☐ Comparison of rule and equation includes a clear statement that both say the same thing in different ways.

Example of an answer a student might write: *Rule use words, equation use symbols. Both say same thing.*

INTERVENTION 5 minutes

BP 6 If students are having difficulty understanding how to write an equation to show rules, use centimeter cubes to demonstrate the pattern and the rule. Distribute centimeter cubes to pairs of students. Say: *Make a chain of 5 cubes. One chain has 5 cubes.* Have partners continue to add chains of 5 cubes until they have 6 chains. Have pairs draw and complete a table to record the number of chains and the total number of cubes. (6; 30) Encourage them to multiply to find the total and then verify by counting. Guide them to write a rule and an equation.

Learn the Vocabulary

Objective Talk and write about function tables using the vocabulary words.

30 minutes

Teach this lesson:
- **Before** introducing lessons on patterns and functions in students' grade-level math textbooks
- **Before** students complete the activities on page 58 of the student worktext

You need these materials:
- tape measure
- masking tape
- sticky notes

Lesson Vocabulary

Essential Vocabulary
function table (input/output table)
rule   to extend

Additional Vocabulary
pattern*   value*   row
input   output   pair

* - Terms that have Vocabulary Cards.

LESSON
2

Learn the Vocabulary

Objective Talk and write about function tables using the vocabulary words.

Learn the Words

Word/Phrase	Definition	Example
function table	a table that shows pairs of related numbers; the first number is the input, and the second number is the output	**Rule: Add 8** Input: 1, 2, 3, 4 Output: 9, 10, 11, 12
rule	an instruction that tells you what to do	The **rule** for the **function table** is: add 8 to the input.
to extend	to make something longer	I can **extend** the function table by adding more numbers.

Example table detail:

Input	1	2	3	4
Output	9	10	11	12

Practice the Words

Directions Use the words in the box on the right to fill in the blanks in the table on the left. You will use some words several times. Then fill in the blanks to complete the sentences. Answer the last question in a complete sentence.

Rule _____ : Subtract 5
Equation: input _____ − 5 = output _____

Input	10	20	30	40	50	60	70	80
Output	5	15	25	35	45	55	65	75

Word box:

extend	function table
input	output rule

1. This function table _____ follows a rule _____.

2. The rule _____ tells me to subtract 5 from the input _____.

3. If I follow the rule _____, I'll find the output _____.

4. I can extend _____ the table by adding more input _____ and output _____ numbers.

5. Use the vocabulary words to explain how to extend the function table. Then add numbers to extend the table above.
   Possible answer: I can add new input numbers. Then I can use the rule to find the new output numbers.

A Introduce

Read aloud the Lesson Objective with students. Ask students to look at page 57 in the student worktext. Ask: *What two things do you need to make a table?* Elicit answers, making sure that students remember that tables have columns and rows. Remind students of the difference between a math table and the piece of furniture. Point out that tables are a way of displaying data. Tell students they will learn about the kind of data that is included in a function table.

B Teach and Learn

Orally introduce the Essential Vocabulary. Say each word or phrase, and have students locate it on page 58. Model the pronunciation, and have students repeat after you.

Draw a 2 × 6 table on the board. Label the rows *Input* and *Output.* Above the table write: *Rule: Subtract 3.* Say: *A function table shows the relationship between pairs of numbers. It shows how they work together.* Point to the word *input* and say: *The first number in the relationship is the input number. We write an input number and then use the rule. The rule tells us what to do with the input number. The result is the output number.* Point out that many function tables are horizontal, like this one, but sometimes they are vertical. When they are vertical, the columns show the input and output numbers.

Highlighted words and phrases may affect student comprehension.

Write 5 as the first input number. Ask: *What is the rule? What do we do next?* (subtract 3 from 5) *What is the output?* (2) *Where do I write the 2?* (in the output row below the 5)

BP 6 Hold up a tape measure. Say: *I can pull out, or extend, the tape measure. When I extend the tape measure, it becomes longer. I can also extend the function table. To extend the function table, I add more numbers.* Pass the tape measure around and have students repeat: *I extend the tape measure.*

Tell students that, together, you will extend the function table on the board. Ask volunteers to come to the board, write an input number, use the rule with that number, and then write the output. Continue until the table is filled in. Show how to write an equation to match the rule. Use *a* as the variable for the input number and *b* for the output number and write: *Rule: Subtract 3. Equation:* $a - 3 = b$

Read the words/phrases, definitions, and examples on page 58 with students. Then model how to analyze the function table on page 58 of the student worktext by thinking aloud:

Think Aloud

Point to the function table on page 58. Say: *I look at the first row of the table. This row is labeled* Input. Point to the word *Input*, and say: *All of the numbers in this row are input numbers. Next, I read the rule.* Point to the rule. Say: *The rule tells me to add 8. This means that I add 8 to each input number. I look at each pair of numbers in the table. The first pair is 1 and 9. 1 is the input number, so I will use the rule with 1. The rule tells me to add 8. 1 + 8 is 9. So, when the input is 1, the output is 9.*

Continue in a similar manner with the other number pairs in the table.

Ask students to examine all input and output numbers in the table. Have a volunteer describe their relationship. Guide students to see that the output number is equal to the input number plus 8. Remind them that the rule is add 8.

Now tell students that they will extend the table. Ask: *What can we do to extend the table?* (add new input numbers, apply the rule, and write the output numbers)

Have students work in small groups. Have them take turns adding a new input number, applying the rule, and finding the output number. Then have students write an equation to express what they did. Ask them to use the vocabulary words as they speak.

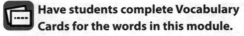 **Have students complete Vocabulary Cards for the words in this module.**

C Review and Practice

BP 6 Divide the class into pairs. Explain that they are going to make a function table with three input numbers. Then they are going to extend their tables. Ask: *How will you extend the function table?* (by adding input numbers and finding output numbers) Have each pair use masking tape on a desk to form the rows and columns of a function table.

- **Ask partners to write *Input* and *Output* on two separate sticky notes.** Have them place the notes in the appropriate rows and columns of the table. Have partners work together to decide on a rule to use. Then they write that rule on a sticky note.

- **One student in the pair writes a number on a sticky note and says to the partner:** *The input is ____. Use the rule to find the output.* The other partner tells how to use the rule and find the output. He or she writes the output number on a sticky note and places it in the correct spot in the table.

- **Partners alternate roles and continue in this manner until their tables contain four to five number pairs.** Finally, they write an equation to go with the rule.

Have pairs use lesson vocabulary to describe their function tables to the class.

Introduce the Practice the Words activity in the student worktext. Make sure students understand the directions. Then have students complete the activity individually. Check students' work.

D Assess and Intervene

Can every student write about function tables using the appropriate vocabulary words based on Practice the Words on page 58? Use the rubric to identify students who need extra support through additional help and the Intervention activity.

Intermediate

- [ ] Writes at least 4 of 5 labels on the table correctly and completes at least 2 extended columns correctly.
- [ ] At least 3 sentences are completed with the appropriate vocabulary words.
- [ ] Explanation of how to extend the table includes the concept of adding more input and output numbers, but may not be clear and complete.

  Example of a sentence a student might write: *Use rule, write numbers, input and output.*

Advanced

- [ ] Writes all labels on the table correctly, and completes 3 extended columns correctly.
- [ ] All 4 sentences are completed with the appropriate vocabulary words.
- [ ] The explanation clearly shows an understanding of how to use the rule to extend the table.

  Example of sentences a student might write: *I write new input number. I use rule. I find new output number.*

INTERVENTION   5 minutes

If students are having difficulty using the correct vocabulary in sentences, have them copy the sentences with the blanks. Then have them write the Essential Vocabulary from the Learn the Words box on sticky notes, read a sentence, and stick the words where they think they should go. Then have them read the sentence aloud and ask themselves if it makes sense. If it does not, have them use another sticky note and try again.

Use More Language

Objective Describe how to extend a function table using *when* and *if*.

---

30 minutes

Teach this lesson:
• **After** lessons on patterns and functions in students' grade-level math textbooks
• **Before** students complete the activities on page 59 of the student worktext

You need these materials:
• Transparency 29
• blank paper

Use More Language

LESSON
3

Objective Describe how to extend a function table using *when* and *if*.

Learn the Language

I made this table. The rule is add 10 to the input. **When** the input is 1, the output is 11. **When** the input is 3, the output is 13.

If I extend the table, I put a new number in the input column. Then I add 10 to the input numbers. **If** the input is 7, the output is 17. **If** the input is 9, the output is 19.

Rule: Add 10

Input	1	3	5	7	9
Output	11	13	15	17	19

When the input is _____, the output is _____.   If the input is _____, the output is _____.

Practice the Language

Directions Write sentences with *when* to describe the inputs and outputs for items 1 to 3 below. In items 4 and 5, use 20 and 25 as new input numbers to extend the table. Then write sentences with *if* to describe the new output numbers. Then answer the last question using a complete sentence.

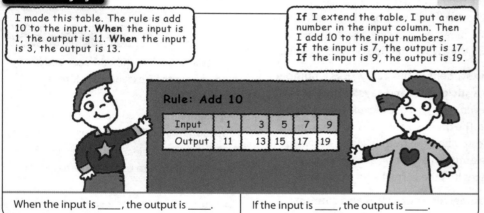

Rule: Subtract 3
Equation: $a - 3 = b$

	①	②	③	④	⑤
Input (a)	5	10	15	20	25
Output (b)	2	7	12	17	22

① When . . . the input is 5, the output is 2.

② When . . . the input is 10, the output is 7.

③ When . . . the input is 15, the output is 12.

④ If . . . the input is 20, the output is 17.

⑤ If . . . the input is 25, the output is 22.

⑥ Does the rule change when you extend the table? Explain why or why not.

Possible answer: The rule doesn't change because it has to be the same for the whole table.

Patterns and Functions • 59

A Introduce

Read the Lesson Objective aloud. Tell students that they are going to learn how to desribe a function table.

Review uses of *if* and *when*. Although these words are often used interchangeably, explain that *when* usually means that the action has been done before or is done on a regular basis. Say: *When I jump into the pool, I get wet. This is something I have done before, so I use the word* when.

• **Tell students that *if* can mean that the action has not been done or is not done regularly.** Say: *If I jump into the pool, I will get wet. Maybe I have done this before, and maybe I haven't. But I know that I will get wet.*

• **Point out that both *if* and *when* can be used to describe something that happens as a result of an action.** Invite students to share some of their own *if* and *when* situations.

B Teach and Learn

Make a list on the board of a variety of actions with which students are familiar. The following are some examples: *exercise, go to bed, go to the beach, walk to school, do homework, buy a game, play with my friends.*

Highlighted words and phrases may affect student comprehension.

- **Above the list of actions, write the words *if* and *when*.** Remind students that *when* often indicates that the action is something they have done before or do regularly. Say: *I try to exercise every morning. When I exercise, I feel great. If I don't exercise in the morning, I feel tired for the rest of the day.*

- **Use the list of actions to develop more *if* and *when* statements.** Ask: *What happens when you go to bed late?* Elicit responses from two or three students using *when*. (When I go to bed late, I am tired in the morning.)

- **Explain that you can ask the same question using the word *if*.** Ask: *What happens if you go to bed late?* Elicit a few responses using *if*.

- **Continue asking questions in this manner.** Have students answer with *if* and *when* statements.

- **Tell students that *if* and *when* statements can be used to describe what happens in a function table.**

Read through the example on page 59 of the student worktext. Have student volunteers read the speech bubbles. Ask: *When the input is 3, what is the output? If the input is 7, what is the output?* Elicit several responses until students understand how to use *if* and *when* statements.

Write on the board the function table below. Include the following numbers:

Rule: Subtract 5							
Input	10	20	30	40			
Output	5	15	25	35			

Model for students how to use *if* and *when* statements to extend the table by thinking aloud.

Think Aloud

Say: *The function table already has some numbers in it. I will look at the input numbers and see how they relate to the output numbers. The rule says subtract 5, so that means that I have to subtract 5 from each input number to find the output number.*

Write this sentence frame about the function table on the board, and model completing it: *When the input is____, the output is____.*

BP 6 Divide the class into small groups. Distribute blank paper. Ask students to copy the function table on the board. As you point to each number pair, ask students to complete the sentence frame on the board chorally with their group. Then have them complete the table.

Model how to extend the table by thinking aloud.

Think Aloud

Say: *I can extend the table by adding more numbers. I'll use 50 as the next input.* Write *50* in the function table and say: *If I subtract 5 from 50, I get 45.* Write *45* in the function table and say: *If the input is 50, the output is 45.*

Write the following sentence frame on the board: *If the input is____, the output is____.* Model completing it as you point to the number pair 50 and 45.

Ask the small groups to continue with other input numbers until the table is filled in. Then ask them to use the sentence frame on the board to describe what they just did.

C Review and Practice

Review the use of *if* and *when* statements in the Learn the Language activity. This time, instead of asking questions, just provide an input number and have students answer with an appropriate *if* or *when* statement.

Show Transparency 29. Divide the class into pairs to practice using the language and to review *input, output, rule,* and *equation.* Chorally read the directions on the transparency with students. Give pairs blank paper to copy and extend the function table.

- **BP 6 Ask partners to start out by reading the rule together.** Then one student says: *When the input is 1, the output is 5.* The partner follows with a statement for the next input. Partners alternate until they have named all of the inputs and outputs in the table.

- **Have partners use the sentence frames on the transparency to describe how to extend the function table using *when* and *if*.** Have partners extend the tables to include an additional four pairs of numbers. Have them take turns describing the function table using the sentence frames.

- After students have had ample time to practice the oral language, have them work individually to complete the Practice the Language activity. Circulate, and assess students as they do the activity.

D Assess and Intervene

How well can students write *if* and *when* statements to describe function tables based on Practice the Language on page 59? Use the rubric to identify students who need extra support through additional help and the Intervention activity.

Intermediate

☐ Uses the sentence frames to write correct *when* and *if* sentences for all input numbers.

☐ The answer to question 6 shows an understanding that the rule does not change, but it may not be clear about why.

Example of a sentence a student might write: *Rule don't change.*

Advanced

☐ Writes complete sentences in own words for all input numbers, with minimal errors.

Example of a sentence a student might write: *When input is 10, output is 7.*

☐ The answer to question 6 shows an understanding that the rule does not change, and clearly explains why.

Example of a sentence a student might write: *Rule doesn't change because has to be same.*

INTERVENTION   5 minutes

If students are having trouble discriminating between the input and output in function tables, introduce the In/Out Box. Have students draw the following on a sheet of paper:

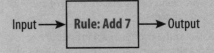

Input ⟶ **Rule: Add 7** ⟶ Output

Explain that a number goes into the box and comes out as a different number. Provide several examples, and write the input and output numbers under the appropriate word.

Solve Math Problems

Objective Make a function table to solve a problem.

---

30 minutes

Teach this lesson:
- **After** lessons on patterns and functions in students' grade-level math textbooks
- **Before** students complete the activities on page 60 of the student worktext

You need these materials:
- Transparency 30
- sticky notes
- Worksheet 15 (one copy per student)

Solve Math Problems

Objective Make a function table to help solve a problem.

Learn to Solve Problems

Problem Dan spends 2 hours each day doing homework. How many hours does he spend doing homework in 2 days? In 3 days? In 4 days?

	Think	Write
Step 1:	Read the problem. Underline the questions. What do you have to find out?	I have to find out the total hours Dan spends doing homework in 2, 3, and 4 days.
Step 2:	Make a function table. Find the input and output.	I use the number of days to find the number of hours. Input = days (d) Output = hours (h)

Days (d)	1	2	3	4
Hours (h)	2	?	?	?

	Think	Write
Step 3:	Circle the facts. Write the rule. Write the equation.	Rule: Multiply by 2 Equation: $d \times 2 = h$
Step 4:	Use the rule to fill in the unknown numbers in the table. Answer the questions in the problem.	

Days (d)	1	2	3	4
Hours (h)	2	4	6	8

He spends 4 hours in 2 days, 3 hours in 6 days, and 8 hours in 4 days.

Practice Solving Math Problems

Directions Follow steps 1 to 4 above to solve the word problems below. Solve the problems on a separate sheet of paper. Write the answers in a complete sentence.

1. Nicolas and 2 friends earn money. They always share the money they earn equally. How much does each boy get if they earn $6? $9? $15? Each boy gets $2 if they earn $6, $3 if they earn $9, and $5 if they earn $15.

2. Joe is 5 years younger than his brother Luis. How old will Joe be when Luis is 17? 20? 24? Joe will be 12 when Luis is 17, 15 when Luis is 20, and 19 when Luis is 24.

3. Lu spends $3 each day. How much does she spend in 2 days? 4 days? 5 days? Lu spends $6 in 2 days, $12 in 4 days, and $15 in 5 days.

4. The prices for tickets are $5, $10, $15, and $25. There is a $2 service charge for each ticket. What is the total cost of a $15 ticket? If the price of a ticket is $25, what is the total cost? The total cost of a $15 ticket is $17. The total cost of a $25 ticket is $27.

60 • Patterns and Functions

EXTENSION AND ENRICHMENT

10 minutes

Divide the class into three or four groups to play **Guess the Rule.** Before the game begins, ask each student to think of a rule to use in creating a function table. Then have them make the table on a sheet of paper, writing the numbers large enough to be viewed when standing in front of the group. On the back of the paper, students write their rule. When the tables are complete, each group member takes a turn displaying his or her table and asking the rest of the group to "Guess the Rule." The others study the numbers and try to be the first to tell what rule was used to make the table.

A Introduce

Read aloud the Lesson Objective with students.

Remind students that there are many ways to solve word problems. Say: *When we solve word problems, it is important to organize our work in a neat and helpful manner. One way to do this is to organize the data in a table.*

Tell students that in this lesson, they will solve word problems by making function tables.

B Teach and Learn

Write this problem on the board, and read it aloud: *Dan spends 2 hours each day doing homework. How many hours does he spend doing homework in 2 days? In 3 days? In 4 days?*

Ask: *What do you notice about the question for this problem? How many question marks are there?* Students should realize that there is more than one question and that the answer to this problem will be more than just one number.

Highlighted words and phrases may affect student comprehension.

Model how to solve the problem using a function table and by thinking aloud.

> **Think Aloud**

Write *Step 1* on the board. Read aloud the instructions for this step. Say: *What do I need to find out?* Underline the questions at the end of the problem on the board, and say: *I need to find out how much time Dan spends doing homework in 2 days, and in 3 days, and 4 days.*

Say: *Dan spends the same amount of time doing homework each day. I have to find out what that amount of time is for different numbers of days.*

Write *Step 2,* and read the instructions aloud. Say: *I have to find more than one answer. I want to make sure that my work is organized. I will make a function table. The data in the problem is about hours of homework and different days. The total number of hours depends on the number of days. So days is the input and hours is the output.* Draw a function table on the board and label the rows *days* and *hours*.

Write *Step 3,* and read the text aloud. Ask: *How much time does Dan spend on homework each day?* (2 hours) Circle this information in the problem on the board. *How can I find out how much time he will spend on homework in 2 days? He spends 2 hours doing homework each day. So the rule is to multiply the number of days by 2.* Write above the table on the board: *Rule: Multiply by 2.* Say: *Now I have to write the equation for the rule. I start with the number of days,* d, *and multiply by 2. That equals the number of hours,* h. Write below the rule on the board: *Equation: $d \times 2 = h$.*

Write *Step 4* and read the text aloud. Say: *Now I will fill in the table. I can look back at the problem and reread the questions. The questions tell me what the input numbers are. I know the number of hours for 1 day, and I have to find the number of hours for 2, 3, and 4 days.* Write *1, 2, 3,* and *4* in the table.

Write the output numbers as you explain how to find them. Say: *In one day, Dan spends two hours doing homework. In two days, he spends two days times two hours each day for a total of four hours.* Continue in this manner, filling in the table for three and four days.

Provide another practice problem for students to solve with a partner. Write the following problem on the board: *Lena's mother is 25 years older than Lena. How old will Lena's mother be when Lena is 12? 16? 20?*

- **Below the problem, write the following questions:** *What goes in the input row? What goes in the output row? What is the rule? What is the equation?*

- **Ask partners to work together to make a function table and solve the problem.** Allow two or three different student pairs to share their solutions with the class.

> ## C Review and Practice

📄 **Give pairs of students two copies of Worksheet 15 of the four-step process and the function table.** Review the steps on the worksheet.

🗔 **Show Transparency 30.** Chorally read the directions on the transparency with students. Read the problems, and explain vocabulary as necessary.

- **BP 6 Tell students that each problem uses a different operation.** Give students sticky notes. Reread each problem, and ask students to talk with a partner to decide which operation to choose. Have students write the number of the problem and the symbol for the operation on a sticky note. When all pairs have finished, ask: *What operation will we use for question 1?* Have students hold up their sticky notes for question 1. Repeat for each problem. Provide assistance as needed on how to choose the correct operation.

- **Tell students that half the pairs will solve problems 1 and 2, and half will solve 3 and 4.** Have pairs copy the problems onto their worksheets and write out the steps to find the solution to each problem. One partner does the writing for the first problem, and the other does the writing for the second problem. Circulate, and assist as necessary.

- **BP 6 Have partners compare their papers with another pair who solved the same problems.** Ask them to find any differences in the rules, the equations, the tables, or the answers. If they find differences, they should discuss why they are different and try to decide what is correct.

- **While students are in the discussion groups, walk around and provide assistance to any groups that can't agree on what is correct.**

Have students individually complete Practice Solving Math Problems in the student worktext. Tell students that each problem uses a different operation. Circulate, and assess how well they are making function tables to solve each problem.

> ## D Assess and Intervene

Do all students understand how to make a function table to solve a word problem based on Practice Study Word Problems on page 60? Use the rubric to identify students who need extra support through additional help and the Intervention activity.

Intermediate

- ☐ Correctly completes at least 2 problems, with accurate rules, equations, and function tables.
- ☐ Answers are written in phrases or sentences, and are comprehensible.

  Example of a sentence a student might write: *All boy earn $6, one boy get $2.*

Advanced

- ☐ Correctly completes at least 3 problems, with accurate rules, equations, and function tables.
- ☐ Answers are written in complete sentences with minimal errors.

  Example of a sentence a student might write: *If boys earn $6, each one get $2.*

INTERVENTION 5 minutes

Are students having difficulty determining which numbers should be used as the input and which should be used as the output? You can help students see the data clearly by using two different colors for the input and output numbers. Once they have both variables, have them identify the pattern. Then ask them: *If _____ goes in, and _____ comes out, what is the rule?* Have them make two rows and label them *input* and *output*. Have them fill in the rows with the data before they use the equation.

Understand the Main Idea

Objective Use a clock or a calendar to talk about time.

45 minutes

Teach this lesson:
- **Before** introducing lessons on using clock and calendar time in students' grade-level math textbooks
- **Before** students complete the activities on page 61 of the student worktext

You need these materials:
- analog clock
- calendar for the current year
- calendar for the current month (1 per student)
- round paper plates (1 per pair)
- sticky notes, markers, and scissors

Prerequisite Background Knowledge
- Telling time
- Units of time
- Days of the week/months of the year

BP 5 *ELL BEST PRACTICE #5:*
Higher-Order Thinking

English language learners are just as capable as any other students of using higher-order thinking, but they may have trouble verbally expressing their thinking. As you ask questions about time and elapsed time, encourage students to think of the ways time is used and expressed, and to analyze and recognize the different uses of clock time and calendar time.

Throughout this module, when you see **BP 5**, you will find an example of higher-order thinking.

Module 16: Time

Understand the Main Idea

LESSON 1

Objective Use a clock or a calendar to talk about time.

Learn the Main Idea

Clock Time

We're going on vacation. Our train leaves at 8:00 A.M. We will get to my grandmother's city at 10:00 A.M. It will take two hours to get there.

Calendar Time

Today is Friday, July 5. Our vacation starts on July 12. It will be one week until our vacation starts.

MAIN IDEA You can use time to tell how long something will take to do or how long it will be until something happens.

Practice Applying the Main Idea

Directions Use the clock and the calendar above to help you. Tell how long something will take or how long it will be until something happens. Using complete sentences, write your answers on a separate sheet of paper.

Example My dance class starts at 4:00 P.M. It will end at 6:00 P.M. How long will it last? Dance class will last two hours.

1. My plane leaves at 3:00 P.M. It will land at 10:00 P.M. How long will the flight take? It will take 7 hours.

2. The sports camp starts on July 14 and ends on July 18. How long will it last? It will last 5 days.

3. Today is July 1. I am going to visit my cousins on July 15. How long will it be until I visit my cousins? It will be 2 weeks until my visit starts.

4. If I start doing my homework at 4:00 P.M. and finish at 6:00 P.M., how long will my homework take? It will take 2 hours.

5. Why is it important to know how long something will take? It is important because I can plan how much time I need.

6. Why is it important to know how long it will be until something happens? It is important because I can count how many hours or days I have to wait.

Highlighted words and phrases may affect student comprehension.

A Introduce

Read aloud the Lesson Objective with students.

Help students activate prior knowledge. Say: *Did you ever want to tell how long it took to do something in hours or minutes, or in days, weeks, or months? How did you describe the time it took?*

BP 5 Display an analog clock and a calendar as you say: *We can measure time in different ways. We use a clock to measure hours, minutes, and seconds. We use a calendar to measure days, weeks, months, and years.* Ask: *Why do we need more than one way to measure time?* Elicit several responses.

Use the artwork on page 61 of the student worktext as a visual introduction to using a clock and a calendar to talk about time and elapsed time. Have pairs look at the pictures and describe what they see to each other.

Point to the suitcase and the clock on the left. Ask: *What do you use a suitcase for? What do you think the girl will do? What time is it?* (the girl is going on vacation; it's 7:00 A.M.) Chorally read the text with students. Summarize what is happening: *It's 7:00 A.M. The girl is going to visit her grandmother in a different city. Her train leaves at 8:00 A.M. The train gets to her grandmother's at 10:00 A.M. I count the hours. It will take two hours to get there.*

Together with students, find 8:00 and 10:00 on the clock in the illustration. Model counting the hours, and say: *How long will it take the girl to get to her grandmother's? It will take her two hours.* Have students repeat.

Point to the calendar on the right. Say: *This is a calendar.* Have students repeat. Ask: *What month does it show?* (July) Chorally read the text with students. Summarize what is happening. Say: *The boy is looking at the calendar. He is counting the time until his vacation starts. Today is July 5. His vacation starts on July 12. It will start in one week.*

Together with students, find July 5 and July 12 on the calendar. Model counting down one row. Say: *One row is one week.* Ask: *How long will it be until the boy's vacation starts?* (1 week)

Read aloud the Main Idea with students. Ask students to tell when they use a clock or a calendar.

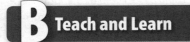

Teach and Learn

Use an analog clock to review telling time. Show a time, and ask: *What time is it?* Say: *It's [8:00].* Practice with vocabulary such as *noon, midnight, half past (30),* and *quarter to/after (15).* As you say each time, write it on the board using numbers and words. Have students repeat each time. (If students have difficulty telling time, conduct a more complete review before proceeding with this lesson.)

BP 5 Have students compare the ways of measuring time in the Learn the Main Idea section. Ask: *How is the girl measuring time?* (in hours) *How is the boy measuring time?* (in weeks) *How are clocks and calendars alike?* (both measure time) *How are they different?*(clocks use seconds, minutes, hours; calendars use days, weeks, months, years)

Have pairs of students make a clock using a paper plate. Demonstrate how to mark the hours and to cut out clock hands from sticky notes, making sure one end of each hand is sticky.

- **Write on the board:** *The bus leaves for the museum at 8:00 in the morning. It will come back at 3:30 in the afternoon.* Model how to mark and label the starting and ending times on the clock with sticky notes. Say: *The starting time is 8:00 A.M. The ending time is 3:30 P.M.*

- **Together, find out how long it will be until the bus comes back.** Say: *We count the hours first, and then the minutes.* Model how to count the hours from 8:00 to 3:00. Say: *When we count minutes, each number on the clock shows 5 minutes.* Together, count the minutes from 3:00 to 3:30 by fives. Say: *That's 30 minutes. It will be 7 hours and 30 minutes until the bus comes back.*

- **Write these sentence frames on the board:** *The starting time is ____. The ending time is ____. How long will ____ take? It will take ____. How long will it be until ____? It will be ____ until ____.* Model how to use these language structures as you provide additional examples.

Use a calendar to review the days of the week, months, and dates. Practice chorally saying dates using ordinal numbers.

BP 5 Demonstrate the U.S. style of writing dates, with the month first, then the date and year. Ask students to share other ways of writing the date. Discuss which style they prefer.

Give each student a calendar for the current month. Write on the board: *I start soccer on October 1. I finish soccer on October 15.* Have students place a small sticky note on the beginning date, count down two rows on the calendar, and place another sticky note on the ending date. Say: *Each row is one week. It will be 2 weeks until practice ends.* Write these sentence frames on the board: *The starting date is ____. The ending date is ____. How long will it be until ____? It will be ____.* Model these structures as you provide additional examples.

Review and Practice

Divide the class into pairs. Have the partners use the sentence frames to ask each other questions about time. Circulate, and make sure students can use their calendars and clocks to find the answers.

Read the directions for the Practice Applying the Main Idea activity. Then have students complete the activity independently. Use the rubric to assess their progress.

Assess and Intervene

Does every student understand how to use a clock and a calendar to talk about time based on Practice Applying the Main Idea on page 61? Use the rubric to identify students who need extra support through additional help and the Intervention activity.

Intermediate

☐ Correctly answers at least 4 of questions 1–4.

☐ Writes logical answers to questions 5 and 6, using phrases or sentences with some errors.

Example of a sentence a student might write: *Important for to plan time.*

Advanced

☐ Correctly answers all of questions 1–4.

☐ Writes logical answers to questions 5 and 6, using complete sentences with minimal errors.

Example of a sentence a student might write: *It is important because I count days I wait.*

INTERVENTION 10 minutes

If students are having difficulty finding elapsed time, use a play clock to show how the hour hand moves during each hour, advancing to the next hour number. Use the minute hand to practice counting minutes by fives. Then help students break a word problem into parts, calculating the minutes until the next hour, then the minutes after the next hour, and adding them together. Use a calendar to model counting days and weeks. Ask questions similar to those in the lesson, and have students practice finding the answers.

Lesson

2

Learn the Vocabulary

Objective Talk and write about time using the vocabulary words.

---

45 minutes

Teach this lesson:
- **Before** introducing lessons on clock and calendar time in students' grade-level math textbooks
- **Before** students complete the activities on page 62 of the student worktext

You need these materials:
- students' analog clocks and calendars from Lesson 1
- play analog clock
- play digital clock or picture of digital clock
- paper, pencils, and small sticky notes
- Transparency 31
- Vocabulary Cards

Lesson Vocabulary

Essential Vocabulary

analog clock	digital clock	elapsed time

Additional Vocabulary

A.M.   P.M.

| half past | noon | midnight |
| ordinal numbers | starting time | ending time |

quarter to (of)/quarter past (after)

LESSON

2

Learn the Vocabulary

Objective Talk and write about time using the vocabulary words.

Learn the Words

Phrase	Definition	Example
analog clock	a clock that shows time with an hour hand and a minute hand	This **analog clock** shows that it is two-thirty. The short hand shows the hour, and the long hand shows the minutes.
digital clock	a clock that shows time with numerals or digits	This **digital clock** shows that it is two-thirty. The digits on the left show the hours, and the digits on the right show the minutes.
elapsed time	the time that it takes to do something from start to finish	My soccer practice starts at 3:00 and ends at 5:15. The **elapsed time** is 2 hours and 15 minutes.

Practice the Words

Directions Complete the story below by filling in the blanks. Use phrases from the chart above. Then answer the questions about the story.

Fabian looks at the clock. It has an hour hand and a minute hand. It is an analog clock _____. It shows 7:30. Fabian leaves for school. When Fabian gets to school, he looks at another clock. It shows time using digits.

It is a digital clock _____. It shows 8:00. School starts at 8:00 A.M. and ends at 3:00 P.M. The elapsed time _____ for the school day is 7 hours.

1. Circle the clock that Fabian saw before school.

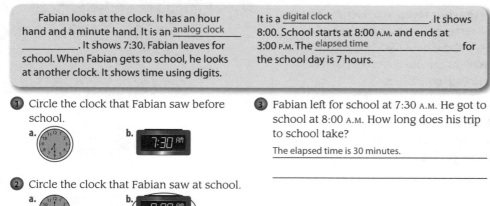
a. _____ b. 7:30 AM

2. Circle the clock that Fabian saw at school.
a. _____ b. 8:00 AM

3. Fabian left for school at 7:30 A.M. He got to school at 8:00 A.M. How long does his trip to school take?

The elapsed time is 30 minutes.

_____

A Introduce

Read aloud the Lesson Objective with students. Ask: *What do you remember about telling time using a clock and a calendar?* Have students tell a partner what they remember about using a calendar and a clock.

As a class, brainstorm ideas for vocabulary words that are important in talking about elapsed time. Write suggested words on the board. Add the Essential Vocabulary to the list, plus words from the Additional Vocabulary box that you think will be useful.

B Teach and Learn

Orally introduce the Essential Vocabulary. Have students open the student worktexts to page 62. Read the Essential Vocabulary phrases, and use the suggestions below to introduce and explain them. As you introduce each phrase, write it on the board and model its pronunciation. Read the definitions and explanations aloud as you point to the key illustrations. Then have students read each word, definition, and example chorally with you.

Hold up a play analog clock and have students show you the analog clocks they made in Lesson 1. Say: *An analog clock uses hour and minute hands to show time. These hands work like our fingers; they point to the hours and minutes. An analog clock has a face.* Ask: *Can you describe what the face has?*

Highlighted words and phrases may affect student comprehension.

(numbers and hands) *What is an analog clock? What does it look like? What does it measure?*

Set your clock to 8:15. Ask students to set their clocks the same way. Say: *We divide the clock face into 4 equal parts, or quarters. Each quarter is 15 minutes. Put the hour hand a little past the 8. Put the minute hand one quarter of the way around the face.* Ask: *What time is it?* Help students answer: *It is 8:15.* Then say: *Let's change the time and make it later.* Model moving the minute hand, 5 minutes at a time, and say each time: *8:20, 8:25, 8:30,* etc. Say: *When we move the minute hand, each number adds 5 minutes.* Model moving the hour hand to show 8:00, 9:00, 10:00, etc. Say: *Each number adds 1 hour as we move the hour hand.*

BP 5 Say: *Set your clock for quarter past nine.* Write: *It is quarter past nine.* Ask: *How do you know your clock says quarter past nine?* (the hour hand is a little past the 9; the minute hand is on 3, so that's 15 minutes; 15 minutes is a quarter of an hour). Explain that there are other ways to say this time. Write and say: *It is quarter after nine. It is 9:15.* Have students repeat.

Hold up a digital clock or a picture of a digital clock, and say: *A digital clock uses only digits to show time.* Explain that *digits* are numbers.

Model how to draw a digital clock. Draw a rectangle with two boxes inside it, and draw a colon between the two boxes. Distribute paper and pencils, and have each student draw a digital clock. Point to the two dots and say: *The colon separates the hours and the minutes.* Then say: *Write the digit 3 in the box on the left side. This side shows the hours. Write the digits 30 in the box on the right side. This side shows the minutes.* Ask: *What time is it?*

Have students erase the time. Dictate other times for them to write. Ask: *What time is it?* Have students answer: *It is _____.* Explain that we always say the digits (instead of phrases like *quarter to*) when we tell time on a digital clock.

BP 5 Point to the illustrations on page 62 of the student worktext. Divide the class into small groups. Ask: *What is a digital clock? How is a digital clock the same as or different from an analog clock? What does a digital clock measure?* Have students discuss the answers in groups.

Say: *Elapsed time is the time that it takes to do an activity from start to finish.* Have students

use the analog clocks they made in Lesson 1. Say: *The starting time is 1:15. The ending time is 3:30. What is the elapsed time?* Together, mark the starting and ending times with small sticky notes. Say: *We count the hours first.* Count off two hours. Then say: *Then we count the minutes. We start at 15 and count by fives until we get to 30. 5, 10, 15. That's 15 minutes. The elapsed time is 2 hours and 15 minutes.*

Provide additional examples. Write starting and ending times on the board, and have groups write the elapsed time on a piece of scrap paper, using the clocks from Lesson 1. Write this question frame on the board: *What is the elapsed time? The elapsed time is _____.* Have groups take turns asking and answering for the class.

Repeat the activity, but have students draw two digital clocks, one for the starting time and one for the ending time.

BP 5 Ask: *What is elapsed time? Why is it important to know how long it takes to do something?*

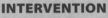 **Have students complete the Vocabulary Cards for the words in this module.**

Review the Essential Vocabulary. Then write and read aloud the following sentences: *Yes, it does. No, it doesn't.*

- **Ask yes/no questions such as:** *Does a digital clock have hands? Does the long hand on an analog clock show minutes? Does elapsed time show how long something takes?* Model using the sentences on the board to answer.

- **Have students form pairs and ask each other similar questions.** Remind them to answer using the sentences on the board.

Use Transparency 31 to give students extra practice. Have pairs work together to do the activity.

Read the directions for the Practice the Words activity. Then read the story aloud, without reading the answers, while students follow along in their books. Answer any questions. Then have students complete the activity individually. Circulate and assess their progress using the assessment below.

Does every student understand the Essential Vocabulary in Practice the Words on page 62? Use the rubric to identify students who need extra support through additional help and the Intervention activity.

Intermediate

☐ Uses at least 2 words correctly to complete the story and correctly identifies at least 1 clock.

☐ Writes a phrase or sentence with minimal errors to tell the elapsed time.

Example of a sentence students might write: *Takes 30 minutes.*

Advanced

☐ Uses all 3 words correctly to complete the story and correctly identifies both clocks.

☐ Writes a complete sentence with no errors to tell the elapsed time.

Example of a sentence students might write: *His trip to school takes 30 minutes.*

INTERVENTION 5 minutes

If students are having difficulty associating the correct name with each type of clock, write and read aloud riddles such as *What tells time with its hands?* (an analog clock) and *What can tell time with only digits?* (a digital clock). Have students use their Vocabulary Cards to complete the riddles. Then pair students to ask and answer their own riddles about the Essential Vocabulary.

Lesson

3

Use More Language

Objective Use *since* and *until* to talk about elapsed time.

45 minutes

Teach this lesson:
- **After** lessons on clock and calendar time in students' grade-level math textbooks
- **Before** students complete the activities on page 63 of the student worktext

You need these materials:
- play analog clock
- clocks and calendars from Lesson 1
- index cards

Use More Language

Objective Use *since* and *until* to talk about elapsed time.

LESSON

3

Learn the Language

I went to bed at 9:00 P.M. last night.
I slept until 7:00 A.M. this morning.
I slept for 10 hours.

It's been raining since Tuesday morning. It's Friday morning now. It's been raining for 3 days.

April

I _____ at (on) _____.
I _____ until _____.
I _____ for _____.

I have (been) _____ since _____.
It's _____ now. I have (been)
_____ for _____.

Practice the Language

Directions Complete sentences 1 to 4 with *since* or *until* and the elapsed time.
Answer questions 5 and 6 in complete sentences. Use *since* or *until*.

① It's 12:00 P.M. now. Juana has been practicing the piano since_____ 9:00 A.M. She has been practicing for _3 hours_____.

② I played basketball until_____ 5:00 P.M. this afternoon. I started playing at 12:00 P.M. I played for _5 hours_____.

③ I got sick on Saturday. I didn't feel better until_____ Tuesday. I was sick for 3 days_____.

④ We have been in fourth grade since_____ the beginning of September. It's the end of January now. We have been in school for 5 months_____.

⑤

AUGUST						
Sunday	Monday	Tuesday	Wednesday	Thursday	Friday	Saturday
	1	2	3	4	5	6
7	8	9	10	11	12	13
14	15	16	17	18	19	20

How long will Chen be in New York?
He will be in New York until Friday, August 5.

⑥

How long has Hoshi been reading?
She has been reading since 4:00.

BP 5 **Remind students what they have learned about telling time and finding elapsed time with clocks and calendars.** Ask: *What is elapsed time? How can we use a clock or a calendar to find elapsed time? Why do we need to know the starting and ending times to find elapsed time?*

Write *elapsed time* on the board. Ask: *What are some words we use to talk about elapsed time?* As students answer, write the words on the board. Then invite students to use each one in a simple phrase or sentence.

Read aloud the Lesson Objective with students. Ask: *Why is it important to know how to talk about elapsed time?* List students' responses on the board, and read them aloud.

B Teach and Learn

Have students open the student worktext to page 63. Point out the first picture, and read the text in the thought bubble. Ask: *What is the boy doing? What time did he go to bed? What time did he wake up? How long did he sleep?* Repeat with the second picture, using questions such as: *When did it start raining? How long has it been raining?*

Highlighted words and phrases may affect student comprehension.

Introduce the meaning of _until_. Write _until_ on the board, and read it aloud. Say: Until _is a word that we use to talk about time. It means up to that time or that moment._ Use a Think Aloud to explain and provide an example:

> **Think Aloud**

Say: _I can use_ until _to show that an action is going on up to a certain time._ Until _tells when something stops happening or ends, so it helps me talk about elapsed time: I slept until 7:00 this morning. I went to bed at 9:00 last night. I slept for 10 hours. The starting time is 9:00 P.M. The ending time is 7:00 A.M. The elapsed time is 10 hours._

Write these sentence frames on the board: _I ____ at (on) ____. I ____ until ____. I ____ for ____._ Model how to choose an activity, a starting time, and an ending time, for both clock time and calendar time: _Friend's house. 10 A.M. Noon: I went to my friend's house at 10 A.M. I stayed until noon. I was at my friend's house for 2 hours. I went to visit my grandmother on July 1. I stayed until July 15. I visited her for 2 weeks._

- **Ask students to work with a partner to choose a clock time activity, a calendar time activity, and starting and ending times for each activity.** Then have them use the sentence frames to tell the rest of the class about their activities.

Introduce the meaning of _since_. Write and read aloud the word _since_. Say: Since _means from the time that something started or from a date in the past._ Use a Think Aloud to explain its meaning:

> **Think Aloud**

Say: _I can use_ since _to show when something started in the past._ Since _tells when something began, so I can use it to talk about elapsed time. I can say something like: It's 8:00 in the evening now. I've been working since 2:00. I've been working for 6 hours. The starting time is 2:00 P.M. The ending time is 8:00 P.M. The elapsed time is 6 hours. I can also use_ since _with a date or a year. For example: I've been in fourth grade since September._

Write these sentence frames on the board: _I have (been) ____ since ____. It's ____ now. I have (been) ____ for ____._ Tell students that they will again choose clock time and calendar time activities, and starting and ending times. Model how to complete the sentence frames: _Playing baseball. 2 P.M. 4:30 P.M.: I have been playing baseball since 2 P.M. It's 4:30 P.M. now. I have been playing baseball for 2½ hours. I have lived here since August. It's February now. I have lived here for 6 months._

- **Have pairs of students pick activities and times, compose sentences, and share them with the class.**

C Review and Practice

Review the Lesson Objective by asking students: _What word can we use to show that something stops or ends?_ (until) _What word can we use to show that something started in the past?_ (since)

BP 5 Divide the class into pairs. Ask students to think about and discuss the difference between the words _since_ and _until_. Have the partners make up an example sentence for each word.

- **Have students copy their sentences on the board with blanks in place of _until_ and _since_.** Then ask the class to complete the sentences. For example: _I have been taking guitar lessons ____ September._ (since) _Jaime took lessons ____ he was 15._ (until)

- **Read aloud the Learn the Language section of page 63 again.** Then ask the pairs to make up examples of their own, using the sentence frames if necessary. Assign each pair _since_ or _until,_ and have the students draw pictures and write sentences about elapsed time, using their worktexts for reference. Remind students that they need an activity, a starting time, and an ending time. Ask them to leave a blank in place of the word _since_ or _until._ When all pairs are finished, have them switch papers with other pairs and complete the sentences. Circulate to check students' work. Explain any errors.

Read the directions aloud. Then have students complete the Practice the Language activity individually. Remind students to look at the Learn the Language section and the sentence frames for help. Assess their work using the rubric below.

D Assess and Intervene

Based on Practice the Language on page 63, how well can students complete and write sentences using _since_ and _until_? Use the rubric to identify students who need extra support through additional help and the Intervention activity.

Intermediate

- ☐ Correctly completes at least 3 sentences with _since_ or _until._
- ☐ Correctly completes at least 3 sentences with the elapsed time.
- ☐ Answers questions 5 and 6 in phrases or sentences containing some errors, but showing comprehension of _since, until,_ and elapsed time.

Example of a sentence students might write: _Chen in New York until August 5._

Advanced

- ☐ Correctly completes all sentences with _since_ or _until._
- ☐ Correctly completes all sentences with the elapsed time.
- ☐ Answers questions 5 and 6 in complete sentences with minimal errors.

Example of a sentence students might write: _Hoshi have been reading since 4:00._

INTERVENTION 10 minutes

If students are having trouble deciding whether to use _until_ or _since_ in sentences about elapsed time, write _starting time (since)_ and _ending time (until)_ on index cards. Tape them to the board or wall as column headings. On separate index cards write problems, such as these:

_I have been writing ____ 5:00. It's 7:00 now. I wrote for 2 hours._

_Tomas visited his cousins ____ June 27. He got there on June 23. He visited his cousins for 4 days._

Read each problem aloud, and ask: _Are we looking for the starting time or the ending time?_ Help students figure this out by identifying the facts. Then have them place each problem in the correct column on the board or wall. After all the cards are sorted into columns, have students read them aloud, filling in the blanks with _until_ or _since._

Solve Math Problems

Objective Decide what unit of time to use to find elapsed time.

45 minutes

Teach this lesson:
- **After** lessons on elapsed time in students' grade-level math textbooks
- **Before** students complete the activities on page 64 of the student worktext

You need these materials:
- Worksheet 16
- Transparency 32
- Students' clocks and calendars from Lesson 1

EXTENSION AND ENRICHMENT 10 minutes

Brainstorm with students words they know to talk about time and elapsed time. Have them write their own lists of words and exchange them with other students. Then introduce the expression *to keep track of (time)*. Model using it in a sentence: *I use a calendar to keep track of the days.* Divide the class into pairs, and have each pair write five sentences. Each sentence should use the expression plus a word from one of their lists.

Solve Math Problems

Objective Decide what unit of time to use to find elapsed time.

Learn to Solve Problems

Problem Tuan went for a bike ride at 10:25 A.M. He came back at 11:05 A.M. How long was his ride?

	Think	Write
Step 1:	Read the problem. Underline the question. Ask yourself what you have to do.	I have to find out how long Tuan rode his bike. The words "how long" mean the time his ride took from start to finish. So I need to find the elapsed time.
Step 2:	Circle the facts. Decide what units of time to use.	The problem is about clock time. The times are less than 1 hour apart, so I need to use minutes.
Step 3:	Solve the problem. Look at a clock when you count hours or minutes. Look at a calendar when you count months, weeks, or days.	end- 11:05 / start- 10:25 — I can look at a clock and count the minutes by fives. I start at 10:25 and count: 5, 10, 15, 20, 25, 30, 35, 40 minutes. Tuan's bike ride was 40 minutes long.

Practice Solving Math Problems

Directions Follow the steps above to solve each problem below. Write your answers on a separate sheet of paper. Tell how you decided what units of time to use for each problem.

1. The movie starts at 1:10 P.M. and ends at 4:10 P.M. How long is the movie? The movie is 3 hours long. I used hours because the answer uses whole hours.

2. Theo gets on the school bus at 8:15 and arrives at school at 9:00. How long is his bus ride? His bus ride is 45 minutes long. I used minutes because the bus ride was less than 1 hour.

3. Tickets go on sale for our school play on March 13. The last day to buy a ticket is March 27. How long will the tickets be on sale? The tickets will be on sale for 2 weeks. I used weeks because the elapsed time is more than a week and less than a month.

4. The art show begins March 1 and ends June 1. How long is the art show? The art show is 3 months long. I used months because the answer uses whole months.

Introduce

Read aloud the Lesson Objective with students. Make sure they remember how to find elapsed time using a clock and a calendar. Review as necessary, using activities from previous lessons.

Explain that reading a problem and thinking about what you have to do will help you decide if you should use a clock or a calendar to find elapsed time. Ask: *What words did we use to talk about elapsed time with clocks and calendars?* Write *Calendar Time* and *Clock Time* on the board.

Elicit words such as *weeks, days, months, hours, minutes,* and write them underneath the correct headings. Say: *These are units of time. As you read a word problem, look for words like these to help you decide what unit of time to use for your answer.*

Say: *In this lesson, you will decide what unit of time to use when finding the elapsed time, by finding the question and the facts in the problem.*

Highlighted words and phrases may affect student comprehension.

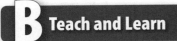

B Teach and Learn

Write the following problem on the board, and read it aloud: *Tuan went for a bike ride at 10:25 A.M. He came back at 11:05 A.M. How long was his ride?*

Have students open their student worktexts to page 64 and look at Learn to Solve Problems. Tell students that the numbered steps will help them find the question, find the facts, and decide what unit of time they need to use to solve the problem.

BP 5 Model how to solve the problem by thinking aloud.

> **Think Aloud**
>
> **Step 1:** Say: *After I read the problem, I look for the question. It begins with the question words* how long *and ends with a question mark. I underline the question:* How long was his ride? *Then I ask myself what I have to do.* How long *means from start to finish, so I know that I have to find the elapsed time of Tuan's bike ride.*
>
> **Step 2:** Say: *I find and circle the facts in the problem. The facts are that Tuan left at 10:25 A.M. and he came back at 11:05 A.M. The times tell me to use clock time. Because they are less than an hour apart, I need to use minutes instead of hours.*
>
> **Step 3:** Say: *Now I will solve the problem. I will look at a clock because I'm using clock time (minutes). I find the starting time, 10:25, and count the minutes by fives until I reach the ending time, 11:05. I count 5, 10, 15, 20, 25, 30, 35, 40. (Demonstrate by pointing to the clock on page 64 or to a play analog clock.) Tuan's bike ride was 40 minutes long.*

Display Transparency 32. Go over the directions, and read the problems chorally. Group students and have them solve the first two problems. Review the answers by calling on volunteers to identify the question, facts, and elapsed time for each problem.

BP 5 Divide the class into pairs. Give each group two copies of Worksheet 16. Assign each pair two elapsed time problems from their grade-level math textbook, or write two problems on the board. The pairs should solve both problems, using one worksheet for each problem. Have students in each pair take turns writing.

As students work, circulate and help as necessary. Model the steps shown in the Think Aloud above. If students need additional help, have them write the question and list the facts on a sheet of paper. Then help them use a clock or a calendar to find the elapsed time. In addition, allow students to use their worktexts for reference.

C Review and Practice

BP 5 Ask volunteers to retell the steps for deciding what unit to use in finding the elapsed time. Prompt them by asking: *Is the question asking about clock time or calendar time? What time words do you see? If the answer is more than one hour, but not only hours, what units do you use? If the answer is less than a year but more than a week, what unit do you use?*

Divide the class into pairs to solve problems. Write on the board an elapsed time problem using clock time, such as *Julian got on the train at 1:25 P.M. He got off the train at 5:15. How long was he on the train?*

- **Read the problem aloud.** Have pairs solve the problem and use these sentence frames to tell the elapsed time and explain their choice of unit: *Julian was on the train for _____. I used _____ because the answer is less than/more than_____.* Use a Think Aloud, similar to the one in Teach and Learn, to assist students if necessary.

- **Write on the board an elapsed time problem using calendar time, such as** *Bella started her science project on May 1. She finished it on May 22. How long did it take her to complete the project?*

- **Read the problem aloud.** Have the pairs solve the problem and use the following sentence frames to tell the elapsed time and explain their choice of unit: *It took Bella _____ to finish her project. I used _____ because the answer is less than/more than_____.* Use a Think Aloud, similar to the one in Teach and Learn, to assist students if necessary.

Use Transparency 32 for additional practice. Have pairs solve the last two problems. Monitor students' work to make sure they understand the steps and are solving the problems correctly.

Read aloud the directions for Practice Solving Math Problems on page 64 of the student worktext. Have students solve the problems individually. Circulate and assess how well they are using the strategy taught in this lesson.

D Assess and Intervene

How well can students use the steps in Learn to Solve Problems to identify the unit of time needed to solve an elapsed time problem? Use the rubric to identify students who need extra support through additional help and the Intervention activity.

Intermediate

- ☐ Correctly solves at least 2 problems using the appropriate unit of time.
- ☐ Explains the choice of unit logically, using phrases or sentences; errors do not impede comprehension.

   Example of an explanation students might write: *Use minutes. Time less that 1 hour.*

Advanced

- ☐ Correctly solves at least 3 problems using the appropriate unit of time.
- ☐ Explains the choice of unit logically, using complete sentences with minimal errors that do not impede comprehension.

   Example of an explanation students might write: *I use minutes because I see clock times less than 1 hour.*

INTERVENTION 10 minutes

If students are having trouble deciding what unit of time to use, remind them of the chart of *Clock Time* and *Calendar Time* that you wrote on the board in at the beginning of this lesson. Have them copy the chart and these sentences: *Use seconds when the answer is less than 1 minute. Use minutes when the answer is less than 1 hour. Use days when the answer is less than 1 week. Use weeks when the answer is less than 1 month. Use months when the answer is less than 1 year.* Then write this sentence frame on the board: *I use _____ if the answer is less than _____.* Read several problems aloud, and have students use the chart and sentence frame to find and tell the correct unit of elapsed time for each problem.

**Prerequisite
Background Knowledge**
• Concepts and vocabulary of
measurement, estimation,
and comparing and
ordering

Understand the Main Idea

Objective Show understanding of different units of length to measure and
compare how long things are.

45 minutes

Teach this lesson:
• **Before** introducing lessons on customary and metric measurements of length in
students' grade-level math textbooks
• **Before** students complete the activities on page 65 of the student worktext

You need these materials:
• 12" rulers, tape measures, and yardsticks (1 of each tool for every 2 students)

 **ELL BEST PRACTICE #6**
Hands-on Activities

For English language learners, hands-on activities are a way to learn academic concepts and
language in ways that are not dependent on
how proficient they are in English. As students
begin to learn different units of length, make
available rulers, yardsticks, and tape measures for
hands-on opportunities with measurements and
comparisons.

Throughout this module, when you see **BP 6**,
this is an example of a hands-on activity.

Module 17: Measures of Length (Customary and Metric)

Understand the Main Idea

LESSON **1**

Objective Show understanding of different units of length to measure
and compare how long things are.

Learn the Main Idea

These skateboards are all different sizes. I want to buy a skateboard that is about 30 inches long.

We have a lot of skateboards in different lengths. Here's a skateboard that's 32 inches long. And here's another one that's 3 feet long.

MAIN IDEA We use units of length to measure and compare how long things are.

Practice Applying the Main Idea

Directions In questions 1 to 3, choose the appropriate unit of length to measure
each thing. Write the letter of the correct answer on each line. In question 4,
write a complete sentence.

1. Which things are best to measure in inches? c, d

2. Which things are best to measure in feet? a, f

3. Which things are best to measure in yards? b, e

   a. the living room wall to be painted
   b. a football field
   c. your index finger
   d. a pencil
   e. the playground
   f. a rug

4. Write about a time you compared how
   long two things were.
   Answers will vary.

A **Introduce**

**Read aloud the Lesson Objective on page
65 of the student worktext with students.**
Have them touch the words: *units of length,
measure,* and *compare* as you say them out
loud.

**Build background knowledge by holding
up a ruler, a yardstick, and a measuring
tape.** Ask: *Have you ever used one of these
tools to measure something to see how long it
is? Why did you decide to measure that object?*
Have students talk with a partner to answer
the questions. Ask volunteers to share with
the whole class.

**Connect learning to students' home and
family.** Say: *You measure things when you
need to know how long they are, their length.
Was there a time when someone in your family
needed to measure something for the house?*
(curtains, rooms for new carpet, size of room
for new furniture) Encourage students to
share.

Read aloud the Main Idea with students.
Tell them they will learn more about the different units of length that we use to measure
and compare how long things are.

Highlighted words and phrases may affect student comprehension.

B. Teach and Learn

Call students' attention to the first picture on page 65 in the student worktext. Ask: *What are the boy and his father doing? Where are they?* Invite pairs of students to study the picture together and answer the questions.

Ask for a volunteer to read the speech bubble in the first picture. Ask: *What do you think the boy and his dad are going to do?* (buy a skateboard) *Are the skateboards all alike?* (no)

Read aloud the speech bubble in the second picture. Ask: *Who is in the second picture besides the boy and his dad?* (a store clerk) *What is she doing?* (showing them some skateboards) *What is different about the two skateboards?* (two different lengths)

Ask students to raise a hand if they own a skateboard. Have a volunteer tell the class what a skateboard is and how to skateboard. Ask the students who raised a hand: *Do you know how long your skateboard is? Did you measure it? What did you use to measure it?*

Write the words *measure* and *length* on the board. Point to each word in turn, pronounce the word, and have students repeat it a few times. Have students pay special attention to the ending of the word *length*. Be sure they have the tip of their tongues between their teeth when they say the ending of *length*.

Ask students to work in groups of four. Have the groups look again at the second picture. Ask: *What does the store clerk have in her hand? What do you think she's going to do with it?* Have the groups discuss the measuring tool (measuring tape) and share their thoughts.

Ask: *Why is it important to measure the skateboards? Will measuring the skateboards help the boy and his dad? How?* Have the small groups discuss and answer these questions.

Show students a tape measure, a ruler, and a yardstick. Name each one and have students repeat. Point out that *yardstick* is a compound word—two words in one.

- **Use the tape measure or yardstick.** Show typical lengths for skateboards: 30 inches for an elementary student; 33 inches for traditional length; 35+ inches for a longboard.

- **Ask:** *Have you ever used a tape measure or a yardstick? What units of length are on a tape measure and a yardstick?* (inches and feet) *What other measuring tools do you know about?* (a ruler) *What units of length are on a ruler?* (inches) Explain that these the units of length are used in the U.S. Students will learn more about these units, and about meters and centimeters, in their math textbooks and in the next lessons.

BP 6 **Pass out a rulers, yardsticks, and tape measures to each small group.** Explain that inches are the smallest unit, a ruler is 1 foot long, and a yardstick is 1 yard long. Have students look at the tools carefully and identify inch marks and foot marks.

Ask: *What are some things you can measure in inches? In feet? In yards?* Have the small groups make lists. Then have a representative from each group come up and write his or her group's list on the board. Ask for hands to see how many agree or disagree with each item.

C. Review and Practice

Review why it is important to know how to measure things. Ask: *Why do you think it is important to know about different units of length?* (because knowing about different units of length can help you choose the measurement tool when you need to measure something)

BP 6 **Have students work in pairs.** Write three headings on the board: *Inches, Feet, Yards.* Give each pair a ruler, a yardstick, and a tape measure. Direct students to walk around the classroom and use the tools to decide which units could best be used for measuring objects such as a desk, table, book, pen, paper, wall, and so forth. They do not need to record any measurements at this time. When they finish, have pairs report on what objects they could measure with each unit. Write the objects under the appropriate headings on the board.

Read the directions for the Practice Applying the Main Idea activity on page 65 in the student worktext. Have the students work independently to complete the activity. Check students' work. Assist with the last question as necessary.

D. Assess and Intervene

Does every student understand that there are different units of length that are used to measure and compare how long things are based on Practice Applying the Main Idea on page 65? Use the rubric to identify students who need extra support through additional help and the Intervention activity.

Intermediate

- ☐ Correctly identifies at least 3 appropriate units of length.
- ☐ Writes phrases or a sentence that show understanding of comparing measurements; may contain errors.

   Example of a sentence a student might write: *Measure 2 piece rope, see what rope more long.*

Advanced

- ☐ Correctly identifies at least 5 appropriate units of length.
- ☐ Writes a complete sentence that clearly shows understanding of comparing measurements; errors do not affect meaning.

   Example of a sentence a student might write: *I measure 2 bicycles for see what bicycle is longer.*

INTERVENTION 5 minutes

If students are having difficulty understanding that there are different units of length, have them work with a partner to identify things they can see in the classroom that might be measured in inches, feet, and yards. Have the partners agree on which is the most appropriate unit of measurement and write down the items and the units for future reference.

Learn the Vocabulary

Objective Use words that will help you talk and write about customary and metric units of measure.

30 minutes

Teach this lesson:
- **Before** introducing grade-level math textbook lessons on linear measurement
- **Before** students complete the activities on page 66 of the student worktext

You need these materials:
- rulers that show inches and centimeters
- sticky notes
- Transparency 33

Lesson Vocabulary

Essential Vocabulary

units of measure	linear units	customary
metric		

Additional Vocabulary

to the nearest _____	half inch	quarter inch
length	width	height
distance		

LESSON
2

Learn the Vocabulary

Objective Use words that will help you talk and write about customary and metric units of measure.

Learn the Words

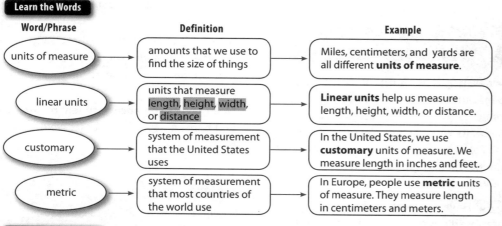

Word/Phrase	Definition	Example
units of measure	amounts that we use to find the size of things	Miles, centimeters, and yards are all different **units of measure**.
linear units	units that measure length, height, width, or distance	**Linear units** help us measure length, height, width, or distance.
customary	system of measurement that the United States uses	In the United States, we use **customary** units of measure. We measure length in inches and feet.
metric	system of measurement that most countries of the world use	In Europe, people use **metric** units of measure. They measure length in centimeters and meters.

Practice the Words

Directions Choose one word or phrase above to fill in each row of squares for questions 1 to 4 in the crossword puzzle below. Then answer question 5 using complete sentences.

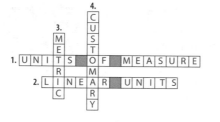

ACROSS

1. amounts that we use to find the size of things
2. units that measure length, height, width, or distance

DOWN

3. system of measurement that most countries of the world use

4. system of measurement that the United States uses

5. What are the two systems of measurement used in the world? Which one did you use in your country? Which one do you use in the United States?

Answers will vary.

A Introduce

Read aloud the Lesson Objective with students. Ask: *What are some words we used in Lesson 1 to talk about length? What units of length were used in measuring the skateboards?* (inches, feet) *Why do we use measuring tools?* (to know how long something is)

Tell students that in this lesson they will learn about the groups that different units of length belong to. They will learn about the terms *units of measure* and *linear units* and about the customary and metric systems for measuring length. Tell students that customary and metric systems use different units to measure.

Remind students that they learned about some units of measure in the last lesson. Elicit *inch, foot,* and *yard,* and list them on the board. Explain that these are all linear units because they measure length, height, width, or distance. (how long, how tall, how wide, how far)

Choose words from the Additional Vocabulary box that you think will be useful, and list them on the board. Elicit examples or definitions.

Highlighted words and phrases may affect student comprehension.

B Teach and Learn

Call students' attention to the ovals with vocabulary terms on page 66 of the student worktext. Remind students that they talked about some units of measure in the last lesson. Point out that linear units of measure are those that measure length, height, width, and distance. Demonstrate and ask students to use their arms with you to show how long, how high, how wide, and how far something is.

Explain to students that linear units of measure include both customary units of measure and metric units. Tell them that customary units of measure are used in the United States. Write the word *customary* on the board, pronounce it, and have students repeat it. Tell students that customary units of measure include inches, feet, yards, and miles. Ask students to think about a time when they might want to talk about distance in miles. (how far away something is, how far we travel on a trip)

Distribute inch/centimeter rulers. Focus students' attention on the smaller units. Write *centimeter* on the board, and explain that this is a metric unit. Elicit other metric units (decimeter, kilometer, meter), and write them on the board. Inform students that these metric units are used in most countries in the world. Ask students if they know whether centimeters, meters, and kilometers are used in their home countries. If a world map is available, point out the students' home countries.

Point out that in the examples of metric units, all the units contain the root word *meter*. Have a volunteer underline the root word *meter* in each of the metric units on the board.

BP 6 Have students work in small groups. Ask them to use their inch/centimeter rulers to measure the approximate length of one shoe of each group member. Tell groups to use both customary and metric units of measure to find out which team member has the longest shoe. Then have groups report to the class what they did, using all four of the vocabulary terms on page 66.

Display Transparency 33. Ask students: *What units of measurement does this ruler show?* (inches and centimeters) Point to the inches side of the ruler and to the centimeters side of the ruler in turn. Ask: *Are inches a customary or metric measure of length? What about centimeters?*

- **Have students work with a partner.** Ask them to look at the crayon above the ruler. Write the sentence frame on the board and read it aloud: *The _____ is longer than the _____.* Have students compare the crayon and the caterpillar using the sentence frame. Have students fill in the blanks using the new vocabulary words.

- **BP 6 Distribute inch/centimeter rulers to groups of four students.** Tell students that the ruler shows both inches and centimeters. Have them check the markings that show an inch, a half inch, and a quarter inch. Then have them find one centimeter, three centimeters, five centimeters, and ten centimeters. Point out that ten centimeters equal one decimeter. Say that the inch and the centimeter are linear units. Ask: *Which is a customary unit of measurement? Which is a metric unit of measurement?*

- **Display Transparency 33 again.** Say: *You can measure parts of inches when you measure things. You can measure things in half inches or quarter inches.*

- **Ask:** *How long is the crayon to the nearest inch? To the nearest half inch? To the nearest quarter inch?* Ask the same questions about the caterpillar.

Have students complete the Vocabulary Cards for the words in this module.

C Review and Practice

Review the vocabulary terms with students. As you say each one, have students try to give a definition or example without looking at the student worktext.

Have students play a category game with the vocabulary. Write two categories on the board in large letters: *Customary Units of Linear Measure* and *Metric Units of Linear Measure*. Distribute sticky notes. Have pairs write on each sticky note an example of a customary or metric unit of measure, and then stick their sticky notes on the board in the correct category. As they post their notes, they must say aloud the heading title and the word on their sticky note.

Introduce the Practice the Words activity on page 66 in the student worktext. Make sure students understand the directions and the crossword puzzle. Have students complete the activity independently. Check students as they work, and then assess them.

D Assess and Intervene

Does every student understand the Essential Vocabulary in the Practice the Words activity on page 66? Use the rubric to identify students who need extra support through additional help and the Intervention activity.

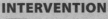

Intermediate

- ☐ Matches at least 3 of the correct words and their definitions.
- ☐ Writes a phrase or sentence, with some errors, that indicates knowledge of where customary and metric systems are used.

Advanced

- ☐ Matches all 4 of the correct words and their definitions.
- ☐ Writes a complete sentence, with few errors, that indicates knowledge of where customary and metric systems are used.

INTERVENTION 5 minutes

Some students may have difficulty understanding the Essential Vocabulary. Help students by paraphrasing and simplifying the terms. For example: customary—measuring that is a <u>custom</u> in the United States; <u>linear</u>—a <u>line</u> can be long (show length), wide (width), high (height), or far (distance). Students may write these in the "Other" box of their Vocabulary Cards to help them learn a new way to remember the vocabulary.

Lesson 3

Use More Language

Objective Use *about* and *actually* to describe estimating and measuring using customary and metric linear units.

40 minutes

Teach this lesson:
- **Before** lessons on linear measurement in students' grade-level math textbooks
- **Before** students complete the activities on page 67 of the student worktext

You need these materials:
- Worksheet 17
- Transparency 34
- customary and metric measuring tools (rulers, yard/meter sticks, tape measures)
- index cards

Lesson Vocabulary

Essential Vocabulary

inch (in.)	foot (ft)	yard (yd)
mile (mi)	millimeter (mm)	centimeter (cm)
decimeter (dm)	meter (m)	kilometer (km)

Use More Language

Objective Use *about* and *actually* to describe estimating and measuring using customary and metric linear units.

Learn the Language

I can guess about how long that caterpillar is. I think the caterpillar is about 3 inches long!

I found a longer caterpillar yesterday. I measured it. The caterpillar was actually 20 centimeters long!

Customary Units of Length
1 foot (ft) = 12 inches (in.)
1 yard (yd) = 3 feet (ft)
1 yard (yd) = 36 inches (in.)
1 mile (mi) = 1,760 yards (yd)

Metric Units of Length
1 centimeter (cm) = 10 millimeters (mm)
1 decimeter (dm) = 10 centimeters (cm)
1 meter (m) = 10 decimeters
1 kilometer (km) = 1,000 meters

Practice the Language

Directions For items 1 to 3, choose *about* or *actually* for the first blank in each of the sentences below. In the second blank, use customary units of measure. For items 4 to 6, choose *about* or *actually* and use metric units of measure.

1. My aunt sent me a music box from Europe. I measured it. It is actually _____ 10 inches _____ long.

2. I think that the kite flying in the sky is about _____ 1 yard _____ long.

3. I measured our new dining table. It is actually _____ 8 feet _____ long.

4. I think Sam's car is about _____ 4 meters _____ long.

5. I measured my mom's cell phone. It is actually _____ 12 centimeters _____ long.

6. I measured that fork. It is actually _____ 2 decimeters _____ long.

A Introduce

Say: *Sometimes when you need to know how long, wide, or tall an object is, you can estimate, or make an educated guess. Other times, it is important that you have an actual measurement.*

Have students work with a partner. Ask: *When is it okay to estimate how many inches, feet, or yards something is? When can I say, It's about 3 inches, or It's about 10 feet, or It's about 50 miles?* Have students discuss with their partner and then report their thoughts.

Connect student's learning to real life. Ask: *When is it important to know the actual length, width, or height of something or someone? When do you need to know how many inches or feet something actually is?* Wait for responses. Say: *If I want to buy carpeting, I have to know exactly how big the room is.*

Read aloud the Lesson Objective on page 67 in the student worktext. Write on the board the words *about* and *actually*. Tell students they will learn to use these two words to describe estimating and measuring when they are using customary and metric linear units.

B Teach and Learn

Point to the words *about* and *actually* on the board. Model the pronunciation of the words, and have students repeat them. Make sure the students stress -*bout* in the first word and *act*- in the second word. Be aware that some students may have difficulty pronouncing *actually*.

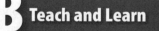

Highlighted words and phrases may affect student comprehension.

Measures of Length (Customary and Metric) • 67

Focus students' attention on the pictures at the top of page 67 in the student worktext. Have students study the pictures and discuss with a partner what they see.

Call for a volunteer to read aloud the speech bubble of the first deer. Ask: *What are the two deer doing? What does the deer on the left see? About how long is the caterpillar?* (3 inches)

Ask students to read together the speech bubble of the second deer. Ask: *What did the second deer find yesterday? What did he do to the caterpillar? What was the actual length of the caterpillar?* (9 centimeters)

Say: *When we estimate the measurement of something, we do not know the exact measurement. We can use the word* about. *We can say, The cat is about 10 inches tall. Or we can say, The dog is about 2 feet long.* Ask students to suggest other times we might use *about* when we measure things.

Write the following sentence frame on the board. *I think ____ is about ____ long.* Model the sentence by saying: *I think your desk is about 2 feet long.* Ask students to come up with other words and estimates, either customary or metric, and use the sentence frame to make sentences of their own. Have volunteers say their sentences aloud.

Say: *When we use a measuring tool, we get an actual measurement. We use the word* actually. *For example, I measured the window with a tape measure. It is actually 78 inches long.*

Write the following sentence frames on the board, and model them for students:
I measured the ____ with a ____. The ____ is actually ____ long.

Provide a few examples for students using the above sentence frame. Emphasize the word *actually*. Then have students work in groups of three or four to create sentences using the frames. Encourage groups to write sentences using both customary and metric units of measure, as well as different measuring tools. Have a volunteer from each group write one of their sentences on the board.

Display Transparency 34. Tell students that these are customary and metric units that we use to measure length. Pronounce the names of the metric units, and have students repeat. Read the directions. Ask students to work with a partner to write the abbreviations and the plurals for each unit on a sheet of paper. Tell them to be careful with the abbreviation of *inch* and the plural of *inch* and *foot*. When they finish, ask volunteers to write their answers on the transparency.

Have students complete the Vocabulary Cards for this lesson.

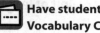 **Review and Practice**

Use the Vocabulary Cards to review customary and metric units of linear measure. Have students shuffle their cards. Then, working in pairs, have them separate the cards into customary and metric and put the cards in each group in order from smallest to largest unit. Have them read the names of the units in order.

Hand out Worksheet 17. Go over the directions with students. Use item 1 to demonstrate reading the name of the item, choosing and recording the correct unit as an estimate, measuring the item, and recording the measurement. Provide metric and customary measuring tools.

- **Have students complete the worksheet in pairs.** Assist as necessary. When pairs have finished, ask them to compare their work with another pair and discuss any differences so they can decide which units are correct.

BP 6 Hand out three index cards to each pair of students. Explain that students will first estimate the length of three classroom items (not previously measured), and then they will actually measure the items. Tell them that they will record the information on the index cards. Write on the board the following sentence frames for students to use to record the estimate and the actual measurement of each item. Remind them they can use customary or metric units.

Estimated measurement: The ____ is about ____ long.

Actual measurement: It is actually ____ long.

- **When pairs have completed and recorded their estimates, give them measuring tools.** After they measure, ask for volunteer pairs to report on one of the items they chose, using the following sentence frames: *We estimated that the ____ was about ____ long. We measured the ____. It was actually ____ long.*

 Assess and Intervene

Are students able to use *about* and *actually* to describe estimating and measuring using customary and metric linear units based on Practice the Language on page 67? Use the rubric to identify students who need extra support through additional help and the Intervention activity.

Intermediate

☐ Completes 4 of 6 sentences by filling *about* or *actually* correctly.

☐ Chooses appropriate customary units for items 1–3 and metric units for items 4–6.

Advanced

☐ Completes 6 of 6 sentences by filling in *about* or *actually* correctly.

☐ Chooses appropriate customary units for items 1–3 and metric units for items 4–6.

INTERVENTION   5 minutes

If students are having difficulty writing sentences using the words *about* and *actually,* write the following chant on the board and help them repeat it, clapping its rhythm as they chant:

About is a guess that I can make!

Actually is a measure I can take!

Lesson

Solve Math Problems

Objective Decide whether to multiply or divide to solve problems where you need to change from one customary unit of length to another.

---

30 minutes

Teach this lesson:
- **After** lesson on changing customary units of measure in students' grade-level math textbooks
- **Before** students complete the activities on page 68 of the student worktext

You need these materials:
- large and small counters

EXTENSION AND ENRICHMENT   10 minutes

Have students estimate in class the length, width, and height of a family (or neighbor's) vehicle (car, van, truck) or bicycle. Ask each student to write their estimate on a piece of paper using a sentence with *about*. Students should exchange their paper with a partner. The partner should change the estimate to another unit of measure, from feet to yards, for example, and then give back the paper. At home, students should measure the object and write a sentence using the word *actually*. During the next class, have students report their findings to the whole class, comparing the actual measurements to their own estimate and their partner's conversion.

LESSON
4

Solve Math Problems

Objective Decide whether to multiply or divide to solve problems where you need to change from one customary unit of length to another.

Learn to Solve Problems

> **Problem** Jung's bedroom at home is 12 feet long. How long is his room in yards?

	Think	Write
Step 1:	Read the problem. Underline the question. What do you need to do to solve the problem?	I have to change feet to yards.
Step 2:	Circle the facts. Decide whether you need to multiply or divide.	I circled **12 feet**. I need to divide because I am changing smaller units (feet) to larger units (yards).
Step 3:	Write a number sentence. Solve the problem.	There are 3 feet in a yard. I will divide 12 by 3. 12 ÷ 3 = 4. Jung's room is 3 yards long.

Practice Solving Math Problems

Directions Use steps 1 to 3 above to solve the problems below. Write *multiply* or *divide* on the line below each problem. Then write a sentence to tell what you will do. Finally, solve the problem and write the answer in a complete sentence.

1 Carla threw a ball 9 yards. How many feet did she throw the ball?

Multiply. I will multiply 9 × 3. She threw the ball 27 feet.

2 Berta's mother is making a tablecloth. She needs 4 yards of fabric. How many feet of fabric does she need?

Multiply. I will multiply 4 × 3. She needs 12 feet of fabric.

3 The classroom is 45 feet long. How many yards long is the classroom?

Divide. I will divide 45 by 3. The classroom is 15 yards long.

4 The length of the flower garden is eight feet. How many inches long is the garden?

Multiply. I will multiply 8 × 12. The garden is 96 inches long.

68 · Measures of Length (Customary and Metric)

A | Introduce

Read aloud the Lesson Objective with students. Remind them that they learned the linear units of measure in Lesson 3.

Say: *Sometimes we need to compare units of measure. If the units are not the same, such as inches and feet, or feet and yards, we need to know how to change from one to another.*

Have students look at page 67 in the student worktext. Point out that metric units can always be divided by 10, so it is easy to change metric units of measure. Point out the Customary Units of Length in the deer hoof print from Lesson 3, and go over the units again. Say: *Sometimes we might need to change inches to feet or feet to yards.*

Ask: *How many inches are there in a foot?* (12) *How many feet are there in a yard?* (3) *How many inches are there in a yard?* (36)

Highlighted words and phrases may affect student comprehension.

B Teach and Learn

Direct students' attention to the problem at the top of page 68 in the student worktext. Ask students to read it aloud with you. Then ask the following comprehension questions, asking students not to look at their worktexts: *What is the problem about?* (Jung's bedroom) *How long is it?* (12 feet) *What problem needs to be solved?* (changing feet to yards)

Go through the steps together, one by one. Have students look at Step 1 and read it aloud. Have students reread the problem and underline the question. Ask students: *What do we have to do to solve the problem?* (change feet to yards)

- **Call students' attention to the box next to Step 1.** Ask students to read what the boy wrote. Ask: *So what are you going to do?* (change feet to yards)

- **Focus students' attention on Step 2.** Ask students to read Step 2 with you. Ask: *So what are you going to do?* (circle the facts; decide whether to multiply or divide) Say: *We change from smaller units to larger units. Feet are smaller than yards. So we need to divide.*

- **Read Step 3 aloud.** Ask: *How many feet are there in a yard?* (3) *I will divide 12 feet (the length of Jung's room) by 3. 12 ÷ 3 = 4. How long is Jung's room?* (4 yards long)

- **Point out to students that if the problem is to change larger units (such as yards) into smaller units (such as feet), you have to multiply.**

Write the following problem on the board:
Kim's mother asked him to measure the length of the flower garden in their yard. Kim took a yardstick and measured the flower garden. He found the flower garden was 6 yards long. His mother wanted to know how many feet the garden was. What should Kim do?

- **Have pairs of students discuss what Kim should do.** Encourage them to look at the steps as they solve the problem. Have the first pair to finish raise their hands and report what they did. (multiply; the garden is 18 feet long)

Direct students to work in groups of four to write two problems of their own. They should write one problem that requires multiplication, and another that requires division. Ask students not to write the solution on the paper. Circulate around the room and listen in as the groups discuss and write their problems. Assist as needed. When the groups are finished writing their problems, have them exchange them with another group. Tell them to be sure to use the steps as they work together to solve the problems.

Write the following on the board:

smaller units   larger units
inches   feet   yards

Explain that when you change from a smaller unit to a larger unit, the number of units will be less, so you divide!

Write the following on the board:

larger units   smaller units
yards   feet   inches

Explain that when you change from a larger unit to a smaller unit, the number of units will be more, so you multiply!

C Review and Practice

Review how to decide whether to multiply or divide. Write on the board for students to copy and learn:

smaller	larger	÷	less
inches	feet	divide	

larger	smaller	×	more
feet	inches	multiply	

Say: *When you change smaller units to larger units, you need fewer of the units, so you divide. When you change larger units to smaller units, you need more of the units, so you multiply.*

Have students work in pairs. Ask them to decide whether they need to multiply or divide to fill in the following chart. Write the chart on the board. Explain that you have provided the first example. Tell students that, working in pairs, they will have to figure out the missing numbers by multiplying or dividing. (Allow students to use calculators if they have not yet learned multiplication and division with regrouping.)

Inches	36	72	144
Feet	3		
Yards	1		

As a check for understanding, have volunteer pairs describe what they had to do (multiply or divide) to find the answer.

D Assess and Intervene

Do students know whether to use multiplication or division when changing customary units of measure based on Practice Solving Math Problems on page 68? Use the following rubric to identify students who need extra support through additional help and the Intervention activity.

Intermediate

☐ Correctly decides in 3 out of 4 word problems whether to multiply or divide.

☐ Writes a correct sentence to solve the problem, with some errors.

Advanced

☐ Correctly decides in 4 out of 4 word problems whether to multiply or divide

☐ Writes a correct sentence to solve the problem, with few errors.

INTERVENTION   10 minutes

BP 6 If students are having difficulty deciding whether to multiply or divide, give them large and small counters. For each problem on page 68, have them identify the larger unit of measure and count out that number of large counters. Then have them take one large counter and exchange it for the appropriate number of small counters. Continue until all the large counters have been exchanged. Ask whether they multiplied the large counters or divided them (multiplied, because each large counter was changed into more small counters).

Repeat the activity. This time identify the smaller unit, and count out that number of small counters. After exchanging the appropriate number of small counters for one larger one, help students explain why they had to divide (because each group of small counters was changed into one large counter).

Lesson 1

Prerequisite Background Knowledge
- Concept of measurement
- Concept and vocabulary of estimation, comparing, and ordering

Understand the Main Idea

Objective Explain when to use units of capacity, weight, and mass.

30 minutes 🕐

Teach this lesson:
- **Before** introducing material on capacity, weight, and mass in students' grade-level math textbooks
- **Before** students complete the activities on page 69 of the student worktext

You need these materials:
- cup, water in a container for pouring
- book, empty milk carton, and toy car or other classroom objects with capacity and weight/mass
- measuring cups, scales, and balances
- Worksheet 18

BP 1 ELL BEST PRACTICE #1:
Comprehensible Language

English language learners are not able to understand everything that is said in the classroom. Teachers can modify their language to help students understand more of the language and concepts presented. Use simple sentences to explain the concepts of capacity, weight, and mass. Speak slowly and clearly and include hands-on and visual links to concepts wherever you can.

Throughout this module, when you see **BP 1**, you will find an example of how you can incorporate comprehensible language into your instruction.

Module 18: Measures of Capacity and Weight/Mass (Customary and Metric)

LESSON 1

Understand the Main Idea

Objective Explain when to use units of capacity, weight, and mass.

Learn the Main Idea

> How heavy is this rock? I can measure to find out. I'll use units of weight or mass to measure.

> Which bucket holds more? I can measure to find out. I'll use units of capacity to measure.

MAIN IDEA Units of capacity, weight, and mass can be used to measure and compare things.

Practice Applying the Main Idea

Directions What units should you use to find an answer? Connect the question with the units you would use to find the answer. Answer question 5 on a separate sheet of paper.

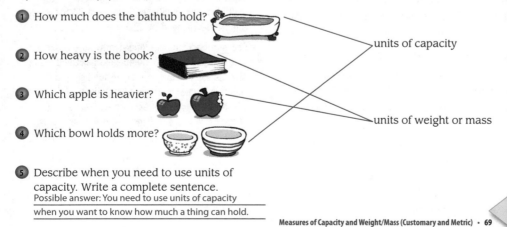

1. How much does the bathtub hold?
2. How heavy is the book?
3. Which apple is heavier?
4. Which bowl holds more?

units of capacity

units of weight or mass

5. Describe when you need to use units of capacity. Write a complete sentence.
Possible answer: You need to use units of capacity when you want to know how much a thing can hold.

Measures of Capacity and Weight/Mass (Customary and Metric) • **69**

A Introduce

Mime picking up something heavy from the floor and placing it on your desk. Be sure to strain your muscles and put a grimace on your face. Then ask students: *What did I just pretend to do? How do you know?* Elicit that you lifted something.

BP 1 Say: *You don't know what I lifted, but you know something about it. Was it heavy or was it light?* Emphasize the words *heavy* and *light*. Ask students how they know the answer.

Establish that the item was heavy because it looked like it was hard to lift. Have students act out lifting a heavy object. Then have them mime lifting something light. Have them say: *This is heavy. It is hard to lift. This is light. It is easy to lift.*

Display an empty cup. Turn it upside down to show it is empty. Then pour water into it. Have students tell you when the cup is full.

Explain that this lesson tells about measuring things that are heavy and things that are full.

Read aloud the Lesson Objective with students. Tell them that *capacity* tells how full something is and that *weight* and *mass* both tell how heavy something is.

Highlighted words and phrases may affect student comprehension.

Call students' attention to the first picture at the top of page 69. Have each student tell the class one thing he or she notices about the picture. Encourage students to say something that hasn't yet been said. Help them to express their ideas in complete sentences. If needed, ask questions, such as: *What is the boy doing? What is he holding?*

- **Read aloud the text in the speech bubble.** Help students break down the ideas by asking: *What does the boy want to know? What will he do to find out?* and *What units will he use?* There is no need to discuss the difference between mass and weight at this point; just explain that they tell how heavy an object is.

- **Tell students that they probably know some units of weight and mass already.** Write *pounds* and *grams* on the board. Read the words aloud. Ask students to tell what they know about these words. Help them form sentences with these words, such as: *I weigh 60 pounds.*

- **BP 1 Touch the words in turn.** Say: *You can measure weight in pounds or measure mass in grams.*

Introduce the second picture. Read aloud the speech bubble and explain that the girl has two buckets. Say: *The girl wants to know which bucket holds more. She needs to find how much water she can put into each bucket.* Have students talk to a partner about which bucket they think holds more, and why.

- **Break down the ideas by asking questions as you did with the first picture.** Ask if students know any units of capacity and record responses. Suggest *liters* and *gallons* if students have no ideas. Help students form sentences with these words. Then touch the words in turn and say: *You can measure capacity in ____.*

Read aloud the Main Idea with students. Have them touch the words *mass, capacity,* and *weight* in their student worktexts.

B Teach and Learn

Write the words *capacity, weight,* and *mass* on the board. Next to *capacity,* write: *How much does it hold?* Next to *weight* and *mass,* write: *How heavy is it?* Read the words and questions with students.

Hold up the cup you displayed earlier. Say: *I want to know how much the cup will hold. Do I measure in units of capacity, mass, or weight?* (capacity) Say: *When I want to know how much a container will hold, I measure its capacity.*

Hold up a book. Say: *I want to know how heavy this book is. Do I measure in units of capacity, or in units of weight or mass?* (weight or mass) Say: *When I want to know how heavy an object is, I measure its _____.* (weight or mass)

BP 1 Repeat, using a milk carton for capacity and a toy car for weight/mass. Have students say as much of the sentences beginning *When I want to know . . .* as they can.

Say: *Look around you. What can you measure in units of capacity? What can you measure in units of weight or mass?* Have students use the sentence frame: *You can measure the capacity/weight/mass of _____.*

Have students work in groups of three. Give each student a copy of Worksheet 18. Instruct students to draw and label objects in and out of the classroom that fit the categories. Then have them talk to another group about their work, using the sentence frame: *You can measure the _____ of a _____.*

Wrap up by reading the Main Idea aloud again. Ask students to summarize what they have learned so far.

C Review and Practice

To review the lesson, play a game with students. Divide them into two teams and have each team form a line.

- **Write on the board:** *How heavy is it? How much does it hold?* Have the first student on one team choose a question and pose it for the first student on the other team. That student must respond *units of weight or mass* or *units of capacity.* If the answer is correct, that team gets a point. Have students take turns asking and answering questions.

Call students' attention to the Practice Applying the Main Idea activity. Read the directions aloud. Point out that question 5 asks students to write a full sentence.

Have students work independently on items 1–5. Check their answers.

D Assess and Intervene

Can students relate concepts of capacity, weight, and mass with various situations, based on their work on page 69? Use the rubric to identify students who need extra support through additional help and the Intervention activity.

Intermediate

- ☐ Connects all 4 questions to the correct unit of measurement.
- ☐ Writes a phrase, with some errors, that tells about capacity but doesn't clearly explain it.

  Example of a sentence a student might write: *Use capacity to know how much in something.*

Advanced

- ☐ Connects all 4 questions to the correct unit of measurement.
- ☐ Writes a complete sentence that clearly explains capacity.

  Example of a sentence a student might write: *You use capacity when you want to know how much bucket hold.*

INTERVENTION   10 minutes

If students are having difficulty with Practice Applying the Main Idea, they may understand the concepts if they use concrete materials. Provide an assortment of measuring cups, scales, and balances for students to work with. Have students talk to each other about the materials and what they learn from using them. Have students relate the words *capacity* and *weight/mass* to what they observe. Encourage students to talk about capacity and weight/mass in complete sentences.

Lesson

2

Learn the Vocabulary

Objective Talk and write about capacity, weight, and mass.

30 minutes 🕐

Teach this lesson:
- **Before** introducing lessons on capacity, weight, and mass in students' grade-level math textbooks
- **Before** students complete the activities on page 70 of the student worktext

You need these materials:
- index cards
- cup or milk carton and stapler
- Transparency 35
- Vocabulary Cards

Lesson Vocabulary

Essential Vocablary

capacity	to hold	weight
to weigh	mass	

Additional Vocablary

customary	metric	unit
container	scale	balance

LESSON 2

Learn the Vocabulary

Objective Talk and write about capacity, weight, and mass.

Learn the Words

Directions Fill in the missing words.

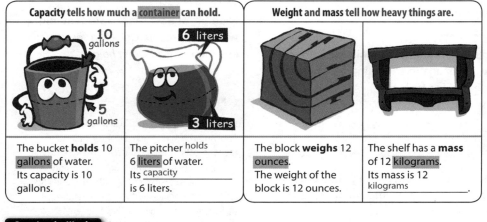

Capacity tells how much a container can hold.		Weight and mass tell how heavy things are.	
10 gallons / 5 gallons	6 liters / 3 liters	(block)	(shelf)
The bucket **holds** 10 gallons of water. Its capacity is 10 gallons.	The pitcher holds 6 liters of water. Its capacity is 6 liters.	The block **weighs** 12 ounces. The weight of the block is 12 ounces.	The shelf has a **mass** of 12 kilograms. Its mass is 12 kilograms.

Practice the Words

Directions Find and circle the hidden vocabulary words. Then write a sentence that tells about each word.

1. p w q u i v r o v m k o r c q p e s (c a p a c i t y) u v m d w x p
Possible sentence: You can use units of capacity to tell how full a thing is.

2. t w j (w e i g h) m p a w g l c f v w o t h z a u p m d w y j g o t
Possible sentence: I can measure something to find out how much it weighs.

3. p b v s r t k l x l f h w e l h f m r w z c h c p o i n (m a s s) p r i
Possible sentence: You can use mass to tell how how heavy something is.

4. t h e l j f q a g b r i j r (w e i g h t) p v s y m s w i l k h i n x o v
Possible sentence: Weight tells me how heavy something is.

5. z e d c (h o l d) p v e y i o a s p j l e e i a u r w y b u o q t z a r l
Possible sentence: When you measure capacity, you find how much a container can hold.

A Introduce

Briefly review the concepts students learned in the first lesson. Go around the room, asking students to tell one thing they remember learning.

Ask students if they have any questions about what they learned. If any students have a question, have them write it on an index card. Collect the questions and use them to guide your teaching of capacity, weight, and mass.

Read aloud the Lesson Objective with students. Ask students to think about vocabulary words that will help them talk and write about capacity, weight, and mass. Write these words on the board. Add any missing Essential Vocabulary words.

BP 1 Circle the Essential Vocabulary words on the board. Read these words slowly and clearly and have students repeat them. Point out that *to hold* and *to weigh* are verbs, or things I can do.

Choose words from the Additional Vocabulary box that you think will be useful. Add these to the list. Elicit or provide examples for all the words on the list.

Highlighted words and phrases may affect student comprehension.

Teach and Learn

Read aloud the statement about capacity at the top of page 70 in the student worktext. Have students follow along. Display a cup or a milk carton and teach students a chant: *CaPAcity TELLS how MUCH this HOLDS.* Have students say the chant several times, clapping to its rhythm, both as a whole group and in smaller groups as well.

Point out the picture of the bucket on page 70. Ask what a bucket is used for. (to hold water) Emphasize that the word *hold* is used in that sentence.

- **Read aloud the text below the picture.** Explain that a gallon is a unit that measures capacity. Ask if 10 gallons seems like a lot or like a little. Help students visualize capacity by asking: *Can the bucket hold as much as a swimming pool?* (no) *Can the bucket hold more than a spoon?* (yes)

- **BP 1 Emphasize that the word *hold* has several meanings.** Be sure students do not think that finding how much the bucket holds implies that they must hold the bucket in their hands. Explain that the meaning used here is *fit inside.* Tell students that the question *How much water will fit inside the bucket?* is the same as the question *How much water does the bucket hold?*

BP 1 Call students' attention to the drawing of the pitcher in the second column on page 70.

- **Ask if students think the pitcher holds more or less than the bucket, and why they think so.** Help them respond, using the sentence frame: *I think the pitcher holds _____ than the bucket because _____.*

- **Read the text with students.** Pause at the blank spaces. Ask students to work in small groups to fill in the blanks. When they finish, have them check their answers with another group. Be sure all students fill in the words *holds* and *capacity.* Wrap up this part of the lesson by displaying the cup again and having students repeat the chant several times: *CaPAcity TELLS how MUCH this HOLDS.*

Continue with the statement about weight and mass. Display a common classroom object, such as a stapler. Teach students the chant: *WEIGHT and MASS tell how HEAvy this IS.* As before, have students repeat the chant several times, clapping to its rhythm.

Have students study the pictures of the block and the shelf. Name each object. Say: *We can measure the weight or mass of these objects to tell how heavy they are.*

Read aloud the text below the pictures. Explain that weight can be measured in units called *ounces.* Mass is sometimes measured in units called *kilograms.* Have students fill in the blank in the right column and check their answers with a partner.

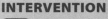 **Display Transparency 35.** Tell students they are going to work in groups of four. They will compare the capacity of two things and the weight or mass of two things. Read the directions aloud and make sure students understand them. Circulate to see that groups are choosing between each two objects and using the correct answer to complete the sentence frame at the bottom of the column.

- **When students are finished, have them share their answers with another group, using the sentence frames.**

 Have students complete the Vocabulary Cards for the words in this lesson.

Review and Practice

Briefly review the Essential Vocabulary words. Then say: *Tell me what* capacity *means.* Call on volunteers to give the meaning of *capacity,* using examples and language from the worktext. Then ask pairs to share their ideas. Repeat with the other words.

Call students' attention to Practice the Words on page 70. Read the directions aloud. Explain that all the words appear from left to right and that each word appears in one row. Point out students will write a complete sentence that uses and describes each word after they have found it.

Have students work through items 1–5 on their own. Note who is having difficulty. Go over possible sentences after everyone has completed the assignment.

Assess and Intervene

Can students use the vocabulary words, as indicated by their work on Practice the Words on page 70? Use the rubric to identify students who need extra support through additional help and the Intervention activity.

Intermediate

- ☐ Finds at least 4 vocabulary words.
- ☐ Writes at least 3 sentences that use the correct words and show some understanding of their meaning.

  Example of a sentence a student might write: *Weigh thing and see if heavy.*

Advanced

- ☐ Finds all 5 vocabulary words.
- ☐ Writes at least 4 sentences that use the correct words and show good understanding of their meaning.

  Example of a sentence a student might write: *You can use mass to see how heavy thing is.*

INTERVENTION 5 minutes

If students cannot write sentences to tell about the vocabulary words, help by giving them partial sentences and having them relate the sentence parts to the vocabulary words. Have students put their Vocabulary Cards in front of them. Then write on the board: *You can use _____ to tell how much something _____.* Have students work with a partner to identify two words that can go in the blanks. (capacity and holds or weight/mass and weighs) If this is still too hard, fill in one of the two missing words. Continue with other sentences as time permits.

Use More Language

Objective Use *greater than*, *less than*, and *equal to* to compare units of capacity, weight, and mass.

---

30 minutes

Teach this lesson:
- **Before** introducing grade-level math textbook lessons on capacity, weight, and mass
- **Before** students complete the activities on page 71 of the student worktext

You need these materials:
- word puzzles
- gallon milk jug and measuring cup
- index cards and tape
- various containers and objects

EXTENSION AND ENRICHMENT 15 minutes

Have students create word puzzles that use the units of measurement mentioned in this lesson. Show students examples of scrambled word puzzles, crosswords, and other types of word puzzles. Have them work with a partner to create a puzzle. Have them write clues to give hints for each of the words. Assemble the puzzles into a booklet and encourage students to solve them as extra practice.

Use More Language

Objective Use *greater than*, *less than*, and *equal to* to compare units of capacity, weight, and mass.

LESSON 3

Learn the Language

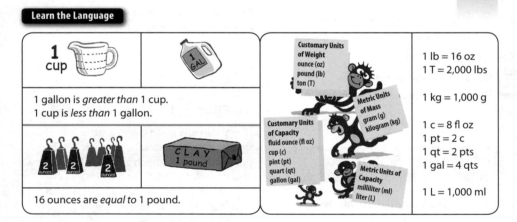

1 gallon is *greater than* 1 cup.
1 cup is *less than* 1 gallon.

16 ounces are *equal to* 1 pound.

1 lb = 16 oz	
1 T = 2,000 lbs	
1 kg = 1,000 g	
1 c = 8 fl oz	
1 pt = 2 c	
1 qt = 2 pts	
1 gal = 4 qts	
1 L = 1,000 ml	

Practice the Language

Directions Write *greater than*, *less than*, or *equal to* to complete the sentences below. Use the information above to help you. Then write a complete sentence for question 6.

1. 1 pound is <u>less than</u> 1 ton.

2. 1 cup is <u>greater than</u> 1 fluid ounce.

3. 1 liter is <u>equal to</u> 1,000 milliliters.

4. 1 gram is <u>less than</u> 1 kilogram.

5. 20 ounces are <u>greater than</u> 1 pound.

6. Write a sentence to compare 1 liter and 1 milliliter.

   Possible answers: 1 liter is greater than 1 milliliter.

   1 milliliter is less than 1 liter.

   _____

A Introduce

Read aloud the Lesson Objective with students.

Introduce a quick warm-up activity to practice the vocabulary of the Lesson Objective. Write the numbers 1 through 10 on the board. Ask students to create sentences that use these numbers and the phrases *is less than* and *is greater than,* such as: *5 is greater than 1.* Be sure students are comfortable using these phrases to compare numbers.

Explain that just like numbers, units of capacity, weight, and mass can be compared. Tell students that they will learn how to compare these units in this lesson.

B Teach and Learn

Hold up a gallon milk jug. Say: *Some units are large. This holds 1 gallon.* Then hold up a measuring cup. Say: *Some units are small. This holds 1 cup. Which holds more, 1 gallon or 1 cup?* (gallon) *We say 1 gallon is* greater than *1 cup.* Then ask: *Is it better to have 1 gallon of ice cream or 1 cup of ice cream? Why?* Have students discuss their answer with a partner.

Highlighted words and phrases may affect student comprehension.

Measures of Capacity and Weight/Mass (Customary and Metric) · **71**

Have students study the first two pictures of containers in the student worktext on page 71. Read aloud the labels *1 cup* and *1 gallon*. Write these words on index cards.

- **Say:** *We just compared cups and gallons. What did we find out?* Say there are two ways of recording the comparison.

- **Write the phrase** *is greater than* **on the board.** Have two students come forward. Give them each one of the cards. Ask them to tape the cards to the board so the sentence is true. Draw out that the sentence should read: *1 gallon is greater than 1 cup.*

- **Now change the phrase so it reads** *is less than.* Ask students how they can make the sentence true. Elicit that the cards need to be switched so the sentence reads: *1 cup is less than 1 gallon.* Point out that these two sentences are written in their student worktexts.

- **BP 1** Then say: *A gallon is greater than a cup. A cup is less than a gallon. You can write the same idea two different ways.*

Continue with the two pictures on the bottom left. Say: *One picture shows 16 ounces.* Explain that ounces are very small units of weight. Point out that the other picture shows 1 pound. Say: *1 pound is greater than 1 ounce. But 1 pound is not greater than 16 ounces!* Tell students that 1 pound is equal to 16 ounces.

- **Call students' attention to the sentence below the pictures.** Test comprehension by asking students if they would rather have 16 ounces or 1 pound of their favorite food. Ask them to discuss their ideas with a partner. Then have students share the highlights of their conversations with the rest of the class. Elicit that since 16 ounces equals 1 pound, the two amounts are identical—it doesn't make any difference which one they have.

Explain that many different units are used to measure capacity, weight, and mass. Focus students' attention on the chart with the monkeys. (Note that if students have not begun work on capacity, weight, and mass in their grade-level math textbooks, they will need extra time to become familiar with some of these terms. If this is the case, it may help to display containers and objects that match some of the units discussed here.) Explain or review the differences between customary and metric units of measure.

- **BP 1** **Say the name of each unit on the list slowly and clearly and have students repeat.** Use some of the units in sentences or have students create sentences that use them, if they are comfortable doing so. Point out that the units are listed from smallest to largest.

Distribute Vocabulary Cards for this lesson. Students are not to fill them out yet.

- **Have students play a game to familiarize themselves with some of the units.** Divide students into groups of three. Have one student shuffle his or her cards and place the top one face up on the table. Ask this student to read the word aloud. Then have the other two students race to identify it as a unit of capacity, mass, or weight. The first to correctly identify the unit wins a point. Continue till each player has gone through all his or her cards for the other two to identify.

- **Read aloud the equivalencies at the bottom of the signs.** Say: *1 pound is equal to 16 ounces. Which is greater, 1 pound or 1 ounce?* Elicit that ounces must be less than pounds. Repeat with other examples.

Have students practice forming sentences that compare these units. Have students work in groups of three again. Have the first student choose two units of measurement that are in the same category, such as grams and kilograms or fluid ounces and pints. Ask that student to place the cards for these two words on the table.

- **Then have the other two students work together to create sentences that compare the two, such as:** *A gram is less than a kilogram.* or *A pint is greater than a fluid ounce.*

Wrap up this part of the lesson by asking students what strategies they used to compare the units. Write students' ideas on the board.

Have students fill out their Vocabulary Cards.

Review and Practice

Have students review the information in this lesson by determining whether sentences are true or false. Write on the board: *1 quart is less than 1 gallon.* Have students read it aloud. Ask whether the sentence is

true or false. (true) Repeat with three or four more sentences, some true, some false.

- **Have students write similar sentences, and have a partner decide if the sentences are true or false.**

Direct students' attention to Practice the Language on page 71. Read the instructions aloud. Have students complete the items independently.

D Assess and Intervene

Can students use *greater than, less than,* and *equal to* to compare units of capacity, weight, and mass, based on Practice the Language on page 71 of the student worktext? Use the rubric to identify students who need extra support through additional help and the Intervention activity.

Intermediate

☐ Fills in at least 4 phrases correctly.

☐ Writes a sentence or phrase that compares the two units correctly, but may contain some errors.

Example of a sentence a student might write: *I liter greater than 1 milliliter.*

Advanced

☐ Fills in all 5 phrases correctly.

☐ Writes a complete sentence, with no errors, that compares the two units correctly.

Example of a sentence a student might write: *1 liter is greater than 1 milliliter.*

INTERVENTION   5 minutes

If students are having difficulty with Practice the Language, they may find the assignment too abstract. Gather containers and objects and label them according to weight, mass, or capacity. For example, use a 1-pint bottle and label it "1 pint." (It is not necessary to be exact when it comes to weight and mass; a picture of a 1-ton object is acceptable). Then have students use the actual materials mentioned in the problem to help them visualize the sentences in questions 1–6 and to determine whether *greater than, less than,* or *equal to* is correct.

Lesson

Solve Math Problems

Objective Explain how to change units to solve a multi-step problem.

30 minutes

Teach this lesson:
- **After** students complete the material on capacity, weight, and mass in their grade-level math textbooks
- **Before** students complete the activities on page 72 of the student worktext

You need these materials:
- Transparency 36
- counters
- index cards
- two problems from grade-level textbooks that require conversion of customary units

LESSON
4

Solve Math Problems

Objective Explain how to change units to solve a multi-step problem.

Learn to Solve Problems

Problem	Mr. Lopez has 1 pound of grapes. He divides the grapes equally among his 4 children. How many ounces do each child's grapes weigh?

	Think	**Write**
Step 1:	Read the problem. Underline the question. Write what you need to do.	I need to divide 1 pound of grapes into 4 equal parts.
Step 2:	Change the units.	1 pound = 16 ounces Mr. Lopez has 16 ounces of grapes.
Step 3:	Solve the problem.	16 ÷ 4 = 4 Each child gets 4 ounces of grapes.

Practice Solving Math Problems

Directions Follow the steps above to solve the word problems below. Show how you change the units. Then write a complete sentence to solve each problem. Use a separate sheet of paper.

1. Some workers put 1 ton of sand on Bluff Beach and 1,800 pounds of sand on Low Beach. Which beach gets more sand? 1 ton = 2,000 pounds; Bluff Beach gets more sand.

2. Zuri makes 1 quart of lemonade. She wants to give half of the lemonade to her sister. How many pints of lemonade will her sister get? 1 quart = 2 pints; her sister gets 1 pint.

3. Minh has a watering can that holds 1 gallon of water. She pours 1 quart of the water onto her lettuce plants. How many quarts of water are still in the can? 1 gallon = 4 quarts; 3 quarts are still in the can.

4. David buys 2 pounds of marbles. If the marbles each weigh 2 ounces, how many marbles does he buy? 2 pounds = 32 ounces; he buys 16 marbles.

A Introduce

Display Transparency 36. Read the directions aloud with students. Tell them they are to work with a partner and choose one of the three words in parentheses to fill in each blank in the sentences. When they finish, they should check their answers with another pair to see if they agree.

- **Go over the sentences with students and be sure they chose the correct words to fill in the blanks.** (holds, mass, heavy, heavier, ounces, capacity, kilograms, gallon, ounce)

Say: *Capacity measures how much a container holds.* Repeat the sentence, leaving out key words and having students fill them in orally. For example, say: *Capacity measures how much _____ and have students supply a container holds*, or say: _____ *measures how much a container holds* and have students fill in *capacity*.

- **Repeat with *weight, mass,* and *measure how heavy an object is,* touching the words weight and mass on the transparency.**

Go over the different units with students. Remind students that they can write number sentences that compare units and that some of these number sentences use an equal sign.

Highlighted words and phrases may affect student comprehension.

- **Write on the board:** *2 pints = 1 quart.* Say: *I can change the units in a problem. Maybe I need to solve a problem that talks about 2 pints of lemonade. I can change 2 pints to 1 quart if that will help me solve the problem. I can change 1 quart of lemonade to 2 pints, too. That's because the amounts are equal.*

Read aloud the Lesson Objective with students. Remind students that a multi-step problem is one that needs more than one step in order to solve the problem. Be sure students know that they will need to change or trade units in order to solve these problems.

B Teach and Learn

Ask students to turn to page 72 in the student worktext. Have volunteers read the problem aloud. Remind students that grapes are a kind of small, round fruit.

BP 1 **Ask students to see in their minds what is happening in the problem.** Have them talk about it in pairs. Encourage them to draw illustrations to help them visualize the problem.

BP 1 **Ask questions to check students' understanding.** Ask: *What does Mr. Lopez have?* (grapes), *How much do the grapes weigh?* (1 pound), and *What will he do with the grapes?* (divide them into 4 equal shares)

Read aloud Step 1. Have students follow along. Point out that the question is underlined in the student worktext. Ask how students can identify the question in a word problem. Elicit that questions end with question marks and that they are usually the last sentence in a word problem.

- **Emphasize that students must use a full sentence to write what they need to do.** Read the sentence to the right of Step 1 with students. Say: *Remember, each child will get 1 equal part.*

Draw a box on the board. Tell students that it represents the grapes in the problem. Draw lines to cut it into four equal parts. Say: *Each of Mr. Lopez's children gets 1 of these parts. We could use fractions to talk about these parts. We could say that each child gets $\frac{1}{4}$ of a pound.* Label each section $\frac{1}{4}$ *lb* and draw a child's face next to it.

- **Then say:** *But that's not what the problem asks. The problem doesn't ask us to use fractions. It doesn't ask us to measure in pounds. It asks us to measure in ____.* (ounces)

Check to make sure students recall that ounces are smaller than pounds. Then continue to Step 2. Read the step aloud. Say: *We need to change pounds to ounces.* Check comprehension by asking students what units they will change (pounds) and what units they will change to. (ounces) Then say *We need to change ____ to ____,* and have students fill in the blanks orally.

- **Move to the equation in the right column and read it aloud.** Point out that students may refer to their textbooks or the student worktext if they are unsure how many of one unit equals another.

- **Then read the sentence with students.** Point out that you have now changed pounds to ounces. Say: *Mr. Lopez has 1 pound of grapes. So he has 16 ounces of grapes.* Draw a square on the board and write *1 lb* next to it. Then draw 3 horizontal and 3 vertical lines to divide it into16 equal sections. Say: *Each of these 16 sections is 1 ounce. So these grapes weigh 1 pound. They also weigh 16 ounces.*

Call students' attention to Step 3. Have a volunteer read the step aloud. Then have students read the information in the right column. Ask students to use counters to demonstrate to a partner that 16 ÷ 4 is 4. Say: *16 ÷ 4 is 4. So 16 ounces ÷ 4 is 4 ounces. Each child gets 4 ounces of grapes.* Say that students need to write a full sentence.

Explain that many word problems ask students to change one unit to another. Write the following problem on the board and ask small groups to use the steps to solve the problem together. *Hai went to the store to buy ice cream. Each of the 4 people in his family wanted a cup of ice cream. Should he buy a quart or a pint of ice cream? How many ounces would each person get?*

C Review and Practice

Review the steps used to solve the sample problem in the student worktext. Ask: *What's the first step? What comes next? What's the last step?*

Select two problems from students' math textbooks that require them to change customary units of capacity and weight/mass from one unit to another. Help students locate the problems in their textbooks, and have them work in pairs to solve them, using the steps from the student worktext. Remind students to use the conversion chart on page 71. Provide assistance as needed. Discuss the problems when all pairs have finished.

Read aloud the directions to Practice Solving Math Problems on page 72. Emphasize that students should write complete sentences to explain or answer each step. Then have students solve the problems on their own.

D Assess and Intervene

Can students convert units while solving multi-step problems, as demonstrated in Practice Solving Math Problems on page 72? Use the rubric to identify students who need extra support through additional help and the Intervention activity.

Intermediate

- ☐ Changes units and solves at least 3 of the problems correctly.
- ☐ Answer questions with complete sentences, with few or no errors.

  Example of a sentence a student might write: *3 quarts water are still in can.*

Advanced

- ☐ Changes units and solves all 4 problems correctly.
- ☐ Answers questions with complete sentences, with few or no errors.

  Example of a sentence a student might write: *3 quarts water are still in can.*

INTERVENTION 10 minutes

You may find that students focus too much on the process of converting units and pay too little attention to which operation they should use to solve each problem. If this is the case, make choosing the operation more explicit. Modify Step 3 so students first state the operation they will use and why. For item 3, for example, have students say: *Minh is pouring out some of the water, so I need to subtract.* Then have students proceed as before.

Lesson

Understand the Main Idea

Objective Recognize and tell how charts and diagrams organize and display data in different ways.

Prerequisite Background Knowledge
- Skip counting by fives
- Basic addition and subtraction skills
- Concept and vocabulary of ordering numbers

---

30 minutes

Teach this lesson:
- **Before** introducing the lessons on collecting and organizing data in the grade-level math textbook
- **Before** students complete the activities on page 73 of the student worktext

You need these materials:
- counters
- small pieces of paper

BP 2 ELL BEST PRACTICE #2:
Assessing, Activating, and Building Background Knowledge

English language learners often have difficulty connecting what they have learned at home or in previous schooling with what they are learning in school. As you discuss concepts about data collection and organization, mention examples that students may be familiar with, such as sports score averages, grades, and surveys about favorite things. Emphasize that this information is derived by collecting several pieces of data, organizing the data in some way, and then making a statement about the pieces of data as a whole group. Throughout this module, when you see **BP 2**, this is an example of assessing, activating, and building background knowledge.

Module 19: Collect and Organize Data

Understand the Main Idea

Objective Recognize and tell how charts and diagrams organize and display data in different ways.

Learn the Main Idea

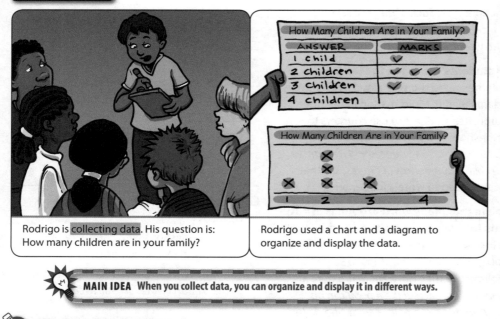

Rodrigo is collecting data. His question is: How many children are in your family?

Rodrigo used a chart and a diagram to organize and display the data.

MAIN IDEA When you collect data, you can organize and display it in different ways.

Practice Applying the Main Idea

Directions Look at the data in the chart and in the diagram below. Answer the questions in complete sentences on a separate sheet of paper.

How Many Books Did You Read Last Month?	
Answer	Marks
1 book	////
2 books	7HL
3 books	7HL
4 books	///

1. How many students read books last month? Seventeen students read books last month.

2. How is the chart like the diagram? How are they different? The chart and the diagram have the same data. The chart uses marks and the diagram uses Xs.

A Introduce

Read aloud the Lesson Objective with students on page 73 of the student worktext.

BP 2 Help students activate their background knowledge. Ask: *Have you ever tried to find out what the school should recycle? How do you think students and teachers would know what to collect?*

Elicit responses. Discuss the idea that the school could collect information or data to help them decide what recyclables they should collect. Point out that one way is to ask people questions about what milk and juice containers people buy if the containers are bottles or cartons, what people do with their newspapers and mail, and what they do with the cans from food and drinks they use.

Talk about the use of surveys in data collection. Say: *Businesses and other groups often take surveys to collect information. The information is called data. The surveys have questions that many people answer. The answers are organized in different ways. Businesses and groups use this information to help them make decisions.*

Highlighted words and phrases may affect student comprehension.

Collect and Organize Data · 73

Point out that surveys can be done in a variety of places, such as classrooms, stores, places where people work, etc. Invite students to describe any surveys in which they or family members have taken part.

Put students in pairs. Have them study the data shown in Learn the Main Idea on student worktext page 73. Encourage them to discuss the answers to the following questions: *What question does Rodrigo ask? How does he organize the information or data? What kinds of symbols does he use? What do the chart and diagram show?*

After giving students time to study the data, discuss their answers. Explain that data can be recorded and displayed in different ways. In this survey, the answers were recorded using marks on the chart and Xs on a diagram.

Read aloud the Main Idea with students. Ask: *Why do you think the boy decided to display data in two different ways?* (The chart helps record data; the diagram shows it like a picture.)

B Teach and Learn

Note: Students will learn the phrases *tally mark*, *tally chart*, and *line plot* in Lesson 2. In this lesson they use the words *mark*, *chart*, and *diagram*.

Make a chart like the one in Learn the Main Idea on page 73. Distribute blank paper. Say: *We will take a survey. We want to find out how many children have pets.* Have students write the number of pets and the marks on their papers as you fill in the chart on the board. Ask: *How many students have no pets? Raise your hand.*

- **Make a mark for each raised hand. Count the marks and hands to see that they are the same number.** After all students have been counted, say: *[Number] students in our classroom have no pets.*

- **Proceed with the next row in the tally chart.** Say: *How many of you have one pet? Raise your hand.* Again, count the raised hands and make marks for each one. Ask students to tell how many people in the class have one pet in the family.

- **Continue until the chart contains each child's information.** Point out that these marks are organized in groups of five.

- **Explain that if there are several groups of marks, then you can skip count by fives to find the total.** Draw some examples on the board and have students count to find the total.

- **Say:** *We have collected data. Now we are going to display it in a diagram.* Draw a blank number line on the board. Ask students to look at the chart to decide which numbers to put on the line (from zero, each whole number up to the highest number of pets). Walk through the process of making a line plot diagram. Have students draw their own diagrams as you model. Ask students to name the number of students for each number of pets in the chart. Invite different students to come to the board and write the appropriate number of Xs.

- **Ask students to summarize the data.** Have them use statements such as: *[Number] students in our classroom have three pets in their family.* Leave the tally chart and line plot diagram on the board.

C Review and Practice

Review the different ways you can organize and display data. Direct students' attention to the chart and diagram at the top of page 73 in the student worktext. Remind students that these displays show the results of a survey like the one you just did with the class. Ask students to tell what the difference is between the two surveys. (the question)

Divide the class into pairs. Ask them to cover the diagram on page 73 with a piece of paper. Give each pair a piece of paper and several counters. Have them look at the chart to get the data they need to make a line plot diagram. Ask them to make a number line on the piece of paper and then use the counters instead of Xs to display the data.

- **When students have completed their diagram, have them uncover the one in the student worktext and compare to see if theirs is correct.** Ask students to make corrections as necessary and then take off the counters one by one and replace them with Xs.

Read the directions for the Practice Applying the Main Idea activity. Point out that in this activity, students will read a chart and a line plot. Check students' work and assist, as needed.

D Assess and Intervene

Does everyone understand how to recognize and tell how charts and line plots display and organize data in different ways based on Practice Applying the Main Idea on page 73? Use the rubric to identify students who need extra support through additional help and the Intervention activity.

Intermediate

☐ Answers question 1 correctly.

☐ Answers question 2 with phrases that explains that both show the same data in different ways.

Example of a sentence a student might write: *Chart and diagram same information in different way.*

Advanced

☐ Answers question 1 correctly.

☐ Writes sentences for question 2 that explains that both show the same data but use different symbols.

Example of sentences a student might write: *Both show same information. Chart show numbers with marks. Diagram show numbers with X.*

INTERVENTION   10 minutes

If students have difficulty recognizing how to read the marks and Xs, use small squares of paper to have them write the word *student* for every mark in a chart. Then have them put an X across each square. Help them paste the correct number of Xs above each category (for example, three books) on the line plot diagram to show the number of students who read that number of books. Show them that the numbers in the chart and on the number line match. Explain that the marks and Xs both represent a student who reads books and was part of the survey. Point out that a mark and an x are both symbols.

Learn the Vocabulary

Objective Talk and write about collecting, organizing, and displaying data using the vocabulary words.

40 minutes

Teach this lesson:
- **Before** introducing lessons on collecting and organizing data in the grade-level math textbook
- **Before** students complete the activities on page 74 of the student worktext

You need these materials:
- index cards, prepared as described in Section C
- blank paper

Lesson Vocabulary

Essential Vocabulary

| data | survey | tally chart |
| line plot | stem-and-leaf plot | |

Additional Vocabulary

| title | label | key |
| results | to record | |

Learn the Vocabulary

Objective Talk and write about collecting, organizing, and displaying data using the vocabulary words.

Learn the Words

A **survey** is a way to collect information. You ask a group of people a survey question. **Data** is the information that you collect from their answers.

Survey group: book club members
Survey question: What is your age?
Data: 8, 9, 11, 10, 9, 11, 9, 10, 11, 8, 10, 11, 10, 9, 8, 9, 10, 10, 11, 11, 17, 17

Ways to record and display data:

A **tally chart** uses tally marks to show data.	**Age of Book Club Members** 8 Years Old: /// 9 Years Old: 卌 10 Years Old: 卌 / 11 Years Old: 卌 / 17 Years Old: //
A **line plot** uses Xs to show data. The Xs are above a number line.	(line plot showing Xs above number line at 8, 9, 10, 11, 17)
A **stem-and-leaf plot** organizes data by place value.	**Age of Book Club Members** Stem / Leaves 0 / 88899999 1 / 00000011111177 stem = tens digit, leaves = ones digit

Practice the Words

Directions Write a vocabulary word for numbers 1 to 3. Write a complete question for number 4.

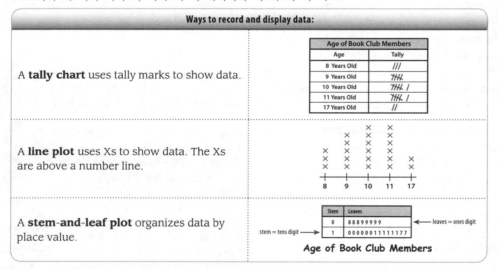

1 line plot _____

(line plot — Goals Scored, 0 1 2 3 4 5 6)

2 stem-and-leaf plot _____

Minutes Spent Doing Homework	
1	05
2	00558
3	0557

3 tally chart _____

Season	Tally
Summer	卌 ////
Fall	卌
Winter	卌 /
Spring	//

4 Write a survey question using the data in number 3. Possible Answer: What is your favorite season?

74 · Collect and Organize Data

A Introduce

BP 2 Read aloud the Lesson Objective with students. Ask: *What are some ways we can collect, organize, and display data?* Remind students of the Main Idea activity and ask: *How did we collect the data about pets in our families? How did we record the data? How did we display the data?* Have students answer the questions with a partner. As they share their answers, ask them to suggest vocabulary words that they need to know. Write these words on the board.

Choose words from the Additional Vocabulary box that you think will be useful and add them to the list. Elicit or provide examples for all the words on the list.

B Teach and Learn

Orally introduce the Essential Vocabulary. Read aloud the text above the data displays in Learn the Words on page 74 of the student worktext. Have students follow along as you read. After you read a sentence with a vocabulary word, write the word on the board and model its pronunciation. Have students say the word.

Explain the word *survey* in more detail. Say: *A survey is a way to collect data. When you do a survey, you ask a lot of people the same questions.* As you say each Essential Vocabulary word, point to it on the board.

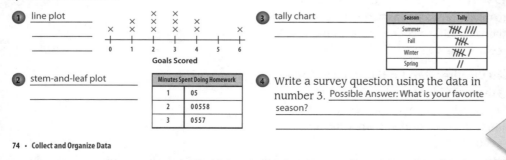

Highlighted words and phrases may affect student comprehension.

Have students read the paragraph on the left above the data displays on page 74. Ask: *What is the question for this survey?* (What is your age?) *What group of people answered the survey question?* (members of the book club) *What kind of data was collected?* (ages of people) *How can you describe the data?* (it includes ages from 8 to 17 years)

Ask students to think of other possible surveys with their partners. What are the questions? Who answers the questions? What kind of information does the survey collect? Have partners share their ideas.

Model and explain the other Essential Vocabulary by thinking aloud. Use the data displays at the top of page 74 in the student worktext.

Think Aloud

Say: *I know different ways to organize and display information, or data. I used marks to record data in a chart. The chart is called a* tally chart. *The marks are* tally marks. *Each mark stands for one person in the book club that is that age. I see that three members are eight years old. I know this because there are three tally marks in the age-eight row.*

Divide the class into small groups. Give them blank paper so they can draw the tally marks and then figure out the number of students. Ask: *How many members are 9 years old? 10 years old? 11 years old? 12 years old? 17 years old? How do you know?* Students should explain that each tally mark for each age represents one member of the club.

Say: *We can use the letter X as a symbol to show data. Can you find a data display that uses Xs to show how many? What is it called?* (line plot) Read the definition of line plot aloud.

Say: *The line plot is labeled with the numbers from eight to eleven. These numbers stand for the possible ages for book club members. Each X on the line plot stands for one member. There are three Xs above the eight. It means that three members are eight years old.*

- **Ask students to draw the line plot and the Xs.** Tell the number of members for each age and compare the data in the line plot with the data in the tally chart. They should discover that it is the same.

BP 2 Say: *Now we are going to learn about another way to display data.* Ask students what a leaf is. Draw a stem and leaf on the board. Say: *A* stem-and-leaf plot *organizes data by place value. In the picture I drew, the stem holds the leaf. In a stem-and-leaf plot, the tens are like the stem, and they hold the ones, which are like the leaves. What two place values do you see in the data?* (tens and ones) *Each tens digit is called a* stem. *Each ones digit is called a* leaf. Draw the plot on the board and show students how to read it. Have students draw a stem and a leaf and write a digit from the *Stem* column on the stem and a digit from the *Leaves* column on the leaf.

Have groups compare the data in each of the three displays. They should conclude that all show the same information in different ways.

 Have students fill out the Vocabulary Cards for this lesson.

C Review and Practice

Students can practice the vocabulary words by playing a game of Display that Data. Create three sets of index cards:

- three *Survey* cards with the question *How old are you?;* one card with answer 9, one with answer 10, one with answer 11.

- three *Number of Times* cards, one each for the numbers 2, 7, and 10.

- three *Display* cards, one each for *tally chart, line plot,* and *stem-and-leaf plot*.

- **Divide the class into three equal groups.** Each group takes one card from each set. Together, they create a data display that combines the information from all three cards. For example, they might show a line plot, labeled *age* with two Xs above the number *11*. Have each student copy the group's data display.

- **Rearrange the class in groups of three by having students count off 1-2-3 in each group and then grouping all 1s together, all 2s, and all 3s.** (Distribute extra students among the three groups.) Have each group of three combine their three data displays into one and copy it on the board.

Introduce the Practice the Words activity in the student worktext. Have students complete the activity individually.

D Assess and Intervene

Can all students name each data display and tell what they do with the data in the tally chart based on Practice the Words on page 74? Use the rubric to identify students who need extra support through additional help and the Intervention activity.

Intermediate

☐ At least 2 of the 3 data displays are correctly identified.

☐ Answers number 4 with a phrase or sentence that shows understanding of *survey* and *data;* may include errors that don't affect meaning.

Example of a question a student might write: *What favorite season?*

Advanced

☐ All three data displays are correctly identified.

☐ Answers number 4 with a complete question that shows understanding of *survey* and *data,* with minimal errors.

Example of a question a student might write: *What your favorite season is?*

INTERVENTION 10 minutes

If students have trouble remembering the Essential Vocabulary, have them draw a tally chart. Point out that tallies are grouped in *fives.* Then have them draw a line plot. Point out that the line is *horizontal* and the Xs are plotted above the numbers. Have them draw a stem-and-leaf plot. Point out that the line between the stem and the leaves is *vertical.* Remind them that to collect *information,* or *data,* they have to ask many people *questions* from a survey.

Suggest that students use the Notes space on their Vocabulary Cards to write the words in italics above. These words will help them remember the Essential Vocabulary.

Use More Language

Objective Use word associations to remember vocabulary.

30 minutes

Teach this lesson:
- **Before** lessons on collecting and organizing data in the grade-level math textbook
- **Before** students complete the activities on page 75 of the student worktext

You need these materials:
- Transparency 37
- Vocabulary Cards
- index cards

Lesson Vocabulary

Essential Vocabulary

mode	mean	median
range	outlier	

A Introduce

BP 2 Build background about summarizing data and finding averages. Ask: *How can you show the number of hours of homework you usually do on a regular day? What data would you need? What would you do with your data?* Tell students to discuss their plan with a partner and then report their ideas back to the class.

Tell students that the way to find out that number is to get the *average* of all the hours of homework you do every week. Write the word *average* on the board. Explain that average means one number that gives you an idea about all the numbers in the data. Brainstorm how you can calculate the average.

Read the Lesson Objective with students. Explain that word associations are other words that help them remember new vocabulary.

Use More Language

Objective Use word associations to remember vocabulary.

LESSON

3

Learn the Language

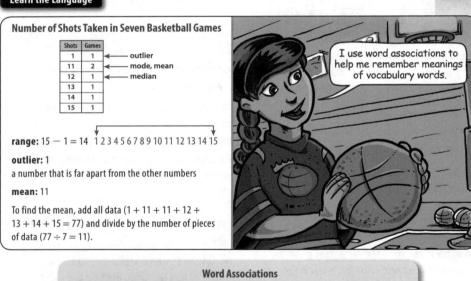

Number of Shots Taken in Seven Basketball Games

Shots	Games	
1	1	← outlier
11	2	← mode, mean
12	1	← median
13	1	
14	1	
15	1	

I use word associations to help me remember meanings of vocabulary words.

range: 15 − 1 = 14   1 2 3 4 5 6 7 8 9 10 11 12 13 14 15

outlier: 1
a number that is far apart from the other numbers

mean: 11

To find the mean, add all data (1 + 11 + 11 + 12 + 13 + 14 + 15 = 77) and divide by the number of pieces of data (77 ÷ 7 = 11).

Word Associations
range: *distance* (distance between largest and smallest numbers)
outlier: *out* of range of other numbers
median: *medium* or the middle number
mode: *most* (the number that appears *most* often)
mean: It's *mean* ☹ that we have to add and then divide to find the *mean*.

Practice the Language

Directions Look at the data in the line plot below. Find the range, median, mode, and mean. Explain how you found each value. Tell if the data has an outlier and explain why. Write your answers on a separate sheet of paper.

```
              ×
              ×
  ×   ×   ×   ×   ×
  +---+---+---+---+
  1   2   3   4   5
```
Miles Walked Each Day

① range The range is 4 miles. Subtract the smallest number from the largest number.

② median The median is 3. Find the middle number.

③ mode The mode is 3. There are more 3s than any other number.

④ mean The mean is 3. Add all numbers to find the total number of miles and divide by the number of pieces of data. 21 ÷ 7 = 3

⑤ outlier The data has no outlier. All of the numbers are close together.

B Teach and Learn

Make a number line on the board. Label it with whole numbers from zero to 15. Plot the data about the shots from Learn the Language on student worktext page 75.

Explain that the line plot shows how many shots a basketball player took in each of seven games. Say that we can use this data to find the number of shots that she usually takes in a game. We can also use the numbers to help us guess how many shots she might take in a new game.

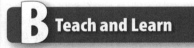

Highlighted words and phrases may affect student comprehension.

Collect and Organize Data · 75

Ask: *What is the greatest number of shots taken in a game?* (15) *What is the least number of shots?* (1)

On the board, write the word *range* **and** *15 − 1 = 14.* Ask students to copy the new words and the numbers they represent as you explain them.

Say: *When we look at a set of data, we can talk about the* range. *One meaning for range is* distance. *Think of the range as the distance between the highest and lowest numbers.* Gesture as you say *highest* and *lowest.* Say: *Look at the table on page 75. Read the numbers aloud.* Copy the numbers on the board. *The range of the shots she took is 14 because the range is the difference, or* distance, *between one and 15.*

Model how to use word associations by thinking aloud.

> **Think Aloud**
>
> **Say:** *There is one number on the line plot that is very different from the others. This number is the* outlier. *Write* outlier *on the board. That word must have something to do with* out. *Maybe it's because that number is outside the group of other numbers. I also see the word* lie *in* outlier. Lie *means to be in one place. I know what the –er at the end of the word means. It's a person or thing that does what the verb means, like* teach, teacher. *So an outlier is a thing that lies (is) out of the range.*

Ask: *Do you see any numbers on the line plot that are out of range of the other numbers?* Students should be able to see that one is far away from the cluster of numbers. Explain that one is an *outlier.*

Say: *Does anyone know the meaning of the word* medium? *It is a size between small and large. It is in the middle. So the word* median *means the number in the middle of a set of data. The first four letters of* medium *and* median *are the same. It's easy to find the median on a line plot. Put one finger on the X at each end of the line. Then touch each pair of Xs until you get to the middle. The middle number in a set of ordered data is the median.*

Above the line plot, make a bracket over the numbers one and 11, and another bracket over 13, 14, and 15. Point to these numbers and say: *There are three Xs on one side and three Xs on the other.* What number is in the middle? (12) *The median is 12.*

Ask: *Is there any number in the data that appears more times than all of the other numbers?* (yes) *What is that number?* (11) *The number 11 appears most often in the data. Most often means the greatest number of times. The number that appears most often is called the* mode. *Think of the beginning sounds of the words* mode *and* most. *The mode has the most numbers that are the same.*

Say: *Look at the number 11 and the word* mean *next to it. One definition of* mean *is* not nice. *Draw this face and think: It's mean that we have to* add *and then* divide *to find the mean. Let's add all the numbers.* (77) *Let's count how many numbers are in the data.* (7) *Divide 77 by 7. The quotient is the mean. So the mean, or the average number of shots taken, is 11.*

> **Have students complete the Vocabulary Cards to this lesson.** Have them write the word associations in the Notes box.

C Review and Practice

Review the new vocabulary. Write the following on the board:

Range = 14	Mode = 11
Outlier = 1	Median = 12
	Mean = 11

Explain that the range and outlier show how the data is spread out. Gesture as you say *spread out.* Explain that he mode, median, and mean show where the data is grouped.

> **Use Vocabulary Cards and Transparency 37 to practice the vocabulary in this module.** Have students copy the three-column chart and work in pairs to put the words in the appropriate column. Explain the meanings of column titles if necessary. Tell them that some words can go in more than one column. Then have them share their work with the class.

For additional practice, write this data set on the board: *2, 14, 14, 17, 18.* Explain that another basketball player played five games. Have students draw a line plot and record the data. Then find the following: range (16), outlier (2), mode (14), median (14), mean (13). Students can use the line plot on the board or in the student worktext for reference. Check their work and progress.

Have individual students complete the Practice the Language activity on page 75 in the student worktext. Circulate and assess students as they complete the activity.

D Assess and Intervene

Are students able to use the word associations to identify vocabulary in Practice the Language on page 75? Use the rubric to identify students who need extra support through additional help and the Intervention activity.

Intermediate

☐ Correctly identifies 3 out of 5 values.

☐ Explanations include general idea of how to find values; some language may be missing or vague.

Examples of sentences a student might write: *Range 2 miles. Range is smallest and biggest number.*

Advanced

☐ Correctly identifies 4 out of 5 values.

☐ Explanations accurately describe how to find the values; may include minor errors.

Example of sentences a student might write: *Range is 2 miles. Subtract smallest number and biggest number.*

INTERVENTION   10 minutes

If students are having difficulty finding the mean, write and explain this equation: $m = (d + d + d + d + d) \div n.$

Use the data in Practice the Language section to model how to calculate the mean:

Step 1: Find the total by adding the data: $1 + 2 + 3 + 3 + 3 + 4 + 5 = 21.$

Step 2: Count the pieces of data. Seven Xs mean seven pieces of data.

Step 3: Divide the total by the number of pieces: $21 \div 7 = 3.$

Relate this operation to the idea of seven children having various numbers of cookies and putting them all together, then sharing them equally. Each child gets three cookies.

Have students write this equation on an index card, practice using it, and keep it to use with lessons on finding the mean.

Solve Math Problems

Objective Decide if a statement about data on a chart or plot is correct or incorrect and explain why.

---

30 minutes

Teach this lesson:
- **After** lessons on collecting and organizing data in the grade-level math textbook
- **Before** students complete the activities on page 76 of the student worktext

You need these materials:
- Worksheet 19
- Transparency 38
- blank paper

LESSON
4

Solve Math Problems

Objective Decide if a statement about data on a chart or plot is correct or incorrect and explain why.

Learn to Solve Problems

What Is Your Favorite Drink?	
Drink	**Tally**
Milk	𝍢𝍢 ///
Juice	////
Water	𝍢𝍢

Problem Lara said that more students in the survey chose milk than all other drinks together. Is she correct? Explain why.

	Think	Write
Step 1:	Read the statement. Underline the question. What do you have to do?	I have to find how many students chose milk and how many chose other drinks.
Step 2:	Study the data in the chart or plot. Find the facts you need.	How many chose milk? (8) How many chose juice and water? (4 + 5 = 9)
Step 3:	Explain why the statement is correct or incorrect.	Lara is incorrect because 8 is less than 9.

Practice Solving Math Problems

Directions Read the data on the line plot and stem-and-leaf plot below. Circle *correct* or *incorrect*. Then explain your answer in a complete sentence.

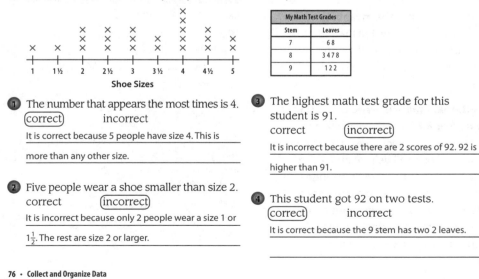

```
                        ×
                        ×
            ×   ×   ×       ×   ×
            ×   ×   ×   ×   ×   ×   ×
    ×   ×   ×   ×   ×   ×   ×   ×   ×
    +   +   +   +   +   +   +   +   +
    1  1½   2  2½   3  3½   4  4½   5
                Shoe Sizes
```

My Math Test Grades	
Stem	**Leaves**
7	6 8
8	3 4 7 8
9	1 2 2

① The number that appears the most times is 4.
(correct)   incorrect
It is correct because 5 people have size 4. This is more than any other size.

② Five people wear a shoe smaller than size 2.
correct   (incorrect)
It is incorrect because only 2 people wear a size 1 or $1\frac{1}{2}$. The rest are size 2 or larger.

③ The highest math test grade for this student is 91.
correct   (incorrect)
It is incorrect because there are 2 scores of 92. 92 is higher than 91.

④ This student got 92 on two tests.
(correct)   incorrect
It is correct because the 9 stem has two 2 leaves.

76 · Collect and Organize Data

Divide the class into groups. Write the prefixes *–in* and *–im* and the following words on the board: *correct, possible, accurate, sufficient, appropriate, polite.* Have groups guess which prefix goes with each word and write the words on a piece of paper. Have them look up the guessed words in the dictionary. Have the groups share their words with the class. Encourage groups to explain the meanings in their own words. Provide assistance if necessary.

 A **Introduce**

Read aloud the Lesson Objective with students.

BP 2 **Review with students the antonyms *correct* and *incorrect*.** Write on the board 6 + 3 = 9 and 6 + 3 = 3. Ask: *Which statement is true? Which statement is correct?* (6 + 3 = 9) *Which statement is not true? Which statement is incorrect?* (6 + 3 = 3)

- **Tell students that statements made about data can be correct or incorrect.** Using descriptions of the classroom of students as data, make a variety of statements. Have students identify which are correct and incorrect. Encourage them to explain why each statement is correct or incorrect.

- **The following are examples of statements you might use:** *There are more girls than boys in the classroom. There are more students in the class with red hair than with brown hair. Eight students in the class are wearing sneakers today.*

Explain that in this lesson, students will read statements about sets of data and identify if the information is correct or incorrect.

Highlighted words and phrases may affect student comprehension.

B Teach and Learn

On the board, copy the tally chart from page 76 of the student worktext. Write this problem on the board: *Lara said that more students in the survey chose milk than all other drinks together. Is she correct?*

Have students open their student worktexts to page 76 and read along as you read the problem aloud. Explain that the numbered steps on the page will show students how to decide if the statement is correct or incorrect.

Model how to analyze the data and the statement given with the problem by thinking aloud.

Think Aloud

Write Step 1. Read aloud the text in the box. Underline the question in the problem on the board and say: *What do I need to do? I need to find out if Lara's statement is correct.*

Write Step 2. Read the directions aloud. Say: *Lara said that more students chose milk than all other drinks together. How many students chose milk? How do you know?* (The row for milk has eight tally marks. That means that eight students chose milk.) *How can I find out how many students chose all other drinks together? What is this number?* (Add together the number who chose juice and the number who chose water: 4 + 5 = 9)

Write this information on the board:

Milk: 8 students
All other drinks: 9 students

Write Step 3. Read aloud the text. Say: *Now that we have looked at the chart and identified the facts, we have to decide if Lara is correct or incorrect.* Point to the numbers on the board and ask: *Which is greater, the number of students who chose milk or the number of students who chose all other drinks? How do you know?* (Eight chose milk and nine chose all other drinks. Eight is less than nine. More students chose all other drinks.) *Is this what Lara said?* (No, she said that more students chose milk.)
Is Lara correct or incorrect? (incorrect)

Write these statements on the board: *Two times as many students chose milk as juice. 13 students chose milk or water.*

Divide the class into pairs. Give each pair a copy of Worksheet 19. Ask pairs to fill in the charts using the data from the favorite drinks tally chart on page 76 of the student worktext to determine whether the statements are correct or incorrect.

- **Walk around the room and observe partners as they work.** Provide assistance as necessary with both language and math concepts. When students have completed the activity, invite a few partners to share their conclusions and explanations about the accuracy of the statements.

C Review and Practice

Direct students' attention to Practice Solving Math Problems on page 76. Discuss the data shown in the line plot. Ask: *What information is shown in the line plot?* (shoe sizes)

- **Put students into small groups.** Say: *I am going to say some statements about the data in the line plot. Talk in your group. Decide if I am correct or incorrect. Write* correct *or* incorrect *on a piece of paper and include an explanation.*

- **Say the following statements, allowing time between each for groups to work on their answers.** Say: *There are five people in this group who wear a size $4\frac{1}{2}$ or 5 shoe.* (correct) *The smallest shoe size in this group is $1\frac{1}{2}$.* (incorrect) *There are five people who wear a size 2 or $2\frac{1}{2}$ shoe.* (incorrect)

- **Invite groups to share their answers and explanations.**

Use Transparency 38 for additional practice. Have students work in pairs to solve the problems, using the steps in Learn to Solve Problems in the student worktext. Select different groups to share their answers and explanations.

Have students individually complete Practice Solving Math Problems in the student worktext. Circulate and assess how well they are using the three-step process and determining the accuracy of the statements.

D Assess and Intervene

Are all students able to analyze the data and determine whether statements are correct or incorrect, based on Solve Math Problems on page 76? Use the rubric to identify students who need additional help and the Intervention activity.

Intermediate

☐ At least 3 of the statements are accurately identified as correct or incorrect.

☐ Explanations include accurate math concepts, although some sentences may be incomplete or include errors that do not affect comprehension.

Example of sentences a student might write: *Incorrect. 2 peoples wear 1 or $\frac{1}{2}$, other peoples more large.*

Advanced

☐ All 4 statements are accurately identified as correct or incorrect.

☐ Explanations are mathematically correct and are written as complete sentences with minimal errors.

Example of sentences a student might write: *It is incorrect because 1 people wear size 1 and 1 people wear size $1\frac{1}{2}$. That is 2 people, not 5.*

INTERVENTION 10 minutes

If students are having difficulty telling if a statement is correct or incorrect, have them find their own answer and compare it to the statement. Make sure they understand that "smaller than size 2" means you do NOT add the data for size 2. For problems with correct statements, have them look for different ways that they could come up with incorrect statements about the data.

Understand the Main Idea

Objective Recognize how different kinds of graphs organize and compare information in different ways.

45 minutes

Teach this lesson:
- **Before** introducing lessons on graphs in students' grade-level math textbook
- **Before** students complete the activities on page 77 of the student worktext

You need these materials:
- chart paper
- graph paper

Prerequisite Background Knowledge
- Skip counting
- Basic concepts of fractions
- Concept and vocabulary of comparing numbers

BP 3 *ELL BEST PRACTICE #3*
Performance Assessment

English language learners often know more than what they can demonstrate on traditional reading- and writing-based assessments. For this reason, it is more effective to evaluate their learning based on observations of their performance on daily classroom tasks. Observe how well students can read, compare data on graphs, and create graphs using the Essential and Additional Vocabulary for this module. In addition, use observation notes, checklists and the rubrics to record students' progress.

Throughout this module, when you see **BP 3**, you will find an example of using performance assessment with students.

Module 20: Read and Make Graphs

LESSON **1**

Understand the Main Idea

Objective Recognize how different kinds of graphs organize and compare information in different ways.

Learn the Main Idea

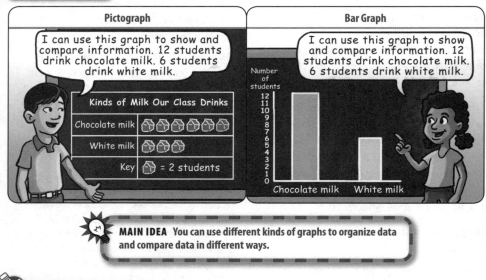

| Pictograph | Bar Graph |

I can use this graph to show and compare information. 12 students drink chocolate milk. 6 students drink white milk.

I can use this graph to show and compare information. 12 students drink chocolate milk. 6 students drink white milk.

Kinds of Milk Our Class Drinks

Chocolate milk
White milk
Key = 2 students

Number of students

Chocolate milk   White milk

MAIN IDEA You can use different kinds of graphs to organize data and compare data in different ways.

Practice Applying the Main Idea

Directions Read the graph below. Answer the first question. Then answer questions 2 to 4 in complete sentences. Use a separate sheet of paper.

4th Grade's Favorite Colors

red	
orange	
green	
blue	
purple	

Key: = 2 votes

(1) Write a list to show how many votes each color got. red: 4 votes; orange: 8 votes; green: 10 votes; blue: 6 votes; purple: 2 votes

(2) What color had the greatest number of votes? Explain how you know. Green had the greatest number of votes. I know because I count 5 green crayons, and each crayon equals 2 votes. So green got 10 votes.

(3) How many more votes did orange have than red? Explain how you know. Orange had 4 more votes than red. I know because I count the crayons, and orange has 2 more crayon.

(4) How does this graph show and compare data? This graph uses pictures and a key to show and compare information.

Highlighted words and phrases may affect student comprehension.

A Introduce

Read aloud the Lesson Objective with students. Make sure students understand what *organize* and *compare* mean. Provide examples as necessary. Ask: *Why is it important to gather information or data and organize it?* (It helps us learn about a subject, and see and understand the information about it.) Have students discuss their responses with a partner.

Help students activate prior knowledge. Ask: *What kinds of data, or information, might you gather or collect?* (weather, friends' favorite sports, etc.) Write students' responses on the board. Ask: *Why might you want this data?* Model answering: *Because I will know what to wear to school* (weather), *Because I can bring the right things to play with at recess* (favorite sports). Invite students to answer using a *because* clause.

Use the artwork on page 77 of the student worktext as a visual introduction to the concept of recognizing different kinds of graphs that show, organize, and compare data.

- **Give students time to look at the visuals on page 77.** Have them describe to each other what they see.

- **Point to panel 1, on the left.** Ask: *What data did the boy gather? Do the pictures make the data easy to understand and organize?*

- **Point to panel 2, on the right.** Ask: *What data did the girl collect? Did the bars show, organize, and compare the data?*

Chorally read aloud the text in each frame with students. Summarize each frame. Say: *The boy collected data about the different kinds of milk his class drinks. He used a picture of a milk carton to show the data. Each milk carton picture equals 2 real cartons. He drew the correct number of symbols to show the data.*

- **Say:** *The girl collected the same kind of data. She labeled the number of students on one side, and the different kinds of milk on the bottom. Then she drew bars to show the number of students that drink chocolate milk and white milk.*

- **Ask:** *Do their graphs show the same data? What did the boy and girl do that was the same/different?*

Read aloud the Main Idea with students. Ask: *What do you already know about using different kinds of graphs to show, organize, and compare data in different ways?* Ask: *How would you organize data for those topics?*

B Teach and Learn

Write and read aloud this sentence frame: *What is your favorite snack food? My favorite snack food is _____.* Have students sit in a circle. Ask the student on your right, and help him or her answer. Then have that student ask the student to his or her left, and continue around the circle. Record the data in a two-column table on chart paper, titled: *Snack Foods* and *Number of Students*. Read the data chorally. Say: *This is the data we collected. We will use it to make graphs.*

- **Divide the class into small groups.** Distribute graph paper to each group. Tell groups they will draw their own graphs as they follow along with you.

- **Model how to draw a bar graph.** Draw the vertical and horizontal axes on chart paper. Point to the horizontal axis. Say: *This side of the graph shows the different snack foods in our class. What should we label it?* Point to the vertical axis. *Say: This side shows the number of students. How many students are there?* Label the vertical axis. Fill in the scale with an appropriate interval. Have students

draw the axes and write the labels. Ask groups to use the table to tell how many students like each snack food. Together, complete the bar graph with the data.

Point out that bar graphs can also have horizontal bars. Pointing to the graph, say: *We can put the number of students on the bottom and the snack foods on the side.*

Use the same data and a Think Aloud to create a pictograph.

> **Think Aloud**
>
> **Say:** *I can also show this data with pictures. I can use a stick figure as a symbol for students. I choose a key to show how many students the symbol represents. Each stick figure equals 2 students. One column lists the snack foods, and the other has the symbols. If I have 1 student, I can use half a symbol.*

- **Model how to make the pictograph, and have students follow along.** Ask groups to use the table to tell how many students like each food. Together, use the data to complete the pictographs.

- **BP 3 Model how to compare the data.** Write on the board: *I know _____ students like _____ because the bar is longer. I know _____ students like _____ because there are more stick figures.* Have students use the sentence frames to compare the data.

C Review and Practice

BP 3 Have groups use their graphs to review the Lesson Objective. Ask: *How did we use different kinds of graphs to organize and compare the same data? How are the graphs the same? How are they different?*

BP 3 Divide the class into pairs. Tell students that they will make a bar graph to show and compare the following data. Write the information on the board. Have pairs read the table, choose a title and a scale, label each axis, and draw a bar for each sport. Have students use their student worktext for reference.

Sports	Students
soccer	6
baseball	4
tennis	2
swimming	2

Have pairs discuss how they showed, organized, and compared the data, and why they used a graph. Each pair should write their explanations. They may use the sentence frames for support.

Read aloud the directions for the Practice Applying the Main Idea activity in the student worktext. Have students complete the activity independently. Use the rubric to assess their work.

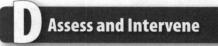 **D Assess and Intervene**

Does everyone understand how to read and compare data on different kinds of graphs, based on the Practice Applying the Main Idea on page 77? Use the rubric below to identify students who need extra support through additional help and the Intervention Activity.

Intermediate

☐ Explanation shows understanding of how to use a graph to organize and compare data; sentence may be incomplete and somewhat difficult to comprehend.

Example of a sentence a student might write: *Use picture show and compare data.*

Advanced

☐ Explanation shows understanding of how to use a graph to organize and compare data; sentence is clear and complete, and minimal errors do not impede comprehension.

Example of a sentence a student might write: *This graph use pictures and key to show and compare data.*

INTERVENTION   10 minutes

If students are having trouble reading the data on the graphs, remind them to look at the key for a pictograph and what the symbol stands for. If one symbol stands for two things, remind them to count the pictures and multiply their answer by two as they compare the data. For bar graphs, have them use their left index finger to find the number on the left side and their right finger to find the item on the bottom. Have them move their right finger up to where their left finger is to read the data correctly.

Lesson

2

Learn the Vocabulary

Objective Use vocabulary words to talk and write about graphs.

---

45 minutes

Teach this lesson:
- **Before** introducing lessons on graphs in students' grade-level math textbook
- **Before** students complete the activities on page 78 of the student worktext

You need these materials:
- Transparency 39
- riddles written on chart paper
- sticky notes

Lesson Vocabulary

Essential Vocabulary

| graph | scale | interval |

Additional Vocabulary

label/to label	title	key
data*	to increase	to decrease
range	horizontal	vertical
trend	axis/axes	

* - Term that has a Vocabulary Card.

LESSON 2

Learn the Vocabulary

Objective Use vocabulary words to talk and write about graphs.

Learn the Words

Word	Definition	Example
graph	a picture that shows different groups of data	**Circle Graph** Types of Sports / football / baseball / soccer **Line Graph** Minutes to Finish Puzzle These are **graphs**. Each one shows different groups of data.
scale	a set of numbers in order with equal distance between them	**Kinds of Milk Our Class Drinks** Scale / Number of Students / Chocolate Milk / White Milk / Interval This **scale** shows the number of students in the class. The **interval** between the two numbers on this scale is 1.
interval	the difference between two numbers on a scale	

Practice the Words

Directions Complete the story below with the vocabulary words above. Answer the questions on a separate sheet of paper. Use complete sentences.

Our class made a <u>graph</u>_____. We wrote this title on the top: *The Weather for Two Weeks*. We labeled the bottom *Different Kinds of Weather*. Each kind of weather had a label: *Rainy, Sunny, Cloudy*, and *Snowy*. We drew 4 bars. They showed the number of days of each kind of weather. We labeled the left side *Number of Days*. The <u>scale</u>_____ had numbers in order with equal distance between them. The numbers 1 to 10 represented 2 school weeks. The scale had an <u>interval</u>_____ of 1. We collected this data: 4 sunny days, 2 cloudy days, 1 snowy day, 3 rainy days. The graph showed that most days were sunny.

1. What does the scale show?
The scale shows the number of days.

2. What is the interval of the scale?
The interval of the scale is 1.

3. Why did the class choose a bar graph?
The class wanted to show and compare data.

4. Tell about another kind of graph to organize and compare information.
Answers will vary.

78 · Read and Make Graphs

A Introduce

Read aloud the Lesson Objective with students. Point to the graphs from Lesson 1 on page 77 of the student worktext. Have students refer to them as you ask: *What do you remember about reading, showing, and comparing data on different kinds of graphs?* Have students share their answers with a partner.

As a class, brainstorm ideas for vocabulary words. Think of words that will be important to know when organizing data and comparing information on graphs. Write suggested words on the board and add Essential Vocabulary Words to the list if needed.

Choose words from the Additional Vocabulary box that you think will be useful. Elicit or provide examples for all the words on the list.

B Teach and Learn

Orally introduce the Essential Vocabulary. Look at the illustrations on page 78 of the student worktext with students.

Write each word on the board as you introduce it and model its pronunciation.

- **Write *graph* on the board.** Ask: *Do you remember how we organized and compared information about different foods? What did we draw to organize the information in different ways?* (numbers, symbols/pictures, bars, graphs) Ask: *Did the drawings use and*

Highlighted words and phrases may affect student comprehension.

---

compare the same data? (Yes, they both told about favorite snack foods.) Say: *A graph is a picture that shows and compares different groups of data.* Chorally read aloud the word, definition, and example.

- **Write the word *scale* on the board.** Point to the scale on the bar graph. Say: *This is a scale on a graph. The numbers on a scale have to be in order. The distance between each number must be the same. A scale is a set or group of numbers in order with equal distance between them. What is the scale on this graph?* (1 to 12) Chorally read aloud the word, definition, and explanation.

- **Write the word *interval* on the board.** Point to the interval on the bar graph in the example. Say: *An interval is the difference between two numbers on a scale. What is the interval on this bar graph?* (1) *How do you know?* (because the difference between each number on the scale is 1) Chorally read aloud the word, meaning, and explanation.

Display Transparency 39. Point to and read the names, titles, and labels on each graph. Then, chorally with students, read the explanations underneath each graph.

Use a Think Aloud to talk about the line graph. As you name each part of the graph and explain it, point to and then write the Essential and Additional Vocabulary words with a marker on the transparency. Discuss and define these words in context: *graph, scale, interval, title, label, data, horizontal axis, vertical axis, line, points.*

Think Aloud

Say: *This is a line graph. I think it is called a line graph because there is a line that connects the points. Line graphs show how data changes over time. The title tells me that this graph is about the number of computers our school had for each year. The vertical axis is the line that goes from the top to the bottom on the graph. It has the numbers 5 to 30. I know those numbers are the scale. I see that they are in order and that the distance between the numbers is the same. The scale has an interval of 5. I can count by fives and go from 5 to 30. The horizontal axis goes from right to left and is on the bottom. The labels for each axis are "Number of Computers" and "Years." I will look at the line. I can see that from 2004 to 2007, the number of computers in the school went up, or increased. I can really see how data changes over time.*

Point to the circle graph. Ask: *Why is this graph called a circle graph?* Elicit responses. Say: *A circle graph shows parts of a whole. Each part is a fraction of a whole.* Read the title and each fraction chorally. Repeat this process for the other two graphs on the transparency.

BP 3 Have students look at Learn the Words on page 78 of the student worktext. Read the words, definitions, and examples chorally. Then divide the class into small groups. Read the directions on the transparency. Have groups use the sentence frame and list of words on the transparency to describe each graph.

Have groups complete the Vocabulary Cards for this module.

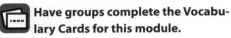
Review and Practice

Review the meaning of the Essential Vocabulary and the different graphs using riddles. Display riddles written on chart paper, and read them aloud. Have groups take turn answering the riddles. If time allows, invite volunteers to draw each graph next to the riddle. For example:

- I show data over time. I have a scale, and my points are connected by lines. What graph am I? (line graph)

- I do not have a scale or an interval. I show parts of a whole. What graph am I? (circle graph)

- I have a scale and an interval. I use bars to compare data. What graph am I? (bar graph)

- I have a symbol and key. I do not have a scale or an interval. I use pictures. What graph am I? (pictograph)

Display Transparency 39. Divide the class into pairs. Have each partner write questions about the different graphs. Then have the other partner answer the questions. Partners take turns asking and answering questions about each graph.

BP 3 Have partners discuss similarities and differences between graphs and then present their findings to the class. Tell them to look for the scale, interval, and axes and to use their student worktext and the Vocabulary Cards for reference. As they present their conclusions, they must use the Essential Vocabulary words.

Have students work independently to complete the Practice the Words activity. Circulate, and assess their progress. Use the rubric to assess their work.

D Assess and Intervene

Does every student understand the Essential Vocabulary based on Practice the Words on page 78? Use the rubric to identify students who need extra support through additional help and the Intervention activity.

Intermediate

- ☐ At least 2 words are correctly filled in to complete the story.
- ☐ Correctly answers at least 2 questions, using simple sentences or phrases.

  Example of a sentence a student might write: *Scale shows days* .

Advanced

- ☐ All words correctly filled in to complete the story.
- ☐ Correctly answers all questions, using complete sentences, with few errors that do not impede comprehension.

  Example of a sentence a student might write: *Interval is 1 in scale of graph.*

INTERVENTION   10 minutes

If students are having trouble understanding word meanings, help them make visual connections. Use Transparency 39 and explain each Essential Vocabulary word again as you point to examples on the graphs. Ask students to write each Essential Vocabulary word on a sticky note. Invite them to place each sticky note in as many places on as many graphs as they can. Then write this sentence frame on the board: *This is the _____ because _____.* Read it aloud, and model completing it. As students place their sticky notes on the graphs, have them complete the sentence frame to explain what each word means.

Lesson

3

Use More Language

Objective Describe the scale and interval of a graph using *large enough* or *small enough*.

---

45 minutes

Teach this lesson:
- **After** introducing lessons on graphs in students' grade-level math textbook.
- **Before** students complete the activities on page 79 of the student worktext.

You need these materials:
- small classroom objects (like erasers)
- envelope and a big box
- paper clips

Use More Language

LESSON 3

Objective Describe the scale and interval of a graph using *large enough* or *small enough*.

Learn the Language

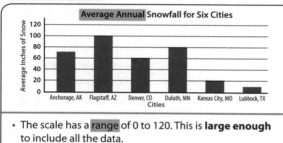

Average Annual Snowfall for Six Cities

(Cities: Anchorage, AK; Flagstaff, AZ; Denver, CO; Duluth, MN; Kansas City, MO; Lubbock, TX)

I chose a scale with a range of 0–120. It is **large enough** to include all the data. I chose the interval 20 inches. It is **small enough** to see the data clearly. The interval is also **large enough** to make a graph that is not too big.

- The scale has a range of 0 to 120. This is **large enough** to include all the data.
- The interval is 20 inches. This is **small enough** to see the data clearly.
- The interval is also **large enough** to make a graph that is not too big.

Practice the Language

Directions Use the data in the table to complete the bar graph. Then answer questions 1 and 2. For questions 3 to 5, use *because* to explain why the scale and interval are good choices or bad choices for this graph.

Animal	Weight
lion	200 pounds
tiger	400 pounds
leopard	100 pounds

1. The range of the scale is __0 to 500.__

2. The interval of the scale is __100.__

3. The range of the scale is a good choice . . .
   because it is large enough to include all the data.

4. The interval for this graph is a good choice . . .
   because it is small enough to show the data clearly. It is large enough so I can make a graph that is not too big.

5. A range of 100 to 200 isn't a good choice . . .
   because it isn't large enough to include all the data.

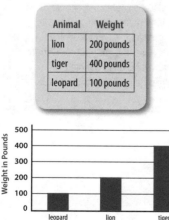

(Bar graph — Weight in Pounds vs. Type of Animals: leopard, lion, tiger)

A Introduce

Remind students what they have learned about using different kinds of graphs to organize data and compare information in different ways. Have students find examples of different kinds of graphs in their textbooks. Have them tell what kind of graph each one is. Allow students to use their student worktexts as a reference.

 Read aloud the Lesson Objective with students. Remind them that they used different kinds of graphs to organize data and compare the information in different ways. Review the Essential Vocabulary words, and write them on the board. Read them aloud with students. Have students use their Vocabulary Cards to find examples of the words on the appropriate graphs and then read or explain what each word means.

Write the phrase *large enough* on the board. Read it aloud. Show students a box and a small object, such as an eraser. Say: *This eraser is small. This box is large. The box is large enough to hold the eraser.* Ask: *What other things are large enough to hold the eraser?* Write on the board: *The _____ is large enough to hold the eraser.* Read the sentence frame aloud. Invite students to walk around the room and put the eraser in different places, such as a bookcase, a desk, etc. Have them use the sentence frame above to talk about the eraser. Explain that if we can put the eraser inside the box, the box is large enough.

Highlighted words and phrases may affect student comprehension.

Write the phrase *small enough* **on the board.** Demonstrate its meaning, using the procedure for *large enough* with a paper clip and an envelope. Say: *The paper clip is small enough to fit in the envelope.* Write this sentence frame on the board: *The _____ is small enough to fit in the envelope.* Invite students to find things in the classroom that fit in the envelope and complete the sentence frame above. Explain that if we can put a paper clip in the envelope, the paper clip is *small enough*.

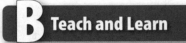

Teach and Learn

Have students open their student worktexts to page 79. As you point to the data, labels, title, and axes on the graph, read aloud the information. Have students follow along and point with you. Then, chorally read the text with students.

Draw this table on the board, and read aloud the data.

Number of Sunny Days This Year	
Month 1	10
Month 2	12
Month 3	15
Month 4	20

- **Draw a vertical and a horizontal axis on the board.** Label the vertical axis *Number of Sunny Days* and the horizontal axis *Month 1, 2, 3, 4.* Draw a scale from 0–25 on the vertical axis (interval of 5). Say: *This is the scale, the numbers arranged in order on the side of a graph. The scale has a range of 0 to 25. I chose this scale because it is large enough to include all the data.*

- **Point out the interval.** Say: *The interval is 5 days. It is small enough to see the data clearly. The interval is also large enough to make a graph that is not too big.*

Write this sentence frame on the board: *The range of the scale is _____. This is _____ to include all the data. The interval is _____. This is _____ to see the data clearly. The interval is also _____ to make a graph that is not too big.* Model how to complete the sentence frames about the scale and interval using the phrases *large enough* and *small enough*.

BP 3 Divide the class into small groups. Distribute graph paper or blank paper. Have

them draw a simple bar graph to show and compare the data in the table. Have them share their graph with the class and use the sentence frames on the board to describe the scale and interval.

Provide similar examples in tables. Include students' favorite foods, fruits, vegetables, sports, movies, authors, etc. As you draw a vertical axis, horizontal axis, scale, and interval on the board, have students draw them on paper. Ask: *What is a good label for the horizontal/vertical axis? What is a good range for the scale? What is a good interval for the scale? Why?* As you elicit answers, complete the scale with students.

Write the following sentence frames on the board: *The range of the scale is _____. The range of the scale is a good choice because it is (large/small) enough to _____. The interval is _____. The interval of the scale is a good choice because it is (large/small) enough to _____.* Model completing the sentence frames about each one of the scales you made. Have groups choose a scale and complete each sentence about the scale by writing it on a sheet of paper. Circulate, and assist as necessary. Invite pairs to share their sentences and show which scale they are writing about.

Review and Practice

Together, create a table that shows students' favorite hobbies. Draw the vertical and horizontal axes. Include the scale and an interval. Use the sentence frames on the board to describe the range of the scale and the interval and whether or not they are a good choice.

BP 3 Divide the class into pairs. Have partners use the table on the board ("Number of Sunny Days This Year"), but change the number of sunny days. Then they create a new scale and interval. Have them use the sentence frames on the board to describe their work. Circulate, and assist as necessary. Have students share their graphs and sentences with the class.

Read aloud the directions for the Practice the Language activity on page 79. Have students complete the activity independently. Circulate and assess their work, using the rubric.

D Assess and Intervene

Does every student understand how to read a scale and interval and explain if the scale/interval is a good choice for the data, based on Practice the Language on page 79 of the student worktext? Use the rubric to identify students who need extra support through additional help and the Intervention activity.

Intermediate

☐ Correctly completes sentences 1–2 to tell what the scale and interval are.

☐ Clearly explains why the scale or interval is large or small enough in at least 2 of sentences #3–5, with some errors that do not impede comprehension.

Example of a sentence students might write: *The range of the scale is a good choice because scale is enough large see all information.*

Advanced

☐ Correctly completes sentences 1–2 to tell what the scale and interval are.

☐ Clearly explains why the scale or interval is large enough or small enough in all sentences. There are few errors and they do not impede comprehension.

Example of a sentence students might write: *The range of the scale is a good choice because is small enough to see all data.*

INTERVENTION 10 minutes

If students are having trouble deciding if a scale is large enough, use visuals to help them see and place data on scales/intervals. Create a scale on paper from 1 to 10 with a range of 1, and write "The Number of Pets in the Class," which is 8. Ask: *Is the scale large enough?* Write these sentences: *The range of this scale is large enough because I can include all the data. The range of this scale is not large enough because I can't fit all the data.* Have students choose the correct sentence about the data for the scale. Repeat the procedure for data that fits and doesn't fit. Use a similar procedure to practice deciding if an interval is large enough to make a graph that will not be too big. Have students choose from these sentences: *This interval is a good choice because it is large enough to make a graph that is not too big. This interval is not a good choice because the the graph will be too big.*

Lesson

4

Solve Math Problems

Objective Choose a graph to help you solve a problem, and explain your choice.

45 minutes

Teach this lesson:
- **After** lessons introducing lessons on graphs in students' grade-level math textbook.
- **Before** students complete activities on page 80 of the student worktext

You need these materials:
- Transparency 39
- Worksheet 20
- Transparency 40

EXTENSION AND ENRICHMENT 15 minutes

Have students work in small groups to make a double bar graph to show and compare the favorite after-school activity for boys and girls. Assign roles in each group: one student asks the questions, one records the data, one draws the table. Each student draws the graph independently. Have them choose two colors for the key. Point out that in this graph, the key tells which color shows which group. Have groups use their student worktexts and math textbooks for reference. Then have them present their graphs to the class. They must use all the Essential and Additional Vocabulary to describe and explain what they did.

LESSON

4

Solve Math Problems

Objective Choose a graph to use to help you solve a problem, and explain your choice.

Learn to Solve Problems

Problem	Average Temperature on Saturday Each Week	
Lisa recorded the temperature at noon every Saturday for 8 weeks. Make a graph that shows whether the temperature changed over the 8 weeks.	Week 1 25° F	Week 5 45° F
	Week 2 30° F	Week 6 50° F
	Week 3 30° F	Week 7 55° F
	Week 4 40° F	Week 8 60° F

	Think	Write
Step 1:	Read the problem. Look at the data. What do you have to do?	I have to make a graph to show whether the temperature changed over time.
Step 2:	How do different kinds of graphs show data?	Pictographs compare data with pictures and a key. Bar graphs compare data and use bars and a scale. Line graphs show changes over time. Circle graphs show parts of a whole.
Step 3:	Which kind of graph will you use? Why? Draw and label the graph.	I should use a line graph because the problem asks about temperature changing over time.

Average Temperature on Saturday Each Week

Practice Solving Math Problems

Directions Choose a graph for each question below. Draw it on a separate sheet of paper. Then write a complete sentence to explain why you chose that graph.

① Tom recorded how many pages of homework his brother Ted, his sister Su, and he did each week. These are the number of pages for each: Ted, 5 pages; Su, 4 pages; Tom, 7 pages. Use the data to make a graph that shows who did the most number of pages of homework.
Answers will vary.

② Our school recorded the number of students in our class from 2004 to 2007. These are the numbers of students for each year: 2004, 18 students; 2005, 22 students; 2006, 20 students; 2007, 24 students. Use the data to make a graph that shows changes over time.
Answers will vary.

80 · Read and Make Graphs

A Introduce

Read aloud the Lesson Objective. Use Transparency 39 from Lesson 2 to review each kind of graph and when to use it. Use the sentence frame on the transparency for review. Model completing the sentence frame about one graph. Point to different graphs on the transparency, and ask students to complete the sentence frame about it. Students may use their Vocabulary Cards to explain what the words mean.

Tell students that they will learn how to choose the correct graph to solve problems.

B Teach and Learn

On the board, ahead of time, write the following table:

Height of Bean Plant for Four Weeks	
Weeks	**Height**
Week 1	1 inch
Week 2	3 inches
Week 3	4 inches
Week 4	7 inches

Highlighted words and phrases may affect student comprehension.

Write this problem above the table: *After Ani planted her garden, she recorded the height of her bean plant for 4 weeks. Make a graph that will show whether the height of the plant changed over 4 weeks.*

Have students open their student worktexts to page 80. Look at the example in Learn to Solve Problems. Tell students that the steps will help them solve the problem.

Model how to solve the problem on the board by thinking aloud.

Think Aloud

Write Step 1, on the board and read it aloud. Say: *First I have to read the problem and look at the data. After I read the problem and the table with the data, I ask myself what I have to do.* Write, and say: *I have to make a graph to show that the height of the plant is changing over time. I have to show if it increases, goes up, or decreases, goes down.*

Write Step 2 on the board, and read it aloud. Say: *What does each kind of graph show?* As you name and explain each graph, point to it on Transparency 39. Say: *Pictographs use pictures and a key to show and compare data. Bar graphs use bars and a scale. Circle graphs use a circle to show parts of a whole. Line graphs use a scale, a line, and points to show how data changes. This problem talks about time. It talks about how the bean plant changed over 4 weeks.*

Write Step 3 on the board, and read it aloud. Ask: *Which kind of graph should I use? Why should I use it? After I answer these questions, I can draw my graph.* Say and write: *I should use a line graph, because this problem is about how the bean plant changed over 4 weeks. First, I look at the heights for each week.* (As you say each of these steps, create the graph on the board.) *This is the title of my graph:* Height of My Bean Plant for Four Weeks. *I draw and label the vertical axis* Number of Inches. *I draw and label the horizontal axis* Number of Weeks. *Underneath, I write* Week 1, Week 2, Week 3, Week 4. *I use a scale to show the inches. I use a range of 8 for my scale, because this is large enough to show all the data and it is just a little larger than my largest data point. I use an interval of 1 because it small enough to show all the data and large enough so that my graph won't be too big.* (Write the numbers 1, 2, 3, 4, 5, 6, 7, 8 on the vertical axis.)

I mark each point on the scale to show the data. (Mark the data.) I connect the points to see if the numbers are changing. The numbers increase, because the line goes up. I answer the question: I drew a line graph because I needed to show the data changing over 4 weeks.

Write the following problem on the board: *Bella measured the amount of snow in inches between the months of December and February. Make a graph that shows whether the snowfall changed over the 3 months.*

Months	Inches of Snow
December	10 inches
January	30 inches
February	20 inches

 Divide the class into groups of four. Distribute copies of Worksheet 20 to each student. Tell them to choose a graph to show and compare the data. They should have a title, scale, interval, and label for each axis. Call on volunteers to explain their solutions to the class.

As students work, circulate, helping students as necessary. If students need additional help, brainstorm ways they can show and compare data using different graphs as you assist them in their thinking process.

C Review and Practice

BP 3 **Use Transparency 40 to provide additional practice.** Have students work in pairs to choose the best graph to show and compare data.

- **Read each problem aloud.** Have pairs discuss which graph is the best choice and why. Have them write their answer and then share it with the class. Write this sentence frame on the board for them to use: *I chose _____ to _____ because _____.* List all responses on the board and explain if necessary. Explain the word results if students don't understand its meaning.

Read aloud the directions for Practice Solving Math Problems on page 80. Tell students that these problems are similar to what they just did. Circulate and assess how well students are solving the problems.

D Assess and Intervene

Does every student understand how to choose a graph to solve a problem and explain why they chose it, based on Practice Solving Math Problems on page 80 of the student worktext? Use the rubric to identify students who need extra support through additional help and the Intervention activity.

Intermediate

☐ Chose an appropriate graph for at least 1 problem, and completed the 1 graph correctly.

☐ Wrote 1 correct explanation using simple sentences or phrases, although errors may make comprehension difficult.

Example of a sentence students might write: *Bars graph because show more number of homework.*

Advanced

☐ Chose an appropriate graph for all 2 problems, and completed all the graphs correctly.

☐ Clearly explained why they chose each graph, using complete sentences, with minimal errors, that do not impede comprehension.

Example of a sentence students might write: *I chose a line graph because I show changes that happened in the years.*

INTERVENTION 10 minutes

If students are having trouble choosing the correct graph to solve problems, have them write the name of each graph on a piece of paper to form columns. Together, think of and write words that will help them recognize the graph and when to use it below each one. After students read each problem, have them look for words in the problems that match or are similar to words on their chart to help them decide which graph to use.

Lesson
1

Prerequisite Background Knowledge
• Concept that things can be measured

Understand the Main Idea

Objective Use geometric terms to identify and talk about things around us.

30 minutes

Teach this lesson:
• **Before** introducing lessons on points, lines, and angles in the grade-level math textbook
• **Before** students complete the activities on page 81 of the student worktext

You need these materials:
• clipboards or other hard surfaces
• ads of kitchens from home decorating magazines
• pushpin

BP 4 ELL BEST PRACTICE #4:
Interaction

For English language learners, extensive interaction with others promotes acquisition of new knowledge, concepts, and language. New language is acquired through modeling and meaning-making provided by interaction in group problem solving. Provide plenty of opportunities for students to compare their work with others as they draw and describe geometric figures. Interaction in which students analyze differences helps develop deeper understanding of new geometric concepts.

Throughout this module, when you see this logo **BP 4**, you will find an example of how you can use interaction in the classroom.

Module 21: Points, Lines, Line Segments, Rays, and Angles

Understand the Main Idea

LESSON
1

Objective Use geometric terms to identify and talk about things around us.

Learn the Main Idea

> I see geometry everywhere! Look at the line segments and angles of the soccer field!

> Look at my favorite spot—the goal! It comes to a point on the side of the net! That's geometry, too.

MAIN IDEA We can use geometry to describe things in our world.

Practice Applying the Main Idea

Directions Find and circle the geometric term in each line of letters for numbers 1 to 3. Then draw an example. Answer question 4 in a complete sentence.

1. X R S A M (P O I N T) B U X L J W P R N M L F
   •A

3. M N B F L M K T Y Q (A N G L E) O B R T S D

2. J N A Z U K R C (L I N E S E G M E N T) B Q H

4. What does geometry help us do?
   Possible answer: Geometry helps us name and talk about things around us.

A Introduce

Read aloud the Lesson Objective on page 81 in the student worktext. Write the words *geometry* and *geometric* on the board.

BP 4 Ask: *Have you ever heard of geometry? What do you know about geometry?* Have students discuss with a partner and then report to the class. Write their ideas on the board.

Hold up a book and say: *Does this book have the shape of a geometric figure? What shape is it?* (rectangle) Point to the clock on the wall and say: *What geometric figure does the face of the clock look like?* (circle) *Look around you and find another geometric shape. Raise your hand when you find one.*

Say: *Knowing about geometry helps us talk and write about things we see in the classroom, at school, on the playground, and at home. When we know geometric terms, such as* point, line, line segment, ray, *and* angle, *we can use them to describe figures and real-life objects.* As necessary, quickly go over these terms with students by providing definitions and drawing pictures of each on the board. Leave this information on the board throughout the lesson.

Highlighted words and phrases may affect student comprehension.

Points, Lines, Line Segments, Rays, and Angles · 81

Read aloud the Main Idea with students. Tell them that they will begin to look around them and see geometric figures in objects wherever they go.

B Teach and Learn

Use the illustrations at the top of page 81 in the student worktext as a visual introduction to geometry. Have student pairs describe to each other what they see in both pictures. Then have volunteers share with the class what is happening.

- **Read aloud with students the girl's speech bubble.** Point to the word *geometry* already written on the board. Underneath, add the words *line segments* and *angles*. Ask: *Are line segments and angles part of geometry?* Elicit that they are. Draw the outline of a soccer field on the board. Ask a volunteer to come up and point to line segments and angles.

- **Write the word *angel* beside the word *angle*.** Have students focus on the different spellings. Have students say both words aloud. Ask for a volunteer to draw a picture of each word on the board and tell the difference between the two words.

- **Read aloud with students the boy's speech bubble.** Add the word *point* to the list on the board. Ask another student to come up and identify the point in the goal.

Say: *The things that you look at every day can show these geometric figures. Right here in our classroom there are things that have points, line segments, rays, and angles. Can you see anything on the wall or bulletin board that has points, line segments, rays, or angles in it?* Give students two minutes to look around and then ask them to name some objects. Write their ideas in a list under a drawing of each: points, line segments, rays, and angles.

BP 4 Give students three minutes to walk around the classroom. Say: *Pretend you are a detective. Walk around the room. Check out everything you can see from the ceiling to the floor. Do not touch anything. Just look. After you look, write down the name of everything you find that has points, line segments, rays, or angles.* Ask for volunteers to point out the objects they observed.

BP 4 Have students work in groups of four. Have the groups draw objects they observed that have points, line segments, rays, and/or angles and then write sentences about them. Write the following example sentence on the board: *The tip of a pushpin is like a point.* As you read the sentence aloud, show students a pushpin and show its pointed tip.

Ask for volunteers from each group. Have them come to the board to draw a picture and write one of their sentences. Have the whole class read aloud their sentences and make suggestions or corrections.

C Review and Practice

Review the concept of geometry by asking: *What have you learned about points? What objects in your world around you have points? What have you learned about line segments? What things that you see in everyday life have line segments? What have you learned about rays and angles? What objects do you know that have rays or angles in them?*

Ask students to think about the equipment on their school playground or at a neighborhood park. If possible, accompany students to the school playground. If this is not possible, have students go to the school cafeteria, gym, library, or office to look for things that have line segments, angles, and points in them. You can also use pictures from magazines to have students look for examples of line segments, angles, rays, and points.

- **BP 4 Ask student pairs to walk around the playground or inside the school with clipboards or other hard surfaces to write on.** Have them observe and draw all the geometric figures they see.

- **BP 4 When they return, ask students and their partners to write four to five sentences describing the objects and the geometric figures they observed.** Ask for volunteers to read aloud their sentences to the class.

Read aloud the directions for Practice Applying the Main Idea on page 81 of the student worktext. Have students do the activity independently. Circulate around the room, checking their progress and assessing their work with the following rubric.

D Assess and Intervene

Do students understand that we can use geometry to describe things in our world, based on Practice Applying the Main Idea on page 81? Use the rubric to identify students who need extra support through additional help and the Intervention activity.

Intermediate

- ☐ Completes 2 out of 3 word searches correctly.
- ☐ Writes a phrase or sentence for question 4 that demonstrates basic understanding of geometry; may include minor errors.

  Example of a sentence a student might write: *Help see point, line.*

Advanced

- ☐ Completes 3 out of 3 word searches correctly.
- ☐ Writes a complete sentence for question 4 that demonstrates a clear understanding of geometry.

  Example of a sentence a student might write: *Geometry helps us describe things in world.*

INTERVENTION 10 minutes

If students are having difficulty understanding geometry, give them some full-page color print advertisements of kitchens cut out of home decorating magazines. Have students identify the objects and describe orally and in writing how the appliances, floor, walls, windows, curtains, etc. contain geometric figures with angles, rays, points, and line segments. If they prefer, students may choose to use sports magazines or books with pictures.

Lesson

2

Learn the Vocabulary

Objective Talk and write about geometry using the vocabulary words.

| 30 minutes |  |

Teach this lesson:
- **Before** introducing lessons on points, lines, and angles in the grade-level math textbooks
- **Before** students complete the activities on page 82 of the student worktext

You need these materials:
- Vocabulary Cards
- pencils
- index cards
- at least one protractor
- Transparency 41

Lesson Vocabulary

Essential Vocabulary

geometry	point	line
endpoint	ray	angle
line segment		

Additional Vocabulary

| degree (°) | protractor | relationship |

LESSON

2

Learn the Vocabulary

Objective Talk and write about geometry using the vocabulary words.

Learn the Words

Word/Phrase	Example/Drawing	Definition
geometry		the study of points, lines, angles, and shapes
point	A	an exact location in space
line	B C	a straight path that goes on without end in both directions
endpoint	endpoint D E	the point at each end of a line segment
line segment	F G	a part of a line that has two endpoints
ray	H I	a part of a line that has one endpoint and goes on without end in the other direction
angle	J K L	two rays that have the same endpoint

Practice the Words

Directions Answer the questions below with a word or a phrase from above. Then draw a picture to show the word or phrase. Answer question 4 with a complete sentence and a drawing.

1. What has no length or width and you cannot measure its size? a point •A

2. What do you call part of a line that has one endpoint and goes on without end in one direction? a ray

3. What geometric figure do the back and seat of a chair form? an angle

4. What is a line? Describe a line in your own words. A line is a straight path that goes on without end in both directions.

82 • Points, Lines, Line Segments, Rays, and Angles

A Introduce

Help students activate prior knowledge. Ask: *What are some geometry words you already learned in Lesson 1?* Write students' responses on the board. (Responses should include *geometry, point, line segment,* and *angle.*)

Connect what students will be learning about to their home and community. Ask: *Have you seen any of these geometric figures in your home or outside?* Have partners tell each other what geometric figures they have seen. Ask volunteers to come to the board and report to the class, drawing and labeling pictures of the things they have seen.

Focus students' attention on page 82 of the student worktext. Read aloud the Lesson Objective with students. Tell them they will learn words to help them talk and write about geometry.

Say: *In this lesson you will learn more about geometric figures, such as endpoints, rays, and line segments. You will learn to recognize what they look like and to know their definitions. You will also learn about a tool called a* protractor *that can measure angles.*

B Teach and Learn

Present each of the Essential Vocabulary words. As you write each word on the board, model its pronunciation and have students repeat the word.

Highlighted words and phrases may affect student comprehension.

Underline *geo-* in the word *geometry* and say: *The word part* geo- *means* the earth. *Another word that has* geo- *in it is* geography. *Geography is the science that teaches about the earth, weather, land forms, lakes, and oceans.*

Underline the letters *-metry.* Say: *This word part means* measuring. *Geometry is about describing and measuring things in our world. Geometry helps us know where things are and what size and shape they are.*

Focus students' attention on the Definition column at the top of page 82 in the student worktext. Read aloud the definition of *geometry.* Point out the different shapes and forms in the drawing.

Have a student read the definition of the word *point.* Explain that a point has no length or width. You cannot measure its size, but you can describe where it is. Each star you see in the sky on a clear night looks like a separate point of light.

BP 4 Have students work in pairs to come up with other examples of points and their locations. (tip of a flagpole, tip of a skyscraper, tip of a pen)

Have a student read the definition for the word *line.* Explain that a line is a straight path that goes on without end in both directions. Point out to students the picture of a line showing arrowheads at both ends. Tell students that you can draw a line through any two points. Explain to students that you can't see a line in the real world because you can't see something that goes on without end. But you can imagine a line.

Say the word *endpoint.* Write it on the board and draw a line segment with two endpoints. Ask a volunteer to tell what an endpoint is. (the point at each end of a line segment)

Read aloud the phrase *line segment.* Ask students if its picture is already on the board. Touch the endpoints on the board. Point out also that most real objects in our world have line segments, not lines, because they have an end.

BP 4 Have students work in pairs to come up with some examples of line segments. Ask the pairs to share their examples with another pair.

Read aloud the word *ray* and have students repeat it. Ask: *Have you ever heard the word* ray? *Have you ever seen a ray of sunshine coming through a window? Have you ever seen*

a ray of light from a flashlight in the dark? Explain that the word *ray* also has a math meaning. Ask a volunteer to read the definition.

Read aloud the word *angle* and have students repeat after you. Demonstrate how angles are formed and how they change. Hold up a book and slowly open it to form different-sized angles. Ask students to describe what you are doing.

- **Demonstrate how angles can be different sizes.** Place two pencils, one on top of the other, and rotate one pencil away from the other, stopping at angles between zero degrees and 180 degrees. Note that the measure of an angle tells how far one side is turned from the other side.

BP 4 **Have groups of four students each use two pencils.** Have them hold one pencil on top of the other and rotate one pencil away from the other, making different angles. Encourage them to talk about what they're doing and to draw a picture of each angle they form. Ask a volunteer to share the group's drawing and tell what the group did and learned.

- **Say:** *The size of an angle can be measured in units called* degrees. *Write the word* degree *on the board and its symbol and have students say the word. Degrees in an angle can be measured with a special tool called a* protractor. *Write the word* protractor *on the board.*

- **Hold up a protractor.** Then display Transparency 41. Point out that a protractor measures angles from zero to 180 degrees. Use the transparency to demonstrate how to use a protractor. If enough protractors are available, give one to each pair or small group. If not, let students take turns using the protractor.

Have students complete the Vocabulary Cards for the words in this lesson.

C Review and Practice

BP 4 **Review the Essential Vocabulary with students.** Point to each word, one at a time, and ask students to define it in their own words. Erase any drawings on the board and have students close their student worktexts. Say each Essential Vocabulary word and have students work with a partner to draw a picture to illustrate each word.

Read aloud the directions for the Practice the Words activity on page 82 of the student worktext. Have students cover the top of the page with a sheet of paper and do the activity independently.

D Assess and Intervene

Can students understand and use the Essential Vocabulary to answer questions based on Practice the Words on page 82? Use the rubric to identify students who need extra support through additional help and the Intervention activity.

Intermediate

☐ Answers at least 3 questions correctly; drawings show a basic understanding of vocabulary words.

☐ Writes a phrase or sentence for question 4 that is correct but may be difficult to understand.

Example of a sentence a student might write: *Line straight no end.*

Advanced

☐ Answers 4 questions correctly; drawings show a clear understanding of vocabulary words.

☐ Writes a clear and correct complete sentence for question 4, with few errors.

Example of a sentence a student might write: *Line is straight with no end.*

INTERVENTION   10 minutes

If students are having difficulty understanding the vocabulary words, have them use index cards to make Concentration game cards. For each vocabulary word, have pairs of students write the word on one card, the definition on another card, and a drawing on the third card. Mix up the cards and place them fact down. A player who chooses three matching cards takes them. If they don't match, the player puts them back. The player with the most sets of three cards wins.

Use More Language

Objective Use geometric terms to describe and identify drawings.

---

45 minutes

Teach this lesson:
- **Before** math textbook lessons on points, lines, and angles in the grade-level math textbook
- **Before** students complete the activities on page 83 of the student worktext

You need these materials:
- index cards
- protractors
- pipe cleaners, straws, toothpicks, dry spaghetti, or pencils
- Transparency 42

Lesson Vocabulary

Essential Vocabulary

vertex/vertices	parallel lines	intersecting lines
straight angle	right angle	acute angle
obtuse angle	perpendicular lines	

 **Introduce**

Read aloud the Lesson Objective on page 83 in the student worktext. Ask students to name some geometry words they learned in the last lesson. Draw a picture of each word on the board. Have students work in pairs to agree on the word for each picture and then say the words. As they say them, label the drawings.

Tell students that in this lesson, they are going to learn more geometry words. Draw a right angle, an acute angle, and an obtuse angle on the board. Ask: *Do these three angles look the same?* Ask if students know the names of any of the angles. If they do, write them on the board. Tell students they will all learn names for each of these angles.

Draw parallel lines, intersecting lines, and perpendicular lines on the board. Say: *Each of these drawings shows two lines. Do the drawings look the same?* Ask if students know the names of any of these pairs of lines. If they do, write them on the board. Tell students they will all learn names for each of these pairs of lines.

Point to the picture of an angle on the board. Ask: *Do you see where the two line segments come together? They come together to form an angle. Does anybody know what this point is called?* If any students know the word *vertex*, write it on the board. Tell students that they will learn more about this word.

Use More Language

Objective Use geometric terms to describe and identify drawings.

Learn the Language

Word/Phrase	Drawing	Definition
vertex/vertices		point where line segments or rays meet and form an angle
parallel lines		lines that never cross and are always the same distance apart
intersecting lines		lines that cross each other at one point
right angle	90°	an angle that measures exactly 90° and forms a square corner
perpendicular lines		lines that cross to form right angles
acute angle		an angle that measures less than 90°
obtuse angle		an angle that measures greater than 90° and less than 180°
straight angle		an angle that measures exactly 180°

Practice the Language

Directions Make a drawing to help you decide if the sentence is true or false. If the sentence is false, write a correct sentence. Use a separate sheet of paper.

1. Parallel lines never meet. True.

2. A straight angle is a straight line. True.

3. A right angle measures more than 90°. False. A right angle measures exactly 90°.

4. Perpendicular lines cross to form an obtuse angle. False. Perpendicular lines cross to form right angles.

5. An acute angle measures 90°. False. An acute angle measures less than 90°.

6. A vertex is the space between two parallel lines. False. A vertex is the endpoint where two line segments or rays meet to form an angle.

7. An obtuse angle measures greater than 90°. True.

8. Intersecting lines never cross each other. False. Intersecting lines always cross each other.

Points, Lines, Line Segments, Rays, and Angles • 83

Highlighted words and phrases may affect student comprehension.

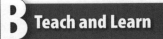 **Teach and Learn**

Introduce the new vocabulary on page 83 of the student worktext. Copy each of the pictures on the board, but in random order. Number the pictures. Then write this question frame on the board: *Why is this a _____?* Tell students they will work in pairs.

- **BP 4 Model the activity: For each picture, pairs write the number of the drawing, find the same picture in their worktext, write the word, and read the definition.** Then one student points to the first picture in the student worktext and asks about it, using the question frame. The other student uses the definition to answer the question. Students then change roles and continue with all the words.

- **BP 4 Have pairs of students complete the activity.** Circulate and provide assistance as necessary.

BP 4 Have students work in groups of four. Tell them they will use their arms and fingers to make figures like the ones in their worktext. Say: *vertex, parallel segments, intersecting segments, perpendicular segments.* Have the groups work together to use their arms and fingers to demonstrate each word as you say it. Give the groups a short time to talk to each other to decide how best to show each word.

Have students walk around the room looking for examples of vertices, parallel segments, intersecting segments, and perpendicular segments. Ask them not to touch anything but just to look. Call on volunteers to take turns reporting on the examples they found. Ask all students to use their fingers to demonstrate the meaning of each word.

Discuss the four kinds of angles with students. Say: *A right angle is like a square corner. An acute angle is smaller than a right angle. An obtuse angle is larger than a right angle. A straight angle looks like a line segment.*

- **BP 4 To demonstrate each angle, use an open book with one cover flat on a surface.** First, show the book with its front cover held vertically to model a right angle. Then close the book slightly to show an acute angle. Open the book almost completely to show an obtuse angle. Then open the book completely with both front and back covers flat on the surface to show a straight angle.

BP 4 Provide students with pipe cleaners, straws, dry spaghetti, or pencils. Have them work with a partner. Have them read the definitions on page 83 of the student worktext and then use the items to form the four angles. Then have them quiz another pair by asking them to identify each of their angles by name.

Have students complete the Vocabulary Cards for the words in this lesson.

 Review and Practice

Lead students in a chant to review the words. Say: *We're going to do a chant to practice the new words. Repeat the words I say:* Angle, angle, angle—right angle! *Clap as you say the first three words with me. I'll give the name of the angle, and then as fast as you can, after you hear its name, use your arms and fingers to make that angle. We can check on each other to see if we have it right.* Say: *Angle, angle, angle—right angle!* Do the same with *acute angle, obtuse angle,* and *straight angle.* Then lead a chant for the vocabulary with line segments. Say: *Line segments, line segments—parallel line segments!* Ask a volunteer to lead the chant, using *intersecting line segments* and *perpendicular line segments* in place of *parallel line segments.* Ask another volunteer to lead, using both angles and line segments.

BP 4 To practice the vocabulary, display Transparency 42. Have students work in groups of three. Point to one of the pictures on the transparency. Have each group of students agree on what the picture shows and its definition, without looking at their student worktexts. Call on a student in one group to respond. Ask the other groups if the response is right and to correct it if not. Continue with all pictures.

Read aloud the directions to the Practice the Language activity on page 83 of the student worktext. Have students do the activity independently. As they are working, circulate through the room and check their progress. Assess their work with the following rubric.

Assess and Intervene

How well do students understand geometric terms and definitions based on their responses to the Practice the Language activity on page 83? Can they draw pictures that represent angles? Use the rubric to identify students who need additional support through extra help and the Intervention activity.

Intermediate

- ☐ Can identify and draw at least 6 correct geometric figures.
- ☐ Corrects false sentences, with some errors; sentences indicate an understanding of the geometric terms.

   Example of a sentence a student might write: *Vertex is point lines meet.*

Advanced

- ☐ Can identify and draw all 8 geometric figures.
- ☐ Corrects false sentences, with very few errors; sentences indicate an understanding of the geometric terms.

   Example of a sentence a student might write: *A vertex is point where lines meet and make angle.*

INTERVENTION   10 minutes

If students are having difficulty using geometric terms to describe and identify drawings, ask them to write the eight vocabulary words on eight separate index cards. Have each student choose a card and read the word. Then have each student make a drawing on a piece of paper to represent the word. Students then describe the drawing to you.

Lesson

4

Solve Math Problems

Objective Understand sentences that have many different phrases in them.

30 minutes

Teach this lesson:
- **After** lessons on points, lines, and angles in the grade-level math textbook
- **Before** students complete the activities on page 84 of the student worktext

You need these materials:
- Worksheet 21
- pipe cleaners
- sentence strips

EXTENSION AND ENRICHMENT   15 minutes

BP 4 Ask students to work with a partner to create a map for an imaginary town or city. Have them draw the streets, roads, and highways, and name them. Have students work together to write a paragraph about the city, using geometric terms. Have them look for representations of various line segments and angles. Collect all the maps and paragraphs and publish a booklet for the class.

LESSON
4

Solve Math Problems

Objective Understand sentences that have many different phrases in them.

Learn to Solve Problems

Sentence Use pipe cleaners to show examples of different kinds of line segments and angles.

	Think	Write
Step 1:	Read the sentence that has many phrases.	I need to read the sentence.
Step 2:	Go back and read one word or phrase at a time. Ask yourself questions about the word or phrase you read.	I'll read one word or phrase at a time: Use use what? pipe cleaners for what? to show to show what? examples examples of what? of different kinds different kinds of what? of line segments and angles.
Step 3:	Say and write the sentence in your own words. Use a few short sentences.	Get some pipe cleaners. Make line segments and angles. Make different kinds.

Practice Solving Math Problems

Directions Follow steps 1 to 3 above to rephrase the sentences below. Write your new sentences on a separate sheet of paper.

1. A line is a straight path of points that goes on without end in both directions. Possible answer: A line is straight. A line goes on without end in both directions.

2. Use a protractor to draw a right angle and an obtuse angle of 100°. Possible answer: Use a protractor. Draw a right angle. Draw an obtuse angle of 100°.

3. An angle that is less than a right angle is called an acute angle. Possible answer: An acute angle is less than a right angle.

4. A ray is a part of a line that has one endpoint and goes on without end in one direction. Possible answer: A ray is part of a line. A ray has an endpoint. A ray goes on without end in one direction.

84 · Points, Lines, Line Segments, Rays, and Angles

A Introduce

Set the scene. Say: *Sometimes when you read a textbook in class or a book at home, you see sentences that are long and difficult. Those sentences may have a lot of different phrases. It can be confusing to have so many words in one sentence.*

Ask: *Have you ever read long and difficult sentences? Do you sometimes find long math word problems hard to understand?*

Have students look at the sentence at the top of page 84 in the student worktext. Write the sentence on the board: *Use pipe cleaners to show examples of different kinds of line segments and angles.* Read it aloud. Say: *This is an example of a long and difficult sentence that has many different phrases in it. Can you tell me what some of the short phrases are?*

Read aloud the Lesson Objective with students. Say: *In this lesson you will learn how to take a sentence with many phrases and break it into shorter parts. Shorter parts are easier to understand.*

Highlighted words and phrases may affect student comprehension.

B Teach and Learn

Focus students' attention on the Think column on page 84 of the student worktext. Tell students that the numbered steps will help them understand long and difficult sentences that have many phrases in them.

Model understanding sentences with many phrases by doing a Think Aloud:

> **Think Aloud**

Write Step 1 on the board and read it aloud. Say: *What do I need to do? I need to read the sentence.* Ask a volunteer to read the sentence aloud. Say: *The sentence is hard to understand because it has so many different phrases, one after another.*

Write Step 2 on the board and read it aloud. Say: *I'll read the first word: use.* Ask students: *What question can I ask about the word* use? Write students' answers on the board. Say: *I have to use something. So I can use the question word* what. *My question is, "Use what?"*

Write the question on the board. Say: *Now I'll read the next word or phrase:* pipe cleaners. Show a pipe cleaner. Say: *I know what pipe cleaners are. I don't need to ask, "What are they?"* Ask: *What other question can I ask about the pipe cleaners?* Write students' suggestions on the board. Say: *I need to know what to use the pipe cleaners for. I'll ask, "For what?" The next phrase is* to show. *I need to use the pipe cleaners to show something. I can use the question word* what *again: "To show what?" The next word says* examples. *I'm going to show examples. I'll ask, "Examples of what?" The next phrase is* of different kinds. *I can use the question word* what *again: "Different kinds of what?" The next phrase is* of line segments and angles. *So I am going to show examples of different kinds of line segments and angles. Now I have a better understanding about what the different phrases in the sentence mean.*

Write Step 3 on the board and read it aloud. Say: *Now I need to say the sentence in my own words. I should use shorter sentences. I'm going to say it like this:* I have to get some pipe cleaners. I have to make line segments and angles. I should make different kinds.

Write the following two sentences on the board.

1. *Use two straws to show a pair of line segments that intersect.*

2. *Find something in the classroom that shows a pair of parallel line segments.*

BP 4 **Distribute Worksheet 21.** Have students work in small groups. Instruct students to use the chart and follow the three steps to help them understand the two sentences on the board. Ask the groups to ask *what*-questions about the words and phrases. Have the group write everything they do as they follow the three steps. As groups work, circulate the room helping as necessary.

C Review and Practice

Ask volunteers to retell the steps for understanding sentences with many phrases in them. Summarize the steps by writing them on the board:

Step 1: *Read the sentence that has many phrases.*

Step 2: *Go back and read one word or phrase at a time. Ask yourself questions about the word or phrase you read.*

Step 3: *Say the sentence in your own words. Use a few short sentences.*

BP 4 **Have students work with a partner.** Have the pairs use the three steps to better understand the following difficult sentences with many phrases in them. Write these three sentences on the board:

1. *Identify the name of each angle according to its size and measure it with a protractor.*

2. *Circle the vertex in the drawing of a right angle on page 83 in your textbook.*

3. *Use the corner of a sheet of paper to identify the kind of angle that is on the worksheet.*

- **When partners have completed the activity, ask them to compare the sentences they wrote in their own words with those of another pair.** Have each pair read the sentences in their own words aloud and then explain how they used the three steps.

Read aloud the directions for the Practice Solving Math Problems activity on page 84 in the student worktext. Have students do the activity on their own. Walk around the room and check their progress as they work. Assess their work with the following rubric.

D Assess and Intervene

How well can students understand sentences with many phrases in them, based on Practice Solving Math Problems on page 84? Can they successfully write the sentences in their own words? Use the rubric to identify students who need additional support through extra help or the Intervention activity.

Intermediate

☐ Shows comprehension of at least 3 sentences by paraphrasing them in own words.

Example of sentences a student might write: *Get protractor. Draw right angle. Draw obtuse angle.*

Advanced

☐ Shows comprehension of all 4 sentences by paraphrasing them in own words.

Example of sentences a student might write: *I get a protractor. I draw a right angle. I draw a obtuse angle. Obtuse angle have 100°.*

INTERVENTION 15 minutes

If students have difficulty knowing how to divide a sentence into words and phrases, have them each copy a sentence onto a sentence strip. Help students separate the sentence into phrases by cutting or tearing them from the sentence strips. Demonstrate separating and cutting. Show students how dividing a long and difficult sentence into phrases and words makes it easier to ask *what*-questions about each part. Explain that once students understand the shorter parts, they can understand the whole sentence. Finally, have students each write a new sentence in their own words, telling what the original sentence with many phrases means.

Understand the Main Idea

Objective Describe how shapes are alike and different.

30 minutes

Teach this lesson:
- **Before** introducing material on polygons and circles in grade-level math textbooks
- **Before** students complete the activities on page 85 of the student worktext

You need these materials:
- cardboard circle and square
- Transparency 43
- index cards
- rulers
- crayons
- blank paper

**Prerequisite
Background Knowledge**
- Concepts of line segments
  and angles

Module 22: Polygons and Circles

Understand the Main Idea

LESSON
1

Objective Describe how shapes are alike and different.

Learn the Main Idea

How are these shapes alike? How are they different?

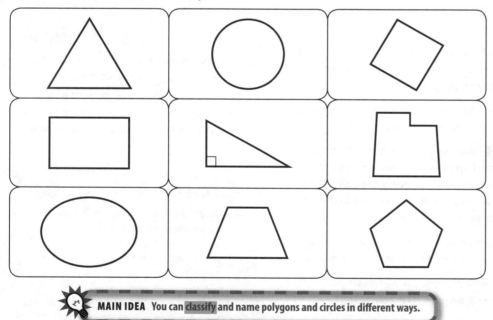

💡 **MAIN IDEA** You can classify and name polygons and circles in different ways.

Practice Applying the Main Idea

Directions Follow the directions below. Color the shapes in the chart above.
Answer the last question in a complete sentence.

1 Color the shapes with curves red. circle and
   oval colored red

2 Color the shapes with only 3 angles blue.
   both triangles colored blue

3 Color the shapes with only 4 sides green.
   rectangle, rhombus, and trapezoid colored green

4 Look at the shapes you did not color.
   Write a sentence to tell how they are alike.
   Then write a sentence to tell how they are
   different. Possible sentences: They are alike

   because they are both polygons. They are different

   because one has 6 sides and the other has 5 sides.

Highlighted words and phrases may affect student comprehension.

ELL BEST PRACTICE #5:
Higher Order Thinking

English language learners are just as capable as
any other students of using higher-order thinking, but are hindered by their inability to express
their thinking in English. Help students by having
them think critically about the plane figures presented in this module. Ask them to analyze, sort,
and describe these figures in a variety of ways,
using words, manipulatives, and pictures. As
students see that they can express even complex
ideas appropriately, they will gain in confidence
and in their willingness to use language.

Throughout this module, when you see the
BP 5, you will find an example of how you can
activate higher-order thinking.

A Introduce

**Activate background knowledge by ask-
ing students to draw some shapes.** Have
them sketch four or five different shapes on a
sheet of paper. Ask them to label the shapes
if they know the names of the figures they
have drawn.

- **BP 5 Then have students get together
  with a partner.** Ask partners to tell each
  other about the shapes they have drawn.
  Circulate through the room, listening to
  conversations and noting the kinds of
  words students are using.

- **Have volunteers share some of their
  shapes and descriptions with the class.**
  Invite them to draw their shapes on the
  board. Write the words they used to name
  the shapes (such as *triangle* and *circle*) and
  make another list of other important words
  (such as *straight* or *curved*). Read aloud the
  word lists. Tell students that these are good
  words for them to know.

**Read aloud the Lesson Objective with
students.**

Have a volunteer read the direction line aloud at the top of page 85 of the student worktext. Then have students study the nine shapes in the chart. Ask if any students drew these shapes or others like them.

Ask students to work with a partner to compare these shapes. Have them report to the whole group. Point out any new words used by students to describe shapes earlier in the lesson and challenge students to identify the classmates who used them. Explain that these are words students can use when they talk about shapes.

Then read aloud the Main Idea with students. Explain that a *polygon* is a closed flat shape with straight sides.

B Teach and Learn

Hold up a large cardboard (or construction paper) circle and a large cardboard square. Have students name each shape. Write the names on the shapes. Ask students to describe the circle. Then ask them to describe the square.

Say: *I am thinking of one of these shapes. It is round. Which shape am I thinking of?* (circle) Have students take turns thinking of one of the shapes and giving the class a clue to its identity.

Display Transparency 43. Point to the octagon and have students repeat its name. Ask: *What can you tell me about an octagon?* Talk about each of the words and drawings on the transparency. Be sure students know the meanings of all the words. Explain that the words on the transparency are helpful in talking about different shapes.

BP 5 Bring students' attention back to the cardboard shapes. Ask: *How are these shapes alike?* Encourage students to use the words on the transparency to help find ways in which the square and the circle are similar. Help them form sentences using frames, such as *They both have _____.* or *Both the circle and the square are _____.* Repeat with the question: *How are these shapes different?* Have students use frames, such as: *The square is/has _____, but the circle is/has _____.*

Again point out the shapes in the student worktext. Invite students to name any shapes they recognize. Ask them to study the shapes for a minute.

Then have each student choose one shape. Ask students to copy the shape onto an index card, using a ruler if necessary to draw the figure correctly.

- **BP 5 Have students find a classmate who has copied a different shape.** Have them compare their shapes to describe how they are alike and how they are different. Remind them to use some of the words on the transparency as a reference. When students have noted several ways in which the shapes are alike and different, have them find a new partner and repeat the process.

- **Gather the whole group together to process the activity.** Have students think about their discussions. Ask: *Who had a shape that was a lot like yours? Who had a shape that was very different from yours?* Ask students to answer each question by naming the correct classmates.

- **BP 5 Then ask volunteers to explain their answers**, using the word *because* if possible. Establish that some pairs of shapes have a lot in common and that other pairs have more differences. Say: *When you look at shapes, you can sort them into groups by thinking about how they are alike and how they are different.*

C Review and Practice

Call students' attention to the figures at the top of page 85 once more. Explain that shapes sometimes go together to make a group. Say: *Shapes can be put in a group if they are all alike in some way.*

BP 5 Invite one student to come forward and display his or her card. Ask students if they have a card that is a lot like the one being displayed. Invite one of these students to come forward and tell how his or her shape is like the first shape. Then say: *These two shapes both have _____. Does anyone else have a shape that fits in this group?* Add more shapes, as possible. Then repeat, having another student display a different shape.

- **Have students move around the room as before, forming groups of shapes that are alike in some way.** Ask students to tell what makes the shapes in their groups alike.

Read aloud the directions for the activity at the bottom of page 85. Explain that these questions ask students to think about groups of shapes and how shapes are alike and different. Have students complete the activity independently.

D Assess and Intervene

How well can students determine how shapes are alike and different, according to Practice Applying the Main Idea on page 85? Use the rubric to identify students who need extra support through additional help and the Intervention activity.

Intermediate

☐ Colors all shapes accurately.

☐ Accurately describes similarities and differences in phrases or sentences, which may lack details.

Example of sentences a student might write: *Alike both have side. Different one have more side.*

Advanced

☐ Colors all shapes accurately.

☐ Accurately describes similarities and differences in complete sentences with details.

Example of sentences a student might write: *They are same because both have sides. They are different because one have more sides.*

INTERVENTION   5 minutes

If students struggle to complete Practice Applying the Main Idea, check to make sure they understand terms such as *side* and *angle*. Draw a large triangle on the board and indicate its sides and angles. Say: *This figure has three sides, here, here, and here.* Repeat with angles. Then do it again with a square and other figures, having students locate, name, and count the various parts of the figure themselves.

Lesson 2

Learn the Vocabulary

Objective Talk and write about shapes using lesson vocabulary.

45 minutes

Teach this lesson:
- **Before** students begin activities on polygons and circles in their grade-level math textbooks
- **Before** students complete the activities on page 86 of the student worktext

You need these materials:
- cardboard circle and square
- marble or tennis ball
- scissors
- index cards

Lesson Vocabulary

Essential Vocabulary		
plane figure	polygon	regular polygon

Additional Vocabulary		
angle *	side	center
radius	diameter	chord
vertex/vertices*		

* - Terms that have Vocabulary Cards.

Lesson 2

Learn the Vocabulary

Objective Talk and write about shapes using lesson vocabulary.

Learn the Words

Directions Draw the shapes in the two blank spaces below.

Plane figures are flat shapes. Here are some plane figures.	⬤	▲	(Georgia shape)
Polygons are closed plane figures made of line segments. Here are some polygons.	◢	⬠	Draw a polygon here: Check students' drawings.
In a **regular polygon**, all sides are equal. All angles are equal, too. Here are some regular polygons.	⬢	⬟	Draw a regular polygon here: Check students' drawings.

Practice the Words

Directions Circle all the words that describe each shape you see. Write a complete sentence for question 4.

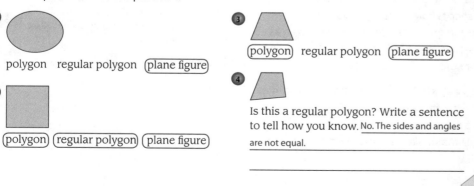

1. polygon   regular polygon   (plane figure)

2. (polygon)   (regular polygon)   plane figure

3. (polygon)   regular polygon   (plane figure)

4. Is this a regular polygon? Write a sentence to tell how you know. No. The sides and angles are not equal.

A Introduce

Read aloud the Lesson Objective with students.

Have students work with a partner to list words that they found useful in the previous lesson. Have students share their lists with the class. Write the words they used on the board. Include small illustrations or examples, if appropriate. Leave the list up throughout the lesson.

Introduce the three Essential Vocabulary words. Write them on the board and say them slowly and carefully. Have students repeat the words after you. Remind students that they heard the word *polygon* in the Main Idea in Lesson 1.

Choose words from the Additional Vocabulary box that you think will be useful. Elicit or provide examples or definitions for these Additional Vocabulary words.

B Teach and Learn

Touch the word *plane figure* on the board and have students read it aloud. Ask students what the word *plane* means. Elicit that *plane* can be short for *airplane* and that the word *plain*, which is pronounced the same, means *regular* or *without anything extra*. Then explain that *plane* in *plane figure* means *a flat surface*. Have students identify *planes* in the room, such as shelf tops or book covers.

Highlighted words and phrases may affect student comprehension.

Read aloud the definition of *plane figure* **on page 86 of the student worktext as students follow along.** Teach students to chant: *A plane figure is a flat shape.* Spread your hands apart along an imaginary plane, like an umpire signaling *safe,* when you say *plane* and again when you say *flat.* Have students repeat the chant, together with the hand motions, three or four times.

- **Hold up a square cut from cardboard.** Ask if this shape is a plane figure. Elicit that it is because it is a flat shape. Repeat with a marble or a tennis ball. Establish that this is not a plane figure because it is not flat.

- **BP 5 Call students' attention to the three plane figures shown in the student worktext.** Have students work with a partner. Ask them to explain to each other how they know that each of the shapes pictured is a plane figure.

Move on to the discussion of the word *polygon.* Tell students that *polygon* is a Greek word that has now become part of English. Explain that *poly-* means *many* and that *-gon* means *angle,* so a polygon is a shape with many angles.

- **Read the definition of** *polygon* **aloud.** Draw closed and not-closed figures on the board to model this concept.

- **Display the cardboard square again.** Elicit that it is a polygon because it is closed and made of line segments. Repeat with a cardboard circle. Elicit that it has curves, so it is not a polygon.

- **BP 5 Give each student a pair of scissors and an index card.** Ask if the index card is a plane figure (yes); then ask if it is a polygon (yes). Have students cut their cards into different kinds of polygons. Then have them compare the polygon they made with one created by a partner. Ask them to talk about how the polygons they made are alike and how they are different.

- **Have students study the examples of polygons in the second row on page 86.** Then have students draw a polygon in the right-hand box of that row. Ask them to check their work with a partner. Conclude by asking if their polygons are also plane figures. (yes)

Continue by introducing the concept of a *regular polygon.* Ask students to use *regular* in a sentence. Explain that *regular* can mean *normal* or *usual,* but in math it often means *equal.*

- **Have students read aloud the definition of** *regular polygon.* Stress that *all* angles and *all* sides must be equal, not just some of them. Call students' attention to the pictures of the scalene triangle and the irregular pentagon in the second row on page 86. Ask students whether these are regular polygons and have them give reasons for their responses. Elicit that neither is regular, since the first has no equal sides or angles and the second has some equal sides and angles, but not all.

- **Have students look at the polygons they cut out from index cards.** Ask if anyone made a regular polygon. If anyone did, invite those students to display their work to the class.

- **Instruct students to study the examples of regular polygons in the third row in the student worktext.** Then have them draw a regular polygon of their own in the space provided. Have students check their work with a partner.

Write the labels *plane figure, polygon,* **and** *regular polygon* **on the board.** Have students form three equal teams. Assign each team a different label. Introduce a relay-style game in which students take turns coming to the board and drawing a figure that matches the label. Students on the *polygon* team, for example, draw a polygon. The winning team is the first one to have each player draw a correct figure. Repeat, switching labels so each team has a different type of figure to draw.

📇 **Have students complete the Vocabulary Cards for the words in this lesson.**

C Review and Practice

BP 5 Ask students how plane figures, polygons, and regular polygons are alike and different. Have them share their ideas with a partner and then with the class. Record their thoughts on the board. Draw out that all regular polygons are polygons and that all polygons are plane figures.

Read aloud the directions for Practice the Words on page 86. Point out that some shapes may fit more than one description. Explain that the last item asks students to write a full sentence.

D Assess and Intervene

Can students determine which vocabulary terms apply to each figure, based on their work in Practice the Words on page 86? Use the rubric to identify students who need extra support through additional help and the Intervention activity.

Intermediate

☐ Identifies the correct terms for at least 2 of the 3 figures.

☐ Writes a correct explanation that includes either sides or angles.

Example of a sentence a student might write: *Sides not equal.*

Advanced

☐ Identifies the correct terms for all 3 figures.

☐ Writes a correct explanation that includes both sides and angles.

Example of a sentence a student might write: *Sides and angles are not equal.*

INTERVENTION 10 minutes

If students are having trouble with the assignments in Practice the Words, create a web for each vocabulary word. Write the word or phrase in the center of the web. Ask students to help you fill in the outside of each web with words and phrases that tell about the vocabulary word. Go over each web with students when they are complete and allow students to use the webs as resources as they do the activity on page 86 again.

Lesson

3

Use More Language

Objective Classify and name shapes.

40 minutes

Teach this lesson:
- **Before** students' grade-level math textbook lessons on polygons and circles
- **Before** students complete the activities on page 87 of the student worktext

You need these materials:
- index cards
- poster board
- Worksheet 22

Lesson Vocabulary

Essential Vocabulary

pentagon	triangle	quadrilateral
hexagon	octagon	trapezoid
rectangle	square	right triangle
parallelogram	rhombus	scalene triangle
obtuse triangle	acute triangle	
isosceles triangle	equilateral triangle	

Use More Language

Objective Classify and name shapes.

LESSON **3**

  Learn the Language

This plane figure has different names.

It's a polygon.
It's a triangle.
It's a right triangle.
It's an isosceles triangle.

polygon
regular polygon
triangle
quadrilateral
pentagon

hexagon
octagon
rectangle
square
trapezoid
parallelogram
rhombus

right triangle
obtuse triangle
acute triangle
equilateral triangle
isosceles triangle
scalene triangle

Practice the Language

Directions Use the word list in the picture above. Write two names for each figure below. Answer number 4 on a separate sheet of paper.

①

possible answers: rectangle; quadrilateral; polygon

③

possible answers: hexagon; regular polygon; polygon

②

possible answers: triangle; equilateral triangle; acute triangle; regular polygon

④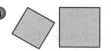

Write a sentence that tells how these two shapes are alike. Use at least one word from the word list. Possible answer: They are alike because they are both polygons/regular polygons/quadrilaterals.

Polygons and Circles • 87

A Introduce

Read aloud the Lesson Objective with students. Remind students that *to classify* means *to sort into groups.*

Ask students to think about a time when they classified, or sorted, objects or numbers. Encourage students to think about how they use classification in daily life. Have them write a description of when they have used classification and share it with a classmate. Possible responses include sorting sports cards by team, classifying coins by value, and separating garbage by sorting out the recycling.

Explain that students can sort polygons, too. Remind students that polygons can belong in more than one group at the same time.

Draw an equilateral triangle on the board. Ask: *Is this a triangle or is it a polygon?* Elicit that it is both a triangle (because it has three sides) and a polygon (because it has only straight sides, no curves). Repeat with a square, asking if it is a square or a plane figure. (both)

Explain that students will learn ways to sort polygons in this lesson.

Highlighted words and phrases may affect student comprehension.

 **Teach and Learn**

Read aloud the text at the top of the Learn the Language box on page 87 of the student worktext. Draw students' attention to the picture of the isosceles triangle.

- **Have students study the figure in the picture.** Then divide the class into groups of four or five students. Have each group sit in a circle. Ask one student in each circle to say one fact about the figure in the picture (for example, that it has three sides). Have the second student repeat or rephrase this information, then add a different fact. The third student repeats the second student's fact before adding a third piece of information, and so on. This activity helps students learn to listen to one another in addition to developing their vocabulary and syntax skills.

- **Discuss the figure in the picture.** Say: *What do I know about this shape? I know that it has only sides. There are no curves. So it must be a _____.* Pause and have students insert the word *polygon*. Call students' attention to the sentence: *It's a polygon.*

- **Point out that some polygons are also regular polygons.** Ask if this shape is a regular polygon. Have students put their thumbs up if they think it is a regular polygon and down if they think it is not regular. If anyone thinks it is a regular polygon or is not sure, have a volunteer explain why it is not regular. (A regular polygon has all sides the same length and all angles equal.)

- **BP 5** **Ask students how many sides the figure has.** Establish that a three-sided figure is called a triangle. Point out that the prefix *tri-* means *three*. Ask if students know the word *tricycle*, which uses the same prefix; if so, challenge them to explain how *tri-* is connected to the word. Students may be interested to know that a person who is trilingual can speak three languages. Point out that *It's a triangle.* appears on the list.

- **Explain that you still have to check what kind of triangle the figure is.** Ask: *Is it an equilateral triangle?* Help students explain that it is not because this triangle's sides are not all the same length. Continue with *right, obtuse, acute, isosceles,* and *scalene,* concluding that it is both right and isosceles triangle.

- **Have students read aloud the four names for the figure.** Point out that these four are highlighted in the word list on the right. Explain that all of these names are correct. Say: *They all tell about the figure in the picture.*

BP 5 **Assign each student one or two words from the list.** Ask students to write their words on index cards. Then draw an obtuse scalene triangle on the board. Invite students to come to the board if one of their words fits the picture. Have them hold up the cards that name the picture. Establish that *polygon, scalene triangle, obtuse triangle,* and *triangle* all match. Repeat with a drawing of a rhombus. (rhombus, quadrilateral, parallelogram, polygon) Wrap up by reminding students that figures can be named in several different ways.

Have students complete the Vocabulary Cards for the words in this lesson.

C **Review and Practice**

To review, distribute copies of Worksheet 22. Direct students to write the names of the figures in the correct column and draw a figure below each name. Then have students discuss with a partner what they did and what they noticed. When they are finished, elicit that some shapes are in just one list, others in two, and some in all three lists.

For additional practice, say: *I am thinking of a shape. It is a regular polygon. It is also a hexagon. What shape am I thinking of? Draw it!* Have students compare their drawings with other students around them. Repeat with a right triangle that is also a scalene triangle.

Have students work with a partner. Have students draw shapes on index cards from the word list. They take turns asking questions about the shape, using the word list and the question form: *Is it a(n) _____?* On the back of the card, students write all the names that apply. Have students do this with at least three or four drawings.

Read aloud the directions for Practice the Language. Point out that students need to use the words in the word list for each item and that they will write a complete sentence for each one. Have students do the activity independently.

D **Assess and Intervene**

Can students identify plane figures in different ways, according to Practice the Language on page 87? Use the rubric to identify students who need extra support through additional help and the Intervention activity.

Intermediate

☐ Accurately names at least 2 figures in 2 different ways.

☐ Writes a phrase or sentence explaining how the shapes are alike; may have errors that don't affect meaning.

Example of a sentence a student might write: *The shape both polygon have 4 side.*

Advanced

☐ Accurately names all 3 figures in 2 different ways.

☐ Writes a sentence with few errors that includes at least one word from the word list and tells how the shapes are alike.

Example of a sentence a student might write: *Rhombus and square are regular polygon.*

INTERVENTION 15 minutes

If students have trouble naming the figures, it is possible that they are not sufficiently familiar with the names of some of the shapes. Help students create a poster showing examples of the various plane figures, together with labels of their characteristics. A picture of a hexagon, for example, would be accompanied by the label: *6 sides/6 angles.* Have students study the poster on a daily basis to help associate the shapes with their names and characteristics.

Lesson

4

Solve Math Problems

Objective Solve problems that are in the form of riddles.

30 minutes

Teach this lesson:
- **After** students complete grade-level math textbook lessons on polygons and circles
- **Before** students complete the activities on page 88 of the student worktext

You need these materials:
- poster board
- glue or tape
- pictures of highway signs
- book of riddles
- Transparency 44

EXTENSION AND ENRICHMENT
15 minutes

Have students use library materials or the Internet to find pictures of road signs. Have students copy or print pictures of these signs and attach them to a sheet of poster board. Then ask them to label all the signs with as many descriptive words and names as they can. For example, a stop sign is a polygon, an octagon, and a regular polygon; a yield sign is an example of an equilateral triangle, a regular polygon, and a plane figure. Have students title their posters and display them.

LESSON

4

Solve Math Problems

Objective Solve problems that are in the form of riddles.

Learn to Solve Problems

> **Riddle** I have 4 equal angles, but my sides are not equal. What am I?

Step 1: Read the riddle.

Remember that *I* means a plane figure. It does not mean a person.

Step 2: Circle the important facts.

Step 3: Draw the figure. Write a sentence to give the answer.

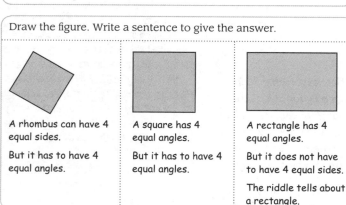

A rhombus can have 4 equal sides.

But it has to have 4 equal angles.

A square has 4 equal angles.

But it has to have 4 equal angles.

A rectangle has 4 equal angles.

But it does not have to have 4 equal sides.

The riddle tells about a rectangle.

Practice Solving Math Problems

Directions Follow steps 1 to 3 above to solve the word problems below. Solve each problem on a separate sheet of paper.

1. All of the points on my outside are the same distance from my center. What am I? [drawing of a circle] Answers will vary, but will refer to circle.

2. I have 1 right angle and 2 other angles. What am I? [drawing of a right triangle] Answers will vary, but will refer to a right triangle.

3. I have 8 angles and 8 sides. What am I? [drawing of an octagon] Answers will vary, but refer to an octagon.

4. I am a quadrilateral. I have one pair of parallel sides. What am I? [drawing a trapezoid] Answers will vary, but refer to a trapezoid.

A Introduce

Ask students if they know what a riddle is. If students are familiar with the term, ask them to define it and invite volunteers to tell riddles that they know. If students do not know the word, explain that a riddle is a question that makes people think. Tell students that many riddles have funny answers. Read an example or two from a riddle book, if possible.

Explain that math problems are sometimes given in the form of riddles. Provide an example by writing this problem on the board: *I am thinking of a number. My number is one more than 10. What is my number?*

- **Ask students to talk to a partner about how they could solve that problem.** Elicit that the solution is 11 because 11 is one more than 10.

Now change the problem slightly so it reads: *I am a number. I am one more than 10. What number am I?* Explain that many riddles in English begin with *I am*. Read the problem aloud with students. Emphasize that the word *I* in this problem refers to a number, not to you or another person.

Highlighted words and phrases may affect student comprehension.

- **BP 5** **Ask students to talk to a partner about how this problem is similar to the first problem and how it is different.** Ask volunteers to summarize their conversations for the class. Elicit that the problems are the same, except that *I am thinking of* has been replaced with *I am*.

Explain that students will learn how to solve problems like these in this lesson, but that the riddles will be about shapes instead of about numbers. Read aloud the Lesson Objective with students. Wrap up by asking students to write a brief definition of a riddle and share it with a classmate.

B Teach and Learn

Have a volunteer read aloud the problem on page 88 of the student worktext. Remind students that in math riddles, the word *I* does not refer to a person. Add that this time it does not refer to a number, either. Point out that numbers do not have sides and angles. Say: *The word I in this problem is talking about ____.* Pause to allow students to fill in the term *a shape* or *a plane figure*.

- **Point out the first step in the discussion of the problem.** Have volunteers read it aloud.

- **Move on to the second step.** Point out that the two important facts are already circled in the student worktext. Stress that the shape has not just four angles, but four *equal* angles. Tell them the shape has four sides, but they are not equal.

- **Have a volunteer read the third step aloud while other students follow along.** Tell students that they should be as specific in their sentences as possible: they should write *equilateral triangle,* for example, rather than just *triangle,* and *rhombus* instead of *quadrilateral*.

- **Say:** *Sometimes, it's easy to know the shape after you finish reading a riddle. Sometimes, you can almost see the shape in your head!* Ask if anyone can mentally picture the shape in the riddle. Then add that visualizing the shapes can sometimes be difficult, too.

Display Transparency 44. Read the names of figures with students. Ask a volunteer to come up and draw and label a picture of a figure on the transparency. Then have the student tell something he or she

knows about the figure using the sentence frames like *An acute triangle has _____.* or *A hexagon has _____.* Go around the room, giving everyone a chance to say something about at least one shape.

Explain that students can use this list to help them visualize and draw the shapes in the riddles.

- **BP 5** **Return students' attention to the sample riddle in the student worktext.** Ask if the shape could be a triangle. Have them explain their answers to a partner and then share their ideas with the class. Help them use the phrase *because* to share their thoughts, as in: *It can't be a triangle because triangles have three sides*.

- **Repeat the above process, asking if the shape can be a quadrilateral.** Have students explain to each other why the shape *must* be a quadrilateral.

- **Say:** *The shape in the riddle is a little like a rhombus. It is a little like a square. It is a little like a rectangle.* Point out the three pictures at the bottom of the Learn to Solve Problems box. Tell students that they can draw shapes like the ones in the pictures to help them decide which shape is the real answer to the riddle.

- **BP 5** **Have students study the pictures and read the text to themselves.** Then ask them to use their own words to explain to a partner how they know the shape cannot be a rhombus or a square, but must be a rectangle.

Write the following riddle on the board: *I have 6 angles and 6 sides. What shape am I?* Have the whole group read it aloud together.

- **Then say:** *First step!* Have students tell you the first step. (reading the problem)

- **Say** *Second step!* **and have students tell you what information to circle.** (6 angles and 6 sides)

- **Finally, say:** *Third step!* Sketch various shapes on the board, or indicate them on the transparency, beginning with shapes that are not hexagons. Have students tell you whether these are or are not the solution to the riddle using the word *because*. Conclude by having students explain why the shape has to be a hexagon.

C Review and Practice

Point out a pentagon on Transparency 44 or draw one on the board. Ask students to help you write a riddle about the pentagon. An example might be: *I have five sides and five angles.* Repeat with *rectangle*.

- **Have students work in pairs.** Ask them to think of a shape and to write a riddle based on that shape. Then have pairs exchange riddles with another pair and solve them using the process described on page 88. Check that they both draw and label the appropriate figures to give their answers.

Read aloud the directions for Practice Solving Math Problems at the bottom of page 88. Have students solve these problems independently using the three steps.

D Assess and Intervene

Can students solve math problems that are expressed in riddles, based on Solving Math Problems on page 88? Use the rubric to identify students who need extra support through additional help and the Intervention activity.

Intermediate

- ☐ Draws and names 3 of the 4 figures accurately.
- ☐ Writes the answer in a phrase or sentence, with some errors.

  Example of a sentence a student might write: *Riddle about circle.*

Advanced

- ☐ Draws and names all 4 figures accurately.
- ☐ Writes the answer in a complete sentence, with few errors.

  Example of a sentence a student might write: *The riddle talk about circle.*

INTERVENTION 10 minutes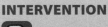

If students have difficulty identifying the correct shape, ask yes/no questions to help students solve riddles by focusing on one shape at a time. Use one of the riddles in the worktext. Ask: *Can the shape be a triangle?* Help students answer *yes* or *no,* using Transparency 44 as a guide. If the answer is *no,* they should explain why and continue with the next shape on the transparency. Be sure they consider each figure carefully before answering the question. Repeat with another riddle when the first is solved.

Understand the Main Idea

Objective Describe movements and see if two sides match in plane figures.

30 minutes

Teach this lesson:
- **Before** introducing lessons on transformations and symmetry in the grade-level math textbook
- **Before** students complete the activities on page 89 of the student worktext

You need these materials:
- scissors (for all students)
- scrap paper
- pattern blocks
- ruler

Prerequisite Background Knowledge
- Names of plane figures

 ELL BEST PRACTICE #6: **Hands-On Activities**

For English language learners, hands-on activities are a way to learn academic concepts and language in ways that are not affected by how much English they understand. The Main Idea in this lesson is a visual concept that can be demonstrated by using a variety of manipulatives. As you introduce and practice geometric movements and symmetry, allow students to work with concrete objects, such as pattern blocks and paper shapes, to provide both visual and physical representations of these concepts.

Throughout this module, when you see **BP 6**, this is an example of a hands-on activity.

Module 23: Transformations and Symmetry

Understand the Main Idea

Objective Describe movements and see if two sides match in plane figures.

Learn the Main Idea

Some children are making shapes. They move, trace, and fold the shapes.

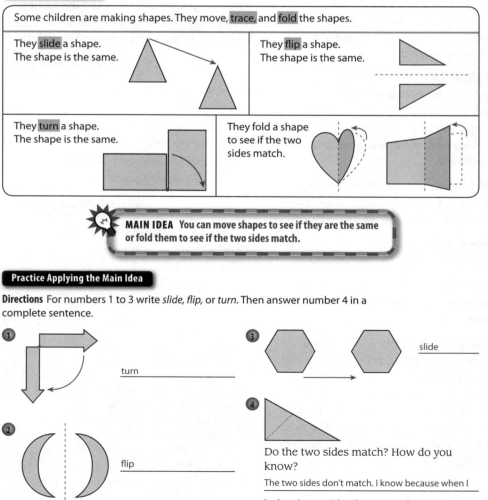

They slide a shape.
The shape is the same.

They flip a shape.
The shape is the same.

They turn a shape.
The shape is the same.

They fold a shape to see if the two sides match.

MAIN IDEA You can move shapes to see if they are the same or fold them to see if the two sides match.

Practice Applying the Main Idea

Directions For numbers 1 to 3 write *slide, flip,* or *turn*. Then answer number 4 in a complete sentence.

1. _turn_

2. _flip_

3. _slide_

4. Do the two sides match? How do you know?

The two sides don't match. I know because when I look at the two sides, they are not the same.

Transformations and Symmetry · 89

A Introduce

Read aloud the Lesson Objective. Tell students that they will learn to write and talk about whether shapes match in this lesson.

Ask if students have ever made paper snowflakes or other designs by folding and cutting paper. If anyone has, invite him or her to describe how these designs are made.

BP 6 Distribute paper and scissors to students. Tell them that you are going to make cut-out designs. Tell them to fold the piece of paper in half twice.

- **Demonstrate how to cut shapes out of each edge of the folded paper.** Ask students to do the same with their pieces of paper. They may cut any shape they want out of the edge: ovals, triangles, circles, etc.

- **When students have finished cutting, ask:** *What do you think your paper will look like when you unfold it?* Students might talk about patterns, matching shapes, etc.

- **Unfold your paper and display it to the class.** Ask students to do the same with theirs. Fold the paper in half again and say: *When I fold the shape in half, both sides match. Both sides are exactly the same.*

Highlighted words and phrases may affect student comprehension.

- **Fold and unfold the paper a few times so students can see that the halves are identical.**

Now change the focus of discussion to movement. Use one of the cutout parts of your paper design. Display it on your desk and ask students to do the same. Have them mimic your movements.

- **Slide the paper on the desk as you say:** *We can move objects in different ways. We can slide them. Slide your paper on the desk.*

- **Hold your finger on one corner of the paper as you turn the paper 360 degrees.** Say: *We can turn objects around a point. Turn your paper.*

- **Put a ruler next to the paper and flip it over the ruler.** Say: *We can flip objects over a line. Flip your paper.*

Read aloud the Main Idea with students. Help them to understand that this statement summarizes what they have just done with their papers.

B Teach and Learn

Refer students to the activity they just did with the paper designs. Ask: *When you moved the piece of paper, did the paper change in any way?*

Discuss that the position of the paper changed—it moved from one place to another. Ask: *Did the size or shape of the paper change when you moved it?* Students should understand that the size and shape of the paper remain the same as it is moved.

BP 6 Give students a few pieces of scrap paper and some scissors. Ask them to fold one piece of paper in half. Demonstrate how to cut the paper to make half of a heart. Have students do the same with their pieces of paper.

- **Unfold the heart and have students do the same.** Say: *Do the two halves match?* (yes) *When we fold some shapes, the two sides match. When we fold other shapes, the sides do not match.*

- **Cut out an irregular shape and then fold it in half.** Say: *When I fold this shape in half, the sides do not match.*

- **Now ask students to cut a shape out of another piece of paper.** Tell them not to fold the paper to cut the shape. Encourage

them to cut a shape in which the two sides do not match. Students may want to draw the shape before cutting the paper. Invite different students to show the class their shapes and what happens when the shapes are folded.

Tell students that they can slide, flip, and turn their shapes. Trace your cut-out heart on the board and then move it to the right and trace it again. Say: *I can slide the shape and it stays the same. I can slide the shape to the left and right, up and down, and diagonally.*

Continue in a similar manner, demonstrating a flip and a turn. Ask student pairs to practice making slides, flips, and turns with their cutout shapes. Emphasize that when the shapes are moved, only the position changes, not the size and shape.

C Review and Practice

Direct students' attention to Learn the Main Idea on student worktext page 89. Read the caption next to the illustrations. Ask: *What do you think will happen with the size when the students move, trace, and fold the shapes? Will the shapes change shape?*

Ask students to name all of the shapes they see on the page. Say the words *flip, turn, slide,* and *fold* and have students point to the appropriate illustrations on the page. Read the text in each box as students point to it.

BP 6 Divide the class into pairs and give each pair some pattern blocks. Tell partners to take turns saying *flip it, fold it, turn it,* and *slide it.* The other student traces a block, moves it appropriately, and traces it again. If the command given is *fold it,* the student traces the figure and then draws what it would look like if it were folded in half.

- **Have partners label the drawings with the appropriate words.** Ask them to continue with the activity until each has drawn a flip, slide, turn, and fold.

Read the directions for the Practice Applying the Main Idea activity. Explain that instead of actually making a drawing, they will identify what kind of movement the drawings show.

Check students' work. Share and discuss students' answers and assist as necessary.

D Assess and Intervene

Do all students understand how to slide, turn, flip, and fold shapes, based on the Practice Applying the Main Idea on page 89? Use the rubric to identify students who need extra support through additional help and the Intervention activity.

Intermediate

☐ Correctly identifies at least 2 of the 3 movements.

☐ Writes an explanation that shows understanding of symmetry with errors that do not affect comprehension.

Example of a sentence a student might write: *No match because sides different.*

Advanced

☐ Correctly identifies all 3 movements.

☐ Writes an explanation that shows understanding of symmetry with minimal errors.

Example of sentences a student might write: *Two sides don't match. I see two sides is not same.*

INTERVENTION 10 minutes

If students have difficulty identifying movements, model some physical movements. Slide your feet apart and then together and say: *I am sliding across the floor.* Next, make a 360-degree rotation with your body and say: *I am turning around and around.* Finally, extend your arm out with palm facing down. Flip your hand so your palm is facing up. Say: *I am flipping my hand.* Have students work with you, practicing these movements while verbalizing them at the same time.

Lesson

2

Learn the Vocabulary

Objective Talk and write about movement and symmetry with figures using the vocabulary words.

---

40 minutes

Teach this lesson:
- **Before** introducing lessons on transformations and symmetry in the grade-level math textbook
- **Before** students complete the activities on page 90 of the student worktext

You need these materials:
- chart paper
- Transparency 45
- pictures of playground scenes
- scissors
- mirror
- Worksheet 23
- chalkboard eraser
- Vocabulary Cards

Lesson Vocabulary

Essential Vocabulary

rotation	congruent	symmetry
transformation	translation	reflection

Additional Vocabulary

slide	flip	turn
similar	line symmetry	line of symmetry
rotational symmetry	quarter (90°) turn	
half (180°) turn	three-quarter (270°) turn	
full (360°) turn		

Learn the Vocabulary

Objective Talk and write about movement and symmetry with figures using the vocabulary words.

Learn the Words

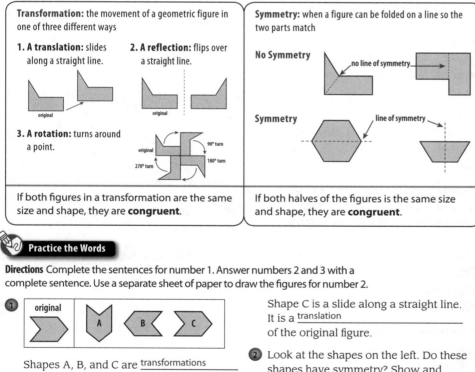

Transformation: the movement of a geometric figure in one of three different ways

1. A translation: slides along a straight line.

2. A reflection: flips over a straight line.

3. A rotation: turns around a point.

If both figures in a transformation are the same size and shape, they are **congruent**.

Symmetry: when a figure can be folded on a line so the two parts match

No Symmetry

no line of symmetry

Symmetry

line of symmetry

If both halves of the figures is the same size and shape, they are **congruent**.

Practice the Words

Directions Complete the sentences for number 1. Answer numbers 2 and 3 with a complete sentence. Use a separate sheet of paper to draw the figures for number 2.

① original | A | B | C

Shapes A, B, and C are <u>transformations</u> of the original figure.

Shape A is a turn around a point. It is a <u>rotation</u> of the original figure.

Shape B is a flip over a straight line. It is a <u>reflection</u> of the original figure.

Shape C is a slide along a straight line. It is a <u>translation</u> of the original figure.

② Look at the shapes on the left. Do these shapes have symmetry? Show and explain. <u>The shapes have symmetry. If you fold on the line, both sides match.</u>

③ original | A | B | C

Are any of the shapes congruent? Explain how you know. <u>All of the shapes are congruent because they are the same shape and size.</u>

A Introduce

Read aloud the Lesson Objective with students. Tell students that they will learn vocabulary words about moving figures and symmetry to talk and write about in this lesson.

BP 6 Review the Main Idea in Lesson 1 of this module with students. Have pairs of students demonstrate how to slide in a straight line, how to flip as two students stand opposite each other with opposite hands up, and how to turn around the same point.

Draw a line on chart paper. Put the chart paper on the floor. Model how to slide, turn, and flip an object over this line. Invite students to come up and do the same with an object of their choice. Tell students that in this lesson, they will learn other names for slides, flips, and turns.

Choose words from the Additional Vocabulary box that you think will be useful. Elicit or provide examples or definitions for the words chosen.

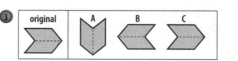

Highlighted words and phrases may affect student comprehension.

B — Teach and Learn

Orally introduce the Essential Vocabulary.
Give students some real-life examples of movements. If possible, show a picture of a playground. Say: *When you go to a playground, you move in different ways. A movement in geometry is called a* transformation. Write *A transformation is a movement.* on the board and have students take turns repeating it to a partner.

Ask: *How do you move from the top of a slide at the playground to the bottom?* (you slide) *Have you ever watched people sliding on ice without turning? When you slide down the slide or on ice, you do not change, you just change places. A slide is also called a* translation. *A translation is a slide along a straight line.* Write *A translation is a slide.* on the board and have partners repeat it to each other.

BP 6 ▶ Model how to turn on your heel around the same point. Then have students stand up and do the same. Say: *We turned around the same point. We made a rotation.* Write *A rotation is a turn.* on the board and explain that rotation is another word for *turn.* Ask students to repeat it to a partner.

BP 6 ▶ Place a mirror in front of a book that has letters on its cover. Point to the book and then to the reflection in the mirror. Have students come up to take a closer look and describe what they see. Pass around the mirror and have students do the same as you say: *The mirror shows a reflection of the book. Look closely at the reflection. It looks like the letters have been flipped.* Write *A reflection is a flip.* on the board.

Ask: *When you move or when you move an object, does the size or shape change?* (no) Trace the chalkboard eraser, then flip it and trace it again. *Are both figures the same size and shape?* (yes) *Both figures are the same size and shape. They are congruent.* Write *Congruent is the same.* on the board.

Model and explain symmetry using the illustrations on page 90 in the student worktext. Make copies of Transparency 45 and have students cut out the figures to use with this activity.

BP 6 ▶ Model how to fold the cutouts and ask students to follow along.

- **Say:** *We can fold these shapes in different ways. Can you show me how to fold these shapes in the middle using only one fold?*

Allow a few students to demonstrate folding the shapes once.

- **Ask students to tell if the sides match.** Say: *No matter how we fold these shapes, the two sides do not match. These shapes do not have symmetry.*

- **Repeat this procedure with the cutouts of the two symmetrical shapes.** Say: *We can fold these shapes so that the two sides match. The fold line is called the* line of symmetry. *When we fold or turn a figure and the parts of the figure match, we say there is symmetry.*

Draw two same-size squares on the board. Read the statements at the bottom of the Learn the Words box. Have students tell if the squares are congruent.

Now draw one smaller square on the board. Model how to identify similar figures by thinking aloud.

Think Aloud

Say: *The two large squares are congruent because they are the same size and shape. The large and small squares are not congruent. They are not the same size. Figures that are the same shape, but may have different sizes, are called* similar. *Similar figures must have the same shape, but they can have different sizes.*

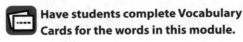 **Distribute Worksheet 23.** Have pairs work together to complete the sentences with the Essential Vocabulary.

Have students complete Vocabulary Cards for the words in this module.

C — Review and Practice

Use the Vocabulary Cards to review and practice the words. Play a game that is a combination of charades and Pictionary™.

- **Divide the class into two teams.** The teams take turns picking a Vocabulary Card and not showing it to the other team. Together, students decide on a way to show the meaning of the word. They can physically move themselves or objects, make gestures, draw a picture, or use the mirror. The other team has to guess the vocabulary word that is being demonstrated.

- **Continue playing until each team has presented each word.** Tell students that they must present the words in a different way than the other team did.

Introduce the Practice the Words activity in the student worktext. Make sure students understand the directions. Have students complete the activity independently. Check students' work.

D — Assess and Intervene

How well can students use the Essential Vocabulary to talk about transformations and symmetry based on Practice the Words on page 90? Use the rubric to identify students who need extra support through additional help and the Intervention activity.

Intermediate

☐ Correctly completes at least 3 of the 4 sentences in number 1.

☐ The sentences for numbers 2 and 3 show basic understanding of word meaning, although some language may be incorrect or vague.

Example of sentences a student might write: *Shapes are symmetry. Sides match.*

Advanced

☐ Correctly completes all 4 sentences in number 1.

☐ The sentences for numbers 2 and 3 clearly demonstrate understanding of word meaning. Most language is accurate.

Example of sentences a student might write: *Shapes have symmetry. You can fold on line and sides are same.*

INTERVENTION — 10 minutes

If students are having difficulty differentiating between the meanings because some of the words have similar initial sounds, introduce the following ideas:

transfor**m**ation: The *m* means movement.

tran**sl**ation: The *sl* means slide.

reflection: A reflection in the mirror is in the opposite direction.

ro**t**a**t**ion: The two *t*'s mean turns.

Students may come up with their own ideas as well.

Use More Language

Objective Use the ending *-tion* to make nouns from verbs and write sentences using the two related words.

---

30 minutes

Teach this lesson:
- **After** lessons on transformations in the grade-level math textbook
- **Before** students complete the activities on page 91 of the student worktext

You need these materials:
- magazines and books with pictures that show transformations
- index cards
- chalkboard eraser
- pattern blocks

EXTENSION AND ENRICHMENT   10 minutes

Work with the class to identify some real-world objects that show transformations. You may want to have students browse through magazines or books. Brainstorm with students and write a list on the board. Some examples include the following: bike pedal (rotation), gymnast (flip), hockey puck (slide). Draw a large three-circle Venn diagram. Label the circles *translation, rotation,* and *reflection.* Go through the list and discuss with students whether each object can perform only one kind of transformation or whether it can do two or all three kinds. As you talk about each object, decide where the word should go in the Venn diagram and write it there.

Use More Language

Objective Use the ending *–tion* to make nouns from verbs and write sentences using the two related words.

Learn the Language

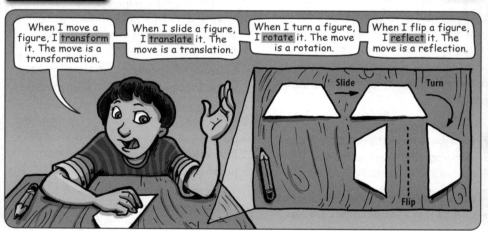

When I move a figure, I transform it. The move is a transformation.

When I slide a figure, I translate it. The move is a translation.

When I turn a figure, I rotate it. The move is a rotation.

When I flip a figure, I reflect it. The move is a reflection.

Slide   Turn

Flip

Practice the Language

Directions Complete the sentences below to describe each picture on the left. Then tell what the move is. Use the related nouns and verbs. Write a complete sentence for number 4.

1. When I . . . flip a figure, I reflect it. The move is a reflection.

2. When I . . . slide a figure, I translate it. The move is a translation.

3. When I . . . turn a figure, I rotate it. The move is a rotation.

4. Explain what happens when you move a figure. When I move a figure, I transform it. It is a transformation.

A   Introduce

As you draw a picture on the board, say: *I am creating a work of art. I am making a creation.* Write *create* and *creation* on the board. Repeat the two sentences and ask students which word is something that you do and which is a thing.

Point out the *-tion* ending in *creation*. Explain that we can add *-ion, -tion,* or *-ation* to some verbs to make nouns. Pronounce *-tion* and have students repeat after you.

Provide other examples or ask students if they can think of any themselves. Write the following word pairs on the board: *act, action; instruct, instruction; construct, construction; add, addition; subtract, subtraction.* Explain or act out the meanings as necessary and ask students to identify the nouns and verbs.

English language learners who are Spanish speakers will find some of these words familiar. They are similar in Spanish.

Read aloud the Lesson Objective. Tell students that they are going to learn some math terms that use these endings to make nouns from verbs.

Highlighted words and phrases may affect student comprehension.

B. Teach and Learn

Remind students of the vocabulary they already learned in this module. Ask: *What word is used to describe movements of shapes?* (transformations) Write on the board *transform* and *transformation*. Underline the suffix. Have students write the words on separate index cards. Ask them to hold up the appropriate cards as you say the words.

Say: *When I* <u>transform</u> *a shape, I move it. I make a* <u>transformation</u>. *We have learned about three different* <u>transformations</u>.

Slide the eraser across the board and ask students to name this movement. If they answer *slide*, say: *Yes and a slide is also called a translation*. Write the words *translate* and *translation* on the board and have students write the words on index cards.

Point out the everyday meaning of *translate/translation*. Say: *Translate means to change words from one language to another. With geometric figures it means to slide from one place to another.*

Ask students to hold up the appropriate cards as you say the words. Gesture and say: *I can translate the eraser across the board. I have made a translation.* You may want to repeat this once or twice.

Continue in the same manner with the word pairs *rotate, rotation* and *reflect, reflection*. Use the eraser or another object to demonstrate the move. Be sure to review the connection between *turn* and *rotation* and *flip* and *reflection*.

Model the language in the Learn the Language section on student worktext page 91 by thinking aloud:

Think Aloud

Say and gesture: *When I slide a figure, I translate it. The move is a translation.* As you ask students these questions, have them hold up the appropriate card and say the word. Ask: *What do I do with the figure?* (translate it) *What is the move called?* (a translation)

Say and gesture: *When I turn a figure, I rotate it. The move is a rotation.* Students hold up the cards and answer the questions: *What do I do with the figure?* (rotate it) *What is the move called?* (a rotation)

Ask: *When I flip a figure, what do I do with it?* (reflect it) *What is the move called?* (reflection). Invite students to hold up the cards and say along with you: *When I flip a figure, I reflect it. The move is a reflection.*

Write the sentence frames on the board: *When I _____ a figure, I _____ it. The move is a _____.*

Have students practice using the sentence frames to describe your actions. Use pattern blocks to demonstrate each of the movements a few times. Check that students can correctly insert the verbs and noun in the sentence frames.

Refer students to the illustration on page 91 of the student worktext. One at a time, point to the pairs of images that show each of the three moves. Have students insert the appropriate words into the sentence frames to describe the movements.

C. Review and Practice

BP 6 **Break the class into pairs and give each pair a set of pattern blocks.** Ask each pair to write the sentence frames on a piece of paper. Tell them to space out the words and sentences so that an index card can be placed in the blanks to complete the sentences. If necessary, display a model for students to copy.

- **Students will use the index cards that they have already made for each word pair.** They will need to make three more cards for the words *slide, turn,* and *flip*.

Tell students that they will take turns performing transformations with the pattern blocks. After one partner shows the transformation, the other puts the index cards with the appropriate words into the sentence frames. Together, students read the sentences.

Allow students to work on this activity for three or four minutes, as you observe their progress. After this practice, have students individually complete the Practice the Language activity on page 91 in the student worktext. Circulate and assess students as they do the activity.

D. Assess and Intervene

Are students able to differentiate between the nouns and verbs and place them correctly in the sentences based on Practice the Language on page 91? Use the rubric to identify students who need extra support through additional help and the Intervention activity.

Intermediate

☐ Correctly completes 2 out of 3 sentences.

☐ Writes an explanation with a few errors that do not affect comprehension and uses the correct noun.

Example of sentences a student might write: *When move one figure, transform. I make transformation.*

Advanced

☐ Correctly completes all sentences.

☐ Writes an explanation with minimal errors and uses the correct noun.

Example of sentences a student might write: *When move a figure, transform it. It is transformation.*

INTERVENTION 5 minutes

If students are having trouble identifying the nouns and verbs in each word pair, have them fold a piece of paper in half vertically and in fourths horizontally, to form eight sections. On the left side, have them write the words *transform, translate, rotate,* and *reflect* at the bottom of each section. On the right side, have them write the matching noun and draw an example. For *transformation,* have them show one of each type. Put a pattern block above the word *transform.* Slide, turn, and flip the block as you say: *When I move a figure, I transform it.* Then point to the drawing and word on the right and say: *The move is a transformation.* Repeat and have students say the sentences with you. Continue in a similar manner with the other words.

Lesson

4

Solve Math Problems

Objective Identify true and false statements with *always, sometimes,* and *never.*

---

30 minutes

Teach this lesson:
- **After** lessons on transformations and symmetry in the grade-level math textbook
- **Before** students complete the activities on page 92 of the student worktext

You need these materials:
- Transparency 46
- blank paper
- magazines and books

LESSON **4**

Solve Math Problems

Objective Identify true and false statements with *always, sometimes,* and *never.*

Learn to Solve Problems

> **Statement** Congruent squares are sometimes the same shape.
> Is this statement true or false?

	Think	Write
Step 1:	Read the problem. Underline the question. What do you have to do?	I underline the question. Then I have to find out if the statement is true or false.
Step 2:	Circle *always, sometimes,* or *never.* What does this word mean?	I circled **sometimes. Sometimes** means that it is true at times, but not all the time.
Step 3:	What kind of figure is in the statement? Write facts you know about the figure.	Congruent squares. I know that congruent shapes are always the same shape and size.
Step 4:	Compare the statement with the facts. Tell if the statement is true or false. If it is false, change it to make it true.	The statement says **sometimes**, but the facts say **always**. The statement is false. Congruent squares are always the same shape.

Practice Solving Math Problems

Directions Follow steps 1 to 3 above to tell if each statement below is true or false. If a statement is false, change it to make true. For question 6, write the steps to show how you corrected one of the false statements on a separate sheet of paper.

① The two halves of a circle are always congruent. True.

_____

② A translation never moves a figure in a straight direction. False. A translation always moves a figure in a straight direction.

③ A quadrilateral sometimes has a line of symmetry. False. A figure that has a line of symmetry always has two parts that match.

④ A figure that has a line of symmetry never has two parts that match. True.

_____

⑤ A transformation is always a translation. False. A transformation is sometimes a translation.

_____

⑥ Pick one of the false statements and write the steps to solve the problem. Answers will vary.

A **Introduce**

Read aloud the Lesson Objective with students.

On the board, write the words *always, sometimes,* and *never.* Review the meanings by stating things that you always, sometimes, and never do. For example, say: *I always brush my teeth before I go to bed at night. Sometimes I go to bed early and sometimes I go to bed late. I never stay up after eleven o'clock.*

Point out the meanings of each word and write them on the board: *Always: every time, each time, at all times, all the time. Sometimes: at times, not all the time. Never: not ever, at no time.* Say: *The words* always *and* never *are antonyms, or opposites. The word* sometimes *is in between; it is not* always *and not* never.

Invite students to share activities of their own that they always, sometimes, and never do.

B **Teach and Learn**

Have students open the student worktext to page 92.

Write this statement on the board and read it aloud: *Congruent squares are sometimes the same shape.* Ask: *Is this statement true or false?* Tell students that when they first read the statement, they might think that it is true.

Highlighted words and phrases may affect student comprehension.

Explain that they need to look at the statement more closely and that the steps on the student worktext page will help them to decide whether it is true or false.

Model analyzing statements by thinking aloud:

> Think Aloud

Write Step 1 on the board. Read aloud the instructions. Say: *I have to read the problem and underline the question. I have to find out if the statement or sentence is true or false.* Underline the question on the board.

Write Step 2 on the board. Read the words to students. Say: *The statement has the word* sometimes. *This means at times, but not all the time.* Circle *sometimes* on the board.

Write Step 3 on the board. Say: *I need to see what figure the statement talks about. Then I have to write facts I know about this figure. The statement talks about squares, and it says congruent squares.* Ask students: *What facts do you know about congruent shapes?* Listen to a few responses and then write on the board: *congruent— same shape and same size.* Emphasize: *Congruent shapes are the same shape and size. They must always be the same shape and size to be congruent.*

Write *Step 4* on the board. Say: *The statement says that congruent squares are sometimes the same shape. Let's compare this with the facts. The facts say that congruent shapes must always be the same shape and size to be congruent.* Ask: *Is the statement true or false? (false) Since the statement is false, I will change it to make it true. What is the word that makes the statement false? (sometimes) What word can I use to make the statement true? (always)* Erase the word *sometimes* from the problem on the board and replace it with *always*. Ask students to read the corrected statement.

Have partners read the text in the Learn to Solve Problems box on page 92. One student can read the Think column and the other can read the Write column.

 Review the names and characteristics of geometric figures. Then display Transparency 46. Divide the class into pairs. Tell students to discuss what they know about each figure with their partner. Have them read the statements quietly. Ask students to decide which is the correct word to complete the

statement. Have them write the complete sentence. Ask pairs to share their statements with the class.

As students work on this activity, walk around and help as necessary. When everyone has completed the sentences, go through the answers and have students make corrections.

C Review and Practice

Have students use the figures on Transparency 46 to practice identifying true and false statements.

- **Ask students to work with their partners.** Distribute blank sheets of paper to each student. Have students copy the figures from the transparency. Partners take turns making statements about the plane figures, using *always, sometimes,* and *never.* The other student tells whether the statement is true or false. If it is false, he or she corrects the statement. Have students draw an example of their statement when possible.

- **For example, one student might say:** *A square sometimes has a line of symmetry.* The partner says: *That is false. A square always has at least one line of symmetry.* Then the partner draws the square and one line of symmetry.

- **Continue until each student has given and commented on four or five statements.**

Allow students to use their drawings as a guide to complete the Practice Solving Math Problems in the student worktext. The answers and illustrations may help them to make sense of the written statements.

Have students work individually to complete the Practice Solving Math Problems activity. Circulate and assess how well they are using the problem-solving procedure and identifying true and false statements.

D Assess and Intervene

Are students able to identify true and false statements and correct false statements to make them true, based on Practice Solving Math Problems on page 92? Use the rubric to identify students who need extra support through additional help and the Intervention activity.

Intermediate

- ☐ Correctly identifies at least 3 of the 5 statements as true or false.
- ☐ Accurately corrects at least 2 of the 3 false statements.
- ☐ Writes the steps to solve the problem correctly, with some errors.

Advanced

- ☐ Correctly identifies all statements as true or false.
- ☐ Accurately corrects all false statements.
- ☐ Writes the steps to solve the problem correctly, with minimal errors.

INTERVENTION   5 minutes

If students are having difficulty reading and understanding the statements, give them visual cues. Make an addendum sheet with a visual for each statement. For problem 1, show a circle with a line of symmetry. For problem 2, show a translation with a straight arrow. For problem 3, show a square with a line of symmetry and an irregular quadrilateral that is not symmetrical. For problem 4, show a figure with a line of symmetry. For problem 5, show a translation, a reflection, and a rotation.

Allow students to use illustrations on the addendum to help them determine if the statements are true or false and to correct the false statements.

Understand the Main Idea

Objective Tell the distance around a figure and the square units that cover a figure.

45 minutes

Teach this lesson:
- **Before** introducing lessons on perimeter and area in students' grade-level math textbooks
- **Before** students complete the activities on page 93 of the student worktext

You need these materials:
- chart paper
- graph paper
- rulers or straight edges
- square paper or square sticky notes
- square or rectangular objects (book, paper, eraser, etc.)
- small objects for measuring: paper clips, popsicle sticks, flat toothpicks, square tiles

Prerequisite Background Knowledge
- Basic concepts of plane figures, estimation, and the ability to add and to multiply

BP 1 **ELL BEST PRACTICE #1:**
Comprehensible Language

English language learners are not able to understand everything that is said in the classroom. Teachers can modify their language in many different ways to help ELLs understand more of the language and concepts presented. When you are explaining perimeter and area, always accompany the language with gestures such as demonstrating covering versus going around or by using visuals such as figure drawings. Use simple sentences to explain what the gestures and visuals show. Emphasize new vocabulary words and pronounce them clearly.

Throughout this module, whenever you see **BP 1**, this is an example comprehensible language.

Module 24: Perimeter and Area

Understand the Main Idea

LESSON **1**

Objective Tell the distance around a figure and the square units that cover a figure.

Learn the Main Idea

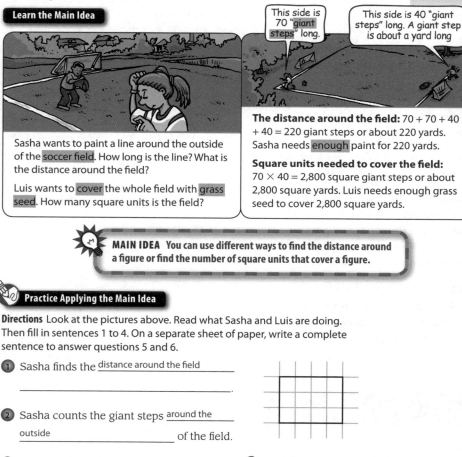

> This side is 70 "giant steps" long.

> This side is 40 "giant steps" long. A giant step is about a yard long

Sasha wants to paint a line around the outside of the soccer field. How long is the line? What is the distance around the field?

Luis wants to cover the whole field with grass seed. How many square units is the field?

The distance around the field: 70 + 70 + 40 + 40 = 220 giant steps or about 220 yards. Sasha needs enough paint for 220 yards.

Square units needed to cover the field: 70 × 40 = 2,800 square giant steps or about 2,800 square yards. Luis needs enough grass seed to cover 2,800 square yards.

MAIN IDEA You can use different ways to find the distance around a figure or find the number of square units that cover a figure.

Practice Applying the Main Idea

Directions Look at the pictures above. Read what Sasha and Luis are doing. Then fill in sentences 1 to 4. On a separate sheet of paper, write a complete sentence to answer questions 5 and 6.

(1) Sasha finds the distance around the field _____

(2) Sasha counts the giant steps around the outside _____ of the field.

(3) Luis finds how much seed he needs to cover the inside of the field

(4) Luis finds the number of square units to cover the field

(5) Explain how you can find the distance around the figure above. I can count the number of squares on each side and add them.

(6) Explain how you can find the number of square units that cover the figure above. I can count the number of squares inside the figure.

A **Introduce**

Read aloud the Lesson Objective with students. Help students activate prior knowledge related to the objective. Ask, emphasizing the underlined words: *Do you play any sports on a field? Does the field have grass that covers it? Does the field have a line that goes around it?*

Use the picture on the left of page 93 of the student worktext as a visual presentation of the concepts of *distance around,* *square units,* **and** *cover.* Point to the first panel and ask: *What sport could these children play on this field? What is the boy, Luis, doing? What is the girl, Sasha, doing?* Encourage students to use the words *covers* and *around.* If they cannot, model describing the picture using these words. Ask a volunteer to read the caption.

- **BP 1** **Restate the problem in simplified language, gesturing as you speak.** Emphasize the underlined words as you say: *Luis wants to know if he has enough seed to cover the field. He needs to know the number of square units.* Place your palm down and move it in a circular motion as you say: *Sasha wants to know if she*

Highlighted words and phrases may affect student comprehension.

has enough paint. *She needs to know the* <u>distance around</u> *the field.* Use your pointer finger to trace the perimeter of the field.

BP 1 **Focus on the second panel, on the right.** Ask: *How did Luis and Sasha measure the distances?* Pantomime walking and counting giant steps. Emphasize the underlined words, and gesture as you ask: *How long is the field? How wide is it?* Read the speech bubbles and captions aloud. Say: *Sasha found the distance around the field by adding all the sides. Luis found the number of yards by measuring giant steps. One giant step is about one yard. Then he multiplied the lengths of the sides to find out the square units that cover the field.* Make a gesture to indicate *area* as you speak.

Have students form pairs to read the text presented in the visuals. Encourage the pairs to use gestures to describe what Luis and Sasha are doing.

BP 1 **Read aloud the Main Idea with students.** Emphasize the *distance around* a figure and the number of *square units* that *cover* a figure.

B Teach and Learn

BP 1 **Introduce the concept of *distance around*.** Ask: *What is the distance around this room?* Gesture to indicate *around* as you speak. Ask: *How can we find out the distance around this room?* Ask volunteers to walk using giant steps to count the length and width of the room. On the board or on chart paper, model how to write the number sentence for perimeter, using the number of giant steps that the students counted. Write and say: *The distance around the room is [X] giant steps, or about [X] yards.*

Introduce the concepts of *area, square units,* and the verb *to cover*. Ask: *About how many square units cover this desk?* Gesture to indicate that you are talking about the whole desk. Cover the desk with square pieces of paper or sticky notes. Count them, and write the number. Say: *You can also multiply the length times the width to find the area. That's what Luis did to find the area of the soccer field.* Model how to write the number sentence for the area of the desk. Write and say: *The number of square units that cover this desk is [X].* Leave the sentences and number sentences on the board or chart paper for students to refer to during the next set of activities.

Have small groups find the perimeter and area of a classroom object. As a class, brainstorm different things you could use as units to measure the distance around and the square units that cover an object. (ruler, paper clips, grid paper, tiles, popsicle sticks, sticky notes) Have students suggest which things can be used to measure perimeter and which can be used to measure area. List students' responses on the board.

- **Ask students to form groups of three or four.** Give each group an object to measure and one of the units to measure with. Allow time for groups to measure, calculate, and write sentences about the distance around and the square units that cover the object. Encourage groups to look at the work on the board as models for their own work. Have each group present their findings to the class. Then say that one way to find the perimeter is by adding the length of each side, as they have done. One way to find area is to cover the object with square units, as they have done. Explain that they will learn other ways to find perimeter and area in the math textbook or in later lessons.

C Review and Practice

Have students work in pairs to draw and discuss the perimeter and area of figures. Give each pair graph paper and rulers or straight edges. Ask each group to draw a rectangle on the graph paper using the boxes as boundaries. Demonstrate if necessary. Circulate to check students' understanding.

- **Ask pairs to exchange their figures with another pair.** Have volunteers suggest the best way to find the distance around and the square units that cover the figures. Ask: *How can we find the distance around these figures? How can we find the number of square units that cover the figures? What should we count?*

Read the directions for the Practice Applying the Main Idea activity in the student worktext. Tell to students to reread the Learn the Main Idea section to answer the questions. Circulate to check comprehension and completion of the activity.

D Assess and Intervene

Can every student tell the distance around a figure and the square units that cover a figure, based on Practice Applying the Language on page 93? Use the rubric to identify students who need extra support through additional help and the Intervention activity.

Intermediate

- ☐ Correctly fills in at least 2 of the 4 sentences.
- ☐ Writes a simple response, using simple clauses and phrases that have been explicitly taught.

  Example of a sentence a student might write: *I count square on sides.*

Advanced

- ☐ Correctly fills in the 4 sentences.
- ☐ Writes a more complex response, with few or no errors.

  Example of a sentence a student might write: *I count how many squares inside figure.*

INTERVENTION 10 minutes

If students are having difficulty telling the distance around or the number of square units that cover a figure, have them make rectangles of paper and use flat toothpicks to measure the distance around the rectangle. Tell them that the toothpick is the unit. Then have them use color tiles or sticky notes to cover the inside of the rectangle. Tell them that the color tiles are the square units. Have them make two cards: one that reads *distance around a figure* and another that reads *square units that cover the inside of a figure*. Give examples of perimeter and area. For example, pick up a square or rectangular object in the room (book, paper, eraser, etc.). Say: *I want to know the distance around this ____.* Point to the perimeter of the object. As you do so, have students hold up the card that corresponds to the concept.

MODULE 24

Perimeter and Area

Lesson 2

Learn the Vocabulary

Objective Talk and write about perimeter and area using the vocabulary words.

 45 minutes

Teach this lesson:
- **Before** introducing lessons on perimeter and area in students' grade-level math textbooks
- **Before** students complete the activities on page 94 of the student worktext

You need these materials:
- countable objects (paper clips, flat toothpicks, square tiles, snap cubes, etc.)
- square and rectangular classroom objects (paper, book, disc, etc.)
- Vocabulary Cards

 LESSON 2

Learn the Vocabulary

Objective Talk and write about perimeter and area using the vocabulary words.

Learn the Words

Directions Fill in the missing words and numbers. Then check your answers with your teacher.

Word/Phrase	Definition
square unit	a unit for measuring area that measures 1 unit × 1 unit
formula	a set of symbols that shows a math rule
area	the number of square units that cover a surface
perimeter	the distance around a figure

The formula for <u>perimeter</u> is: $p = l + w + l + w$

The formula for perimeter is: length + width + <u>length</u> + <u>width</u>.

The formula for <u>area</u> is: $a = l \times w$.

The formula for area is: length × <u>width</u>.

Practice the Words

Directions Write the missing vocabulary words to complete numbers 1 to 4. On a separate sheet of paper, write a complete sentence for numbers 5 and 6.

1 You measure <u>perimeter</u> when you measure the distance around the door.

2 You measure the <u>area</u> when you measure the surface to cover the table.

3 You use <u>square units</u> to measure area.

4 When you use a set of symbols to show a math rule, you use a <u>formula</u>.

5 Explain how you measure the perimeter of a playground. **Possible answer: I measure the distance around the playground.**

6 Explain how you measure the surface of the playground. What unit do you use? **Possible answer: I measure the area. I use square units.**

94 · Perimeter and Area

Lesson Vocabulary

Essential Vocabulary

perimeter	square unit	area
formula		

Additional Vocabulary

unit	standard unit	figure
length	width	variable*

* - Term that has a Vocabulary Card.

A Introduce

Ask students to open to page 93 of the student worktext. Ask: *What does Sasha need to know about the field? What does Luis need to know? How do they measure the field?* Write student responses on the board. Remind students of the words *distance around, square units,* and *covers.* Add these words if necessary.

Read aloud the Lesson Objective with students. Say, and write on the board: *The distance around a figure is called the perimeter. The number of square units that cover a figure is called the area.* Read the sentences and use gestures to indicate each concept as you do so.

BP 1 Play a brief game of Charades. Divide the class into two teams. Pantomime walking the perimeter of the room. The first team to shout "perimeter" wins a point. Model measuring the length and width of a book and calculating the area. The first team to shout "area" wins a point. Invite volunteers to come to the front of the room to pantomime for the class to guess.

Add the Essential Vocabulary words to the list, along with any of the Additional Vocabulary words you think will be useful. Read all the words on the list, and have students repeat them.

Highlighted words and phrases may affect student comprehension.

B — Teach and Learn

Orally and visually introduce the Essential Vocabulary. Circle the four Essential Vocabulary words on the board. Ask students to open the student worktexts to Lesson 1 on page 93. Have pairs of students discuss the visual and find parts that show each vocabulary word they know. Have students share.

BP 1 **To define and explain** *square unit,* **return students' attention to Lesson 1.** Draw a soccer field on the board. Begin drawing footprints across and down the field. Ask volunteers to tell what unit Luis and Sasha used to measure the length and width of the field. (giant steps about a yard long) Tell students that one yard will be the unit of measurement. Then point and say: *Luis used square yards to measure the area of the field. A square yard is one yard long on each side.* Draw a square and label it *1 yard* on each side. Say: *That's 1 yard times 1 yard.* Write the definition for square unit on the board, and have students read it aloud with you.

Introduce the word *formula,* **pointing to the number sentences on the visual on page 93.** Ask: *Who can think of a way to write a rule that uses symbols to show how to measure perimeter and area?* Guide students to come up with the formulas for perimeter and area.

BP 1 **Demonstrate the definitions of area and perimeter by drawing figures and using countable objects.** Draw several square and rectangular figures on the board. Invite volunteers to come to the board to measure the figures' lengths and widths in different ways (using their hands or other countable objects). Then identify how to find the figures' perimeter and area. If necessary, provide sentence frames such as: *The perimeter is the _____ around _____. The area is _____ square _____ =*

Ask pairs of students to complete the Learn the Words section on page 94. Then review the answers and concepts as a class. Read the definitions of the Essential Vocabulary words aloud together, and use the figure on the page to discuss them as necessary.

Have students complete Vocabulary Cards for the words in this module.

C — Review and Practice

BP 1 **Ask students to form small groups.** Have the groups choose a classroom object, decide the best way to measure its length and width, and identify how to find the perimeter and area, without necessarily solving them. Then have students write complete sentences to present their findings to the class. Model the activity by thinking aloud.

Think Aloud

Say: *I want to know the perimeter and area of the door. What is the best way of measuring the door? I can use paper clips, but that takes a long time because they are much smaller than the door. I can use my hands, but it's hard to reach the top of the door. I'll use a one-foot stick, a ruler. It can easily reach up the door, and it's about the right size.* Walk to the door, and continue: *To find perimeter and area, I need to know the length and width of the figure. I measure how long and wide the door is.* Measure the door, and record the length and width on the board. Say: *To calculate the perimeter of a rectangle, I use the formula: length + width + length + width.* Then say and write a complete sentence saying what the perimeter is. Repeat the process with area.

- **Once groups have identified and written how they measured perimeter and area, have a class sharing of their work.** If necessary, encourage students to use your sentences as models for their own.

As a class, discuss real-life situations to calculate perimeter and area. Ask students to think of square and rectangular objects or rooms in their homes or surroundings. Record their ideas on the board. Ask specific questions about each one, such as *Why might you need to know the area of your living room?*

- **Choose one of the ideas for pairs to discuss how to identify perimeter and area.** Ask them to decide on a unit and then come up with a formula. Have them share their work with the class. For example, say: *We want to buy new tile for the kitchen floor. How do we find the perimeter and the area? What unit can we use? We can use feet to find the perimeter. We can use square feet to find the area. We need to know how much tile to buy. The kitchen floor is 5 feet wide and 7 feet long. How many square feet of tile do we*

need for the area? How much tile do we need for the perimeter? Write the word problem on the board as you say it.

- **Ask a volunteer to read the problem for the class.** Underline the questions for students to use as a model. Encourage pairs to come up with different units and rooms to measure. Then write a formula.

Together read the Practice the Words directions aloud. As a class, complete the first item.

Have students work individually to complete the Practice the Words activity. Circulate and assess their progress, using the assessment below.

D — Assess and Intervene

Is every student able to use the Essential Vocabulary to talk and write about perimeter and area based on Practice the Words on page 94? Use the rubric to identify students who need extra support through additional help and the Intervention activity.

Intermediate

☐ Completes at least 3 of numbers 1–4 correctly.

☐ Ideas are correct in 5–6, but errors may somewhat impede communication.

Example of a sentence a student might write: *Measure distance around playground.*

Advanced

☐ Completes all of numbers 1–4 correctly.

☐ Writes sentences with minimal errors that do not impede overall meaning.

Example of a sentence a student might write: *I measure area, use squares units.*

INTERVENTION 10 minutes

If students are unable to use the Essential Vocabulary to talk about perimeter and area, encourage them to use the Vocabulary Cards. Have students work across from a partner. One partner places his or her cards face down on the desk. The other places his or her cards face up. Each takes a turn choosing two matching cards and reading the word and definition. After several rounds, partners place all the cards face down and take turns identifying the words. Then they place the cards face up and take turns giving the definitions.

MODULE 24

Perimeter and Area

Lesson 3

Use More Language

Objective Use *alike* and *different* to compare and contrast perimeter and area.

40 minutes

Teach this lesson:
- **After** lessons on perimeter and area in students' grade-level math textbooks
- **Before** students complete the activities on page 95 of the student worktext

You need these materials:
- Transparency 47
- a metric ruler and a yardstick to compare and contrast
- Transparency 48
- 3 different colored transparency markers
- Worksheet 24

Use More Language

Objective Use *alike* and *different* to compare and contrast perimeter and area.

LESSON 3

Learn the Language

How are perimeter and area alike? How are they different?

Perimeter and area are alike because they are both measures of plane figures.

They are different because perimeter is a measure around the figure …

…and area is a measure of how many units you need to cover the figure.

Perimeter and area are alike because _____.
They are different because perimeter _____ and area _____.

Practice the Language

Directions Write two complete sentences telling how area and perimeter are alike and two complete sentences telling how they are different. Use the sentence frames above to help you. Then answer question 5 in a complete sentence.

1. Possible response: Perimeter and area are alike because I use standard units to measure them.

2. Possible response: They are alike because they both measure plane figures.

3. Possible response: Perimeter and area are different because perimeter is a measure of the distance around the figure, and area is a measure of the number of units you need to cover the figure.

4. Possible response: They are different because I use linear units to measure perimeter and square units to measure area.

5. Why is it important to know how perimeter and area are alike and different?
   Possible response: It is important because then I know how to measure perimeter and area.

A Introduce

Read the Lesson Objective with students. Write the words *alike* and *different* on the board. Ask: *When do we use the words* alike *and* different*?* List students' responses on the board.

BP 1 **Introduce the concepts of alike and different, and compare and contrast.** Draw a T-chart on the board. Label one column *ruler*, the other *yardstick*. Display a metric ruler and a yardstick. Say, emphasizing the underlined words: *Let's compare these objects; let's tell how they are alike.* Ask: *How are these objects alike?* Record responses in the T-chart. Then say: *Let's contrast these objects; let's tell how they are different. How are these objects different?* Record their responses in the T-chart. Reread, and review the chart with students.

B Teach and Learn

Have students open the student worktext to page 95 on the far left. Read the text for the first visual. Say: *We can also compare and contrast math ideas. We can find how perimeter and area are alike and different.* Tell students that we can use a diagram to compare and contrast two objects or concepts.

Highlighted words and phrases may affect student comprehension.

Perimeter and Area · 95

- **Use Transparency 47 to make a list of what students know about perimeter and area.** Have students make their own T-chart on a sheet of paper. Ask volunteers to write on the transparency what they know about either term using the words in the word bank. Tell students they may use some words more than once. Reread the lists with the class. Make any necessary corrections.

- **Show the Venn Diagram on Transparency 48.** Tell students that they will now use what they know about perimeter and area to look at the similarities and differences between them. The Venn diagram will help students to record and visually show similarities and differences between perimeter and area. Explain that things in the middle of the diagram show how the two terms are the same. Things in the outer parts of the circle show how they are different. Return students' focus to the T-charts that they completed. Say: *Let's look at what we know about perimeter and area. How are perimeter and area alike? How are perimeter and area different?* Ask volunteers to read a similarity and a difference as you record these in the Venn diagram on the transparency. Save the completed Venn diagram to be used throughout this lesson.

BP 1 **To help students understand the visual, point to ideas on the Venn diagram from Transparency 48.** Then gesture to help explain each idea. For example, use your pointer finger to draw around an imaginary figure and say: *Perimeter measures the distance around a figure.*

Review and Practice

Turn students' attention back to the student worktext on page 95. Read the text in the second two panels aloud with students. Point out the use of *because* and the two parts of the sentence that tells about differences. Ask a volunteer to read the sentence frames aloud as you write them on the board. Model using the sentence frames and the Venn diagram to compare and contrast a different aspect of perimeter and area.

Use Transparency 48 to practice the sentence frames. Have students work in pairs. Have each pair of students write sentences for each of the similarities and differences listed in the Venn diagram. Have a class sharing of the sentences by asking each pair to read one example aloud.

BP 1 **As a class, discuss the importance of comparing and contrasting perimeter and area.** Ask: *Why do we compare and contrast perimeter and area? How does that help us?* Record student responses on the board, rereading and gesturing to clarify each one.

Distribute copies of Worksheet 24 to pairs of students. Say: *We have learned how perimeter and area are alike and how they are different. Now, let's look at two word problems. In one word problem, you have to find the perimeter. In the other word problem, you have to find the area. Understanding how perimeter and area are alike and different will help you decide how to solve the problems.*

- **Read the first problem aloud chorally.** Gesture to show perimeter. Then read the second problem, gesturing to show area.

- **Display the completed Venn diagram on Transparency 48.** Say: *This Venn diagram has information about how perimeter and area are alike and how they are different. How can we use that information to solve these word problems? I see that the phrase* distance around *is only under* perimeter. *I know that in problem 1, Mei wants to put wire fencing around her patio. So I need to find the perimeter. In problem 2, Mei wants to cover her bedroom floor. I look at the Venn diagram and see that the word* cover *is only under* area. *So I need to find the area for problem 2.*

- **Ask pairs of students to complete Worksheet 24.** You may display Transparency 48 again for reference. When students complete their work, review the answers by asking volunteers to write their answers on the board. Also review the formation for completing the sentences.

Together, read the directions for the Practice the Language activity on page 95 of the student worktext. Ask a volunteer to come to the board to model completing the first problem as an example.

Have students work individually on the Practice the Language activity. Circulate, and assess students as they complete the activity.

D Assess and Intervene

Can students use *alike* and *different* to compare and contrast perimeter and area based on Practice the Language on page 95? Use the rubric to identify students who need extra support through additional help and the Intervention activity.

Intermediate

☐ Uses sentence frames to correctly write at least 3 complete compare and contrast sentences.

☐ Writes a phrase or sentence with a logical explanation for the importance of comparing and contrasting.

Example of a sentence a student might write: *Help know how measure.*

Advanced

☐ Correctly writes 4 complete compare and contrast sentences in own words.

☐ Writes a complete sentences with a logical explanation for the importance of comparing and contrasting.

Example of a sentence a student might write: *It help me understand how to measure.*

INTERVENTION   10 minutes

BP 1 **If students have trouble using *alike* and *different* to compare and contrast perimeter and area,** use simplified language to write possible compare-and-contrast sentences about perimeter and area on a sheet of paper, leaving out the words *alike* and *different*. Read the sentences aloud. After each one, ask: *Does this tell how they are* alike *or how they are* different? Have students complete the sentences with *alike* or *different*.

Solve Math Problems

Objective Use the information you know to help you solve problems with words you don't know.

45 minutes

Teach this lesson:
- **After** lessons on perimeter and area in students' grade-level math textbooks
- **Before** students complete the activities on page 96 of the student worktext

You need these materials:
- completed Worksheet 24
- different colored chalk, transparency marker
- chart paper
- word problems about perimeter and area, with challenging vocabulary, from the grade-level math textbook

EXTENSION AND ENRICHMENT 15 minutes

Ask students to write a story about finding an area or perimeter. Brainstorm ideas as a class. Ask: *When might you need to find the area of something? When might you need to find the perimeter of something? For what kinds of projects do you need to find perimeter or area?* Encourage students to use the visuals in the student worktext and their grade-level texts to answer these questions. Record all responses on the board. Remind students that stories have a beginning, middle, and end. If necessary, model thinking about and writing a story about finding a perimeter or area. When students have completed their stories, ask them to briefly illustrate them, and display them around the room. Then allow time for the students to walk around the room to read the stories.

LESSON
4

Solve Math Problems

Objective Use the information you know to help you solve problems with words you don't know.

Learn to Solve Problems

Problem	Manny's father is building a (credenza) for the dining room. The top of the credenza is 5 feet long and 2 feet wide. <u>How much wood does Manny's father need to cover the top? How much (veneer) does he need to cover the edges</u> around the top?

	Think	**Write**
Step 1:	Read the problem. Circle the words you don't know. Tell what you know about the words.	A credenza is something I can build. It goes in a dining room. Maybe it is furniture. Veneer is something that goes around the edge of the top of the furniture.
	Can you solve the problem without knowing more?	Yes. If not, I can ask for help to find out what the word means.
Step 2:	Underline the questions. Tell what you have to do.	How much wood to cover the top = area. How much veneer to go around the top = perimeter.
		I have to find the area and perimeter.
Step 3:	Write number sentences or formulas and solve. Write the answers in complete sentences.	area = 5 ft × 2 ft. The area is 10 square feet.
		perimeter = 5 ft + 2 ft + 5 ft + 2 ft. The perimeter is 14 feet.

Practice Solving Math Problems

Directions Use the steps above to solve the problems below. Show your work on a separate sheet of paper. Answer the questions in complete sentences.

1. Tran and his mother are buying a carpet that will cover the floor of the guest bedroom. The room is 8 feet wide and 9 feet long. How many square feet must the carpet be? The carpet must be 72 square feet.

2. Diya wants to make a fabric border for a page in her scrapbook. The page is 10 inches wide and 12 inches long. How many inches of fabric will she need to go around the outside of the page? She will need 44 inches of fabric.

3. Keesha and her father are building a slate-covered patio that will be 7 feet long and 5 feet wide. They also want to put a row of bricks around the patio. How many square feet of slate do they need to buy? How many feet of brick do they need? They need to buy 35 square feet of slate and 24 feet of bricks.

4. Explain why you can sometimes solve a problem when you don't know all the words. Possible answer: Sometimes it is not necessary to know the exact meanings of all the words to solve the problem.

96 · Perimeter and Area

A Introduce

Read aloud the Lesson Objective with the class. Display Worksheet 24 or write the word problems from Worksheet 24 on the board. Ask: *Were there any vocabulary words in these problems that you didn't know?* If so, write the words on the board. Say: *Sometimes you don't understand every word in a word problem. But you can still understand enough to figure out the problem.* Ask: *How did you solve the problem without knowing these words? What words helped you solve the problem?* Create a list of the helpful words on the board.

Tell students that they will learn how to solve more problems with some vocabulary that they don't know.

Highlighted words and phrases may affect student comprehension.

B | Teach and Learn

Ask students to open their student worktext to page 96. Write the problem on the board, and read it aloud to the class. Have students follow along on the chart as you use a Think Aloud to model solving a problem with unfamiliar vocabulary.

> **Think Aloud**

Read Step 1 aloud. Say: *What do I have to do? I have to read the problem and circle the words I do not know.* Read the problem aloud. Circle the words *credenza* and *veneer.* Say: *Now I have to tell what I know about these words. What does the problem tell me about these words? The problem says that Manny's father is building a credenza. So, a credenza is something you can build, maybe from wood. Then it says that the credenza is for the dining room. It's probably some kind of furniture. Veneer must be something that goes around the edge of the top.*

Ask: *How do I know if I can I solve the problem without knowing more? Here's what I can do. I can read the problem again, but read* something *instead of the words I don't know.* Demonstrate, and then say: *Can I solve the problem? Yes, I can. I don't need to know the exact meanings of* credenza *and* veneer *to solve the problem. I have the information I need. Sometimes I can't solve the problem when I read it with* something *instead of the words I don't know. Then I need to ask for help with the meaning of the words.*

Have student pairs read Step 1 together and explain in their own words what it tells them to do.

BP 1 **Read Step 2 aloud.** Say: *I have to underline the questions.* Underline the two questions, and say: *I look at the words in the questions to help me understand what I have to do.* With vocal stress and different colored chalk, emphasize the words *cover* and *around* as you say: Cover *tells me I have to find the area.* Around *tells me I have to find the perimeter.*

Have student pairs read Step 2 together and explain in their own words what it tells them to do.

Read Step 3 aloud. Say and do the following: *I will write number sentences or formulas for the area and perimeter. Then I can solve the problem and write the answers.*

Have student pairs read Step 2 together and explain in their own words what it tells them to do.

For visual learners and kinesthetic learners, invite volunteers to the board to draw diagrams for the problem. Have volunteers label their diagrams with number of feet for length and width.

Find two word problems with challenging vocabulary in students' grade-level textbook from lessons on perimeter and area. Have pairs of students solve the problems using the steps on page 96. Then have them exchange their solutions with other pairs to check each other's work.

Monitor, and provide assistance as needed. Circulate around the room, and answer questions as students work. Then ask pairs to share their explanations. Correct as necessary.

C | Review and Practice

Ask volunteers to retell the steps for solving problems with unfamiliar vocabulary. Record their summary on the board. As students retell the steps, ask them prompting questions. For example, say: (Step 1) *What is the first step in solving any problem? What can you do if there are unfamiliar words? What information do you look for in the problem to help you understand what the word means? Can you solve the problem without knowing the meaning of the word?* (Step 2) *How do you know what a problem is asking you to do?* (Step 3) *What is the final step? What do you have to write to solve the problem?*

Write the following problem on the board. Have students work in pairs to solve it following the strategies and steps you modeled:

Dania is making a velvet rug for the living-room floor of her antique dollhouse. The room is 14 inches by 10 inches. How much velvet does she need to cover the floor?

Read aloud the directions for Practice Solving Math Problems on page 96. Remind students to circle all the unfamiliar words and to use the information in the problem to figure out what they know about the words before they try to solve the problem.

As students work on problems individually, assess how well they are using the steps taught in this lesson.

D | Assess and Intervene

How well can students solve problems that include vocabulary they don't know based on Practice Solving Math Problems on page 96? Use the rubric to identify students who need extra support through additional help and the Intervention activity.

Intermediate

☐ Follows the steps to solve at least 2 problems correctly.

☐ Explains using simple sentence structure and some errors that impede communication somewhat.

Example of a sentence a student might write: *Sometime not have know meaning.*

Advanced

☐ Follows the steps to solve all 3 problems correctly.

☐ Explains with more complex sentence structure and minimal errors that do not impede overall meaning.

Example of a sentence a student might write: *Sometimes I don't have to know exact meaning.*

INTERVENTION 10 minutes

BP 1 Some students may not be able to learn enough information about the meaning of a word from the context of the problem. Use the problem from page 96 to model how to draw a picture that will help students visualize the context of the problem. Then encourage students to draw visuals for the problems in Practice Solving Math Problems.

Understand the Main Idea

Objective Measure the space inside a solid figure and make a model of a solid figure.

30 minutes

Teach this lesson:
- **Before** introducing lessons on solid figures and volume in the grade-level math textbook
- **Before** students complete the activities on page 97 of the student worktext

You need these materials:
- wooden block or plastic cube
- one-inch cubes and 8–10 small boxes of different sizes
- Worksheet 25, scissors, tape for each group of three
- rulers
- empty cereal box

Prerequisite Background Knowledge
- Concept of estimation
- Names of plane figures

BP 2 **ELL BEST PRACTICE #2:**
Assessing, Activating, and Building Background Knowledge

English language learners often have difficulty connecting what they have learned in their previous education in school and at home with what they are currently learning in school. In this module teachers can help ELLs activate their prior knowledge by helping them recall plane figures and learn about how they are different from solid figures. Teachers can also help students recognize and talk about solid figures that they see at school, at home, and in stores.

Throughout this module, when you see **BP 2**, you will find an example of how you can assess, activate, and build background knowledge.

Module 25: Solid Figures and Volume

Understand the Main Idea

Objective Measure the space inside a solid figure and make a model of a solid figure.

Learn the Main Idea

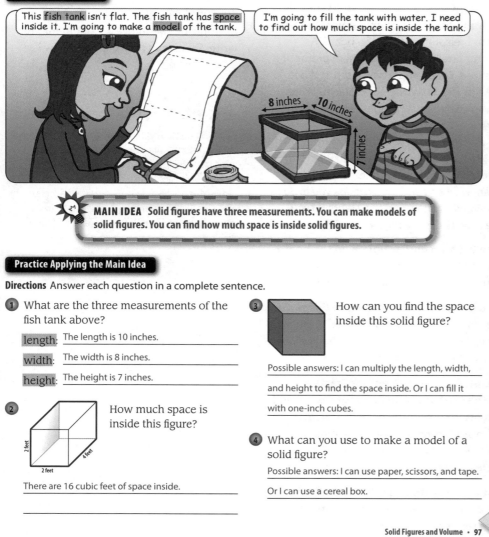

"This fish tank isn't flat. The fish tank has space inside it. I'm going to make a model of the tank."

"I'm going to fill the tank with water. I need to find out how much space is inside the tank."

8 inches | 10 inches | 7 inches

MAIN IDEA Solid figures have three measurements. You can make models of solid figures. You can find how much space is inside solid figures.

Practice Applying the Main Idea

Directions Answer each question in a complete sentence.

1. What are the three measurements of the fish tank above?

   length: The length is 10 inches.

   width: The width is 8 inches.

   height: The height is 7 inches.

2. How much space is inside this figure?

   2 feet, 2 feet, 4 feet

   There are 16 cubic feet of space inside.

3. How can you find the space inside this solid figure?

   Possible answers: I can multiply the length, width, and height to find the space inside. Or I can fill it with one-inch cubes.

4. What can you use to make a model of a solid figure?

   Possible answers: I can use paper, scissors, and tape. Or I can use a cereal box.

Solid Figures and Volume · 97

Highlighted words and phrases may affect student comprehension.

A Introduce

BP 2 **Help students activate their previous knowledge about plane and solid figures.** Draw a rectangle on the board. Ask: *What can you tell me about this object?* Have students tell a partner what they know and then share with another pair. Elicit that it is a rectangle and that it has two dimensions: length and width. Make sure students understand what length and width mean by showing it on the rectangle you drew on the board. Explain that a *dimension* is a measure in one direction. Say that a dimension is also flat and is a plane figure.

Hold up a block or cube and ask: *How is this block different from the drawing on the board?* Have student pairs discuss and share with another pair and then with the whole group. Elicit that it is a square block and that it has three dimensions, not two, as the drawing on the board has. You can measure length and width. But you can also measure a third dimension, height. Show students what height means by pointing at the height of the block or cube. Point out that the block is a solid figure and it takes up space. You can measure the space inside it.

Read aloud the Lesson Objective on page 97. Tell students that in this lesson they'll learn more about solid figures, make models of them, and learn how to measure the space inside some of them. You may want to point out to Spanish-speaking students that *solid figure* is a cognate of *figura sólida*.

B Teach and Learn

Focus students' attention on the picture at the top of page 97 in the student worktext. Have a volunteer read the girl's speech bubble aloud. Ask students to describe to a partner what the girl is doing. Have them share their thoughts with the class. Write their ideas on the board.

Say: *The girl sees that the fish tank isn't flat. Is the fish tank a plane figure?* (no) *What is inside the fish tank?* (space) *What is the girl going to do?* (make a model of the fish tank)

Have students look at the boy on the right. Have a volunteer read his speech bubble. Ask: *What is the boy planning to do?* (fill the tank with water) *What does he need to do first?* (find out how much space is in the tank) Ask: *How do you think the boy is going to measure the space in the tank?* Have groups of four discuss measuring ideas. Have volunteers share with the whole class.

BP 2 Say: *You already learned about plane figures. Do you remember how you measured a rectangle?* Have several students share what they recall. Elicit that rectangular plane figures have two dimensions that you can measure: length and width. You can multiply them to find the area. Or you can add the length and width of each side to find the perimeter. Draw a rectangle on the board and label the length 10 inches and the width 7 inches. Have the groups work together to find the area of the rectangle.

Read aloud with students the Main Idea on page 97 in the student worktext. Ask students how many dimensions rectangular solid figures have. (3)

Say: *Rectangular solid figures have three measurements: length, width, and height. If you want to find out how much space is inside a rectangular solid figure, you multiply all three measurements to get your answer.*

Draw a picture on the board of a fish tank with the same measurements as in the illustration. Say: *To find how much space is in the tank, we need to multiply the length (10 in.) by the width (8 in.) by the height (7 in.). That's* $10 \times 8 \times 7 =$. Help students come up with the answer of 560. Tell them that the space inside a solid figure is measured in cubic units, so the answer is 560 cubic inches.

Ask: *Can anyone think of another way to find the space inside a rectangular solid figure?* Elicit that you can fill the solid figure with one-inch blocks, but you would need 560 one-inch blocks!

BP 2 Pantomime sewing and ask students if they have ever seen a family member sew. Encourage students to tell what people who sew do before they can begin sewing. (buy thread, buy cloth, get scissors, cut the right size out of the cloth, etc.) Elicit that people who sew clothing either buy or make a model to use to cut the cloth just the right size.

Hold up an empty cereal box. Pull or cut the box apart along the seams so you have one flat piece of cardboard. Cut off any tabs. Lay the box on a large sheet of paper and ask a volunteer to draw around the box. Hold up the paper and say: *This is a model of the cereal box. If I fold it, I can make a shape just like the cereal box.*

Distribute a copy of Worksheet 25 to each group of three students. Pass out scissors and tape. Inform groups that each student in the group will use one of the models to make a solid figure. Have the groups display their completed solid figures.

C Review and Practice

Review with students two of the ways to measure the space inside a rectangular solid figure. You can count the number of cubic units that will fit inside. For some figures you can multiply the length, width, and height of a solid figure.

Distribute a small box and lots of one-inch cubes to groups of four students. Tell students they will measure the space inside their box. After the groups have filled their boxes with one-inch blocks, ask each group to report to the rest of the class what they found. Write the group findings on the board.

- **Provide rulers and have the groups discuss another way to measure space inside their boxes without filling them with blocks.** Have students write a number sentence. Go around the room and assist as the students measure and then write a number sentence that multiplies the three dimensions. Have groups share their number sentences with the class.

Read aloud the directions for the Practice Applying the Main Idea activity on page 97 of the student worktext. Have students do the activity independently. Circulate and check understanding.

D Assess and Intervene

Can students use different ways to find measurements of solid figures? Do they understand how to make models of solid figures, based on Practice Applying the Main Idea on page 97? Use the rubric to identify students who need extra support through additional help and the Intervention activity.

Intermediate

☐ Correctly identifies 3 of the 4 dimensions or volume in questions 1 and 2.

☐ Uses phrases that are correct, but may be somewhat difficult to understand, to describe how to find volume and make a model.

Advanced

☐ Correctly identifies all 4 dimensions and volume in questions 1 and 2.

☐ Uses complete, correct, and comprehensible sentences to describe how to find volume and make a model.

INTERVENTION 10 minutes

For students who are having difficulty understanding how to measure the space inside rectangular solid figures, provide empty boxes. Have students fill up a box with blocks to show how to measure the space inside a box. Help students talk about the three dimensions and point them out: length, width, height. Have students use sticky notes to label each dimension of the box. Then have them write a number sentence they can use to measure the space inside.

Learn the Vocabulary

Objective Talk and write about solid figures and volume using the vocabulary.

45 minutes

Teach this lesson:
- **Before** introducing lessons on solid figures and volume in the grade-level math textbook
- **Before** students complete the activities on page 98 of the student worktext

You need these materials:
- wooden block, plastic cube, or tissue box
- Vocabulary Cards
- Transparency 49
- index cards

Lesson Vocabulary

Essential Vocabulary

| solid figure | face | edge |
| net | volume | cubic unit |

Additional Vobabulary

vertex/vertices*	formula*	height
width	length	pattern
dimension	two-dimensional	three-dimensional

* – These words have Vocabulary Cards.

Learn the Vocabulary

Objective Talk and write about solid figures and volume using the vocabulary.

Learn the Words

Word/Phrase	Definition	Example
solid figure	a figure that has three dimensions: length, width, height	
face	a flat surface of some solid figures	
edge	line segment where two faces of a solid figure meet	edge ← → face
net	a pattern that can be used to make a model of a solid figure	
volume	the amount a solid figure holds	
cubic units	a unit that measures volume	height width length

Practice the Words

Directions Write words in the blanks to complete the sentences. Write a complete sentence to answer numbers 4 and 5.

1. An <u>edge</u> is a line segment where two <u>faces</u> of a solid figure meet.

2. A <u>faces</u> of some solid figures is a <u>flat surface.</u>

3. A pattern that we use to make a model of a solid <u>figure</u> is called a <u>net</u>.

4. What do we call the amount that a solid figure holds? <u>We call the amount a solid figure holds the volume.</u>

5. What kind of units do we use to measure volume? <u>We use cubic units to measure volume.</u>

A Introduce

Write the word *plane figure* on the board. Have students repeat it. Beside the term, about three feet away from it on the board, write the word *solid figure*. Have students repeat the word. Draw a circle around both words.

BP 2 Help students recall some differences between solid figures and plane figures. Ask them to discuss with a partner what they remember from Lesson 1 and previous modules. As they are talking, make a web for each word on the board. Draw eight lines out from each circled word. Ask volunteers to come to the board and write one of their ideas on each web. Elicit that plane figures are flat with just two measurements. Elicit that solid figures have at least three measurements, that they take up space, and that the space can be measured.

Read aloud with students the Lesson Objective. Explain that *volume* is another word for the amount a solid figure holds. Tell students they will learn some new vocabulary words that will help them talk and write about solid figures. They will also find out how to measure the volume, or the space inside solid figures.

Choose words from the Additional Vocabulary box that you think will be useful. Elicit or provide examples or definitions for the words you have chosen.

Highlighted words and phrases may affect student comprehension.

B Teach and Learn

Write the word *face* on the board. Tell students that most of the words they will learn in this lesson have an everyday meaning and also a math meaning. Ask: *When I say the word* face, *what do you think of?* Have students discuss with a partner. Then have them share their ideas with the group. (happy face, person's face, animal's face, the face of a clock, face your problems, etc.)

- **Point out that there is also a math meaning for the word *face*.** Say: *Look at the chart on page 98 of the student worktext. Look at the picture in the second row on the right. What do you think a face is in math?* (flat surface of some solid figures)

- **Hold up a block or a tissue box.** Ask a volunteer to point out the faces of the solid figure. Elicit that some objects have several faces.

BP 2 Write the word *edge* on the board and say: *Everybody sit on the edge of your seat! Have you ever sat on the edge of your seat before? Why?* Have partners discuss and then share their experiences with another pair. Ask volunteers to report to the class. Elicit that you might sit on the edge of your seat if you watch an exciting or scary movie, if you were nervous about a test, or if you were giving a class report.

- **BP 2 Ask:** *How many of you have fallen off a couch, sofa, or bed because you got too close to the edge? Have you ever climbed a hill or a mountain? Did your parents warn you not to go too close to the edge? Why did they give you that warning?* Encourage students to share experiences with a partner and then with the whole class

- **Ask students to talk with their partners about what they think an edge on a solid figure is.** Hold up the block or tissue box again. Ask a volunteer to show where the edges are. Explain that the *edge* of a solid figure is the line segment where two faces come together.

BP 2 Write the word *net* on the board. Say: *When you hear the word* net, *what do you think of?* Have students discuss in groups of four their experiences with the word *net*. Have the groups report to the class. Elicit that there are basketball nets, fishing nets, hair nets, and volleyball, tennis, badminton, and ping pong nets.

- **Say:** *In the last lesson, you used a model to make a solid figure. You cut it out and taped it together. Two other words for* model *are* net *and* pattern. (Point to some of the displayed solid figures the students made.) *These were made from nets; now they're solid figures.* Have students stand and repeat a chant with you, clapping their hands to the rhythm: *I used a net to make a solid figure! I used a pattern to make a solid figure!*

Write the word *volume* on the board. Ask volunteers to say what they think of when they hear the word *volume*. (My mom always tells my sister to turn down the volume on her radio, etc.) Elicit that *volume* means *loudness or softness of the music or sound*.

- **Say:** *That's the everyday meaning of volume. The math meaning of volume is* the amount or how much a solid figure can hold. Ask students to look at the picture of the cube in the last row of the chart on page 98 in the student worktext. Say: *You can fill a solid figure like this with one-inch cubes and count them to find the volume. The volume of the solid figure will be measured in cubic units.* Write the word *cubic units* on the board.

Have students turn back to page 97 in their student worktexts. Have them read aloud with you the Main Idea on page 97. Ask students if they have any questions. Ask: *What are the three measurements that solid figures have?* (length, width, height) *What are two other words for models for making solid figures?* (net, pattern) *What's another word for how much space there is inside solid figures?* (volume)

 Have students work with a partner to complete the Vocabulary Cards for the words in this lesson.

C Review and Practice

Point to the words *solid figure, face, edge, net, volume,* and *cubic unit* on the board. Review both their math meanings and their everyday meanings.

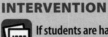 **Display Transparency 49.** Have students work in pairs to decide which word goes with each picture and whether the picture shows a math meaning or an everyday meaning. When all students are finished, have them direct you to write the name under each picture and to write the letter *E* (everyday) or the letter *M* (math).

Have students work independently to complete the Practice the Words activity in the student worktext on page 98. Circulate around the room, check students' progress, and assess their work.

D Assess and Intervene

Can students talk and write about the Essential Vocabulary, based on the Practice the Words activity on page 98? Use the rubric to identify students who need extra support through additional help and the Intervention activity.

Intermediate

- ☐ Correctly completes 4 out of the 6 missing words in numbers 1–3.
- ☐ Writes phrases or sentences that indicate an understanding of volume and the units used to measure volume; errors may make comprehension difficult.

  Example of a sentence a student might write: *Amount solid figure hold call volume.*

Advanced

- ☐ Correctly completes all 6 missing words in numbers 1–3.
- ☐ Writes complete sentences that indicate a clear understanding of volume and units used to measure volume, with only a few errors.

  Example of a sentence a student might write: *What kind of units we use is cubic units.*

INTERVENTION 10 minutes

If students are having difficulty understanding the Essential Vocabulary, call out a word and ask students to work with a partner to draw a picture of the word on an index card. Then have them write a definition on the other side in their own words. Have them find the matching Vocabulary Card, compare the definitions, and revise the one on the index card if necessary.

Lesson 3

Use More Language

Objective Use riddles to describe solid figures.

---

30 minutes ⏱

Teach this lesson:
- **Before** or during lessons on solid figures in the grade-level math textbook
- **Before** students complete the activities on page 99 of the student worktext

You need these materials:
- Transparency 50
- Vocabulary Cards

Lesson Vocabulary

Essential Vocabulary

pyramid	cube	sphere
cone	cylinder	rectangular prism

A Introduce

BP 2 **Write the word *riddle* on the board.** Have students pronounce the word. Ask: *Who can tell me what a riddle is?* Have students share their experiences with riddles, if any, in groups of four. As they are discussing, write this riddle on the board: *What has four wheels and flies?*

Ask volunteers to share their ideas with the class. Have them ask a riddle if they know one.

Say: *A riddle is like a word puzzle you have to solve. Riddles are usually funny, so you can find them in books of jokes in the library.*

Call students' attention to the riddle on the board. Have them read it aloud with you. Challenge students to solve the riddle. (a garbage truck) Explain that the word *flies* can be a form of the verb *to fly,* but in this case it means *insects.*

Practice pronouncing the sound *-dle* in the word *riddle*. Write this phrase on the board, and have students practice saying it: *A riddle in the* middle *of a* puddle *with a* poodle. Explain the words *puddle* and *poodle* if students don't understand them. Have students say the sentence several times as fast as they can. Ask a volunteer to come to the board and draw a picture of a riddle (written on a piece of paper) in the middle of a puddle with a poodle. Say: *Sentences like this are hard to say. They are called tongue twisters—they twist your tongue!*

Read aloud the Lesson Objective at the top of page 99 in the student worktext. Tell students that in this lesson they will learn the names of solid figures and will learn to write riddles to tell about them.

Use More Language

Objective Use riddles to describe solid figures.

Learn the Language

Mom, I've got a riddle for you! I'm a box that you want near you when you have to blow your nose. What am I?

I know! You're a box of tissues. You are a cube!

rectangular prism
cube
sphere
cone
cylinder
triangular pyramid

Practice the Language

Directions Solve the riddles below. Write a sentence for each question. Create your own riddle for number 4.

1 I have 6 square faces, 12 edges, and 8 vertices. What solid figure am I?
You are a cube.

2 I have 6 rectangular faces. What solid figure am I?
You are a rectangular prism.

3 I am a solid figure with one curved surface, one flat surface, and one vertex. What solid figure am I?
You are a cone.

4 Write your own riddle about any solid figure. Write the clues and the question. Then give the answer in a complete sentence.

Answers will vary.

Solid Figures and Volume · 99

Highlighted words and phrases may affect student comprehension.

B Teach and Learn

Focus students' attention on the illustration on page 99 of the student worktext. Ask: *Who do you see in the picture? Where are they? What do you think they are doing?* (mom and daughter, in a store, shopping)

Have students talk with a partner about everything they see on the shelves in the store, for example: "I see boxes of tissues"; "I see big beach balls." When the pairs are finished, have them share what they saw with the whole group.

BP 2 **Say:** *Take out a piece of paper and a pencil. I want you to draw a picture of a solid figure as I say its name. Don't look at anyone else's picture. When you finish drawing the figure, hold it up for me to see.* Then say one at a time: *cylinder, rectangular prism, cone, pyramid, cube, sphere.* Check students' drawings to see who needs to know more information about solid figures.

BP 2 **Say:** *You have learned about solid figures before. Look closely at the picture. Do you see any of the solid figures you know about on the shelves in the store?* (cylinder, cube, rectangular prism, pyramid, sphere, cone) *How many different solid figures do you see on the shelves?* (6)

Ask a volunteer to read the girl's speech bubble. Ask: *What does the girl have for her mother?* (a riddle) *Together, let's all say the riddle again: "I'm a box that you want near you when you have to blow your nose. What am I?" What's the answer?* (a tissue box; a cube)

Tell students that there is an *I* in the riddle and that the *I* stands for a solid figure, not for the girl. Say that many riddles use *I*.

Focus students' attention on the illustrations of the six solid figures on the right. Read aloud the name of each solid figure. Write each name on the board, model its pronunciation, and have students repeat the name after you: rectangular prism, cube, sphere, cone, cylinder, pyramid.

Say: *All these figures have three measurements. They are all three-dimensional solid figures.*

Have students work in groups of four and match the store items in the picture with the solid figures on the right. Then have them talk about the shapes of the figures, their dimensions (height, width, length), and their faces, edges, and vertices. When

students are finished, have them report to the whole group. Draw pictures of each solid figure on the board and add students' findings to the pictures.

Say: *One of the ways to learn the names of solid figures is to make up riddles about them. Take a piece of paper now, listen carefully, and write down the information I am going to give you. Here is a riddle for you:*

I have 6 square faces, 12 edges, and 8 vertices. What am I?

Say: *Discuss the information with a partner, look at the pictures on page 99, and come up with your answer. When you know the answer, stand up!*

When all pairs are standing up, have them all say their answer at the same time, on the count of three. If any pair had an answer other than a cube, help them to see why the answer is a cube.

Display Transparency 50. Ask students to work with a partner to solve the five riddles. Invite them to keep page 99 in their student worktexts open. When student pairs have solved the riddles, have them check with another pair to see if they solved them correctly.

Have students work with a partner to complete the Vocabulary Cards for the words in this lesson.

C Review and Practice

Review solid figures and their characteristics. Write the name of a solid figure on the board and ask students to call out names of real things they know that have the same shape or things they know about that figure, for example: cone. Students call out: ice cream cone, emergency cone, has a point on one end and is round on the other end.

Have students play The Riddle Game in pairs. Each pair creates a riddle about a solid figure and has another pair answer the riddle. Circulate through the room. Make sure the riddles make sense and the information in them is correct.

Read the directions to the Practice the Language Activity on page 99 in the student worktext. Have students work independently. Tell them they will solve riddles and write a complete sentence for their answers.

D Assess and Intervene

How well can students write and answer riddles to describe solid figures, based on Practice the Language on page 99? Use the rubric to identify students who need extra support through additional help and the Intervention activity.

Intermediate

☐ Solves 2 out of 3 riddles about solid figures.

☐ Writes a riddle that describes a solid figure accurately enough to be able to identify it, although errors may make it difficult.

Example of a riddle a student might write: *Have 6 face, 12 edge, 8 vertex. What I am?*

Advanced

☐ Solves 3 out of 3 riddles about solid figures.

☐ Writes a riddle that clearly describes a solid figure so it is easy to identify.

Example of a riddle a student might write: *I have 6 faces, 12 edges, and 8 vertexes. What am I?*

INTERVENTION 10 minutes

If students are having difficulty using riddles to describe solid figures, have pairs use the Vocabulary Cards to see if they know what the solid figures look like and can describe something about them. Student take turns choosing a card and reading the word to a partner. The partner then has to draw the solid figure that was named and describe that figure.

Solve Math Problems

Objective Understand the use of the phrase *can be* _____ in word problems.

30 minutes

Teach this lesson:
- **After** lessons on solid figures and volume in the grade-level math textbook
- **Before** students complete the activities on page 100 of the student worktext

You need these materials:
- plain paper and pens or pencils

EXTENSION AND ENRICHMENT 15 minutes

Have students choose common everyday objects and solid figures and write riddles about them. For example: I can be found on a kitchen wall. My face is usually round, but it can also be square. What am I? (a clock)

Students may work alone or with a partner. When the riddles are completed, ask a partner or another pair to answer them. Then put all the riddles together and make a riddle book for the whole class to enjoy.

Solve Math Problems

Objective Understand the use of the phrase *can be* _____ in word problems.

Learn to Solve Problems

> **Problem**
> What solid figure (can be made) with this drawing of a net?

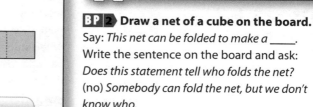

	Think	Write
Step 1:	Read the problem. Circle the phrase *can be* and the verb after it.	I'll circle: <u>can be made</u>.
Step 2:	Underline the question.	I'll underline: <u>What solid figure can be made with this drawing of a net?</u>
Step 3:	Solve the problem.	It's a cube!

 Practice Solving Math Problems

Directions Follow steps 1 to 3 above to solve the word problems below. Use a separate sheet of paper when you answer number 4.

① Which solid figures can be combined to make this figure?

a cylinder and a cone

② Laura thinks that this net can be folded to make a cube. Is she right or wrong? Why or why not?

Laura is wrong. The net should have 4 sides, 1 top, and 1 bottom.

③ What solid figure can be made with this net?

a rectangular prism

④ Write a word problem using the words *can be* _____. Then solve the problem.

Answers will vary.

A Introduce

BP 2 Draw a net of a cube on the board.
Say: *This net can be folded to make a* _____. Write the sentence on the board and ask: *Does this statement tell who folds the net?* (no) *Somebody can fold the net, but we don't know who.*

Write two other examples that use *can be* on the board.

1. *A short book can be read in an hour.*

2. *Two solid figures can be combined to make a new figure.*

Write on the board: _____ *can be* _____. Below the second blank, write these words in a vertical list: *made, cut, painted, cleaned, repaired, washed, eaten, driven, done.*

Ask students to work with a partner to make sentences using these verbs or others. Have volunteers write their sentences on the board and read them aloud. After each sentence is read, point out that we don't know who did the action that the verb tells about. The person who did it is not important; it could be anybody.

Read aloud the Lesson Objective at the top of page 100 in the student worktext. Tell students that in this lesson they will learn to recognize and to understand the phrase *can be* with verbs in math word problems.

> Highlighted words and phrases may affect student comprehension.

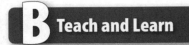

Teach and Learn

BP 2 Have students recall what a *net* is. Accept all answers. Elicit that a *net* is a pattern that can be used to make a model of a solid figure. Say: *In this lesson we're going to look at a math word problem that has the word* net *in it.*

Have students open their student worktexts to page 100. Write the problem on the board and read it aloud. Tell students that this is a word problem that has the words *can be made* in it, as well as the word *net*.

Focus students' attention on the chart on page 100. Say: *Notice the two headings,* Think *and* Write. *We're going to think through this problem together and see if we can solve it.*

Think Aloud

Read Step 1 and say: *First, I'm going to read the problem.* Read the problem on the board. *Then I will circle the words* can be *and the verb that follows.* Circle the phrase *can be made* on the board.

Ask a student volunteer to read aloud Step 2. Then say: *I am going to underline the question.* Underline the question and read it aloud. Ask: *Does the question mean I should use the net to make a solid figure? No, it means that* anybody *can use the net to solve the problem.*

Read aloud Step 3. Ask: *What do I have to do to solve the problem? I can use the net to make a solid figure if I need to. Or I can imagine what the solid figure looks like.*

Have students work in pairs to find the answer to the problem. Mention that if students have to, they can trace the net onto a separate sheet of paper, cut it out, and fold it to find the answer. When they have solved the problem, ask students to share their answers with the group. Keep a tally on the board to see how many correctly named the solid figure that can be made. (a cube)

Tell students that there are many different possible verbs that can be used with the phrase *can be* in word problems. Write on the board the following examples: *can be made, can be used, can be combined, can be cut, can be folded, can be taped, can be described.* Ask students for other phrases that could be

used in word problems and add those to the phrases on the board. Leave this list on the board for use in Section C.

To summarize, ask for volunteers to walk the class through the steps and how they used them to come up with their answer. Ask other students what they will probably do the next time they see *can be* plus a verb in a word problem. Ask if any students have different ideas about solving this type of word problem. Encourage others to comment on the different ideas and add suggestions of their own.

Review and Practice

Review the three steps for solving word problems with the phrase *can be* and a verb. Ask students to write the three steps without looking at their student worktexts. Then instruct students to stand up. When all are standing, ask them to say the three steps by memory, without looking at their papers.

Practice phrases with *can be* and a verb. Read aloud with students the list of *can be* phrases on the board. Clarify the meanings of any of the verbs, if necessary. Assign two of the phrases to each pair and ask them to use them to write a problem about solid figures. Have pairs exchange their problems with another pair and solve them.

Read aloud the directions for Practice Solving Math Problems on page 100 in the student worktext. As students work on the problems individually, go around the room and check how well they have learned the problem-solving strategy.

Assess and Intervene

How well can students understand phrases with *can be* in word problems, based on Practice Solving Math Problems on page 100? Use the rubric to identify students who need extra support through additional help and the Intervention activity.

Intermediate

☐ Answers at least 2 of the word problems correctly, using *can be* and a verb in the answer.

☐ Writes a word problem using *can be* and a verb. The problem may not be logical and may be difficult to understand.

Example of a problem a student might write: *Sphere can be make with net?*

Advanced

☐ Answers all 3 of the word problems correctly, using *can be* and a verb in the answer.

☐ Writes a logical word problem using *can be* and a verb. The problem may include errors, but they do not affect comprehension.

Example of a problem a student might write: *Luis say a sphere can be make with net. Is correct?*

INTERVENTION 10 minutes

If students are having difficulty understanding the phrase can be with a verb in word problems, have them practice asking and answering simple riddles about everyday things and solid figures with the phrase *can be* and a verb. Suggest that they use some of these phrases: *can be made, can be used, can be cut, can be folded, can be taped, can be described*, etc., for example:

1. I can be made in the morning after somebody gets out of me. What am I? (a bed)

2. I can be used to make a solid figure. What am I? (a net or a pattern)

3. I can be used to make somebody's hair look good? What am I? (a brush or a comb)

4. I can be taped together if I get torn. What am I? (paper)

5. I can be described as having triangles for my four faces. What am I? (pyramid)

Understand the Main Idea

Objective Describe the kinds of things that fractions name.

Prerequisite Background Knowledge
- Concept of division into parts
- Concept of equal parts

30 minutes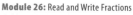

Teach this lesson:
- **Before** introducing material on fractions in students' grade-level math textbooks
- **Before** students complete the activities on page 101 of the student worktext

You need these materials:
- a strip of paper
- counters
- Transparency 51
- scissors

Module 26: Read and Write Fractions

Understand the Main Idea

Objective Describe different kinds of things that fractions name.

BP 3 **ELL BEST PRACTICE #3:** **Performance Assessment**

English language learners often know more than what they can demonstrate on traditional reading- and writing-based assessments. For this reason, it is often more effective to evaluate students' learning based on their work in ordinary classroom tasks. Pay attention to students' ability to read, write, and understand fractions as they carry out written, oral, and hands-on activities in the module. Take notes on what you observe.

Throughout this module, when you see **BP 3**, you will find an example of how you can use performance assessment to evaluate students' comprehension of fractions.

Learn the Main Idea

This picture shows a whole pizza.	This picture shows a group of baseballs.	This picture shows a number line.
The whole has 3 equal parts.	The group has 3 equal parts.	The number line shows $\frac{1}{3}$ and $\frac{2}{3}$.
Fractions can name equal parts of a whole.	Fractions can name equal parts of a group.	Fractions can name points on a number line.

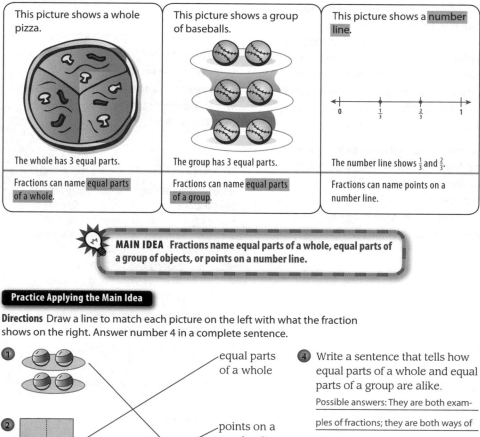

MAIN IDEA Fractions name equal parts of a whole, equal parts of a group of objects, or points on a number line.

Practice Applying the Main Idea

Directions Draw a line to match each picture on the left with what the fraction shows on the right. Answer number 4 in a complete sentence.

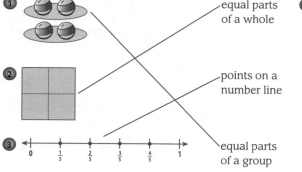

equal parts of a whole

points on a number line

equal parts of a group

4 Write a sentence that tells how equal parts of a whole and equal parts of a group are alike.

Possible answers: They are both examples of fractions; they are both ways of dividing things.

A Introduce

Activate students' background knowledge by taking a strip of paper and folding it into two equal pieces. Ask students to tell what you just did, using whatever words they can. Have each student tell a partner what he or she thinks. Then have partners share their ideas with the class.

Elicit that you folded the paper in half, or into two halves. Ask questions such as: *How many pieces did I make?* (2) *Are the pieces the same size?* (yes)

Write the word *fraction* on the board and read it aloud. Explain that the word *fraction* comes from a root meaning *to break*. Say: *When you break things into equal parts, you make fractions.*

Display the strip of paper you folded earlier. Ask students if this strip shows fractions. Have students explain their thinking. Elicit that the strip was folded into two equal parts, so the halves are an example of a fraction.

Invite students to tell about past experiences when they have made or used fractions.

Highlighted words and phrases may affect student comprehension.

Together with students, read aloud the Lesson Objective on page 101 in the student worktext. Then call students' attention to the first picture in the Learn the Main Idea box. Ask students to describe what they see.

- **Read the caption at the top of the picture,** emphasizing the word *whole*. Say: *There is just one pizza. It is a whole pizza.* Point out that the word *whole,* meaning *entire* or *complete,* is different from the word *hole.*

- **Then read aloud the statements below the picture.** Have students check that the three parts are equal. Say: *Fractions can name equal parts of a whole,* while drawing a circle in the air with your finger. Have students repeat your words and actions.

- **Repeat with the second picture, emphasizing the word** *group.* Stress that a *group* or *set* of objects includes not just one thing, but several. Say: *Fractions can name equal parts of a group.* Draw small circles in the air with your finger. Again, have students repeat.

- **Move on to the last picture.** Establish that number lines are divided into equal parts. Say: *You can show fractions on a number line, too.* Point out that the numbers marked between 0 and 1 are fractions. Say: *Fractions can name equal parts or distances on a number line.* Read aloud the text below the number line.

Conclude by reading aloud the Main Idea on page 101 of the student worktext. Have volunteers point to parts of whole, parts of a group, and the number line in the visual in the student worktext.

B Teach and Learn

Draw a square on the board. Explain that the square is one *whole* object. Draw lines to form four equal vertical slices. Explain that your picture now shows fractions. Say: *I had a whole square. I divided it into four equal parts.*

- **Then say:** *Fractions can name equal parts of a whole.* Have students practice this sentence by filling in missing phrases. For instance, say: *Fractions can name ____ of a whole,* and have students fill in *equal parts.* Or say: *Fractions can name equal parts of ____,* and have students supply *a whole.*

- **BP 3 Have students work with a partner.** Give each pair a sheet of paper.

Explain that the sheet of paper is a whole. Ask them to show fractions by folding the sheet to show equal parts. When they have done one number of equal parts, have them fold another sheet into a different number of equal parts. Then have them talk about their work with another pair. Go over this work with the class as a whole.

- **Wrap up this part of the lesson by having students clap and chant:** *Fractions can name equal parts of a whole.*

Draw four triangles on the board. Establish that this is a group of objects and is also called a set. Draw two loops around pairs of triangles. Point out that this picture now shows fractions. Say: *I had a group of triangles. I divided the group into two equal parts.*

- **Say:** *Fractions can name equal parts of a group.* As before, leave out phrases for students to say.

- **BP 3 Distribute twelve counters to each pair.** Instruct them to make equal parts and draw the results. Encourage them to find two to three different ways of making equal parts and then talk about their work with another pair.

- **Wrap up by having students clap and chant:** *Fractions can name equal parts of a group.*

Draw a number line on the board and label it 0, $\frac{1}{4}$, $\frac{2}{4}$, $\frac{3}{4}$, and 1. Say: *This number line goes from 0 to ____.* Pause and let students complete the sentence with *1.* Say: *The number line has been broken into equal parts. Each part shows an equal distance.* Explain that the other numbers on the number line are fractions. Say: *Fractions can name points on a number line.* Have students finish the sentence: *Fractions can name points on ____.*

C Review and Practice

Display Transparency 51. Point to each picture in turn. Have students respond *equal parts of a whole, equal parts of a group,* or *equal parts of a number line,* and then say the sentence: *Fractions can name equal parts of a whole, equal parts of a group, or equal parts of a number line.*

BP 3 Have students work with a partner. Have them take turns drawing wholes or groups and dividing them into equal parts. The student who is not drawing should

identify the picture as showing a whole or a group and then say the appropriate sentence beginning *Fractions can name equal parts of ____.*

Read aloud the directions for Practice Applying the Main Idea on page 101. Have students draw lines to match the picture with the kind of fraction it names. Have students complete numbers 1–4 on their own. Check their work.

D Assess and Intervene

Can students describe the different things that fractions name, based on Practice Applying the Main Idea on page 101? Use the rubric to identify students who need extra support through additional help and the Intervention activity.

Intermediate

- ☐ Connects all 3 pictures with the correct names.
- ☐ Writes a sentence that mentions fractions or dividing; errors may make comprehension difficult.

  Example of a sentence a student might write: *Both are make fraction.*

Advanced

- ☐ Connects all 3 pictures with the correct names.
- ☐ Writes a sentence that mentions fractions or dividing; minimal errors do not affect comprehension.

  Example of a sentence a student might write: *Both show equal part.*

INTERVENTION 5 minutes

If students have trouble with the activities on page 101, they may not be sure what the phrase *equal parts* means. Provide scissors and paper. Help students cut one sheet of paper into two equal parts. Have them say, *These are two equal parts.* Explain that these parts are a fraction of the whole. Then repeat, having students cut another sheet into two parts that are not equal. Have them say, *These are two unequal parts.* Explain that these are not fractions because they are not equal. Have students try making equal and unequal parts on their own.

Learn the Vocabulary

Objective Talk and write about fractions using the vocabulary words.

30 minutes

Teach this lesson:
- **Before** students begin work on fractions in their grade-level math textbooks
- **Before** students complete the activities on page 102 of the student worktext

You need these materials:
- egg carton
- scored crackers
- books
- Worksheet 26
- large sheet of chart paper and markers

Lesson Vocabulary

Essential Vocabulary

fraction	numerator	denominator
group (set)	whole (region)	

Additional Vocabulary

half/halves	third/thirds	fourth/fourths
eighth/eighths		

Learn the Vocabulary

Objective Talk and write about fractions using the vocabulary words.

Learn the Words

Directions Write the missing numbers and words.

A **fraction** names equal parts.

Fractions can name equal parts of a **whole** or a **region**. 3 out of 4 equal parts are shaded. $\frac{3}{4}$ of the whole is shaded.	Fractions can name equal parts of a **group** or a **set**. 3 _____ out of 4 _____ equal parts are shaded. $\frac{3}{4}$ _____ of the group is shaded.
The **numerator** tells how many equal parts you are choosing or shading. $\frac{3}{4}$ ⟵ numerator	The **denominator** tells how many equal parts in all. $\frac{3}{4}$ ⟵ denominator _____

Practice the Words

Directions Write the missing vocabulary words in the blanks. Then answer question 6 using a complete sentence.

1. The top number in a fraction is the numerator _____.

2. The bottom number in a fraction is the denominator _____.

3. A fraction _____ shows equal parts.

4. Some fractions show equal parts of a group or whole _____.

5. Other fractions show equal parts of a whole or group _____.

6. What information does the denominator of a fraction tell you? Use your own words to explain. Possible answer: The denominator tells how many equal parts there are in all. _____

_____

A Introduce

Introduce students to the game Hangman. Use *fractions* as the word to be guessed. When they guess a letter correctly, they get another turn. When they guess wrong, draw a head, neck, arm, etc.

Read the word *fractions* aloud with students when the letters have been guessed. Ask students to write a sentence about fractions in their own words. They may include information from the previous lesson. Encourage them to provide drawings or numbers if it would help them.

Have students form small groups and talk about their writing. Move around the room, helping students clarify their ideas.

Bring the group back together. Ask students to list words that were helpful in talking about fractions. Repeat each of these words, and write them on the board. Add other important words you heard in conversations, even if students don't mention them. For example, say: *I heard [Miguel] use the word* group *to tell about fractions. That's a good word! I'll add it to the list.*

Read the word list aloud. Add sketches or other examples that will help students understand the meanings of the words. Then add any other words from the Essential Vocabulary list that have not yet been brought up.

Choose any words from the Additional Vocabulary box that you think will be useful. Elicit or provide examples or definitions for these words.

Highlighted words and phrases may affect student comprehension.

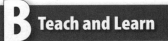

B Teach and Learn

Read aloud with students the Lesson Objective on page 102 in the student worktext. Explain that the words on the board will help them talk and write about fractions.

Read aloud the first line in the Learn the Words box. Ask students to point to classmates who used the phrase *equal parts* when talking about fractions in their small groups.

Remind students that there are two kinds of equal parts. Say: *One kind is _____. The other is _____.* Allow students to complete the sentences with *equal parts of a whole* and *equal parts of a group.* Say that there is also a third kind of equal parts: *equal parts of a number line.*

Point out the text above the two pictures in the Learn the Words box. Have volunteers read the text aloud. Explain that the words *whole* and *region* refer to the same thing, and *group* and *set* refer to the same thing.

Briefly review the difference between whole (or region) and group (or set). Display an egg carton. Establish that this is a whole because it is a single object. Then hold up several pencils. Establish that the pencils represent a group, because they are multiple objects. Finally, display ordinary objects such as a scored cracker (example of a whole) and a few books (example of a group). Have students tell if they are wholes or groups.

Draw students' attention to the pictures in the Learn the Words box. Ask students to talk with a partner about the two pictures. Ask them to tell each other how they are alike and how they are different. Establish that both pictures show equal parts, but the one on the left shows equal parts of a whole and the one on the right shows equal parts of a group.

Introduce the word *shaded*. Relate the word *shaded* to the *shade* that results when light is blocked; explain that *shaded* areas are darker, like areas that are in the shade. Have students point to the *shaded* triangles in the two pictures.

Say: *We can use fractions to tell about these pictures. We can use fractions because the pictures show _____.* Allow students to fill in the phrase *equal groups.*

Read aloud the text beside the left-hand picture. Ask: *How many parts are shaded?* (3) *How many are there in all?* (4) Explain that 3 of the 4 parts of the figure are shaded. Read aloud the fraction $\frac{3}{4}$ as *three-fourths* and have students repeat. Then read the line: $\frac{3}{4}$ *of the whole is shaded.*

Move on to the picture on the right. Have students work with a partner to read the text and fill in the missing numbers. Move around the room, offering help as necessary.

Point out the words *numerator* and *denominator* on the bottom row of the Learn the Words box. Say the words carefully and slowly, and have students repeat several times. You may find it useful to teach the words one syllable at a time, writing the syllables separately on the board and building up their pronunciation in parts.

Use the pictures and arrows to show students that the numerator is the top number in a fraction. Explain that the *numerator* refers to the number of equal parts that are shaded or chosen. Repeat with the denominator, the bottom number. Explain that the denominator refers to the total number of equal parts. Have students fill in the missing word *denominator* in the blank space.

📇 **Have students complete the Vocabulary Cards for the words in this module.**

C Review and Practice

BP 3 ▸ **Return to the list of Essential Vocabulary terms on the board.** Have students sketch a picture to show what each word means. Then have them talk about their pictures with a partner. Pay special attention to *numerator* and *denominator*, which are easy to confuse even for fluent speakers of English.

📄 **BP 3** ▸ **Distribute one copy of Worksheet 26 to pairs of students.** Have students work together to identify the numerators and the denominators. Encourage them to use their Vocabulary Cards and the information on page 102 of the student worktext.

Read aloud the directions for Practice the Words on page 102. Point out that question 6 asks for a complete sentence. Then have students solve the problems independently.

D Assess and Intervene

How well do students understand the meaning of the vocabulary words, judging from their work in Practice the Words on page 102? Use the rubric to identify students who need extra support through additional help and the Intervention activity.

Intermediate

☐ Identifies 4 of the words correctly.

☐ Writes a phrase or sentence that includes the idea of total equal parts; errors may make comprehension difficult.

Example of a sentence a student might write: *Tell you how many part.*

Advanced

☐ Identifies all the words correctly.

☐ Writes a complete sentence that includes the idea of total equal parts, with minimal errors.

Example of a sentence a student might write: *Denominator tell you the number of equal part there is.*

INTERVENTION   5 minutes

📇 Students who cannot identify all of the vocabulary words may benefit from creating a web to organize information about them. Have students use markers to create a web on a large sheet of chart paper. In the center of the web, have them place a Vocabulary Card with a word they are not yet familiar with. Help them list information about the word in the strands of the web going out from the center. If possible, have students work with others who struggle with different words, so they can help each other.

Use More Language

Objective Use *is* and *are* to ask and answer questions about fractions.

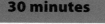

30 minutes

Teach this lesson:
- **After** students complete work on fractions in their grade-level math textbooks
- **Before** students complete the activities on page 103 of the student worktext

You need these materials:
- Transparency 52
- markers (4 red and 1 blue)

EXTENSION AND ENRICHMENT   10 minutes

Challenge students to find examples of fractions in everyday life. Help them get started by listing and describing two to three sample fractions, such as a *half* moon, a pizza cut into *eighths*, or a dime (which is one *tenth* of a dollar). Then have students work with a partner or in small groups to think of other examples. Ask them to talk about these examples with the rest of the group. Then have them write and draw the examples to create a class book.

Use More Language

Objective Use *is* and *are* to ask and answer questions about fractions.

LESSON
3

Learn the Language

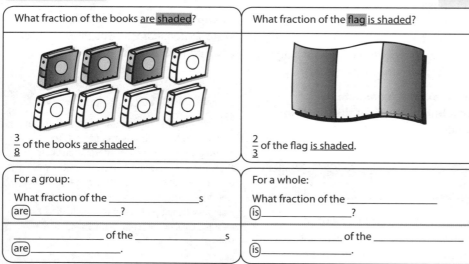

What fraction of the books <u>are shaded</u>?

$\frac{3}{8}$ of the books <u>are shaded</u>.

What fraction of the <u>flag</u> <u>is shaded</u>?

$\frac{2}{3}$ of the flag <u>is shaded</u>.

For a group:

What fraction of the _____s (are)_____?

_____ of the _____s (are)_____.

For a whole:

What fraction of the _____ (is)_____?

_____ of the _____ (is)_____.

Practice the Language

Directions Write a question and an answer about fractions for each picture below. Use *is* and *are* to tell about fractions.

1 Question: Answers will vary. Possible question: What fraction of the balloons are black?

Answer: Possible answer: $\frac{3}{5}$ of the balloons are black.

2 Question: Answers will vary. Possible question: What fraction of the ducks are painted?

Answer: Possible answer: $\frac{1}{4}$ of the ducks are painted.

A Introduce

Read aloud the Lesson Objective on page 103 in the student worktext with students.

Briefly discuss the words *is* and *are*. Write the two words on the board. Point out that they mean the same thing but are used with different words. Write the following sentence on the board: *The dog ____ little.* Ask students which of the two words *is* and *are* goes in the blank. Read the sentence aloud both ways if necessary. Elicit that *is* goes in the sentence. Then repeat, using the sentence *The dogs ____ brown.* (are)

Have students discuss with a partner why they think one sentence uses *is* and the other uses *are*. List their ideas on the board. Reinforce that *is* is used with singular subjects, and *are* is used with plural subjects.

Explain that *is* and *are* can be important words in talking about fractions. Tell students that they should look for the words *is* and *are* as they work through page 103.

Highlighted words and phrases may affect student comprehension.

Teach and Learn

Draw students' attention to the upper left corner of the Learn the Language box. Have students read the sentence aloud. Point out that some of the words are underlined. Explain that the words refer to the picture below the text.

- **Ask students how they know that this sentence is a question.** (question mark) Establish also that a question asks for information instead of giving information, and that this sentence asks for information.

- **Have students close their eyes.** Ask them to recall if the question used the word *is* or if it used *are*. (are)

- **Move to the answer below the picture.** Have students tell a partner how they know this is an answer (because it gives information and ends with a period) and how they know the answer is $\frac{3}{8}$ (3 of 8 books are shaded).

- **Review Essential Vocabulary terms by asking students which part of the fraction is the numerator and which is the denominator.** (3 is the numerator; 8 is the denominator) Then ask students if the example shows equal parts of a *whole* or equal parts of a *group*. Establish that the example shows equal parts of a group.

Repeat the above procedure with the example on the right. Be sure students notice that *is* has replaced *are* in both question and answer. Be sure students also see that this example shows equal parts of a whole, not equal parts of a group.

Challenge students to identify when to use *is* and when to use *are* in asking and answering questions about fractions. Encourage them to think back to the discussion about *is* and *are* in the lesson introduction. Have students talk with partners, and then ask them to share their ideas with the rest of the class. Establish that *is* should be used with fractions of a whole, because a whole is only one object. This is the same as when we say: *The dog is little. Are* applies to fractions of a group because a group includes more than one object. This is the same as when we say: *The dogs are brown*.

Assign students to work in pairs. Have them ask and answer the questions in the Learn the Language box as if they were

dialogue. For example, one student would say *What fraction of the flag is shaded?* and the other would reply $\frac{2}{3}$ *of the flag is shaded*. Have them repeat these dialogues a few times. Allow students to read from the text at first, but encourage them to do as much from memory as they can. You can model this process with a volunteer before students break into pairs.

Point out the sentence frames in the student worktext. Be sure students see that one of the frames applies to equal parts of a group and the other to equal parts of a whole. Read the frames aloud with students.

 Display Transparency 52. Model for students a question and answer about the first picture. Say: *What fraction of the flag is shaded? That's the question.* Together repeat the question. Then say: *Can anyone tell me the answer to this question?* Help students answer *Two thirds of the flag is shaded*.

- **BP 3 Have students ask and answer questions about the other pictures on the transparency.** Ask them to have a dialogue with their partners, one asking the question, the other answering the question. Circulate through the room, offering help and clarification as needed.

- **Discuss the activity with students.** Ask what they found hard or easy about it. Wrap up by explaining that they will often use *is* and *are* to ask and answer questions about fractions.

Review and Practice

Hold up four red markers and one blue marker. Say: $\frac{4}{5}$ *of the markers are red*. Write that sentence on the board. Then ask: *What question goes with that answer?* Refer students to the sentence frames in the text. Help them see that the answer fits the question *What fraction of the markers are red?*

Repeat by drawing a square divided into fourths on the board and shading one part. Give students the answer $\frac{1}{4}$ *of the square is shaded*. Help them see that the question is *What fraction of the square is shaded?*

Have students work independently to complete the Practice the Language activity on page 103 in their student worktexts. Ask them to use the sentence frames only if they have to. Check and then assess the students.

Assess and Intervene

Can students use *is* and *are* to ask and answer questions about fractions, based on Practice the Language on page 103 of the student worktext? Use the rubric to identify students who need extra support through additional help and the Intervention activity.

Intermediate

☐ Uses *is* or *are* correctly in 1 question and answer.

☐ Questions and answers use sentence frames with few errors.

Example of a sentence a student might write: *What fraction of duck is paint?*

Advanced

☐ Uses *is* or *are* correctly in both questions and answers.

☐ Questions are answer are written in students' own words, with few errors.

Example of a sentence a student might write: *How much of duck is paint?*

INTERVENTION 10 minutes

It is often difficult for students to write fractions of groups accurately. Help students by having them draw pictures. To model the fraction of black balloons in item 1 of Practice the Language, for example, have them draw all the black balloons above a fraction bar. Explain that this shows the numerator of the fraction. Then have them draw *all* the balloons at the bottom of the fraction bar. Explain that this shows the fraction's denominator. Help them count to see that there are 3 black balloons out of 5 in all, so $\frac{3}{5}$ of the balloons are black.

Solve Math Problems

Objective Use *would* to answer questions with *suppose* in word problems.

30 minutes

Teach this lesson:
- **After** completing work on fractions in students' grade-level math textbooks
- **Before** students complete the activities on page 104 of the student worktext

You need these materials:
- poster board or butcher paper
- a penny and a quarter

Solve Math Problems

Objective Use *would* to answer questions with *suppose* in word problems.

Learn to Solve Problems

Problem Kenji and Rosario bought a pizza to share equally. They cut the pizza in half. Suppose they cut the pizza into fourths instead. Would the pieces be larger or smaller?

	Read	Write/Think
Step 1:	Read the problem. Circle what the children did with the pizza.	I will circle "They cut the pizza in half."
Step 2:	Draw a square around what you should suppose or pretend.	I will put a square around "Suppose they cut the pizza in fourths instead."
Step 3:	Underline the question. What do you need to do?	I will underline "Would the pieces be larger or smaller?" I need to compare halves and fourths.
Step 4:	Solve the problem. Draw a picture if that will help.	$\frac{1}{2}$ $\frac{1}{4}$ Fourths are smaller than halves. So if the children cut the pizza in fourths, the pieces would be smaller.

Practice Solving Math Problems

Directions Follow steps 1 to 4 above to solve the word problems below. Solve the problems on a separate sheet of paper. Write the answers in complete sentences.

1. Roshni had 8 markers. She gave Elena half of the markers. Suppose she gave Elena a quarter of the markers. Would Elena have more markers or fewer markers? Elena would have fewer markers.

2. Timo painted a third of a wall. Suppose he had painted half of the wall. Would more or less of the wall be painted? More of the wall would be painted.

3. Julio made a flag with 4 equal stripes. Suppose he made the flag with 5 equal stripes. Would the stripes be larger or smaller? The stripes would be smaller.

4. Sarina folded a dinner napkin into 4 equal parts. Suppose she folded it into 3 equal parts instead. Would the equal parts be larger or smaller? The parts would be larger.

Write the word *suppose* in the center of a sheet of butcher paper. Circle it and read it aloud. Ask if students have ever heard or used this word before. Encourage students to share their experiences.

- **Explain that the word *suppose* means *pretend* or *imagine*.** Say: *When you use the word* suppose, *you are talking about something that isn't necessarily true. It's a* what if? *word. You're thinking about what would happen* if *it were really true.*

- **Draw four lines radiating from the word *suppose* so they form a web.** Write *pretend, imagine, not necessarily true,* and *what if?* on the lines and have students read them aloud. They may need extra practice on the phrase *not necessarily true.* The web should look like this:

- **Ask students why you wrote these words on the lines.** Elicit that the words help explain the meaning of *suppose.* Display the web so students may refer to it as they work through the lesson.

- **Provide practice in using the word *suppose* in its everyday meaning.** Say: *Suppose today were Saturday. What would you be doing right now?* Point out that today is *not* Saturday, but you are asking students to pretend that it is. Have students answer using the sentence frame *I would be _____.*

Highlighted words and phrases may affect student comprehension.

- **Repeat with other situations and sentences, such as** *Suppose you were 10 feet tall.* **and** *Suppose your pencil came to life!* Encourage students to be creative in their responses. Have them share their ideas with a partner. Instruct students to ask their partners *suppose* questions of their own as well, if they are comfortable doing so at this point.

Explain that math word problems sometimes use the word *suppose.* Ask students to give the meaning of this word using the web you created earlier. Then together with students, read the Lesson Objective on page 104 in the student worktext.

B Teach and Learn

Ask students to look at the problem on page 104 of the student worktext. Call on a volunteer to read the first sentence of the problem statement.

Point out that it can be helpful for students to picture a problem in their minds. Invite students to visualize what they know so far. Establish that two children are going to share a pizza. Help students add detail to their mental images by asking guiding questions, such as *What color hair do you think the children have?*, *Are either of the children wearing glasses?*, and *What toppings do you think they put on their pizza?*

Have students share their ideas in groups of four. Make it clear that students' answers to these questions are neither right nor wrong, but that thinking about these details helps make the problem more real.

Read aloud the rest of the problem. Model the meaning of *larger* and *smaller* with a penny and a quarter. Say, and have students repeat: *The quarter is larger than the penny. The penny is smaller than the quarter.*

Call students' attention to Step 1. Read the step aloud. Explain that students should circle what the children *really* did with the pizza. Point out that the information is circled in the problem and written next to Step 1. Have volunteers read the sentence aloud.

Read Step 2 aloud. Help students find the word *suppose* in the problem statement. Refer them to the web you created earlier to help them remember what *suppose* means.

- **Read aloud the sentence beginning** *Suppose. . . .* Say: *Kenji and Rosario didn't* really *cut the pizza into fourths. But what if they did? What would that look like?*

Move on to the third step. Read it aloud. Ask students to find the question in the problem and read it chorally. Say: *I need to compare two things. I need to compare the halves of the pizza with the fourths of the pizza. I need to see which is larger.* Check students' comprehension of *suppose* by asking them if the children really did cut the pizza in half (yes) or into fourths (no).

Walk students through the fourth step. Read the text aloud. Emphasize the value of drawing a picture. Have students explain the picture in the text to a partner. Then point out the text below the picture. Say: *You can see that fourths are smaller than halves.* If *the children cut their pizza in fourths, the pieces would be smaller.* Explain that because the question says *suppose,* and *suppose* means that what you say is not necessarily true, the answer has to be *would.*

Write the following problem on the board: *Franca had 6 rings. She gave a third of her rings to her sister. Suppose she gave her sister half of the rings. Would her sister have more or fewer rings?*

- **BP 3** **Read the problem aloud.** Have students work with a partner to solve it, following the sequence of steps given in the student worktext. Circulate through the room, noting where students have difficulty. Remind them to talk to each other about the problem and to give their final answer in a full sentence.

- **BP 3** **When students are done, help them discuss the problem.** Ask them to talk about which steps they found easy and which ones were harder. Encourage students to share their strategies for understanding the problem. Summarize these strategies, and write them on the board.

C Review and Practice

Play a game with the class to reinforce the meaning of *suppose.* Tell students that you will say a sentence, and they should respond with *True, Not true,* or *Not necessarily true.* Have students repeat the phrase, *Not necessarily true,* several times with a beat. Say a true sentence, such as *There are ____ students*

in this class. Students should respond *True.* Then say *There are 45 students in this class* and have students respond *Not true.* Say: *Suppose there were 325 students in this class.* Students should respond with *Not necessarily true.* Repeat with other examples.

- **BP 3** **Have students play this game with a partner.** Help them form and interpret sentences with *suppose.*

Read aloud the directions for Practice Solving Math Problems at the bottom of the page. Have students work on these problems independently. Move through the room, and check students' work.

D Assess and Intervene

Based on Practice Solving Math Problems on page 104, can students use *would* when answering problems that use *suppose*? Use the rubric to identify students who need extra support through additional help and the Intervention activity.

Intermediate

☐ Solves at least 3 problems correctly.

☐ Answers are given in phrases or sentences sentences; errors do not interfere with understanding.

Advanced

☐ Solves all 4 problems correctly.

☐ Answers are given in complete sentences with few if any errors.

INTERVENTION 5 minutes

Have students act out the problems in Practice Solving Math Problems. Help them use materials or pictures to model each problem two different ways: once as it really happened, and once including the *suppose* part. For item 1, for example, have two students play the parts of Roshni and Elena, using 8 markers. Have Roshni give Elena half the markers. (4) Then have Roshni give Elena a quarter of the markers. (2) Have students reread the question and answer it, using a complete sentence. Continue with other examples.

Understand the Main Idea

Objective Compare and order fractions that name the same amount and fractions that name different amounts.

Lesson

1

Prerequisite Background Knowledge
- Concepts of fractions
- Concepts of multiplication and division and comparing and ordering numbers

30 minutes

Teach this lesson:
- **Before** introducing lessons on equivalent fractions and comparing and ordering fractions in the grade-level math textbook
- **Before** students complete the activities on page 105 of the student worktext

You need these materials:
- rulers
- Transparency 53
- clay, plastic knives
- fraction bars
- construction paper

BP 4 ELL BEST PRACTICE #4:
Interaction

For English language learners, extensive interaction with others promotes acquisition of new knowledge. Interaction with the teacher through modeling will help students acquire the language and concepts related to comparing and ordering fractions. Group and pair work will provide students opportunities to practice and strengthen fraction concepts and develop the language used to discuss these topics.

Throughout this module, when you see **BP 4**, this is an example of interaction.

Module 27: Compare and Order Equivalent Fractions

Understand the Main Idea

LESSON
1

Objective Compare and order fractions that name the same amount and fractions that name different amounts.

Learn the Main Idea

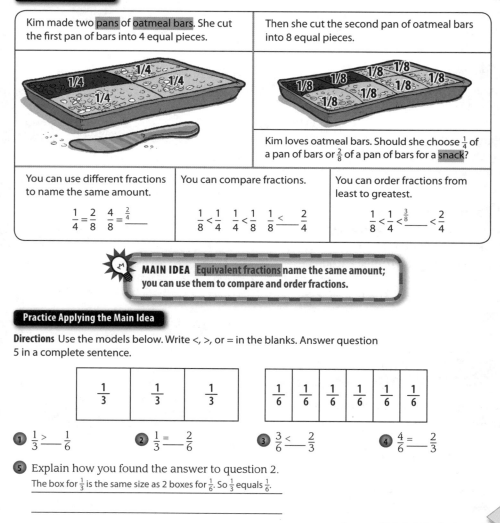

Kim made two pans of oatmeal bars. She cut the first pan of bars into 4 equal pieces.

1/4 1/4 1/4 1/4

Then she cut the second pan of oatmeal bars into 8 equal pieces.

1/8 1/8 1/8 1/8 1/8 1/8 1/8 1/8

Kim loves oatmeal bars. Should she choose $\frac{1}{4}$ of a pan of bars or $\frac{2}{8}$ of a pan of bars for a snack?

You can use different fractions to name the same amount.

$\frac{1}{4} = \frac{2}{8}$ $\frac{4}{8} = \frac{2}{4}$

You can compare fractions.

$\frac{1}{8} < \frac{1}{4}$ $\frac{1}{4} < \frac{1}{8}$ $\frac{1}{8} < \underline{\quad} \frac{2}{4}$

You can order fractions from least to greatest.

$\frac{1}{8} < \frac{1}{4} < \frac{3}{8} \underline{\quad} < \frac{2}{4}$

MAIN IDEA Equivalent fractions name the same amount; you can use them to compare and order fractions.

Practice Applying the Main Idea

Directions Use the models below. Write <, >, or = in the blanks. Answer question 5 in a complete sentence.

$\frac{1}{3}$	$\frac{1}{3}$	$\frac{1}{3}$

$\frac{1}{6}$	$\frac{1}{6}$	$\frac{1}{6}$	$\frac{1}{6}$	$\frac{1}{6}$	$\frac{1}{6}$

1. $\frac{1}{3} > \underline{\quad} \frac{1}{6}$ 2. $\frac{1}{3} = \underline{\quad} \frac{2}{6}$ 3. $\frac{3}{6} < \underline{\quad} \frac{2}{3}$ 4. $\frac{4}{6} = \underline{\quad} \frac{2}{3}$

5. Explain how you found the answer to question 2.
   The box for $\frac{1}{3}$ is the same size as 2 boxes for $\frac{1}{6}$. So $\frac{1}{3}$ equals $\frac{1}{6}$.

A Introduce

Read aloud the Lesson Objective with students.

Use Transparency 53 to activate and/ or build background knowledge.
Give a quick overview of measurements in fractions of an inch. Discuss with students that this ruler measures length in $\frac{1}{2}$-inch, $\frac{1}{4}$-inch, and $\frac{1}{8}$-inch units. Other rulers also measure in 16ths.

- **Have students look at the transparency.** Ask them to discuss with a partner how many of each kind of fraction there are in an inch, then share with the class. Tell them that classroom items, such as index cards, notebooks, and sticky notes, can be measured in inches or in fractions of an inch.

BP 4 Give students rulers. Have them identify the marks for $\frac{1}{8}$ inch, $\frac{1}{4}$ inch, and $\frac{1}{2}$ inch. Brainstorm real-life experiences using these fractions to measure. Ask: *What kinds of things have you measured using fractions of an inch?* Listen to several responses. Ask: *What fractions can we use to measure length?*

Highlighted words and phrases may affect student comprehension.

Help students understand that different fractions can name the same amount. Say: *Look at $\frac{1}{2}$ inch on the ruler. How many quarter inches are in $\frac{1}{2}$ inch?* (2) *So two quarters or $\frac{2}{4}$ are equal to $\frac{1}{2}$.* You may need to remind students that one quarter is the same as $\frac{1}{4}$. Use the ruler to show that $\frac{1}{4}$ inch equals $\frac{2}{8}$ inch. Tell students that they can also use the ruler to see which measurements (or fractions) are bigger and smaller than others.

Say: *Find $\frac{1}{2}$ inch and $\frac{1}{4}$ inch on the ruler. Which is bigger, $\frac{1}{2}$ or $\frac{1}{4}$? How can you tell?* Students should indicate that $\frac{1}{2}$ inch takes up more space and is longer on the ruler than $\frac{1}{4}$ inch.

Have students count by eighths to find $\frac{2}{8}$ inch and by fourths to find $\frac{1}{4}$ inch on the ruler. Ask: *Which is bigger, $\frac{2}{8}$ or $\frac{1}{4}$? How can you tell?* Students should realize that these fractions show the same amount because they take up the same amount of space on the ruler.

Read aloud the Main Idea on page 105 with students. Discuss with them how this statement relates to the activity you just completed with the ruler.

B **Teach and Learn**

BP 4 **Put students in pairs.** Have them open their student worktexts to page 105. Give each student a piece of clay and a plastic knife. Have students flatten and shape the clay into a rectangle so that it resembles the illustration of a pan of oatmeal bars in Learn the Main Idea on page 105 of the student worktext.

- **Read the text above the first illustration.** Say: *Use the knife to cut your clay into four equal pieces like the picture in the textbook.*

- **Ask:** *What fraction names each piece that you cut?* Write $\frac{1}{4}$ on the board. Say: *Each piece is $\frac{1}{4}$ of a pan.*

- **Read the text above the second illustration.** Say: *One partner should leave his or her clay in four pieces. The other partner should cut the clay into eight equal pieces, as in the second picture. What fraction names each piece that you cut?* ($\frac{1}{8}$) Write $\frac{1}{8}$ on the board. Say: *Each piece is $\frac{1}{8}$ of the pan.*

- **Encourage students to compare the sizes of the pieces of clay.** Say: *Which piece is bigger, $\frac{1}{4}$ or $\frac{1}{8}$?* ($\frac{1}{4}$) $\frac{1}{4}$ *is greater than $\frac{1}{8}$. $\frac{1}{8}$ is less than $\frac{1}{4}$.* Write on the board and spell

out: $\frac{1}{4} > \frac{1}{8}$ and $\frac{1}{8} < \frac{1}{4}$. Chorally read the sentence with students.

Refer students to the illustrations of the oatmeal bars in the student worktext. Ask: *Should Kim choose the pan with $\frac{1}{4}$ or $\frac{2}{8}$ of a pan of oatmeal bars? Tell your partner.* Allow students to discuss the answer. Ask: *How many fourths does the shaded section name?* ($\frac{1}{4}$) *How many eighths does the shaded section name?* ($\frac{2}{8}$) *The shaded sections of both rectangles are the same size.* Explain that since both sections are equal, this means that $\frac{1}{4}$ is the same as $\frac{2}{8}$. Both fractions name the same amount.

Tell students that these are fractions that name the same amount and that they have compared the sizes of different fractions. Explain that they can use these ideas to order three fractions from least to greatest.

Say: *We know that $\frac{1}{8}$ is smaller, or less than, $\frac{1}{4}$. Look at the picture. Is $\frac{3}{8}$ smaller or bigger than $\frac{1}{4}$?* (bigger)

Write on the board: $\frac{1}{8} < \frac{1}{4} < \frac{3}{8}$. Explain that these fractions are in order from smallest to largest (least to greatest).

C **Review and Practice**

To review equivalence, comparing, and ordering, guide students to fill in the blanks in Learn the Main Idea. Say: *Shade in another fourth next to the fourth that is shaded. Now $\frac{2}{4}$ of the rectangle is shaded. $\frac{2}{4}$ is the same as how many eighths?* ($\frac{4}{8}$) *Is $\frac{2}{4}$ bigger or smaller than $\frac{3}{8}$?* (bigger) Help students use this information to fill in the blanks.

BP 4 **Divide the class into groups of four.** Give each group a set of fraction bars and set out 1 whole for reference. Each student in the group takes one of the following bars: $\frac{1}{2}, \frac{1}{3}, \frac{1}{4}, \frac{1}{5}$. One at a time, students take turns showing their bars and naming the fraction. That student asks another group member to find two bars that together make the same size. Another group member finds a bar that is smaller, and a third student finds a bar that is larger.

- **Have the group work together to discuss and write equality and inequality statements for each of the fractions.** Continue until all group members have had a turn. Invite groups to share their fraction statements with the class.

Read the directions for the Practice Applying the Main Idea activity. Have students work independently to complete the activity.

Check students' work and assist with the language for number 5, as needed.

D **Assess and Intervene**

Do students know which fractions name the same amount? Can students compare and order fractions based on Practice Applying the Main Idea on page 105?

Intermediate

- ☐ Correctly completes at least 3 comparison statements.

- ☐ Explanation includes the idea that the $\frac{1}{3}$ section is the same size as two $\frac{1}{6}$ sections. Language may be vague or incomplete.

  Example of a sentence a student might write: $\frac{1}{3} \frac{2}{6}$ *size same.* $\frac{1}{3} = \frac{2}{6}$.

Advanced

- ☐ Correctly completes all comparison statements.

- ☐ Explanation clearly states that the sections for $\frac{1}{3}$ and $\frac{2}{6}$ are the same size and concludes that the two fractions are equal.

  Example of a sentence a student might write: $\frac{1}{3}$ *is same size* $\frac{2}{6}$. $\frac{1}{3} = \frac{2}{6}$.

INTERVENTION 5 minutes

It may be helpful for some students to participate in a kinesthetic activity for comparing fractions. Cut a piece of construction paper in half and label each half with the fraction $\frac{1}{2}$. Use a different color paper folded and cut in fourths and label each section $\frac{1}{4}$. Fold, cut, and label a third piece of paper in a different color for eighths. Allow students to place the cutouts on top of one another to compare, order, and find equivalent fractions. Use the cutouts to model statements such as: $\frac{1}{2} = \frac{2}{4} = \frac{4}{8}, \frac{1}{4} = \frac{2}{8}, \frac{1}{8} < \frac{1}{4}$ and $\frac{1}{4} < \frac{1}{2}, \frac{1}{8} < \frac{1}{4} < \frac{1}{2}$.

Learn the Vocabulary

Objective Talk about equivalent fractions using vocabulary words.

30 minutes

Teach this lesson:
- **Before** introducing lessons on equivalent fractions and comparing and ordering fractions in the grade-level math textbook
- **Before** students complete the activities on page 106 of the student worktext

You need these materials:
- Vocabulary Cards
- index cards

Lesson Vocabulary

Essential Vocabulary
equivalent fractions   simplest form
common factor

Additional Vocabulary
factor   numerator*
denominator*   like denominators*

* - These terms have Vocabulary Cards.

LESSON
2

Learn the Vocabulary

Objective Talk and write about equivalent fractions using the vocabulary words.

Learn the Words

Directions Fill in the blanks below.

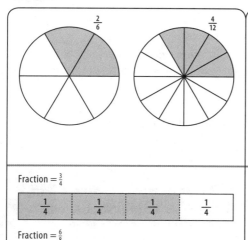

$\frac{2}{6}$ $\frac{4}{12}$

Equivalent fractions are fractions that name the same amount. Two sixths ($\frac{2}{6}$) and four twelfths ($\frac{4}{12}$) are equivalent fractions.

Common factors are factors that are the same for two different numbers. 2 is a common factor of 4 and 12. $2 \times 3 = 6$. $2 \times 6 = 12$.

The **simplest form** of a fraction is the form where 1 is the only common factor of the numerator and the denominator. $\frac{1}{3}$ is a fraction in simplest form. $\frac{2}{6}$ is not in simplest form because it can be changed to the simpler form $\frac{1}{3}$.

Fraction $= \frac{3}{4}$

| $\frac{1}{4}$ | $\frac{1}{4}$ | $\frac{1}{4}$ | $\frac{1}{4}$ |

Fraction $= \frac{6}{8}$

| $\frac{1}{8}$ | $\frac{1}{8}$ | $\frac{1}{8}$ | $\frac{1}{8}$ | $\frac{1}{8}$ | $\frac{1}{8}$ | $\frac{1}{8}$ | $\frac{1}{8}$ |

$\frac{3}{4}$ and $\frac{6}{8}$ are <u>equivalent fractions.</u>

2 is a <u>common factor of 6 and 8.</u>

$\frac{3}{4}$ is in <u>simplest form.</u>

Practice the Words

Directions Write the vocabulary words on the blanks below. Write a sentence to answer number 6.

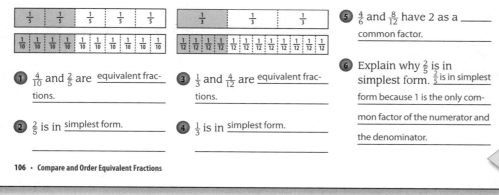

| $\frac{1}{5}$ | $\frac{1}{5}$ | $\frac{1}{5}$ | $\frac{1}{5}$ | $\frac{1}{5}$ |

| $\frac{1}{10}$ | $\frac{1}{10}$ | $\frac{1}{10}$ | $\frac{1}{10}$ | $\frac{1}{10}$ | $\frac{1}{10}$ | $\frac{1}{10}$ | $\frac{1}{10}$ | $\frac{1}{10}$ | $\frac{1}{10}$ |

| $\frac{1}{3}$ | $\frac{1}{3}$ | $\frac{1}{3}$ |

| $\frac{1}{12}$ | $\frac{1}{12}$ | $\frac{1}{12}$ | $\frac{1}{12}$ | $\frac{1}{12}$ | $\frac{1}{12}$ | $\frac{1}{12}$ | $\frac{1}{12}$ | $\frac{1}{12}$ | $\frac{1}{12}$ | $\frac{1}{12}$ | $\frac{1}{12}$ |

❶ $\frac{4}{10}$ and $\frac{2}{5}$ are <u>equivalent frac-</u> <u>tions.</u>

❷ $\frac{2}{5}$ is in <u>simplest form.</u>

❸ $\frac{1}{3}$ and $\frac{4}{12}$ are <u>equivalent frac-</u> <u>tions.</u>

❹ $\frac{1}{3}$ is in <u>simplest form.</u>

❺ $\frac{4}{6}$ and $\frac{8}{12}$ have 2 as a <u>_____</u> common factor.

❻ Explain why $\frac{2}{5}$ is in simplest form. <u>$\frac{2}{5}$ is in simplest</u> <u>form because 1 is the only com-</u> <u>mon factor of the numerator and</u> <u>the denominator.</u>

106 · Compare and Order Equivalent Fractions

A Introduce

BP 4 **Read aloud the Lesson Objective with students.** Then read aloud the Main Idea statement from Lesson 1. Have students discuss with a partner what this Main Idea means in their own words. Review with the class that they have discovered how to find different fractions that name the same amount and how to tell whether fractions are bigger or smaller than others.

Emphasize that the vocabulary in this lesson will help students talk about fractions that name the same amount.

Choose words from the Additional Vocabulary box that you think will be useful. Elicit or provide examples or definitions for these words.

B Teach and Learn

Orally introduce the Essential Vocabulary. Begin by discussing the circles on student worktext page 106. Ask: *How many equal parts are in the first circle?* (6) *What fraction names each equal part?* ($\frac{1}{6}$) *How many equal parts are in the second circle?* (12) *What fraction names each equal part?* ($\frac{1}{12}$) Ask students how many sections in the second circle take up the same amount of space as one section in the first circle. (2)

Highlighted words and phrases may affect student comprehension.

Say: $\frac{4}{12}$ of the circle is the same size as $\frac{2}{6}$ of the circle. $\frac{4}{12}$ and $\frac{2}{6}$ name the same amount. They are equivalent fractions. Write $\frac{2}{6} = \frac{4}{2}$ on the board. Then write *equivalent fractions*. Provide ample practice with the pronunciation of the fraction names.

Write on the board: $\frac{2}{6} = \frac{4}{12}$. Circle $\frac{4}{12}$. Say: *Let's make a list of the factors of 4: 1 × 4, 2 × 2.* Write them on the board. Do the same with the factors of 12: *1 × 12, 2 × 6, 3 × 4.* Rewrite the lists in order:

1, 2, 4

1, 2, 3, 4, 6, 12

Ask: *Which numbers are the same in both lists?* (1, 2, 4) Circle these numbers on the board. Say: *These are the* common factors *of 4 and 12.* Write this phrase on the board and explain that students will learn how to use common factors to find equivalent fractions in their grade-level textbooks.

Now direct attention to the fraction $\frac{2}{6}$. Ask students to work with a partner and find the common factors of 2 and 6. Remind them to find the factors of each number, write them in order, and circle the ones that are the same in both lists. (Students should list 1, 2 as factors of 4, and 1, 2, 3, 6 as factors of 6. They should circle 1 and 2.)

Write the fractions $\frac{1}{3}$ and $\frac{2}{6}$ on the board. Explain: *We can only divide 1 and 3 by 1. 1 is the only common factor of 1 and 3. So we say that $\frac{1}{3}$ is in* simplest form *because the only common factor of the numerator and denominator is 1. $\frac{1}{3}$ can't be changed to a simpler form any more.* Write *simplest form* on the board.

Say the sentence above about simplest form two or three times. Ask students to repeat it after you.

Point out to students that *simplest* here means *the fraction that uses the smallest numbers possible when the numerator and the denominator are divided by the same number.*

Point to the illustration for $\frac{3}{4}$ in the student worktext. Say: *I see that three out of the four sections of this rectangle are shaded. What fraction names the shaded sections?* ($\frac{3}{4}$)

Point to the illustration for $\frac{6}{8}$ and say: *This rectangle is the same size as the other one. I see that six out of eight sections of this rectangle are shaded. What fraction names the shaded section?* ($\frac{6}{8}$)

Ask: *Can you name the two equivalent fractions? Explain why they are equivalent.* ($\frac{3}{4}$ and $\frac{6}{8}$ are equivalent fractions because they name the same amount.)

Say: *Now let's see if one of these fractions is in simplest form. Look at $\frac{6}{8}$. What are common factors of 6 and 8?* (2 and 1) *So, 1 is not the only common factor. Is $\frac{6}{8}$ in simplest form?* (no)

Ask: *What are the common factors of 3 and 4?* (only 1) *The only common factor of 3 and 4 is 1. So, $\frac{3}{4}$ is in simplest form.*

BP 4 **Have students work with a partner.** Have the pairs discuss why these fractions are equivalent and why $\frac{3}{4}$ is in simplest form. Then have partners work together to complete the blanks in Learn the Words.

Write examples of fractions in simplest form and not in simplest form on the board. Have students show thumbs up for fractions in simplest form or thumbs down for fractions not in simplest form.

Read the definitions and examples of the three Essential Vocabulary words on page 106. Then have students complete Vocabulary Cards for these words.

C Review and Practice

Use the Vocabulary Cards in a group activity to help students practice the lesson vocabulary.

- **Make sets of equivalent fractions on index cards.** Include fractions such as $\frac{1}{4} = \frac{2}{8}$, $\frac{2}{4} = \frac{4}{8}$, $\frac{3}{4} = \frac{6}{8}$, etc.

- **BP 4** **Put students in small groups.** Ask them to take turns picking a Vocabulary Card and an equivalent fraction card. Students describe the fractions on the card using the word on the Vocabulary Card and the following sentence frame: _____ *are/are not/is/is not* _____ *because* _____ . For example: $\frac{2}{4}$ *and $\frac{4}{8}$ are equivalent fractions because they name the same amount.* OR $\frac{2}{4}$ *is not in simplest form because 2 is a common factor of 2 and 4.* OR $\frac{1}{4}$ *is in simplest form because 1 is the only common factor of 1 and 4.*

- **Team members decide if each statement is correct.** When errors are made, team members suggest changes. Allow students to continue until all players have had several turns.

Introduce the Practice the Words activity in the student worktext. Make sure students understand the directions. Have students complete the activity individually. Check students' work and assist as necessary.

D Assess and Intervene

Do all students understand the Essential Vocabulary in Practice the Words on page 106? Use the rubric to identify students who need extra support through additional help and the Intervention activity.

Intermediate

☐ At least 3 blanks are correctly completed with vocabulary words.

☐ Explanation shows understanding of concept of simplest form. Sentence may be incomplete.

Example of a sentence a student might write: *Simplest form because 1 only factor common.*

Advanced

☐ At least 4 blanks are correctly completed with vocabulary words.

☐ Explanation is written as a complete sentence and shows clear understanding of the concept of simplest form.

Example of a sentence a student might write: $\frac{4}{5}$ *and $\frac{1}{3}$ are simplest forms because common factor only 1.*

INTERVENTION   5 minutes

If students are still having trouble associating the vocabulary words with their meanings, provide additional word clues. Make the connection between *equivalent* and *equal*: *Equivalent* fractions *are* equal *amounts.* Emphasize that fractions in simplest form use the smallest numbers possible for the numerators and denominators. Use the visual in the student worktext. Say: $\frac{3}{4}$ *and $\frac{6}{8}$ are equivalent fractions. They are equal amounts. $\frac{3}{4}$ is in* simplest form. *We cannot write an equivalent fraction with smaller numbers than $\frac{3}{4}$.*

Use More Language

Objective Describe rules for finding equivalent fractions using the synonyms *other than* and *except*.

30 minutes

Teach this lesson:
- **After** lessons on equivalent fractions and comparing and ordering fractions in the grade-level math textbook
- **Before** students complete the activities on page 107 of the student worktext

You need these materials:
- whiteboards or paper
- Transparency 54
- centimeter cubes

 **Introduce**

Find out what students already know about the words *other than* and *except*. Say: *Take everything off of your desk* except *a pencil. Put everything away* other than *a pencil.* Look around to see if students understand this directive. Then say both sentences again as you model and use gestures.

BP 4 Put students into pairs. Ask them to discuss what they learned about equivalent fractions and simplest form in Lesson 2. Invite a couple of different pairs to summarize their discussion for the class.

Read aloud the Lesson Objective with students. Remind students that finding a fraction's simplest form is one way to find an equivalent fraction. Encourage students to think about what they know about simplest form and how this information might relate to a rule about finding equivalent fractions.

B Teach and Learn

Give students each a whiteboard or a piece of paper. Say: *Can you write all of the one-digit numbers other than zero?* If students don't understand, say: *If I want to write the one-digit numbers other than zero, I can include all one-digit numbers that I can think of, but I can't include zero.*

Give students time to write. Review what they wrote and then write the numbers *1* through *9* on the board. Say: *This list includes all of the numbers from 1 through 9, but it does not include zero. It includes nine one-digit numbers other than zero.*

Tell students that *except* is another way to say *other than*. Provide examples of its use. Say: *These are some one-digit numbers. Are there any one-digit numbers that are missing?* (Yes, zero.) *These are all of the one-digit numbers* except *zero.*

Use More Language

Objective Describe rules for finding equivalent fractions using the synonyms *other than* and *except*.

Learn the Language

I can find equivalent fractions by multiplying both the numerator and denominator by any number **other than** 1 or 0.

I can find equivalent fractions by dividing both the numerator and denominator by any number **except** 1 or 0.

Practice the Language

Directions Follow the directions for numbers 1 and 2. Fill in the blanks for numbers 3 and 4. Answer number 5 in a complete sentence.

1. Cross out all numbers **other than** zero.

2. Cross out all numbers **except** 1.

3. $\frac{1}{3} \times \frac{2}{2} = \frac{2}{6}$ $\frac{1}{3} \times \frac{3}{3} = \frac{3}{9}$

   I can find equivalent fractions by multiplying both the numerator and denominator by any number <u>except (or other than)</u> _____ 1 or 0.

4. $\frac{9}{12} \div \frac{3}{3} = \frac{3}{4}$

   I can find equivalent fractions by dividing both the numerator and denominator by any number <u>other than (or except)</u> _____ 1 or 0.

5. When you multiply to find equivalent fractions, what number can you use? Answer with *except* or *other than*. <u>I can use any number other than (or except) 1 or zero.</u>

 Highlighted words and phrases may affect student comprehension.

Repeat this sentence frame a few times. Encourage students to insert both *except* and *other than* in the pause: *These are all of the one-digit numbers (pause) zero.*

Model how to use these words in rules for finding equivalent fractions. Use the circular arrows and the common factor above or below each arrow to show how to multiply the numerator and denominator, as shown on page 107 of the worktext.

Think Aloud

Write the fraction $\frac{1}{2}$ on the board. Say: *I can find equivalent fractions by multiplying both the numerator and denominator by any number other than zero or 1. What happens if I multiply the numerator and denominator by 1?* (I get the same fraction.) *What happens if I multiply the numerator and denominator by zero?* (I get zero.)

Say: *Let's name some numbers other than zero or 1.* Students should count 2, 3, and so on.

Have students write in their notebooks as you discuss the components of the number sentence $\frac{1}{2} \times \frac{2}{2} = \frac{2}{4}$. Say: *What rule did I use to find the equivalent fractions?* (Multiply the numerator and denominator by a number other than zero or 1.) *What number other than zero or 1 did I use?* (2) *What are the equivalent fractions?* ($\frac{1}{2}$ and $\frac{2}{4}$) Continue with $\frac{1}{2} \times \frac{3}{3} = \frac{3}{6}$.

Say: *If a fraction is not in simplest form, I can divide to find equivalent fractions. I can find equivalent fractions by dividing both the numerator and denominator by any number except 1 or zero. What happens if I divide the numerator and denominator by 1?* (I get the same fraction.) *What happens if I divide the numerator and denominator by zero?* (I can't divide by zero.)

Have students write in their notebooks as you discuss the components of the number sentence:

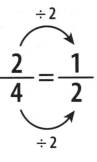

Say: *What rule did I use to find the equivalent fractions?* (Divide the numerator and denominator by any number except 1 or zero.) *What number other than 1 did I use?* (2) *What are the equivalent fractions?* ($\frac{1}{2}$ and $\frac{2}{4}$) Continue in a similar manner with $\frac{4}{8} \div \frac{4}{4} = \frac{1}{2}$, making sure to draw the arrows from numerator to numerator and from denominator to denominator.

Now refer students to Learn the Language on student worktext page 107. Read aloud the text in the speech bubbles. Have students repeat the rules a few times to practice the pronunciation, if needed.

Write the following number sentence on the board:

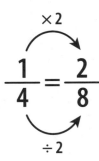

Ask: *What are the two equivalent fractions?* ($\frac{1}{4}$ and $\frac{2}{8}$) *How can you use multiplication to find equivalent fractions?* (Multiply both the numerator and denominator by a number other than zero or 1.) Ask students to state the division rule, using *except,* and identify the equivalent fractions in the number sentence: $\frac{4}{16} \div \frac{4}{4} = \frac{1}{4}$.

C Review and Practice

Use Transparency 54 to review the sentence frames used to describe rules to find equivalent fractions. Write a fraction and an equivalent fraction on the transparency. Ask volunteers to come to the front and write on the transparency the common factor you used to find the equivalent fraction. Then the volunteer uses the sentence frame on the transparency to tell the rule and the common factor. Repeat the process several times. Have students write equivalent fractions, write the common factor, and describe what they did.

BP 4 **Put students in pairs to review and discuss the number sentences in Learn the Language.** Ask one student to read the first rule (multiplication), while the partner explains how this rule is used to find the

equivalent fractions on the right. Partners then switch roles to discuss the division rule for finding equivalent fractions.

Ask pairs to reread the rules to one another and suggest other numbers that, according to the rules, can be used to find equivalent fractions for $\frac{4}{10}$.

Have students work independently to complete the Practice the Language activity on page 107 in the student worktext. Circulate and assess students as they do the activity.

D Assess and Intervene

How well can students use the words *other than* and *except* to describe rules for finding equivalent fractions in Practice the Language on page 107? Use the rubric to identify students who need extra support through additional help and the Intervention activity.

Intermediate

☐ Crosses out the correct numbers in numbers 1 and 2.

☐ Correctly completes the rules with the terms *other than* or *except*.

☐ Answers in a phrase or sentence that includes either *except* or *other than* and the correct numbers.

Advanced

☐ Crosses out the correct numbers in numbers 1 and 2.

☐ Correctly completes the rules with the terms *other than* or *except*.

☐ Answers in a complete sentence that includes either *except* or *other than* and the correct numbers.

INTERVENTION 5 minutes

If students have trouble understanding the terms *other than* and *except*, present a variety of situations that do not include numbers. Place some centimeter cubes of different colors in front of a student. Say: *Pick up all cubes* other than *the yellow ones. Put all cubes in the cup* except *the red ones.* Similar activities can be performed using other manipulatives or common classroom objects.

Solve Math Problems

Objective Identify information you do not need to solve word problems.

---

30 minutes

Teach this lesson:
- **After** lessons on equivalent fractions and comparing and ordering fractions in the grade-level math textbook
- **Before** students complete the activities on page 108 of the student worktext

You need these materials:
- paper
- Worksheet 27

EXTENSION AND ENRICHMENT   10 minutes

Review with students the two ways they have learned for finding equivalent fractions and comparing using a model or using rules. Have students make a poster to illustrate these ways with the same pair of equivalent fractions. On the left, they show a visual model and on the right, they present the mathematical ways. Create a display of students' posters in the classroom.

LESSON
4

Solve Math Problems

Objective Identify information you do not need to solve word problems.

Learn to Solve Problems

Problem   At his birthday party, Oren ate $\frac{1}{2}$ of the cake. His brother Eitan ate $\frac{3}{12}$. His brother Aaron ate $\frac{1}{6}$, and his sister Noa ate $\frac{1}{12}$. Which brother ate the most? Which brother ate the least?

	Think	Write
Step 1:	Read the problem and underline the question(s).	I underlined the questions: <u>Which brother ate the most? Which brother ate the least?</u>
Step 2:	A. Circle the facts. B. Which facts do you need to solve the problem? Which fact(s) do you not need? C. Cross off the fact(s) you don't need.	A. I circled: **Oren ate** $\frac{1}{2}$; **Eitan ate** $\frac{3}{12}$; **Aaron ate** $\frac{1}{6}$ and **Noa ate** $\frac{1}{12}$. B. I need the amount the brothers ate. I don't need to know how much Noa ate. She is a sister. C. So I will cross off $\frac{1}{12}$.
Step 3:	Solve the problem. Answer the question(s) in complete sentences.	Now I can solve the problem. I compare $\frac{1}{2}$, $\frac{3}{12}$, and $\frac{1}{6}$. $\frac{1}{2} > \frac{3}{12}$ and $\frac{3}{12} > \frac{1}{6}$. Oren ate the most and Aaron ate the least.

Practice Solving Math Problems

Directions Use steps 1 to 3 above to solve the problems below on a separate sheet of paper. Write your answers in complete sentences.

1. On a math test, Max got $\frac{4}{5}$ of the problems correct. Lia got $\frac{9}{10}$ of the problems correct and Raul got $\frac{8}{10}$ of the problems correct. Who got more problems correct, Lia or Max? Lia got more problems correct.

2. Look at the recipe for fruit salad below. Are there more blueberries or raisins in the salad?

Fruit Salad	There are more blueberries in the salad.
1/3 cup raisins 3/4 cup apple slices 1/2 cup blueberries	

3. Look at the recipe for fruit salad in question 2. Abiel has $\frac{5}{8}$ of a cup of apple slices and $\frac{5}{8}$ of a cup of blueberries. Does he have enough apple slices to make the fruit salad?   Abiel does not have enough apples slices. $\frac{5}{8} < \frac{3}{4}$

4. Elsa put some flowers in a vase. $\frac{1}{2}$ of the flowers are roses, $\frac{2}{8}$ of the flowers are tulips, and $\frac{4}{16}$ of the flowers are daisies. Are there more tulips or daisies in the vase? There are the same amount of tulips and daisies.

A **Introduce**

Read aloud the Lesson Objective with students.

BP 4 **Divide the class into an equal number of small groups.** Explain that the class will be gathering information to make a list of things needed to take on a camping trip.

Give half of the groups a piece of paper telling them to suggest items that are *necessary* for a camping trip. Give the other half of the groups a piece of paper telling them to suggest items that are *not necessary* for a camping trip. Have students work on their lists with their group. Tell students not to let the other groups know which type of list they are making.

Assemble the class back together. Write two headings on the board: *Needed* and *Not Needed*. Ask volunteers from each group to name items on their lists. Have students from other groups suggest whether each item belongs on the *Needed* list or the *Not Needed* list. Record the items on the board under the headings as you go through each group's list.

Explain to students that math problems usually include the information you need to solve the problem. But sometimes they also include other information that you don't need. It is important to look at all of the information in the problem and decide if it is necessary information or not necessary.

Highlighted words and phrases may affect student comprehension.

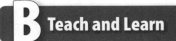

B Teach and Learn

Have students open their student work-texts to page 108. Have students refer to the page as you walk through the problem in Learn to Solve Problems.

Write the problem on the board and read it aloud. Then model solving the problem by thinking aloud.

Think Aloud

Write Step 1. Read aloud the text in the *Think* column. Say: *The problem asks two questions: Which brother ate the most? Which brother ate the least?* Underline the questions in the problem on the board.

Write Step 2. Read aloud the text in *A*, *B*, and *C.* Say: *I need to look at all of the information in the problem. Then I can decide what information I need and what information I don't need.* Circle the facts as you say: *Oren ate $\frac{1}{2}$, Eitan ate $\frac{3}{12}$, Aaron ate $\frac{1}{6}$, and Noa ate $\frac{1}{12}$. The questions I need to answer are which brother ate the most and which brother ate the least.*

Ask: *Do I need to know how much Oren ate?* (yes) *So, I won't cross off this information. Do I need to know how much Eitan ate?* (yes) *I'll leave this information in the problem. Do I need to know how much Aaron ate?* (yes) *So this information stays, too. Do I need to know how much Noa ate?* (no) *No, I don't need this information because Noa is a sister and I only need to find out which brother ate the most and which brother ate the least. So I'll cross off this information.* Cross off this fact in the problem on the board.

Write Step 3. Read the text aloud. Say: *I have the facts I need to use. Now what do I have to do to solve the problem? I can compare the fractions to solve the problem. I have to find the greatest fraction and the smallest fraction.*

Ask students to name the fractions that must be compared to solve the problem. Write on the board: $\frac{1}{2}, \frac{3}{12}, \frac{1}{6}$. Discuss with students two ways to order the fractions from smallest to greatest: use fraction strips, models, or drawings; change the fractions to equivalent fractions with the same denominator and compare the numerators. Demonstrate each way.

- **Have students identify the greatest and the least fractions.** ($\frac{1}{2}$ is the greatest; $\frac{1}{6}$ is the least) Then have them answer the questions in complete sentences. (Oren ate the most cake. Aaron ate the least.)

BP 4 **Distribute copies of Worksheet 27.** Have students work with a partner to first discuss and then solve the problems. For the first problem, one partner reads the steps and the other does the writing. For the second problem, partners reverse roles. In both problems, partners discuss what to do before writing.

Walk around the room and observe partners' work. Assist as necessary.

C Review and Practice

Review the problem-solving process from the student worktext. Go through the problems students solved on Worksheet 27.

Invite partners to share their solutions. One student reads the text in the *Think* column. The partner reads what he or she wrote in the corresponding *Write* column. Encourage other students to comment about the ideas presented or explain alternative strategies used.

Have students individually complete Practice Solving Math Problems in the student worktext. Circulate and assess how well they can analyze the information in the problems to determine necessary and unnecessary facts.

D Assess and Intervene

Are all students able to identify the unnecessary information and then solve problems, based on Practice Solving Math Problems on page 108? Use the rubric to identify students who need extra support through additional help and the Intervention activity.

Intermediate

☐ At least 3 of the problems are solved correctly.

☐ Answers are written in phrases or sentences and answer the question that was asked, but may include some errors.

Example of a sentence a student might write: *Lia not Max more problems correct.*

Advanced

☐ All 4 problems are solved correctly.

☐ Answers are written in complete sentences and answer the question that was asked, with minimal errors.

Example of a sentence a student might write: *Lia got more of problems correct.*

INTERVENTION 10 minutes

If students have difficulty determining what information is needed and what information is not needed, suggest that they first think about what is happening in the problem. Have students write the problem from page 108 at the top of a sheet of paper. Have students look carefully at the question. Does it have any clues that suggest some facts are important and some are not? Have students highlight important facts in the problem. For the problem in Learn to Solve Problems, students will highlight *brother*, *most,* and *least* in the questions. Underneath the problem, have students make a list of all the facts in the problem. Go through each fact individually and ask: *Does this information help you find out which brother ate the most? Does this information help you find out which brother ate the least?* Have students take notes on their list to help them decide which facts help them answer the questions.

Prerequisite Background Knowledge
- Concepts of fractions
- Concepts of multiplication and division

Understand the Main Idea

Objective Tell if a fraction is greater than, equal to, or less than 1.

30 minutes

Teach this lesson:
- **Before** introducing material on mixed numbers and improper fractions in the grade-level math textbook
- **Before** students complete the activities on page 109 of the student worktext

You need these materials:
- chart paper
- scissors, construction paper
- 12-inch rulers
- Transparency 55

BP 5 **ELL BEST PRACTICE #5:** Higher-Order Thinking

English language learners are just as capable of using higher-order thinking skills as any other students, but are hindered by their inability to express their thinking in English. As students explore mixed numbers and improper fractions, do not simply ask students to recall information. Instead, encourage them to make connections and to formulate questions of their own to explore the differences in these two types of fractions. As students recognize that their language skills need not keep them from thinking critically, they will be more likely to use more complex language and to describe more complex ideas as well.

Throughout this module, when you see **BP 5**, this is an example of higher-order thinking.

Module 28: Mixed Numbers and Improper Fractions

Understand the Main Idea

Objective Tell if a fraction is greater than, equal to, or less than 1.

LESSON **1**

Learn the Main Idea

Some fractions show less than 1 whole.	Jon shades $\frac{2}{3}$. He shades less than 1 whole triangle.	The caterpillar is $\frac{3}{4}$ inches long. It is less than 1 whole inch.	
Some fractions show more than 1 whole.	Jon shades $\frac{4}{3}$. He shades more than 1 whole triangle.	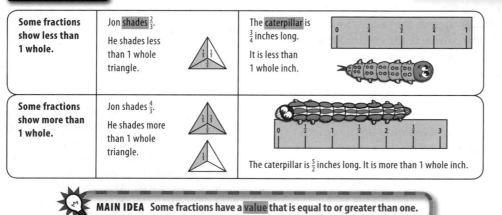 The caterpillar is $\frac{5}{2}$ inches long. It is more than 1 whole inch.	

MAIN IDEA Some fractions have a value that is equal to or greater than one.

Practice Applying the Main Idea

Directions Circle *less than 1, equal to 1,* or *more than 1* to tell how big the fraction is. Answer question 4 on a separate sheet of paper.

1

Anya shades $\frac{4}{4}$. $\frac{4}{4}$ is. . .

less than 1 whole square
(equal to 1 whole square)
more than 1 whole square

2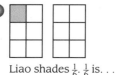

Liao shades $\frac{1}{6}$. $\frac{1}{6}$ is. . .

(less than 1 whole rectangle)
equal to 2 whole rectangles
more than 1 whole rectangle

3

Tarik measures $1\frac{1}{2}$ cups of water. $1\frac{1}{2}$ is. . .

less than 1 whole cup
equal to 1 whole cup
(more than 1 whole cup)

4 Write a sentence to explain how you knew the answer to question 3. Possible answer: $1\frac{1}{2}$ is higher than the mark for 1 on the side of the cup, so it is more.

A Introduce

Write the word *fraction* on the board and read it aloud. Build background knowledge by having students write for two or three minutes, telling what they know about fractions. Encourage them to use numbers, words, and pictures.

Ask students to share their work with a partner. Then ask them to choose one idea or example that was part of their partner's work. Ask them to share that idea with the class, beginning: *Leo says . . .* Record highlights of this discussion on the board.

Read aloud the Lesson Objective with students. Explain that students have learned a lot about fractions that are less than 1. Point out examples that students used in their descriptions of fractions or provide examples of your own. Stress, however, that some fractions can be more than 1 or equal to 1. Ask students if they have ever seen or used a fraction that was greater than 1. Encourage students to talk about these fractions with the same partner.

Highlighted words and phrases may affect student comprehension.

Call students' attention to the first of two rows of art and text at the top of page 109 of the student worktext. Read aloud the captions for the two pictures. Have students study the two pictures on their own.

- **BP 5 Ask students to explain the scenarios in the top two panels to a partner.** Ask students to discuss how the two situations are alike and how they are different. Circulate through the room, helping students express their ideas in sentences.

Move on to the bottom set of pictures. Read aloud the captions. Emphasize that these pictures show fractions that are greater than 1 whole.

- **BP 5 Have students work with a partner.** Ask them to make a list of questions about the pictures and the fractions used in the descriptions. Collect the questions and write them on chart paper. Revisit them as students work through the lessons in this module, helping them answer as many of the questions as possible.

Read aloud the Main Idea with students. Explain that a *value greater than 1* means that the fraction shows more than 1 whole.

B Teach and Learn

BP 5 Give each student a sheet of construction paper and a pair of scissors. Ask students to predict what they will be doing with these materials. If they have trouble guessing, remind them of the discussion they had in Section A, above. Elicit that they will be making fractions.

- **Have students fold their sheets of paper into fourths.** Have them label each section $\frac{1}{4}$.

- **BP 5 Ask students to talk to a partner about what the 1 and the 4 mean in the fraction $\frac{1}{4}$.** Establish that the 4 is the denominator, which tells how many equal parts, and that the 1 is the numerator, which tells how many parts are being chosen. On the board write $\frac{1}{4}$ and circle and label *numerator* and *denominator*.

- **Have students cut the fractional parts along the creases and put them in a pile.** Then have them place $\frac{1}{4}$ in front of them. Repeat with $\frac{2}{4}$, then with $\frac{3}{4}$. (Be sure pieces do not overlap or stack.) Write these fractions on the board, or have students tell

you how to write them. Ask if the fractions are less than a whole or greater than a whole. (less) Have students tell you how they know.

- **Have students place $\frac{4}{4}$ in front of them.** Ask what $\frac{4}{4}$ represent. (whole) Ask students how they know.

- **Explain that students will now model a fraction that is greater than 1.** Have them combine their fractional pieces into a stack with those of their partner. Then challenge each pair to display $\frac{5}{4}$. Have them arrange the pieces so they recreate one whole sheet of paper and an extra fourth beside it. Ask students how they know this fraction is greater than 1 whole.

- **Challenge partners to use their fractional pieces to model another fraction that is greater than 1.** Have pairs compare answers with another pair.

Explain that fractions equal to 1 or greater than 1 are also used in measurement. Distribute 12-inch rulers to each pair. Check students' understanding of rulers by having students find the 1-inch mark, the 2-inch mark, and the 10-inch mark.

- **Ask students to work with a partner to find the half-inch mark.** Model how to find the mark if needed. Say: *This mark shows $\frac{1}{2}$ inch. Is $\frac{1}{2}$ inch more or less than 1 whole inch?* Draw out that it is less.

- **Repeat, having students find the $1\frac{1}{2}$ inch mark.** Point out that this mark is halfway between the 1-inch mark and the 2-inch mark. Elicit that $1\frac{1}{2}$ inches is greater than 1 whole inch. Repeat with $2\frac{1}{2}$ inches and $3\frac{1}{2}$ inches.

Wrap up this part of the lesson by having students return to the second set of pictures on page 109 of their student worktexts. Have them talk about these pictures and what they show. Record highlights of their discussions.

C Review and Practice

Display Transparency 55. Go through the pictures one at a time with students. For each image, ask: *Does this show more than 1 whole, the same as 1 whole, or less than 1 whole? How do you know?* Encourage students to talk about their ideas with partners and then share their answers with the class. Help students create a list of

strategies for telling whether a given fraction is greater than, equal to, or less than 1.

Read aloud the directions for Practice Applying the Main Idea on page 109. Point out that the assignment is the same as in the previous activity, but that students will need to work on these problems independently. Explain that the last item asks students to write a full sentence.

D Assess and Intervene

Can students tell whether fractions are more than, equal to, or less than 1, based on Practice Applying the Main Idea on page 109? Use the rubric to identify students who need extra support through additional help and the Intervention activity.

Intermediate

- ☐ Correctly answers 2–3 questions.
- ☐ Writes an appropriate phrase or sentence; errors do not interfere with meaning.

    Example of a sentence a student might write: *Is over line with 1.*

Advanced

- ☐ Correctly answers all 3 questions.
- ☐ Writes an appropriate sentence with few or no significant errors.

    Example of a sentence a student might write: *Water is over 1 cup line, so is greater than 1 whole.*

INTERVENTION — 5 minutes

If students are struggling to understand fractions that are greater than, equal to, or less than 1, use visual cues. Have students refer to the Practice section in their worktexts to find wholes in the pictures and circle or otherwise mark them to show that all the pieces are being counted. For example, students can circle the left-hand square for item 1, or draw a heavy line across the 1-cup mark for item 3. Provide other examples of fractions that are equal to or greater than 1 and have students draw them.

Learn the Vocabulary

Objective   Talk and write about fractions that are greater than or equal to 1, using the vocabulary words.

45 minutes

Teach this lesson:
- **Before** introducing material on improper fractions and mixed numbers in the grade-level math textbook
- **Before** students complete the activities on page 110 of the student worktext

You need these materials:
- crackers
- Vocabulary Cards
- Worksheet 28
- red and blue crayons or colored pencils

Lesson Vocabulary

Essential Vocabulary

mixed number	improper fraction

Additional Vocabulary

| quotient | rename _____ as _____ |
| numerator* | denominator*   remainder* |

* - Terms that have Vocabulary Cards.

 **Introduce**

Write the numbers $1\frac{3}{4}$ and $\frac{7}{4}$ on the board. Read them aloud (one and three fourths, seven fourths) and have students repeat the numbers. Emphasize proper pronunciation of *fourths*; be sure students are not saying *fours*.

BP 5 **Ask students to form small groups.** Have them talk to their groups about the two numbers on the board. Ask them to explain how the numbers are alike and how they are different. Encourage them to draw diagrams or other pictures to help them talk about the numbers. Assign one member of each group to record highlights of the conversation. Then have groups share what they discussed.

Note some of the important words about fractions that students used in their conversations. Write these words on the board and read them aloud. Say: *Words such as part and* whole *are very useful when you are talking about fractions.*

Explain that students can use other important terms to talk about fractions that are greater than 1. Write the phrases *mixed number* and *improper fraction* on the board. Read them aloud and have students repeat.

Touch the number $1\frac{3}{4}$ and say: *This is a mixed number.* Touch the number $\frac{7}{4}$ and say: *This is an improper fraction.* Do not explain what these are just yet, but tell students that they will be learning about mixed numbers and improper fractions in this lesson.

Learn the Vocabulary

Objective   Talk and write about fractions that are greater than or equal to 1 using the vocabulary words.

Learn the Words

Directions Write the correct numbers in the four blanks below.

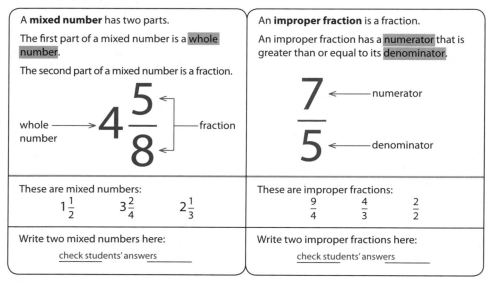

A **mixed number** has two parts.

The first part of a mixed number is a whole number.

The second part of a mixed number is a fraction.

$$4\frac{5}{8}$$

whole number ⟶   ⟵ fraction

These are mixed numbers:

$$1\frac{1}{2} \qquad 3\frac{2}{4} \qquad 2\frac{1}{3}$$

Write two mixed numbers here:
check students' answers

An **improper fraction** is a fraction.

An improper fraction has a numerator that is greater than or equal to its denominator.

$$\frac{7}{5}$$

⟵ numerator

⟵ denominator

These are improper fractions:

$$\frac{9}{4} \qquad \frac{4}{3} \qquad \frac{2}{2}$$

Write two improper fractions here:
check students' answers

Practice the Words

Directions Color the boxes red that show a mixed number. Color the boxes blue that show an improper fraction. The red boxes will spell out a secret message. Answer question 2 in a complete sentence.

1

red $1\frac{1}{2}$	blue $\frac{7}{4}$	red $2\frac{1}{10}$	blue $\frac{8}{5}$	red $6\frac{1}{3}$	blue $\frac{10}{3}$	red $9\frac{1}{8}$
red $4\frac{5}{8}$	blue $\frac{3}{2}$	red $8\frac{1}{3}$	blue $\frac{9}{9}$	red $9\frac{3}{4}$	blue $\frac{9}{4}$	red $7\frac{6}{10}$
red $2\frac{3}{4}$	red $4\frac{1}{4}$	red $4\frac{3}{4}$	blue $\frac{10}{2}$	red $3\frac{9}{10}$	blue $\frac{6}{2}$	red $2\frac{4}{5}$
red $6\frac{1}{2}$	blue $\frac{3}{3}$	red $5\frac{2}{5}$	blue $\frac{8}{4}$	red $4\frac{5}{7}$	blue $\frac{8}{8}$	blue $\frac{6}{4}$
red $8\frac{1}{10}$	blue $\frac{10}{5}$	red $7\frac{1}{8}$	blue $\frac{12}{6}$	red $3\frac{2}{5}$	blue $\frac{10}{10}$	red $1\frac{1}{9}$

2 Describe how mixed numbers and improper fractions are alike.

Possible answer: They both show fractions that are
greater than 1.

_____

_____

_____

_____

Highlighted words and phrases may affect student comprehension.

Read aloud the Lesson Objective with students.

Choose words from the Additional Vocabulary box that you think will be useful. Elicit or provide examples or definitions for all the words you have chosen.

B Teach and Learn

Call students' attention to the two numbers on the board, $1\frac{3}{4}$ and $\frac{7}{4}$. Ask students to recall which is the mixed number ($1\frac{3}{4}$) and which the improper fraction ($\frac{7}{4}$). Then play a quick game with students to give them practice in using these terms. Touch $\frac{7}{4}$ and have students say *improper fraction*. Then touch $1\frac{3}{4}$ and have students say *mixed number*. Continue as above, varying the order in which you touch the two numbers.

Write $3\frac{2}{3}$ on the board. Remind students that they haven't yet learned the definitions of mixed numbers and improper fractions, but tell them that they can probably guess whether $3\frac{2}{3}$ is a mixed number or an improper fraction.

- **BP 5** **Have students make guesses and explain their thinking to a partner using the following sentence frame:** *I think it's a mixed number/an improper fraction because _____.* Elicit that $3\frac{2}{3}$ is a mixed number. Repeat with the improper fraction $\frac{9}{2}$.

Call students' attention to the information on mixed numbers in the box on the top left of page 110 in the student worktext. Read the text aloud or have a volunteer do so. Ask students what it means to *mix* things together. Stress that a *mixed* number combines two parts: a whole number part and a fraction part.

Explain that a whole number is a number you use to count, such as 1, 2, 3, and so on. Say: *A mixed number tells about a number of whole things and some more parts left over.*

Use scored crackers to model the mixed number $2\frac{1}{2}$. Write $2\frac{1}{2}$ on the board. Point out that the 2 is written bigger than the $\frac{1}{2}$. Have one student hold up two whole crackers. Have a second student hold up a half of a third cracker. Indicate the first student and say: *[Maritza] has two whole crackers. Two is the whole number part of the mixed number.* Then indicate the second student and say:

[Lee] has $\frac{1}{2}$ of a cracker. $\frac{1}{2}$ is the fraction part of the mixed number. Repeat with other examples, such as $3\frac{1}{2}$ and $1\frac{1}{4}$.

Call students' attention to the three examples of mixed numbers in the Learn the Words box. Help students read the mixed numbers chorally; be sure they include the word *and* between the whole number and fractional parts of the number. Then have them write two mixed numbers of their own. Ask them to talk about their mixed numbers with a partner.

Move on to the information about improper fractions in the first box on the right. Read the text aloud. Help students remind each other what the numerator and the denominator of a fraction are and what they mean. Point out that students are accustomed to working with fractions in which the denominator is greater than the numerator, but that this is not true for improper fractions. Tell students that improper fractions are also sometimes called *fractions greater than 1.*

Call students' attention to the three examples of improper fractions in the Learn the Words box. Ask students how they know these are improper fractions. (because the numerator is greater than or equal to the denominator) Then have students write two improper fractions of their own and talk about them with a partner.

BP 5 **Sum up the discussion by returning to $1\frac{3}{4}$ and $\frac{7}{4}$, the numbers you wrote on the board at the beginning of the lesson.** Ask students to talk again about how the numbers are alike and different, using the terms *mixed number* and *improper fraction* and other concepts they have learned in this section of the lesson.

Have students complete the Vocabulary Cards for the words in this module.

C Review and Practice

Give each pair a copy of Worksheet 28. Have students read the statements. Have them determine whether each statement is true or false. Then have them compare their answers with another pair and discuss any disagreements. Go over the answers with the class.

Call students' attention to Practice the Words at the bottom of page 110. Read the directions aloud with students. Then have them complete the section on their own. Point out that the last item asks them to write a complete sentence. Check students' work.

D Assess and Intervene

Can students use and understand *mixed number* and *improper fraction*, based on Learn the Words on page 110? Use the rubric to identify students who need extra support through additional help and the Intervention activity.

Intermediate

- ☐ Shades the diagram and makes no more than 2 errors.
- ☐ Writes a phrase or sentence that includes the idea of greater than 1, with no errors that interfere with comprehension.

Advanced

- ☐ Shades the whole diagram correctly.
- ☐ Writes a complete sentence that includes the idea of greater than 1, with minimal errors.

INTERVENTION 5 minutes

If students have trouble distinguishing mixed numbers from improper fractions, have them use colored pencils to help distinguish between the two. Have students write the mixed number $3\frac{1}{2}$. (Be sure they write the 3 so it is larger than the $\frac{1}{2}$.) Then have them shade the 3 with a colored pencil, indicating that it is a whole number and not a fraction. Repeat with other mixed numbers. Many students will respond well to this extra visual cue.

Lesson

3

Use More Language

Objective Give and follow commands to rename improper fractions and mixed numbers.

30 minutes

Teach this lesson:
- **After** students complete the material on mixed numbers and improper fractions in the grade-level math textbook
- **Before** students complete the activities on page 111 of the student worktext

You need these materials:
- rulers
- fraction strips
- Transparency 56

EXTENSION AND ENRICHMENT
10 minutes

Have students use rulers to measure the lengths of various objects in the room. Instruct them to measure in inches and round each length to the nearest eighth or fourth inch. Then have them write each length as a mixed number. Ask them to talk about the lengths and put them in order from largest to smallest when they are finished.

Use More Language

LESSON 3

Objective Give and follow commands to rename improper fractions and mixed numbers.

Learn the Language

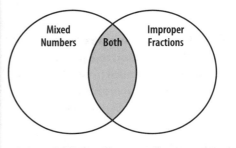

Write the improper fraction $\frac{4}{3}$ as a mixed number.

1 whole and 1 third left over $\frac{4}{3} = 1\frac{1}{3}$

Change the mixed number $1\frac{1}{2}$ to an improper fraction.

3 halves in all $1\frac{1}{2} = \frac{3}{2}$

Rewrite the mixed number $1\frac{7}{8}$ as an improper fraction.

1 whole = 8 eighths
8 eighths + 7 eighths = 15 eighths
$1\frac{7}{8} = \frac{15}{8}$

Rename the improper fraction $\frac{7}{2}$ as a mixed number.

$\frac{7}{2} = \frac{2}{2} + \frac{2}{2} + \frac{2}{2} + \frac{1}{2}$
$\frac{7}{2} = 1 + 1 + 1 + \frac{1}{2}$
$\frac{7}{2} = 3\frac{1}{2}$

Commands
Write _____ as _____.   Change _____ to _____.
Rewrite _____ as _____.   Rename _____ as _____.

Practice the Language

Directions Solve the problems below. Write your answer to number 5 on a separate sheet of paper.

1. Write the fraction $\frac{7}{4}$ as a mixed number.
$1\frac{3}{4}$

2. Rename the mixed number $1\frac{4}{5}$ as an improper fraction.
$\frac{9}{5}$

3. Rewrite the fraction $\frac{8}{3}$ as a mixed number.
$2\frac{2}{3}$

4. Change the mixed number $3\frac{1}{4}$ to an improper fraction.
$1\frac{3}{4}$

5.
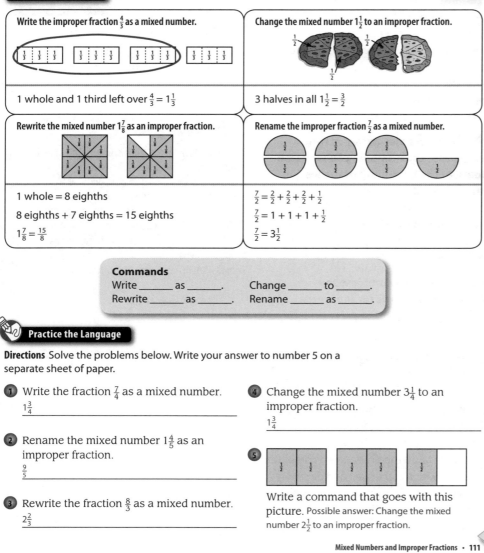
Write a command that goes with this picture. Possible answer: Change the mixed number $2\frac{1}{2}$ to an improper fraction.

Mixed Numbers and Improper Fractions · 111

A Introduce

Draw a Venn diagram on the board. Label the left circle *Mixed Numbers* and the right circle *Improper Fractions*. Label the center area *Both*. See the model below.

Mixed Numbers   Both   Improper Fractions

- **Have volunteers read aloud the labels.**

- **BP 5 Have students use the diagram to help them compare mixed numbers and improper fractions.** Have them say a fact about fractions greater than 1, then tell whether the statement belongs in the left circle, the right circle, or both. For example, the statement *One part is a whole number and the other part is a fraction.* belongs in the left circle only, while *It can be greater than 1.* should go in the intersection of the circles. Write suggestions in bullet form in the appropriate places as they are given.

Explain that this lesson will help students think about the connections between improper fractions and mixed numbers. Then read aloud the Lesson Objective with students. Explain that you give a command when you tell someone to do something.

Highlighted words and phrases may affect student comprehension.

Teach and Learn

Write the mixed number $1\frac{1}{2}$ **on the board.** Next to it, write the improper fraction $\frac{3}{2}$.

- **BP 5** **Ask students whether these numbers are equal or not.** Then have students explain to a partner how they know. Encourage them to draw diagrams or pictures to illustrate their thinking. Elicit that the numbers are equal.

- **Have students work with a partner to list other mixed numbers and improper fractions that are equal, such as** $1\frac{1}{5}$ **and** $\frac{6}{5}$ **or** $2\frac{1}{4}$ **and** $\frac{9}{4}$.

- **Say:** *Sometimes it is best to use a mixed number and sometimes it is best to use an _____.* Pause and allow students to complete the sentence with the phrase *improper fraction*.

- **Then say:** *Some words and phrases tell you to change a mixed number to an improper fraction or to change an improper fraction to a _____.* Pause and allow students to complete the sentence with the phrase *mixed number*.

Call students' attention to the top left section of the Learn the Language box on page 111. Have a volunteer read the first sentence aloud. Point out that this is an example of a command since students are being told to do something.

- **Have students circle the word** *write* **and the word** *as.* Explain that when you *write* something *as* something else, you *change it into* that thing. Write the phrase *write _____ as* on the board.

- **BP 5** **Highlight the drawing of the fraction strips and the explanation below it.** Have students use fraction strips to model $\frac{4}{3}$. Then have them place three of the thirds together and replace them with a whole strip to model $1\frac{1}{3}$. Have students explain to a partner how they know that the two amounts are equal.

- **Summarize by saying:** *We had the improper fraction* $\frac{4}{3}$. *We wrote that fraction as* $1\frac{1}{3}$. *We changed it to a mixed number. Which words told us to change it?* Elicit that the words *write _____ as* told students to change the improper fraction to a mixed number.

Continue a similar process with the other three boxes. Have students circle the words that require them to turn each improper fraction to a mixed number or vice versa. Spend as much time as you need on the examples and how to make the conversions, but focus most heavily on the vocabulary *change _____ to, rewrite _____ as,* and *rename _____ as.*

- **Read aloud the sentence frames below the Learn the Language box with students.** Remind them that all four expressions mean the same thing.

Have students work with a partner. Instruct one member of each pair to use fraction strips or to draw a picture showing a fraction that is greater than 1. Have them write the amount as a mixed number or an improper fraction below the drawing or the strips. Check students' work.

- **Next, have students give their partners a command such as:** *Write this mixed number as an improper fraction.* or *Rename this improper fraction as a mixed number.* Be sure they use one of the four expressions on the board. The partner should carry out the command. Encourage them to sum up their work by saying *I wrote the mixed number as an improper fraction.* or *I changed the improper fraction to a mixed number.*

Continue, having students take turns giving and carrying out commands. Circulate through the room, offering help as needed and checking how well students can use the sentence frames on the board to formulate their ideas.

Discuss the activity with students when all pairs have had the opportunity to take several turns. Ask students what parts of the activity they thought were easy and what parts they thought were hard. Repeat, asking students to talk about what they liked and didn't like about the activity. End this section of the lesson by having students write a number from one to five to indicate how good they think they are at carrying out commands like these, with one being *not good at all* and five being *excellent.* Check students' self-ratings and make a note to offer extra help to those who gave themselves a one or a two.

Review and Practice

Display Transparency 56. Have students tell which commands ask them to change a mixed number to a fraction, or vice versa, and which do not.

Call students' attention to Practice the Language at the bottom of page 111. Point out that the last item requires students to write a command of their own. Tell them not to use the student worktext unless they need it for extra support.

Assess and Intervene

Can students write and follow the commands introduced in this lesson based on Practice the Language on page 111? Use the rubric to identify students who need extra support through additional help and the Intervention activity.

Intermediate

- ☐ Successfully follows at least 3 of the commands.
- ☐ Uses a sentence frame to write an appropriate command.

Advanced

- ☐ Successfully follows all of the commands.
- ☐ Writes an appropriate command without the use of a sentence frame.

INTERVENTION 10 minutes

If students struggle to convert fractions greater than 1, have them use fraction strips or drawings to model the mixed numbers or improper fractions in Practice the Language. For example, have students use seven $\frac{1}{4}$ fraction strips to model $\frac{7}{4}$. Then show how they can combine four of the strips to equal 1 whole, thus renaming the improper fraction as *1 whole and* $\frac{3}{4}$, or $1\frac{3}{4}$. Continue with other examples.

Lesson

4

Solve Math Problems

Objective Solve multi-step problems that use fractions greater than 1.

---

30 minutes

Teach this lesson:
- **After** completing the work on fractions greater than 1 in the grade-level math textbooks
- **Before** students complete the activities on page 112 of the student worktext

You need these materials:
- chart paper
- measuring cup
- fraction strips
- index cards

LESSON
4

Solve Math Problems

Objective Solve multi-step problems that use fractions greater than 1.

Learn to Solve Problems

| Problem | Lisette wants to make a special kind of bread. She needs $1\frac{2}{3}$ cups of flour. She has $\frac{3}{2}$ cups of flour. Does she have enough flour to make the bread? |

	Think	Write
Step 1:	Read the problem. Underline the question. What do you need to do?	I need to find out if Lisette has enough flour.
Step 2:	Circle the facts. Plan what you need to do.	I need to compare $1\frac{2}{3}$ and $\frac{3}{2}$.
Step 3:	Solve. Rewrite mixed numbers or improper fractions if you need to.	Rewrite the improper fraction as a mixed number: $\frac{3}{2} = 1\frac{1}{2}$. Compare the mixed numbers: $1\frac{2}{3} > 1\frac{1}{2}$. Lisette does not have enough flour.

Practice Solving Math Problems

Directions Follow steps 1 to 3 above to solve the word problems below. Solve each problem on a separate sheet of paper. Write the answers in complete sentences.

1. Miko walks $1\frac{3}{10}$ miles before lunch. After lunch, he walks $\frac{11}{10}$ miles. Does he walk more miles before lunch or after lunch? Miko walks more miles before lunch than after lunch.

2. Sanjay's red pencil is $5\frac{1}{2}$ inches long. His blue pencil is $\frac{10}{2}$ inches long. Which pencil is longer? Sanjay's red pencil is longer.

3. Han and Ismael each find rocks near a river. Han's rock weighs $1\frac{4}{5}$ pounds. Ismael's rock weighs $\frac{14}{10}$ pounds. Whose rock weighs more? Han's rock weighs more than Ismael's.

4. Falina's pet cats drink $\frac{7}{4}$ cups of water each day. Falina pours $1\frac{6}{8}$ cups of water into her cats' bowls. Will that be enough water for the cats? It will be enough water for the cats.

112 · Mixed Numbers and Improper Fractions

A Introduce

Have students look through their grade-level math textbooks to find word problems that use fractions greater than 1. Have them discuss these problems with a partner. If the problems have been done in class or as homework, have students explain how they solved them. If the problems haven't been completed, have students brainstorm ways of solving them.

Ask students to share problem solving-strategies that they used or would think about using. Write these ideas on chart paper. Accept general strategies, such as: *draw a picture* or *use logical thinking*. Also accept strategies that are specific to fractions, such as *compare the numerators* or *decide if the number is a mixed number or an improper fraction*. Read the list of strategies aloud with students. Display the chart in the classroom.

Read aloud the Lesson Objective with students. Point out that a *multi-step* problem asks students to do two or more things in order to find the answer. Explain that students will learn some strategies for solving multi-step problems in this lesson.

B Teach and Learn

Tell students that the first problem in the student worktext is about cooking. Have students turn to page 112 in the student worktext. Help build background by asking students if they have ever cooked. Ask: *Who likes to cook? What have you cooked? Tell us about a time when you helped cook something.* Have students answer in sentences beginning *Once I cooked ____.* or *I like to cook ____.*

Ask students what tools they need for cooking. Help them express their ideas in complete sentences, such as: *You need a stove/pan/bowl to cook.* If students mention measuring cups, highlight these on the list; if not, add them to the list yourself.

Highlighted words and phrases may affect student comprehension.

Display a measuring cup, preferably one with fractional markings on the side. Identify it as a measuring cup and say: *You use this measuring cup to tell how much to use when you cook.* Explain that cooking measurements are often given in whole numbers, such as *2 cups of raisins,* but that measurements can also be given in mixed numbers, such as $1\frac{1}{2}$ *cups of milk.*

Read the sample problem aloud with students. Then walk students through the Learn to Solve Problems box.

Read aloud Step 1. Say: *I need to find the question so I can underline it. How do I know where to find the question?* Elicit that questions in word problems usually come at the end of the problem statement and that they always end with a question mark.

- **Have students touch the question.** Ask them to check their responses with a partner. Point out that the question is already underlined in the student worktext. Remind students that they will have to do their own underlining as they work through other word problems.

- **Be sure students comprehend the question by asking:** *What do I need to find out?* Elicit that you need to find out if Lisette has enough flour to make the bread. Point out that the question has already been written as a statement.

Continue to Step 2. Read it aloud. Say: *I need to circle the facts in the problem. In many word problems, the facts are numbers.* Point out that this problem includes units, so students should circle them, too. Have students identify the facts in the problem.

- **BP 5** Say: *Next, I need to make a plan.* Ask students why it is wise to make a plan. If planning appears on the list of strategies students created earlier in the lesson, highlight it where it appears. If not, add it to the list.

- **Then say:** *I need to use the facts to see if Lisette has enough flour to make the bread. I have to compare the amount of flour she has with the amount of flour she needs.* Ask students how much flour she has ($\frac{3}{2}$ cups) and how much she needs ($1\frac{2}{3}$ cups).

- **Move on to Step 3.** Read it aloud. Point out that the amount Lisette has is a mixed number and the amount she needs is an improper fraction. Say: *It's hard to compare mixed numbers and improper fractions. Before I compare, I'll need to change the improper fraction to a mixed number.* Point out that it would also be fine to change the mixed number to a fraction. The important thing is that the two amounts be expressed in the same form.

- **Have volunteers help you convert $\frac{3}{2}$ to $1\frac{1}{2}$.** Say: *Now we know that Lisette has $1\frac{1}{2}$ cups of flour. She needs $1\frac{2}{3}$ cups of flour. Which is more?*

- **BP 5** **Have students explain to a partner how they can determine which of $1\frac{1}{2}$ and $1\frac{2}{3}$ is greater.** Encourage them to use drawings or fraction strips to help.

- **Elicit that $1\frac{2}{3}$ is greater.** Have students write the number sentence: $1\frac{2}{3} > 1\frac{1}{2}$ (or $1\frac{1}{2} < 1\frac{2}{3}$). Say: *Lisette has less flour than she needs. So, she does not have enough flour.* Point out that the answer is written in a full sentence.

Point out that the problem was multi-step because students had to do two things. First, they had to change the improper fraction to a mixed number; second, they had to compare the two amounts.

BP 5 **Talk about the solving process with students.** Read aloud the steps in turn. Ask students if they found the steps easy or hard to understand. Have them put their thumbs straight up for easy, straight down for hard, and in the middle for in between. Then invite students to discuss what they do and do not understand. Have students answer each other's questions if they can.

Wrap up this section by calling students' attention to the problem-solving strategy chart they created earlier in the lesson. Go through the list of strategies. Help students to think about which strategies you did and did not use while solving the sample problem. Highlight the ones that were used. Encourage students to use these again as they continue with the lesson.

C Review and Practice

Quickly review the three steps in the student worktext. Ask students what they do *first, second,* and *third.*

Have pairs write each step on an index card without including the number of the step. Have students mix the cards and set them on the table in front of them. Then ask them to put the cards in order. Encourage them to try to do so without checking the student worktext.

Read aloud the directions for Practice Solving Math Problems at the bottom of page 112. Instruct students to solve these problems independently. Remind them to write their answers in complete sentences.

D Assess and Intervene

Can students solve multi-step problems that use fractions greater than 1, as shown in Practice Solving Math Problems on page 112? Use the rubric to identify students who need extra support through additional help and the Intervention activity.

Intermediate

- ☐ Solves 3–4 problems correctly.
- ☐ Gives at least 3 answers in phrases or sentences, with some errors.

Advanced

- ☐ Solves all 4 problems correctly.
- ☐ Gives all 4 answers in complete sentences, with minor errors only.

INTERVENTION   5 minutes

If students have trouble with **Practice Solving Math Problems**, help them act out the problems. Acting out the problems can help students understand the scenario and gain confidence with the numbers and concepts. For number 1, for example, have a student play the part of Miko and walk two separate distances (pausing for "lunch"). Talk about how far Miko went on each part of the walk. Repeat with other examples.

Lesson

1

Prerequisite Background Knowledge
- Concepts and vocabulary of addition and subtraction
- Concepts of fractions and equivalent fractions

Understand the Main Idea

Objective Identify when you use different rules to add or subtract fractions and mixed numbers.

30 minutes

Teach this lesson:
- **Before** introducing material on adding and subtracting fractions in students' grade-level math textbooks
- **Before** students complete the activities on page 113 of the student worktext

You need these materials:
- fraction strips

BP 6 ***ELL BEST PRACTICE #6:***
Hands-On Activities

For English language learners, hands-on activities can teach academic concepts and language in ways that are not affected by how much English they understand. Have students use manipulatives such as fraction strips as they learn how to add and subtract fractions. Students will associate the language they hear with these activities, thus gaining greater proficiency in English as well as understanding how to add and subtract fractions and mixed numbers.

Throughout this module, when you see **BP 6**, it indicates a chance to introduce a hands-on activity.

Module 29: Add and Subtract Fractions and Mixed Numbers with Like and Unlike Denominators

LESSON 1

Understand the Main Idea

Objective Identify when you use different rules to add or subtract fractions and mixed numbers.

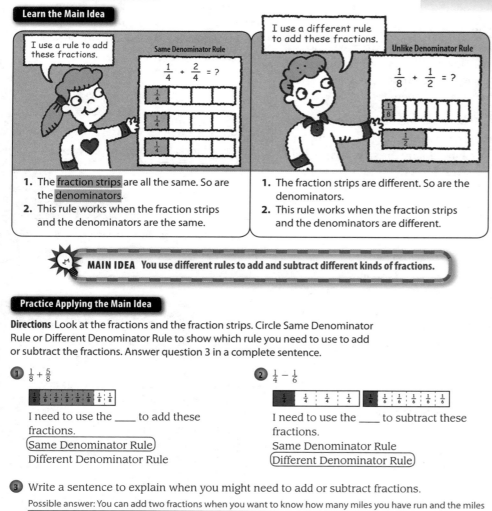

Learn the Main Idea

I use a rule to add these fractions.

Same Denominator Rule

$\frac{1}{4} + \frac{2}{4} = ?$

1. The fraction strips are all the same. So are the denominators.
2. This rule works when the fraction strips and the denominators are the same.

I use a different rule to add these fractions.

Unlike Denominator Rule

$\frac{1}{8} + \frac{1}{2} = ?$

1. The fraction strips are different. So are the denominators.
2. This rule works when the fraction strips and the denominators are different.

MAIN IDEA You use different rules to add and subtract different kinds of fractions.

Practice Applying the Main Idea

Directions Look at the fractions and the fraction strips. Circle Same Denominator Rule or Different Denominator Rule to show which rule you need to use to add or subtract the fractions. Answer question 3 in a complete sentence.

1 $\frac{1}{8} + \frac{5}{8}$

I need to use the ____ to add these fractions.
(Same Denominator Rule)
Different Denominator Rule

2 $\frac{1}{4} - \frac{1}{6}$

I need to use the ____ to subtract these fractions.
Same Denominator Rule
(Different Denominator Rule)

3 Write a sentence to explain when you might need to add or subtract fractions.
Possible answer: You can add two fractions when you want to know how many miles you have run and the miles are fractions.

Add and Subtract Fractions and Mixed Numbers with Like and Unlike Denominators • 113

A **Introduce**

Briefly review what a fraction is and what a mixed number is. Have students explain to a partner how fractions and mixed numbers are alike and different.

Say: *Sometimes, you need to add or subtract fractions or mixed numbers.* Introduce the following two scenarios:

- **Run in place and have students do the same.** Say: *I like to run. I run $\frac{3}{4}$ of a mile in the morning. Then I run $\frac{3}{4}$ of a mile in the evening. How far do I run in all?* Explain that students can add the fractions to find the total. Say: *I can add fractions when I want to know how many miles I run in all.*

- **Then mime stretching out a short rope and have students imitate you.** Say: *I have $1\frac{1}{2}$ feet of rope.* Repeat with another, longer rope. Say: *Cesar has $2\frac{3}{4}$ feet of rope. How much longer is Cesar's rope than my rope?* Tell students that they can subtract the mixed numbers to find the answer. Say: *I can subtract mixed numbers when I want to compare two lengths of rope.*

Read aloud the Lesson Objective with students. Explain that the word *rules* is used here to mean *steps that you need to follow.*

Highlighted words and phrases may affect student comprehension.

Say: *There are two ways to solve these kinds of problems.*

Call attention to the illustration on page 113 of the student worktext. Have students study the panels and talk about what they see with a classmate.

Read aloud the Main Idea with students. Explain that they will learn more about using different rules when they are adding and subtracting different types of fractions.

B Teach and Learn

BP 6 Distribute fraction strips to pairs of students. Briefly review that fraction strips model fractions.

Have partners find and hold up two fraction strips that are the same, such as $\frac{1}{4}$ and $\frac{1}{4}$ or $\frac{1}{8}$ and $\frac{1}{8}$. Then repeat, having the partners hold up two strips that are different, such as $\frac{1}{2}$ and $\frac{1}{4}$. Check that all students can find pairs of fraction strips that are the same and pairs that are different.

Review what students said earlier about the artwork in the panels at the top of page 113. Tell students that there are two important rules for adding and subtracting fractions and mixed numbers. Explain that they will learn when they should use each rule, but emphasize that students will not need to know all about each rule until they begin work in their grade-level math textbook.

Call students' attention, on the left panel. Ask: *What problem is the girl trying to solve?* ($\frac{1}{4} + \frac{2}{4}$) Have students use their fraction strips to model the problem shown. Be sure students understand that $\frac{2}{4}$ is made by joining two $\frac{1}{4}$ strips together.

- **Say:** *The girl used these fraction strips. Are they the same or are they different?* Elicit that they are the same.

- **Point out the denominators in the two fractions.** Ask students what they know about the denominators in the fractions $\frac{1}{4}$ and $\frac{2}{4}$. Elicit again that they are the same.

Have a volunteer read aloud the text in the girl's speech bubble. Then read aloud the text beneath the picture. Say: *This does not tell us what this rule is called. But it does tell us when we can use the rule. It tells us when this rule works. When does the rule work?* Elicit

that when the denominators are the same, we can add or subtract the numerators. Tell students that we can call this rule the Same Denominator Rule. Write this term on the board.

Repeat with the second illustration on page 113 of the student worktext. Say: *This does not tell us what this rule is called either. But it does tell us* when *we can use this rule. When does this rule work?* Draw out that when the denominators are different, we have to make the denominators the same. Then we can add or subtract the numerators. We can call this rule the Different Denominator Rule. Write this term on the board.

BP 6 Write on the board: $\frac{3}{8} - \frac{1}{8}$. Have students model the problem with fraction strips. (three $\frac{1}{8}$ strips and one $\frac{1}{8}$ strip) Ask if the denominators of the two fractions are the same or different. (the same)

- **Ask students if the Same Denominator Rule or the Different Denominator Rule would work to subtract the fractions.** Have them discuss this question with their partners. Ask them to give their answer and explain why. Establish that the Same Denominator Rule applies because the denominators are the same. Repeat for the problem $\frac{5}{8} - \frac{1}{2}$. (Different Denominator Rule, because the denominators are different.)

Wrap up this section by explaining that the same two rules are used to add and subtract mixed numbers.

C Review and Practice

Review rules for adding and subtracting fractions by holding up a fraction strip marked $\frac{1}{4}$ and another marked $\frac{1}{8}$. Say: *I want to add these fractions. Which rule do I use? Why?* Have students discuss the answer in pairs. Draw out that the Different Denominator Rule applies, as the strips are different.

Repeat with $\frac{3}{8}$ and $\frac{2}{8}$. Ask which rule you would use to subtract $\frac{2}{8}$ from $\frac{3}{8}$. (the Same Denominator Rule)

Read aloud the directions for Practice Applying the Main Idea. Tell students these problems are like the ones they just solved. Have students solve the problems independently. Then assess their work.

D Assess and Intervene

Can students identify which rule applies to each situation, based on Practice Applying the Main Idea on page 113 of the student worktext? Use the rubric to identify students who need extra support through additional help and the Intervention activity.

Intermediate

- ☐ Items 1 and 2 are both answered correctly.
- ☐ Writes a simple sentence with an accurate example of adding or subtracting mixed numbers or fractions. Any errors do not affect communication.

  Example of a sentence a student might write: *You need adding fractions when you run 2 time.*

Advanced

- ☐ Items 1 and 2 are both answered correctly.
- ☐ Writes a sentence clearly describing the addition or subtraction of mixed numbers or fractions. There are few errors.

  Example of a sentence a student might write: *You can subtract fractions to compare how much longer is one rope than the other rope.*

INTERVENTION 5 minutes

The use of the word *rule(s)* may be confusing to some students. They may interpret the word to refer to a requirement, such as a rule in a game, rather than a series of steps for solving a problem. If this is an issue, provide students with concrete opportunities to use this vocabulary. For example, have students use the addition algorithm to find the sum $24 + 49$; then point out that they have used a rule to compute the answer. Do the same with other procedures familiar to students. Relate these to the use of *rule* in the lesson.

Lesson **2**

Learn the Vocabulary

Objective Talk and write about adding and subtracting fractions and mixed numbers, using the vocabulary words.

30 minutes

Teach this lesson:
- **Before** introducing material on adding and subtracting fractions in students' grade-level math textbooks
- **Before** students complete the activities on page 114 of the student worktext

You need these materials:
- index cards and highlighters
- Transparency 57
- Vocabulary Cards

Lesson Vocabulary

Essential Vocabulary

like denominators   unlike denominators

Additional Vocabulary

denominator*   numerator*   simplest form*
to simplify*

* – Terms that have Vocabulary Cards.

Introduce

Write the fractions $\frac{1}{8}$ and $\frac{1}{4}$ on the board. Have students read the fractions aloud.

Have students form small groups. Ask groups to share what they know about the two fractions. Encourage them to talk about how the fractions are alike and how they are different.

Emphasize the fact that the denominators of the two fractions are not the same, or point this out if students do not mention it. Ask: *What would I do if I wanted to add these two fractions?* Remind students that in the previous lesson, they learned that there are two rules for adding or subtracting fractions: the Same Denominator Rule and the Different Denominator Rule. Elicit that the Different Denominator Rule would apply in this case because the denominators of the two fractions are different.

Repeat with $\frac{1}{6}$ and $\frac{5}{6}$. Draw out that if these two fractions were added or subtracted, the Same Denominator Rule would apply because the denominators are the same.

Read aloud the Lesson Objective with students. Explain that this lesson will teach students new terms to use in talking about adding or subtracting fractions and deciding whether the denominators are the same or different.

LESSON **2**

Learn the Vocabulary

Objective Talk and write about adding and subtracting fractions and mixed numbers using the vocabulary words.

Learn the Words

Directions Write the missing denominators to make the statements true.

$\frac{1}{8}$ $\frac{3}{8}$	$\frac{1}{2}$ $\frac{3}{4}$
These fractions have the same denominator.	These fractions do not have the same denominator.
The denominators are alike.	The denominators are not alike.
These are fractions with **like denominators**.	These are fractions with **unlike denominators**.
These pairs show like denominators: $\frac{2}{4}$ $\frac{3}{4}$ | $\frac{1}{12}$ $\frac{2}{12}$ | $\frac{5}{6}$ $\frac{1}{6}$	These pairs show unlike denominators: $\frac{1}{4}$ $\frac{5}{8}$ | $\frac{3}{10}$ $\frac{3}{12}$ | $\frac{2}{5}$ $\frac{3}{\text{any number but 5}}$

Practice the Words

Directions Look at the pairs of fractions. Draw a line to show if they have like denominators or unlike denominators.

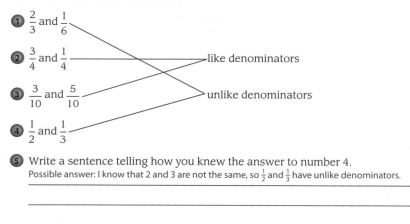

1. $\frac{2}{3}$ and $\frac{1}{6}$

2. $\frac{3}{4}$ and $\frac{1}{4}$ ——————— like denominators

3. $\frac{3}{10}$ and $\frac{5}{10}$ ——————— unlike denominators

4. $\frac{1}{2}$ and $\frac{1}{3}$

5. Write a sentence telling how you knew the answer to number 4.
Possible answer: I know that 2 and 3 are not the same, so $\frac{1}{2}$ and $\frac{1}{3}$ have unlike denominators.

Highlighted words and phrases may affect student comprehension.

B · Teach and Learn

Write the word *like* on the board. Have volunteers read it aloud. Ask students to use the word in a sentence. Point out that *like* has multiple meanings. It can express fondness for someone or something, as in *I like the color red,* or it can mean *similar to,* as in *I look like my big brother.* Explain that the students will be using the second meaning of *like* in this lesson.

Write the word *denominators* after *like*. Have students read the phrase *like denominators* aloud. Distribute index cards and have students write what they think the phrase *like denominators* means. Then have students share their writing with a partner.

Say: *When two fractions have* like *denominators, they have denominators that are the same.*

Write $\frac{3}{10}$ and $\frac{7}{10}$ on the board. Touch the first fraction. Say: *This fraction is $\frac{3}{10}$. The denominator is 10.* Have students name the second fraction and give the denominator. Ask: *Do these fractions have like denominators? How do you know?* Elicit that the denominators are the same, so the fractions have like denominators.

Display Transparency 57 and call students' attention to the fractions listed on it. Divide students into two teams. Call out one of the fractions. The first team to identify a fraction on the transparency that has the same denominator wins a point. Have the winning team then use both fractions in a complete sentence such as: *$\frac{1}{8}$ and $\frac{5}{8}$ are fractions with like denominators.*

Write the phrase *unlike denominators* on the board. As before, have students write what they think this term means on an index card and share it with a partner.

Explain that *unlike* is the opposite of *like*. Say: *When two fractions have denominators that are different, we say they have* unlike *denominators.* Ask volunteers to give examples of fractions with unlike denominators, such as $\frac{1}{2}$ and $\frac{1}{3}$.

Have students study the examples in the Learn the Words box on page 114 of the student worktext. Read the text aloud with students. Point out the similarity of the words *like* and *alike*.

Call students' attention to the bottom rows of the Learn the Words boxes. Have students verify with a partner that the first set of fractions in the box on the left has like denominators and that the second set does as well. Have students complete the third set so that the two fractions in the pair have like denominators. Repeat with the second set of examples on the right. Point out that the first two sets of fractions have different denominators, or unlike denominators. Go around the room and check students' work.

End this part of the lesson by having students complete the Vocabulary Cards for the Essential Vocabulary words.

C · Review and Practice

BP 6 Review like and unlike denominators with students by playing a game to practice identifying like and unlike denominators. Give each student five index cards and highlighters. Instruct them to write a different fraction on each card. Tell them that the denominators may not exceed 12.

Divide students into pairs. Explain that the first player puts down any fraction card in his or her hand, face up so the other player can see it, and says it aloud. The partner then chooses a card from his or her hand, plays it, and reads it aloud. If the denominators on the two cards match, the second player then says *Like Denominators* and gets two points. If the denominators do not match, the second player says *Unlike Denominators* and gets one point. Then the second player takes a turn. Play until all cards are used. The winner has the most points at the end of the game.

Read aloud the directions for Practice the Words at the bottom of page 114. Have students solve the problems on their own.

Circulate around the room and observe students as they work. Take notes on their progress and comprehension of the vocabulary.

D · Assess and Intervene

How well do students associate the terms *like denominators* and *unlike denominators* with pairs of fractions, based on Practice the Words on page 114 of the student worktext? Use the rubric to identify students who need extra support through additional help and the Intervention activity.

Intermediate

☐ Correctly identifies like or unlike denominators for at least 3 pairs.

☐ Writes a complete sentence, with some errors, containing a rough description of the student's thinking.

   Example of a sentence a student might write: *One number have 2 on bottom and other have 3.*

Advanced

☐ Correctly identifies like or unlike denominators for all 4 pairs.

☐ Writes a grammatically correct sentence that uses math terms such as *denominator(s)* or *fraction*.

   Example of a sentence a student might write: *The denominators of the fractions are different, so unlike was the good answer.*

INTERVENTION   5 minutes

If students have trouble with the questions at the bottom of page 114, they may be unclear about which part of the fraction is the numerator and which is the denominator. To help, teach them the phrase *The Denominator is Down,* emphasizing that *denominator* and *down* both begin with the same letter, D. Also, have students highlight the denominators where they appear in the student worktext.

MODULE 29

Add and Subtract
Fractions and
Mixed Numbers
with Like
and Unlike
Denominators

Lesson

3

Use More Language

Objective Use prefixes and suffixes to show relationships among words that tell about fractions.

45 minutes

Teach this lesson:
- **After** students complete the lessons on adding and subtracting fractions and mixed numbers in students' grade-level math textbooks
- **Before** students complete the activities on page 115 of the student worktext

You need these materials:
- fraction strips
- Worksheet 29
- index cards

Use More Language

Objective Use prefixes and suffixes to show relationships among words that tell about fractions.

LESSON
3

Learn the Language

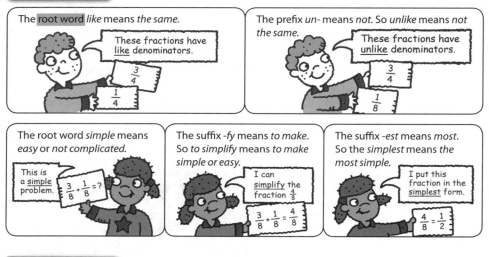

The root word *like* means *the same.*

These fractions have like denominators.

$\frac{3}{4}$
$\frac{1}{4}$

The prefix *un-* means *not.* So *unlike* means *not the same.*

These fractions have unlike denominators.

$\frac{3}{4}$
$\frac{1}{8}$

The root word *simple* means *easy* or *not complicated.*

This is a simple problem. $\frac{3}{8} + \frac{1}{8} = ?$

The suffix *-fy* means *to make.* So *to simplify* means *to make simple or easy.*

I can simplify the fraction $\frac{4}{8}$

$\frac{3}{8} + \frac{1}{8} = \frac{4}{8}$

The suffix *-est* means *most.* So the *simplest* means *the most simple.*

I put this fraction in the simplest form.

$\frac{4}{8} = \frac{1}{2}$

Practice the Language

Directions Write the correct word on the first line. Then write the definition of the word on the second set of lines.

1. This word is formed from the root word *simple* and the suffix *-fy.* simplify

   It means possible definition: to make something easier/less complicated

2. This word is formed from the root word *like* and the prefix *un-.* unlike

   It means possible definition: different

3. This word is formed from the root word *simple* and the suffix *-est.* simplest

   It means possible definition: easiest/least complicated

4. Write a sentence to explain how the words *like* and *unlike* are related.

   Possible answer: *Unlike* is the opposite of *like.*

EXTENSION AND ENRICHMENT

 15 minutes

Have students brainstorm other math words they have studied this year or in the past. Challenge them to think of prefixes and suffixes that will change the forms of these words. Offer examples, such as the word *possible* becoming *impossible* with the prefix *im-*, or the word *angle* becoming *triangle* by adding the prefix *tri-*. Have students create a list of these words and their meanings.

A Introduce

Write the phrase *root word* on the board. Draw a box around the phrase and tell students that a root word is the main part of a word. Write the word *prefix* to the left of *root word* and draw a box around it. Say that a prefix always comes before the root word, for example, write, rewrite.

Write the word *suffix* on the board to the right of *root word* and draw a box around it. Explain that a suffix comes after a root word, for example, write, writing.

BP 6 Have students model root words, prefixes, and suffixes. Ask a student to come to the front of the room. Write *root word* on an index card and have the student hold it up. Then have another student come forward. Give this student a card reading *prefix* and have the student stand to the right (as students face the class) of the *root word* card. Say: *Prefixes always come before the root word.*

Repeat with another student and the word *suffix*, pointing out that suffixes always follow the root word. Give the cards to three other students and ask them to place themselves in the correct order.

Tell students that root words, prefixes, and suffixes can also help them learn about fractions. Read aloud the Lesson Objective with students and discuss. Make sure students understand the meaning of relationships.

Highlighted words and phrases may affect student comprehension.

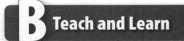

B Teach and Learn

Call students' attention to the first set of panels on page 115 of the student worktext. Remind students that they learned the terms *like denominators* and *unlike denominators* in Lesson 2.

Read aloud the text at the top of each panel in the first row. Stress that the prefix *un-* means *not* or *the opposite*. Say: *Like means the same, so* unlike *means _____.* Have students complete the sentence with the words *not the same* or *different.*

Draw attention to the first panel in the second row on page 115. Have a volunteer read aloud the text at the top.

- **Invite students to suggest sentences that use the word *simple.*** Write some of these sentences on the board.•

- **Ask students to focus on the card pictured in the panel and the speech bubble in the drawing.** Read the speech bubble aloud. Say: *When the girl says the problem is simple, she means that it is _____.* Pause and allow students to fill in words such as *easy,* or *not complicated.*

- **Have students give you examples of other math problems that they think are *simple* or *not simple.***

- **Emphasize that *simple* is a root word.** Say: *You can add suffixes to the word* simple. *Some of these suffixes will give you new words that you can use to describe fractions.*

Move on to the second panel. Write the word *simplify* on the board. Show students how the word comes from *simple* plus the suffix *-fy*, meaning *to make.* Have students study the picture and read the speech bubble. Repeat with the third panel and the word *simplest.*

Say: *Now you know where the words* simplify *and* simplest form *come from. They come from the root word* simple. *They are related to this root word.*

Review the meanings of *simplify* and *simplest form* as follows:

- **BP 6 Distribute fraction strips to pairs of students.** Ask them to form $\frac{3}{6}$ with the strips. Say: *Is this fraction in its simplest form? Why or why not?* Have students discuss the question with their partner before answering.

- **Establish that the fraction is not in simplest form.** Say: *We can simplify this fraction. We can make it simpler. We can make it less complicated. We do not need three fraction strips to show the fraction!*

- **Challenge students to work with their partners to simplify $\frac{3}{6}$, using the fraction strips.** Check that students are showing the correct answer, $\frac{1}{2}$.

- **Repeat with $\frac{6}{8}$ (which is $\frac{3}{4}$ in simplest form) and $\frac{4}{12}$ ($\frac{1}{3}$ in simplest form).** Write the original fractions and the simplified forms of each on the board. Say: *We simplified these fractions. Now they are in simplest form.*

Wrap up by saying: *Some math words use prefixes and suffixes. When you look at math words, look for prefixes and suffixes. They will help you understand these words and see how they are related to root words.*

C Review and Practice

Review root words, suffixes, and prefixes by writing these three words on the board and asking volunteers to explain them. Then write *like, write, do, call* on the board and have students add suffixes and prefixes to make new words. (likely, rewrite, writing, redo, doer, recall, calling)

Distribute Worksheet 29 to pairs of students. Have pairs read the words and work together to write a sentence that includes the first word, *simple.* Ask them to be sure the sentence makes sense and uses *simple* correctly. Suggest that students read the sentence aloud to see if it sounds right.

- **Have students continue with the other four words, writing a sentence for each.**

- **Ask pairs to work with another pair when they have completed the worksheet.** Ask pairs to take turns sharing their sentences with each other. Then read several good sentences to the class. Discuss why they think the sentences are good.

Call students' attention to the Practice the Language activity. Remind students to look for root words, prefixes, and suffixes to help them. Have students complete the activity independently.

D Assess and Intervene

Can students use prefixes and suffixes to identify words and their meanings, based on Practice the Language on page 115 of the student worktext? Use the rubric to identify students who need extra support through additional help and the Intervention activity.

Intermediate

- ☐ Identifies and defines at least 2 of the three words
- ☐ Writes a sentence that addresses the question and contains no major errors affecting meaning.

  Example of a sentence a student might write: *The word each has like in them.*

Advanced

- ☐ Identifies and defines all 3 words.
- ☐ Writes a sentence that contains only minor errors and clearly explains how the 2 words are related, using terms such as *opposite, prefix, not,* and *root word.*

  Example of a sentence a student might write: *Unlike and like are opposites because the prefix un- means not.*

INTERVENTION 5 minutes

Students may have trouble visualizing the words they are asked to form in items 1–3 at the bottom of page 115. To help, have them write the root word on an index card and the prefix or suffix on another. Then have them arrange the cards to "build" each of the words as follows: *like* and *un-; like* and *-ly.* Point out that the words *simplify* and *simplest* require small spelling modifications before they can be written, but that students should now be able to find the correct word in the Learn the Language section at the top of the page.

Lesson
4

Solve Math Problems

Objective Explain what is wrong when solutions to problems are not correct.

---

45 minutes

Teach this lesson:
- **After** teaching lessons on adding and subtracting fractions and mixed numbers in students' grade-level math textbooks
- **Before** students complete the activities on page 116 of the student worktext

You need these materials:
- fraction strips
- Transparency 58

LESSON
4

Solve Math Problems

Objective Explain what is wrong when solutions to problems are not correct.

Learn to Solve Problems

> **Problem** Luisa solved the problem $\frac{2}{8} + \frac{5}{8} =$. She said the sum was $\frac{7}{16}$. Her answer was not correct. Explain what she did wrong.

Step 1: Read the problem. What do you have to do? Write a complete sentence.
I have to explain why Luisa's answer was wrong.

Step 2: Solve the problem yourself. Explain what you did.
I need to add $\frac{2}{8} + \frac{5}{8}$. The denominators are alike, so I add the numerators and keep the denominator the same. $\frac{2}{8} + \frac{5}{8} = \frac{7}{8}$.

Step 3: Look at the answer. Why is the solution incorrect?
Luisa's answer was $\frac{7}{16}$. She added the numerators. Then she added the denominators, too.

Step 4: Explain why the answer is wrong. Use complete sentences.
The denominators of $\frac{2}{8}$ and $\frac{5}{8}$ are the same. They have the same denominator, 8. You don't add the denominators to find the sum.

Practice Solving Math Problems

Directions Explain why each answer is wrong. Use a separate sheet of paper. Answer in complete sentences.

1. Bai Yong says that $\frac{3}{8} + \frac{3}{8} = \frac{3}{16}$. What did she do wrong? Possible answer: She added the denominators and kept the numerators the same, not the other way around.

2. Zu says that $\frac{8}{10} - \frac{7}{10} = \frac{1}{0}$. What did Zu do wrong? Possible answer: He subtracted the denominators.

3. Ricardo says that $\frac{3}{8} - \frac{1}{4} = \frac{2}{4}$. What did he do wrong? Possible answer: He subtracted both the numerator and the denominator without changing one fraction so both would have the same denominator.

4. Tam says that $\frac{9}{9} - \frac{3}{9} = \frac{12}{9}$. What did she do wrong? Possible answer: She added the numerators instead of subtracting them.

A Introduce

Read aloud the Lesson Objective with students. Explain that a *solution* is an answer to a math problem.

Ask students to raise their hands if they have ever gotten a wrong answer to a math problem. Be sure to raise your hand yourself! This will help students recognize that making mistakes is a natural part of learning, even for teachers.

Say: *Sometimes, when you make a mistake, it is easy to find what you did wrong. Sometimes, finding your mistake can be harder.* Explain that looking for mistakes in other people's work can help students improve their own math skills.

B Teach and Learn

Have students open their worktexts to page 116. Direct their attention to the problem at the top of the page. Ask a volunteer to read the problem aloud.

Say: *Luisa's answer is not correct. It's a wrong answer. Let's see if we can find the mistake that she made. These steps will show us how.*

Direct students' attention to the first step. Have a volunteer read it aloud.

- **Point out that most math word problems end with a question.** Explain that this problem does not end with a question; instead, it ends with a statement, or a direction.

- **Say**: *What do you have to do?* Elicit that the problem asks students to explain why Luisa's answer was not correct. Show students that this statement appears on the right side of the page next to Step 1.

Have students look at the second step. Have a volunteer read the step aloud, or do it yourself as students follow along in their worktext.

Highlighted words and phrases may affect student comprehension.

- **Say**: *One good way to find the mistake is to solve the problem yourself. If you get a different answer, that will help you see what Luisa did wrong.*

BP 6 **Distribute fraction strips or other fraction manipulatives to students.** Explain that students can use these materials to help them find the actual answer to Luisa's problem.

Walk students through the process of adding the fractions with the fraction strips, as follows:

- **Have pairs of students model $\frac{2}{8}$ with the fraction strips.** Ask students to use complete sentences to explain what strips they can use to model $\frac{2}{8}$. Help them put their ideas into words.

- **Next, have students use the fraction strips to model $\frac{5}{8}$.** Again, have students use complete sentences to explain how to create $\frac{5}{8}$ with the fraction strips. Offer help as needed.

- **Ask students to solve this problem by using the fraction strips.** Then have them get together with another pair of students. Ask them to check each other's answers. If there are disagreements, ask students to try to resolve them on their own before involving you. Finally, ask students to explain their thinking to the other pair, even if they arrived at the same answer.

- **Circulate through the room, listening to students' conversations.** Ask guiding questions, such as *Did you have to trade any of the fraction strips?* (no) and *What makes $\frac{2}{8}$ and $\frac{5}{8}$ alike?* (the denominators are the same)

Return to Step 2 of Learn to Solve Problems. Establish that $\frac{2}{8} + \frac{5}{8} = \frac{7}{8}$, referring to the fraction strips model if necessary.

- **Point out that the problem asks students to explain their thinking.** Call students' attention to the explanation on the right side of the page. Read it aloud.

- **Instruct students to reflect on this explanation with their partner.** Ask: *Who explained their thinking this way? Who explained it differently?*

- **Point out that Luisa did not get the answer $\frac{7}{8}$.** Ask students what answer Luisa got instead. ($\frac{7}{16}$)

Read Step 3 aloud. Write the numbers $\frac{2}{8}$ and $\frac{5}{8}$ on the board. Use the following Think Aloud to show students what Luisa might have done wrong:

> **Think Aloud**

- **Say:** *Let's see . . . I know that Luisa's answer was wrong. But part of it was correct. Which part was correct?* Establish that the numerator was correct. Then say: *It looks like Luisa added the numerators. Good for her! She knew she was supposed to do that when adding fractions with like denominators.*

- **Tap the two denominators.** Say: *Luisa got the numerator right. But she got the denominator wrong.* Ask students what denominator she got (16) and what denominator she should have gotten. (8) Say: *Now I know what part of the problem she missed. That will help me find her mistake.*

- **Look at the two fractions again.** Say: *The fractions both have an 8 in the denominator. Luisa said the denominator should be 16. I think I see what she did!* Ask students how the numbers *8* and *16* are related.

- **Invite students to describe what they think happened.** Summarize by saying: *I think Luisa added the denominators. She added 8 and 8 and got 16!* Point out that this explanation is given in the box to the right of Step 3.

Move on to the fourth step. Read the step aloud and emphasize that students will need to use complete sentences.

- **Read aloud the explanation on the right side of the page with students.** Emphasize that Luisa added the denominators, but she shouldn't have. Have students explain what Luisa did and then talk about it with a partner. Then have them share their explanation with the whole group.

> **C** **Review and Practice**

Review briefly with students what to do when the solution to a problem is incorrect. Ask students to tell you the steps that are helpful when solutions are wrong.

Display Transparency 58. Point to the first problem. Take students through the problem step by step, as you did with the sample problem on page 116 of the student worktext. Help students record their thinking as you write numbers and full sentences on the transparency. Ask pairs of students to work together to solve the other three problems, using the top of page 116 as reference.

Call students' attention to the Practice Solving Math Problems activity. Read the directions aloud. Tell students that the assignment is similar to those they solved in the worktext and on the transparency.

Have students solve the problems at the bottom of the page on their own. Go around the room and assess each one.

> **D** **Assess and Intervene**

Can students identify errors in problems, based on Practice Solving Math problems on page 116? Use the rubric to identify students who need extra support through additional help and the Intervention activity.

Intermediate

- ☐ The errors in at least 3 problems are correctly identified.
- ☐ Three explanations are correct, though sentences may have errors that make comprehension difficult.

Advanced

- ☐ The errors in all 4 problems are correctly identified.
- ☐ All explanations are written in sentences, with errors that do not affect the meaning.

INTERVENTION 10 minutes

BP 6 Students who have trouble identifying what is wrong with the problems may benefit from using manipulatives to model each problem. Provide fraction strips for students to use in solving the problems. You can also help by asking guided questions, such as *Did he add the numerators correctly?* or *What is wrong with the denominators?*

Understand the Main Idea

Objective Identify and describe fractions and decimal numbers.

30 minutes ⏱

Teach this lesson:
- **Before** introducing material on decimals in the grade-level textbooks
- **Before** students complete the activities on page 117 of the student worktext

You need these materials:
- meter stick
- posterboard or butcher paper
- Transparency 59

Prerequisite Background Knowledge
- Basic concepts of place value
- Basic concepts of fractions

BP 1 ***ELL BEST PRACTICE #1:*** **Comprehensible Language**

English language learners are not able to understand everything that is said in the classroom. Teachers can modify their language in various ways to help students understand more of the language and concepts presented. When explaining and talking about decimals, use visuals, charts, and hands-on materials whenever you can. Speak in simple sentences and try to provide students with answer choices when you ask questions.

Throughout this module, when you see **BP 1**, you will find an example of how you can make language more comprehensible for students.

Module 30: Decimal Concepts

Understand the Main Idea

Lesson **1**

Objective Identify and describe fractions and decimal numbers.

Learn the Main Idea

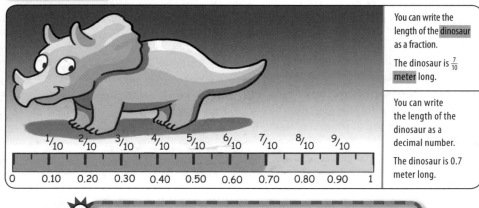

You can write the length of the dinosaur as a fraction.

The dinosaur is $\frac{7}{10}$ meter long.

You can write the length of the dinosaur as a decimal number.

The dinosaur is 0.7 meter long.

MAIN IDEA Decimal numbers and fractions both show parts of a whole.

Practice Applying the Main Idea

Directions Use the picture below. Write *decimal* if the number is a decimal number. Answer question 5 in a complete sentence. Write *fraction* if the number is a fraction.

1. $\frac{6}{10}$ of the square is shaded. ____fraction____

2. 0.6 of the square is shaded. ____decimal____

3. 0.40 of the square is not shaded. ____decimal____

4. $\frac{40}{100}$ of the square is not shaded. ____fraction____

5. Write a sentence that tells how fractions and decimals are alike. Then write a sentence that tells how they are different. Possible answers: They both tell about parts of a whole. One uses a fraction bar and the other uses a decimal point.

A Introduce

Write $7.25 on the board. Build background by asking where students have seen numbers that look like this. Elicit that this is a money amount. Establish that the symbol at the front is a dollar sign, which indicates the number is dollars.

- **Then point out the decimal point (.) after the 7.** Name the decimal point and explain that it is used to separate the dollars on the left from the cents on the right.

- **BP 1** **Touch the dollar sign and the 7 and say:** *seven dollars.* Touch the decimal point and say: *and.* Finally, touch the 25 and say: *twenty-five cents.* Repeat, having students say the phrase *seven dollars and twenty-five cents* with you; then have them say it chorally without your support.

- **Follow the same procedure with $3.80, $0.79, and $10.95.**

Read aloud the Lesson Objective. Stress that students already know many things about fractions. Explain that they will learn about decimals in this module.

Call students' attention to the picture at the top of page 117.

Highlighted words and phrases may affect student comprehension.

- **Have students talk to a partner about what they see.** Elicit that the picture shows a dinosaur and a meter stick. Display a meter stick. Establish that meter sticks measure length.

- **Ask the following questions:** *Is the stick longer than the dinosaur, or is the dinosaur longer than the stick?* (the stick is longer) *Is the dinosaur longer or shorter than one meter long?* (shorter) Have students explain their answers.

Point out that the meter stick in the picture is divided into equal parts. Check comprehension by having students count the parts. Say: *There are 10 equal parts. So the parts are called ____ .* Have students fill in the word *tenths.*

Point out the markings on the meter stick in the picture. Ask whether the top or the bottom of the meter stick shows fractions. (the top) Explain that the numbers on the bottom are *decimals.* Add that decimals are like fractions in some important ways.

Read aloud the text below the picture. Say: *We write the decimal 0.7 as zero point seven, but we say it as seven tenths.* Then read aloud the Main Idea with students.

B Teach and Learn

Write the words *fraction* and *decimal* on the board. Have students read them aloud.

Circle the word *fraction*. Have students explain to a partner what a fraction is. Then ask them to summarize their discussions for the class.

- **BP 1 Work with students to create a fractions chart on posterboard or butcher paper.** Help students come up with true statements about fractions, such as: *A fraction is a number. A fraction has a numerator and a denominator. A fraction shows equal parts.* List these on the chart and read them aloud with students.

- **Emphasize that fractions show equal parts.** Say: *There is another way to show equal parts, too. You can use decimal numbers to show equal parts.*

Circle the word *decimal* on the board. Underline the prefix *deci-.* Say: *Decimal comes from the root word* deci-, *which means one-tenth.*

- **BP 1 Refer students to the picture of the meter stick in student worktext.** Ask them if the decimal numbers are at the top or the bottom of the meter stick. (the bottom)

- **Then have students talk about the decimal numbers on the meter stick.** Ask questions, such as: *What do you notice? How are these numbers alike? How are they different from fractions?*

- **Have students summarize their conversations.** Write their ideas on the board. If necessary, ask guiding questions, such as *What does each decimal number have?* or *How do decimals remind you of money amounts?* Establish that every decimal number on the meter stick has a decimal point and begins with zero. Explain that while some decimals do not include the zero, *all* decimals have a decimal point.

Create a K-W-L chart for decimals with students. Draw a three-column chart on a sheet of butcher paper as follows:

What I Know	What I Want to Know	What I Learned

- **Have students tell what they know about decimals, either from this lesson or from previous knowledge.** Write these ideas in the first column.

- **Then have students generate questions that they have about decimals.** Write these questions in the second column. Read the lists aloud. Complete the chart when students have finished the material on decimals in their grade-level textbooks.

C Review and Practice

 **Display Transparency 59.** Point to a fraction. Ask students whether it is a fraction or a decimal and how they know. Repeat with a decimal.

- **Then have students work with a partner.** Have them sort the remaining decimals and fractions by making a two-column chart, labeling the columns *Fractions* and

Decimals, and copying the numbers from the transparency into the appropriate column. Walk around the room, checking students' work.

Read aloud the directions for Practice Applying the Main Idea on page 117. Point out that questions 1–4 refer to the pictured grid and that question 5 must be answered in a full sentence. Have students complete the items on their own.

D Assess and Intervene

Based on Practice the Main Idea on page 117, can students identify and describe fractions and decimals? Use the rubric to identify students who need extra support through additional help and the Intervention activity.

Intermediate

☐ Answers questions 1–4 correctly.

☐ Writes a correct difference and a correct similarity between fractions and decimals, using phrases or sentences; errors may make comprehension difficult.

Example of sentences a student might write: *Alike show equal part. Different show with two numbers or with point.*

Advanced

☐ Answers questions 1–4 correctly.

☐ Writes a correct difference and a correct similarity between fractions and decimals, using complete sentences; errors do not affect comprehension.

Example of sentences a student might write: *They are alike because the two show equal parts. They are different because fraction have numerator and denominator, decimal have decimal point.*

INTERVENTION 5 minutes

If students have difficulty telling fractions and decimals apart, it is often helpful to have them write some of their own. Have them write fractions, such as $\frac{3}{10}$ and $\frac{94}{100}$. Teach them a simple chant to help, as in *THREE on the TOP with a FRACtion BAR* for $\frac{3}{10}$. Repeat with decimals such as 0.3 and 0.94, using a chant: *ALways USE a DECimal POINT!* Then show students some more decimals and fractions for them to identify.

Learn the Vocabulary

Objective Talk and write about decimal numbers using vocabulary words.

⏱ **30 minutes**

Teach this lesson:
- **Before** students begin work on decimals in the grade-level textbooks
- **Before** students complete the activities on page 118 of the student worktext

You need these materials:
- meter stick and 2 decimeter rods
- string cut to a length of 1.2 meters
- Vocabulary Cards

Lesson Vocabulary

Essential Vocabulary

decimal	decimal point	tenths
hundredths	thousandths	

Additional Vocabulary

expanded form	word form	
equal parts	mixed numbers*	standard form

* - Term that has a Vocabulary Card.

LESSON
2

Learn the Vocabulary

Objective Talk and write about decimal numbers using the vocabulary words.

Learn the Words

Directions Write the missing numbers in the spaces below.

These are **decimal** numbers. They have digits to the right of the **decimal point**. The decimal point separates the whole numbers from the fractional parts. 0. 45 3.1 0.8 2.50	These are not decimal numbers. They do not have decimal points. $\frac{1}{2}$ 17 $1\frac{1}{4}$ 6
Write two decimal numbers. Check students' answers. All numbers should include decimal points. _____ _____	Write two numbers that are not decimal numbers. Check students' answers. No numbers should have decimal points. _____ _____

Each digit has its own place in a decimal number.

Ones	Decimal Point	Tenths	Hundredths	Thousandths
0	.	7	8	2

7 **tenths** = $\frac{7}{10}$ = 0.7

78 **hundredths** = $\frac{78}{100}$ = 0.78

782 **thousandths** = $\frac{782}{1,000}$ = 0.782

Practice the Words

Directions Use the number **3.159**. Write the words or numbers that will make each sentence true. Answer question 5 in a complete sentence.

① The digit 5 is in the <u>hundredths</u> place.

② The digit in the thousandths place is <u>9</u>.

③ The digit before the decimal point is <u>3</u>.

④ The digit 1 tells how many <u>tenths</u> there are in that place.

⑤ Write a sentence explaining how you know that 3.159 is a decimal number.

Possible answer: The number has a decimal point,

so it's a decimal number.

_____

_____

A **Introduce**

Read aloud the Lesson Objective on page 118 of the student worktext with students. Remind them that they learned about fractions and decimals in the previous lesson. Give students a chance to look back over their work in Lesson 1 and talk about it with a partner.

Go around the room and have students take turns saying one thing they remember about the lesson. Help them form complete sentences. Encourage students to share ideas no one else has mentioned.

- **After every three or four students, pause and say:** *Point to the person who said that decimals show equal parts. That's right, [Leo] said that decimals show equal parts.* This will model sentence form and encourage students to listen as others talk.

Ask students to think about important words they used, or heard used, in these descriptions. List these words on the board. Help students define as many of the words as possible in speech or pictures. Add any Essential Vocabulary words not mentioned by students.

BP 1 **Read aloud the words in the list.** Say the words slowly and carefully and have students repeat. Be sure they hear and include the final *ths* sound in *tenths, hundredths,* and *thousandths*. These words will be difficult for students from some language backgrounds.

Highlighted words and phrases may affect student comprehension.

Choose words from the Additional Vocabulary box that you think will be useful. Elicit or provide examples or definitions for these words.

B Teach and Learn

Write the number _1.2_ on the board. Say: *This is a* decimal, *or a decimal number. We know it's a decimal because it has a decimal point.* Have students locate the decimal point and explain to a partner where the decimal point is in this number. (between the 1 and the 2) Stress that all decimals have decimal points.

Offer a brief introduction to decimals and decimal vocabulary, as follows:

- **Say:** *The decimal point divides a decimal number into two parts. The first part is to the left of the decimal point. These digits tell how many wholes there are.* Ask students how many wholes the number on the board shows. Elicit that it shows one whole. Underline the 1. Say: *This number tells that there is 1 _____.* Pause and have students complete the sentence with the word *whole*.

- **Then explain that the digits to the right of the decimal point tell how many tenths, hundredths, or thousandths.** Touch 1.2. Say: *This means 1 whole and two tenths of another whole.* Have students say that sentence. Point out that the decimal point is read as *and*.

- **BP 1 Use a meter stick and two rods from base-ten blocks to model 1.2.** Hold up the meter stick. Say *1 whole* with students. Then hold up the rods. Help students say: *and two tenths.*

- **Lay out a 1.2 meter length of string so students can see it clearly.** Lay the stick and the rods flat beside it. Touch the ends of the length of string and say: *The string is one and two tenths meters long.*

- **Challenge students in small groups of four to write 1.2 as a mixed number.** Have them explain their thinking to another group and compare answers. Elicit that 1.2 is equal to $1\frac{2}{10}$. Tell students that we read the fraction and the decimal exactly the same.

Read aloud the text at the top of the Learn the Words box on page 118. Read the decimals aloud with students, but do not spend much time on which show tenths

and which show hundredths. Have students describe how the numbers on the left are different from the numbers on the right. Tell students that whole numbers can be written as decimals.

Ask students to work with a partner. Have them write two decimal numbers and two numbers that are not decimals in the appropriate spaces on page 118. Instruct each pair to compare their answers with another pair. Remind students that there are multiple correct answers. Check students' work.

Draw a four-digit place value chart on the board. Label the boxes *thousands, hundreds, tens, ones.* Write the number 4,539 in the boxes, one digit per space. Review how place value charts work. Ask students questions, such as: *What is the value of 5 in this number?* (500) Conclude by having students read the number aloud. Repeat with 375 and 2,390.

Move to the place value chart at the bottom of the Learn the Words box. Explain that decimal numbers use places, too, but that the places to the right of the decimal point show fractional amounts.

- **BP 1 Read the column headers aloud with students, emphasizing proper pronunciation of _tenths, hundredths,_ and _thousandths_.** Explain that decimals are like fractions in which the denominator is 10, 100, or 1,000.

- **Ask questions as you did above, using the decimal place value chart in the student worktext.** For example, ask students to name the value of the digit 7 in the number. (7 tenths) Then walk students through the table of equivalents beside the place value chart. Emphasize that the value of 0.782 is *seven tenths, eight hundredths,* and *two thousandths.* However, it is read as *782 thousandths.*

📇 **Have students complete Vocabulary Cards for the words in this module.**

C Review and Practice

📇 **Shuffle a set of Vocabulary Cards and choose two at random.** Model how you can create a sentence with those two cards. For example, for the words *decimal* and *hundredths,* you could say: *Some decimals have a hundredths place.* Repeat with two other cards, asking volunteers to think of a sentence.

- **Have students work in pairs, taking turns drawing two cards and creating sentences for them.** Circulate through the room, helping students say full sentences. Allow some students to use just one card if using two is too difficult.

Read aloud the directions for Practice the Words on page 118. Be sure students understand that they are to use the number 3.159 to do the activity. Then have them complete the activity independently.

D Assess and Intervene

Can students use and understand the vocabulary terms, based on their work in Practice the Words on page 118? Use the rubric to identify students who need extra support through additional help and the Intervention activity.

Intermediate

☐ Writes at least 3 correct answers.
☐ Answers question 5 with a phrase or sentence that mentions a decimal point.
Example of a sentence a student might write: *Have decimal point.*

Advanced

☐ Writes all 4 correct answers.
☐ Answers question 5 with a complete sentence, including *because* or *so* and mentioning a decimal point.
Example of a sentence a student might write: *It's decimal because it have decimal point.*

INTERVENTION 5 minutes

Students who have difficulty identifying tenths, hundredths, and thousandths may benefit from having a choice of possible answers. Give them two possible selections for each of questions 1–4. For example, have students choose between *tenths* and *thousandths* for the correct answer to question 4. Seeing or hearing the answer as a choice can often help students who may have trouble generating the answer on their own.

Use More Language

Objective Write and follow directions about decimals.

45 minutes

Teach this lesson:
- **After** students complete the material on decimals in the grade-level textbooks
- **Before** students complete the activities on page 119 of the student worktext

You need these materials:
- newspaper or magazines
- glue
- Transparency 60
- markers
- index cards
- Worksheet 30

EXTENSION AND ENRICHMENT   10 minutes

Have students cut money amounts out of newspaper and magazine articles and advertisements. Have them glue these money amounts to a sheet of paper and write the corresponding decimals in word form beneath the numbers. For example, if a student cuts out the amount $24.99, have that student write *twenty-four dollars and ninety-nine cents* below the number. Ask students to fit four or five money amounts on a page and share their work with a classmate.

Use More Language

Objective Write and follow directions about decimals.

LESSON **3**

Learn the Language

You can write the directions.

Write a number that has _____ in the _____ place, _____ in the _____ place, and _____ in the _____ place.

You can follow the directions.

The number is _____ and _____.

Practice the Language

Directions Write the correct decimal number on the line in questions 1 to 4. Write directions for question 5.

① Write a number that has 7 in the tens place, 4 in the ones place, and 9 in the tenths place.

74.9

② Write a number that has 8 in the ones place, 5 in the tenths place, 6 in the hundredths place, and 3 in the thousandths place.

8.563

③ Write a number that has 1 in the hundredths place, 2 in the tenths place, 4 in the ones place, and 5 in the tens place.

54.21

④ Write a number that has 6 in the hundreds place, 0 in the tens place, 3 in the ones place, 7 in the tenths place, and 8 in the hundredths place.

603.78

⑤ Write directions about the number 8.934.

Possible answer: Write a number that has 8 in the

ones place, 9 in the tenths place, 3 in the hundredths

place, and 4 in the thousandths place.

_____

Highlighted words and phrases may affect student comprehension.

A Introduce

Briefly review the concept of directions. Give students a series of commands, such as: *Stand up. Raise one arm in the air. Pat your head. Touch your toes.* Have students follow the directions as you say them one-by-one. Model any that seem difficult for students to carry out. Explain that these are called *directions* and that directions tell people what to do.

Have a few volunteers each give a direction, such as the ones above. Have the rest of the class carry out each action. Once you are sure that students can express and understand directions, divide the class into pairs. Have students practice giving directions to their partners.

Read aloud the Lesson Objective with students. Check comprehension by asking: *What will these directions be about?* Elicit that the answer is *decimals*.

B Teach and Learn

Call students' attention to the left-hand picture at the top of page 119. Have a volunteer read aloud the text in the speech bubble. Be sure the student says *tenths* rather than *tens*.

Use the following procedure to walk students through the information at the top of page 119:

- **Point out that the girl in the picture is giving the boy a direction.** Say: *She is asking the boy to write a number. The number is a decimal. How do I know the boy has to write a decimal?* Draw out that the number includes tenths, so it must contain a decimal point.

- **BP 1 Ask a few brief comprehension questions to make sure students understand the direction.** For example, check that students know what number must be in the tenths place (6) and what place the 3 belongs in (the ones).

- **Say:** *I can write this number. I'll start by putting in a decimal point.* Write a decimal point on the board. Explain that the decimal point helps you by dividing the number into two parts. Use gestures and words to explain that the whole number goes on the left of the decimal point and the fractional part goes on the right.

- **Say:** *This number has no hundreds or tens. But it does have ones. How many ones does it have?* Establish that the girl is asking for a number with three ones.

- **BP 1 Ask students if the ones place is to the left or the right of the decimal point.** Elicit that the ones place is to the left of the decimal point. Write *3* in the ones place.

- **Repeat with the tenths place.** Establish that this place is just to the right of the decimal point and that the digit *6* belongs there.

- **Ask if there are any more digits or places.** Establish that there are not. Have students read the resulting number aloud as: *three and six tenths*.

Move on to the second picture. Point out that the boy is answering the question by writing the number and by saying it aloud. Help students check to see that the answer in the student worktext is the same as the number you wrote on the board.

Call students' attention to the sentence frames at the bottom of the Learn the Language box. Point out that the sentence frame on the left includes space for describing three digits, not two, and that students may be asked to describe a number with more than three digits as well.

Tell students that you will give them some more directions. Divide the class into pairs. Then display Transparency 60. Tell the class that these directions are like the ones they did in the lesson, but they will have to use tens, ones, tenths, hundredths, and thousandths. Point out the set of directions at the top of the transparency. Read them aloud or have a volunteer do it. Have students work together to follow the directions and write the number with a marker on an index card.

- **Have students hold up their index cards when they are finished with the first problem.** This will make it easy for you to check students' work by scanning the classroom. Pull aside pairs who do not have the correct answer for a quick refresher; allow other pairs to continue to the next problems.

- **Circulate through the classroom as students work, checking answers and asking students to read the decimals aloud.** Be sure they say *tenths* and *hundredths* rather than *tens* and *hundreds*.

When partners have solved all four problems, give them each a copy of Worksheet 30. Ask them to use the sentence frames on the worksheet to create four sets of directions, each describing a different decimal.

- **Have them exchange papers with their partners.** Have the partner solve each problem and write and say the number. For example, if a problem asks for a number that has 7 in the tens place, 6 in the ones place, and 9 in the tenths place, the partner should write 76.9 and read it as *seventy-six and nine tenths*. Have partners check each other's work.

Review and Practice

Give four students index cards, one with a decimal point on it and the others with the numbers 1, 2, and 3.

Ask the other students which of the digits *1, 2,* and *3* they would like to have in the ones place, the tenths place, and the hundredths place. Record the directions on the board, using a simple form, such as: *3 in the tenths place*. Then have the four students with the cards form the number described.

Repeat, having other students hold the cards and form the number.

Call students' attention to Practice the Language at the bottom of page 119. Explain that directions have already been written for students in numbers 1–4 and that students will need to follow the commands to write the appropriate number. Point out that number 5 asks students to write directions about the decimal number. Tell students that they should use the sentence frame when they write directions only if they have to. Have students solve these problems on their own.

D Assess and Intervene

Can students give and respond to directions involving decimals, judging by their work on page 119? Use the rubric to identify students who need extra support through additional help and the Intervention activity.

Intermediate

- ☐ Writes at least 3 decimal numbers correctly.
- ☐ Writes a correct direction, with no errors, but using the sentence frame.

Advanced

- ☐ Writes all 4 decimal numbers correctly.
- ☐ Writes a correct direction with some errors, but without using the sentence frame.

INTERVENTION   10 minutes

If students have trouble writing the correct numbers, have them use a place value chart with six columns and a decimal point. Help students label each of the columns from hundreds to thousandths. Then write a set of directions on the board and help students place the digits in the right places on the chart, with the help of the labeled columns.

Solve Math Problems

Objective Explain your answers to word problems.

---

30 minutes

Teach this lesson:
- **After** students complete the work on decimals in the grade-level math textbooks
- **Before** students complete the activities on page 120 of the student worktext

You need these materials:
- base-ten blocks
- graph paper
- large playground ball
- index cards

LESSON

4

Solve Math Problems

Objective Explain your answers to word problems.

Learn to Solve Problems

> **Problem** Lee ran (1.90 miles). Suu ran (1$\frac{8}{10}$ miles). <u>Who ran farther? How do you know?</u>

	Think	Write
Step 1:	Read the problem. Underline the questions. What do the questions tell you to do?	There are two questions. First I need to solve the problem. Then I need to explain how I know the answer.
Step 2:	Circle the facts. What do you know? What do you have to do to solve the problem?	I know how far each person ran. I have to compare the distances to see who ran farther.
Step 3:	Solve the problem. Explain your answer.	I need to write both numbers as decimals. Then I need to compare them. 1.90 1$\frac{8}{10}$ 1.90 1$\frac{8}{10}$ = 1.8 1.90 > 1.8 Lee ran farther because 1.90 is greater than 1$\frac{8}{10}$.

Practice Solving Math Problems

Directions Follow steps 1 to 3 above to solve the word problems below. Solve each problem on a separate sheet of paper. Write answers in complete sentences.

1. Katja is 1.6 meters tall. Dolores is 1$\frac{6}{10}$ meters tall. Which girl is taller? How do you know? They are the same height because 1.6 and 1$\frac{6}{10}$ are equivalent.

2. Ramon ate 0.10 pounds of cheese. Kai ate 0.15 pounds of cheese. Which boy ate $\frac{15}{100}$ pounds of cheese? How can you tell? Kai because 0.15 is equivalent to $\frac{15}{100}$.

3. Adem draws a rectangle with a perimeter of 6.40 inches. Then he draws a square with a perimeter of 6$\frac{20}{100}$ inches. Which shape has the greater perimeter? Why? The rectangle, because 6.40 > 6$\frac{20}{100}$.

4. Joni buys a brown rug that is 2.25 yards long. She buys a blue rug that is 2$\frac{1}{4}$ yards long. Which rug is longer? How do you know? They are the same length because 2.25 and 2$\frac{1}{4}$ are equivalent.

120 · Decimal Concepts

A Introduce

Write the following phrases on the board and read them aloud: *How do you know? How can you tell? Why?* Tell students that they often see these phrases at the end of word problems.

Ask students what makes all of these phrases alike. Elicit that they all are ways of asking students to explain their answers. Ask students to think of times when they had to explain their answers. Encourage them to describe briefly what people do when they explain an answer.

Provide practice in explaining by writing the following problem on the board: *How many students are in class today? How do you know?* Read the problem aloud; then have students repeat chorally. Point out that there are two different questions in the problem.

- **Have students work with a partner to solve the problem and explain their answers.** Invite students to share their answers and explanations with the class. Summarize by putting the information into a full sentence, for example: *Miguel and Tomi say there are 15 students today. They know this because they counted* or *because they know that no one is absent.* Establish that the same answer can have several different explanations.

Have students reflect on the explanations they gave and heard. Then have them list words that they found useful in explaining answers. Draw out that words such as *because* and *so* can help students describe their thought processes.

Read aloud the Lesson Objective on page 120 with students. Tell students that these problems will all include decimals.

Highlighted words and phrases may affect student comprehension.

B Teach and Learn

Call students' attention to the problem on top of page 120 of the student worktext. Have students read it aloud. Build background by asking students if a *mile* is a long distance or a short distance. Help students describe a mile in terms that make sense to them, or explain that your school is about one mile from a well-known place in your community.

- **Then ask students whether the people in the problem ran more than a mile or less than a mile.** Have them say their answer to a partner and explain how they know. Elicit that the students each ran more than a mile because each of the numbers given in the problem is greater than one. Repeat, asking students if the runners ran more or less than two miles. (less, because one mile and a part of another mile is less than two miles)

Have students read Step 1 aloud. Point out that there are two questions in this problem and that both are underlined in the student worktext.

- **Read aloud the text to the right.** Say: *First, I need to solve the problem. Then I need to explain how I know.* Have students repeat.

- **BP 1 Divide students into two groups.** Point to one group. Say: *First, I need to ____.* Have students respond with: *solve the problem.* Point to the other group and say: *Then I need to ____.* Have students respond with: *explain how I know.* Repeat several times.

- **Wrap up Step 1 by explaining that students will need to *solve* and *explain* each problem in this lesson.**

Move on to Step 2. Ask students why it is wise to circle the facts in a word problem. Draw out that circling information helps you notice it. Point out that the circling has been done for students. Add that students should always circle the units as well as the numbers.

BP 1 Have students briefly close their worktexts, marking their place for easy reference. Ask them to work with a small group to brainstorm ways of solving the problem. Write the facts of the problem on the board to help remind students of what they need to do. Circulate through the room, listening to students' ideas and helping to put them into sentence form. Provide materials such as base-ten blocks and graph paper to help students.

- **Ask students to share their ideas with the rest of the class.** Make notes on the board and summarize their thinking. Highlight words and phrases. such as *compare* and *write both numbers as ____,* if students have used them.

Have students reopen their student worktexts. Read aloud the first column of Step 3. Walk students through the explanation in the second column of how to solve the problem Say: *Decimals are another way to write fractions that have 10, 100, or 1,000 in the denominator, so it makes sense to change fractions to decimals to solve this problem.*

- **Explain that you could also change the decimal to a fraction.** Demonstrate on the board. Single out any pairs or groups who mentioned changing fractions to decimals or decimals to fractions during the class discussion.

Move on to the last sentence in the Learn to Solve Problems box. Read the explanation aloud with students. Emphasize the word *because* and point out that the explanation compares the two numbers in the problem.

Locate two problems about decimals in students' grade-level textbooks that require explaining how they know the answer. Have students solve the problems and write an explanation. Encourage them to use *because* in their explanations.

Conclude by discussing students' explanations. Ask what parts of the explanations were easy to write and which were harder to write. Invite students to share words and phrases that they found helpful.

C Review and Practice

Review with students what two things they must do when problems ask for explanations. Help them respond with the sentences they used earlier: *First, I need to solve the problem. Then I need to explain how I know.*

Review Steps 1–3 in the Learn to Solve Problems box. Ask students to tell you what Step 1 is, then Step 2, and Step 3.

Remind students that they can solve problems like these by expressing all numbers either as fractions or as decimals. Have students stand in a circle.

Say: *You can make both numbers into ____* (bounce a playground ball at a student, who catches it and says *fractions* or *decimals*). Then have the student bounce it back to you, saying: *Or you can make both numbers into ____.* Finish the sentence with the word the student did not say earlier. Repeat.

Have students solve problems 1–4 at the bottom of page 120 on their own.

D Assess and Intervene

Can students solve word problems and explain their answers, based on their work in Practice Solving Math Problems on page 120? Use the rubric to identify students who need extra support through additional help and the Intervention activity.

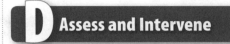

☐ Solves at least 3 problems correctly.
☐ Explains the answer in a phrase or sentence that includes the idea of equivalent, greater than, or less than.

Example of a sentence a student might write: *Rectangle greater because number greater.*

Advanced

☐ Solves all 4 problems correctly.
☐ Explains the answer in a complete sentence that includes the idea of equivalent, greater than, or less than.

Example of a sentence a student might write: *Rectangle have greater perimeter because 6.40 greater than $6\frac{20}{100}$.*

INTERVENTION 10 minutes

The relationship of fractions to decimals may be unclear for students who struggled to solve problems 1–4. Give these students extra practice reading and writing decimals. Have them count the number of places after the decimal point. Help them make a chart on an index card, showing that one place means the number is in the tenths, whereas two places means it is in the hundredths. Have students practice writing a decimal number with hundredths and then write it in fraction form. Repeat with tenths.

ADDITIONAL ACTIVITIES

The following activities can be used as needed to provide extra practice, review, and individual intervention.

Activity Key	
W	**Whole class activity**
G	**Small group activity**
I	**Individual activity**

Activity	Purpose	Materials Needed	Time	Directions
Detail Cluster (***W***)	To engage students in thinking and talking about the Main Idea	• Chalk or white-board and tools to write with	10–15 minutes per cluster	Write the Main Idea of an *ALN* lesson in the middle of a cluster. As you ask students what details they recall from the lesson, add the details to the cluster. Encourage students to provide specific examples from the student worktext, using their memory.

Multiple Meanings (***G***)	To help ELLs understand the difference between everyday meanings and math meanings for words	• Chalk or white board and tools to write with
		• Paper for students to write on and pencils to write with
			10–15 minutes per word	Write math words on the board that have everyday meanings, such as: *table, bill, foot, face, key, mass, label, product, property, plane, slide, yard,* etc. Under each word, write four or five answers, two true and two or three false. For example, write:
				  A table is _____.
				  a) a place to eat lunch
				  b) a way to show data
				  c) a kind of triangle
				  d) a way to measure in the metric system
				  e) the numbers on a thermometer
				Have students work in small groups, with each group working on a different word. When all groups are finished, have them present their answers to the class.

Quickwrite (***I, G***)	To encourage students to think, write, and speak about topics they will learn more about	• Paper for students to write on and pencils to write with	5 minutes	Before beginning a new module or lesson, ask students to think about a time when they needed to know or used a particular math concept (such as estimating). Have students write for three minutes on the topic, without stopping. Then have pairs of students share their stories with each other.

ADDITIONAL ACTIVITIES

Activity	Purpose	Materials Needed	Time	Directions
Math Riddles (*G*)	To encourage students to think and communicate (verbally and in writing) about math problems and concepts in a fun environment	• Pencil and paper for students to write on • Math riddles. (These can be found in a variety of places: in books, in students' grade-level text books, and on some websites. Check the Additional Resources on the accompanying Teacher Resource CD-ROM for more information.)	10–15 minutes per riddle	Write math riddles on the board or on a piece of paper. Have students work in small groups to come up with answers to the riddles. When they have completed a riddle, let them present the answer to the class. Make sure students take turns being the writer and the speaker.
Fill in the Blanks (*I*)	To help students practice vocabulary words and concepts	• Pencil and paper for students to write on	10 minutes	Make short stories using vocabulary words from *ALN* lessons, leaving a blank line for the vocabulary words. Have students fill in the blanks using their student worktext. Go over the answers in class or with each student individually.
Context Analysis (*W, I*)	To engage students in examining the mathematical context in which a term appears	• Chalk or white board or overhead projector and tools to write with	10 minutes	Write three or more sentences on the board or overhead that have the math word replaced with a nonsense word. Provide a list of correct words to the right of the sentences. For example, write: *Seth has to dulimp* (estimate) *the cost of a bag of apples to see if he has enough money*. Have students check their answers using the student worktext Glossary or by referring to the lesson.

ADDITIONAL ACTIVITIES

Activity	Purpose	Materials Needed	Time	Directions
Tic-Tac-Toe (*G*)	To give students practice applying mathematical concepts	• Markers and paper to create tic-tac-toe grids	20 minutes	Have students work together in pairs. Create a large tic-tac-toe grid on the board. Have students make their own tic-tac-toe grids on their paper. Write nine math problems on the board that correspond to the lesson you're teaching. Have students write one question randomly in each space. Working in pairs, students take turns answering the problems correctly. The student who answers the problem correctly places their X or O in the corresponding box. Students continue taking turns until one student gets three in a row.
Bingo! (*W*)	To reinforce mathematical definitions and concepts	• Markers and paper • Bingo markers, like buttons or tiles	20 minutes	Have students make a nine-space bingo grid, with three rows and three columns. Have students write FREE in the middle. Give students bingo markers, such as tiles, buttons, etc. Explain the rules of bingo: three in a row wins; students can place a marker in the center space because it is free. Then make Bingo! specific to the math topic you're teaching. For example, write 10 or more fractions on the board. Have students write fractions on their bingo grids that are equivalent fractions to the ones you write on the board. When you call out a fraction, students must find if they have an equivalent fraction on their grid and cover the space with a marker.
True-or-False Trivia (*G, W*)	To reinforce mathematical definitions and concepts	• Blank index cards • Markers	15 minutes	Using index cards, write Essential or Additional Vocabulary words and their definitions on one side. Give some words incorrect definitions. On the other side, write whether the definition is true or false. Have students work in groups or show the whole class each card, giving the group points for each correct answer. Make sure students can explain why the answer is true or false and are not just guessing.

ADDITIONAL ACTIVITIES

Activity	Purpose	Materials Needed	Time	Directions
Memory (*I*)	To reinforce math-ematical definitions and concepts	• Blank index cards • Markers	10 minutes	Using a pair of index cards for each vocabulary word, draw a picture of a vocabulary word on one card, and on the other card, write the definition. For example, on one card draw a sphere and on the second card write: *a solid figure that is shaped like a ball*. Make several pairs of cards and then lay the cards face down on the desk. Have students choose one and try to find the matching card.

Chanting
(*W*)
	To reinforce recur-ring patterns in language	None	5 minutes	Create chants for exercises prior to teaching the module to students. Chants begin with a simple question posed by the teacher and are followed by a repetitive response.
				For example:
				  Teacher: On a number line, which number is less?
				  Students: The number on the left is less; left is less.

Act It Out! (*W*)	To engage students in practicing math vocabulary words and concepts	• Various items to create a skit or patomime (costumes, sets, etc.)	30 minutes	Using math concepts, have one student or a small group of students act out a word or phrase while the rest of the stu-dents try to guess the word or phrase from a list on the board.
Link It with Literature (*W*)	To allow students the chance to link mathematical facts with stories	• Age-level appropriate math books (suggestions can be found in the Additional Resources on the Teacher Resource CD-ROM) • Chart paper and markers	15 minutes	Read aloud a book that incorporates mathematical concepts. Discuss the mathematical aspects of the story with the class. Reread those parts if neces-sary. Use chart paper to help students solve the math problem. Discuss the solution as a group.

ADDITIONAL ACTIVITIES

Activity	Purpose	Materials Needed	Time	Directions
Problem & Solution Game (**W**)	To practice problem solving skills	• Word problems • Pencil and paper for students to write on • Chalk or white board and tools to write with, or an overhead projector	20 minutes	As students read through a math problem, create a mini game board on a transparency or on the board. The game board should have a home where the question that needs to be solved is placed. There should be a winner's circle and a path to get to the circle, with as many spaces as are necessary to solve the problem. In each space, students must write the step needed to solve the problem. The first student comes to the board and writes the problem in the home space. The next student writes the first step, and the next student writes the second step, and so on, until the problem is solved.
Structure Analysis (**W**)	To help students learn the meaning of a word by looking at its base	• Chalk or whiteboard and tools to write with	10 minutes	Write a list of math terms on the board with bases that may be familiar to students, such as *polygon*, *tenths*, or *measurement*. Read the words aloud. Ask: Can you tell what these words might mean by looking at them? Have students take turns drawing a box around each base word, correcting if necessary. Share the answers with the group.
Round Robin (**W**)	To assess which math concepts students have understood and which they may need further assistance with	None	10 minutes	Using a lesson from the *ALN* student worktext, have students takes turns describing what happened until they have finished retelling the entire story. Encourage them to use key vocabulary words.

GLOSSARY

WHAT IS A GLOSSARY?

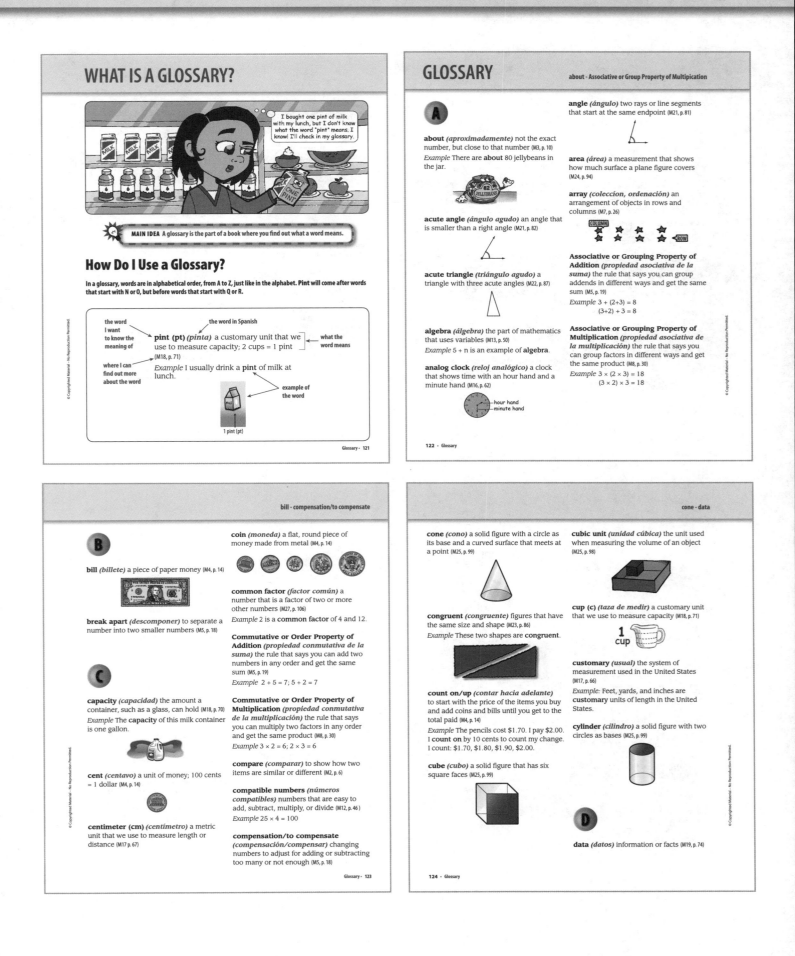

I bought one pint of milk with my lunch, but I don't know what the word "pint" means. I know! I'll check in my glossary.

MAIN IDEA A glossary is the part of a book where you find out what a word means.

How Do I Use a Glossary?

In a glossary, words are in alphabetical order, from A to Z, just like in the alphabet. Pint will come after words that start with N or O, but before words that start with Q or R.

the word I want to know the meaning of

the word in Spanish

pint (pt) *(pinta)* a customary unit that we use to measure capacity; 2 cups = 1 pint

what the word means

where I can find out more about the word

(M18, p. 71)

Example I usually drink a **pint** of milk at lunch.

example of the word

1 pint (pt)

Glossary · 121

GLOSSARY

about - Associative or Group Property of Multipication

A

about *(aproximadamente)* not the exact number, but close to that number (M3, p. 10)
Example There are **about** 80 jellybeans in the jar.

acute angle *(ángulo agudo)* an angle that is smaller than a right angle (M21, p. 82)

acute triangle *(triángulo agudo)* a triangle with three acute angles (M22, p. 87)

algebra *(álgebra)* the part of mathematics that uses variables (M13, p. 50)
Example 5 + n is an example of **algebra**.

analog clock *(reloj analógico)* a clock that shows time with an hour hand and a minute hand (M16, p. 62)

hour hand
minute hand

angle *(ángulo)* two rays or line segments that start at the same endpoint (M21, p. 81)

area *(área)* a measurement that shows how much surface a plane figure covers (M24, p. 94)

array *(coleccion, ordenación)* an arrangement of objects in rows and columns (M7, p. 26)

COLUMN
ROW

Associative or Grouping Property of Addition *(propiedad asociativa de la suma)* the rule that says you can group addends in different ways and get the same sum (M5, p. 19)
Example 3 + (2+3) = 8
(3+2) + 3 = 8

Associative or Grouping Property of Multiplication *(propiedad asociativa de la multiplicación)* the rule that says you can group factors in different ways and get the same product (M8, p. 30)
Example 3 × (2 × 3) = 18
(3 × 2) × 3 = 18

122 · Glossary

---

bill - compensation/to compensate

B

bill *(billete)* a piece of paper money (M4, p. 14)

break apart *(descomponer)* to separate a number into two smaller numbers (M5, p. 18)

C

capacity *(capacidad)* the amount a container, such as a glass, can hold (M18, p. 70)
Example The **capacity** of this milk container is one gallon.

cent *(centavo)* a unit of money; 100 cents = 1 dollar (M4, p. 14)

centimeter (cm) *(centímetro)* a metric unit that we use to measure length or distance (M17 p. 67)

coin *(moneda)* a flat, round piece of money made from metal (M4, p. 14)

common factor *(factor común)* a number that is a factor of two or more other numbers (M27, p. 106)
Example 2 is a **common factor** of 4 and 12.

Commutative or Order Property of Addition *(propiedad conmutativa de la suma)* the rule that says you can add two numbers in any order and get the same sum (M5, p. 19)
Example 2 + 5 = 7; 5 + 2 = 7

Commutative or Order Property of Multiplication *(propiedad conmutativa de la multiplicación)* the rule that says you can multiply two factors in any order and get the same product (M8, p. 30)
Example 3 × 2 = 6; 2 × 3 = 6

compare *(comparar)* to show how two items are similar or different (M2, p. 6)

compatible numbers *(números compatibles)* numbers that are easy to add, subtract, multiply, or divide (M12, p. 46)
Example 25 × 4 = 100

compensation/to compensate *(compensación/compensar)* changing numbers to adjust for adding or subtracting too many or not enough (M5, p. 18)

Glossary · 123

---

cone - data

cone *(cono)* a solid figure with a circle as its base and a curved surface that meets at a point (M25, p. 99)

congruent *(congruente)* figures that have the same size and shape (M23, p. 86)
Example These two shapes are **congruent**.

count on/up *(contar hacia adelante)* to start with the price of the items you buy and add coins and bills until you get to the total paid (M4, p. 14)
Example The pencils cost $1.70. I pay $2.00. I **count on** by 10 cents to count my change. I count: $1.70, $1.80, $1.90, $2.00.

cube *(cubo)* a solid figure that has six square faces (M25, p. 99)

cubic unit *(unidad cúbica)* the unit used when measuring the volume of an object (M25, p. 98)

cup (c) *(taza de medir)* a customary unit that we use to measure capacity (M18, p. 71)

1 cup

customary *(usual)* the system of measurement used in the United States (M17, p. 66)
Example: Feet, yards, and inches are **customary** units of length in the United States.

cylinder *(cilindro)* a solid figure with two circles as bases (M25, p. 99)

D

data *(datos)* information or facts (M19, p. 74)

124 · Glossary

GLOSSARY

decimal *(decimal)* a number that shows parts of a whole (M30, p. 118)

Example 0.50 is a decimal that shows half of one whole.

decimal point (.) *(punto decimal)* the dot that separates whole numbers from fractional parts in a decimal number (M30, p. 118)

Ones	Decimal Point	Tenths	Hundredths	Thousandths
0	.	7	8	2

decimeter (dm) *(decímetro)* a metric unit that we use to measure distance or length; 10 centimeters = 1 decimeter (M17, p. 67)

denominator *(denominador)* the bottom part of a fraction; it shows the total number of equal parts (M26, p. 102)

$$\frac{3}{6} = \frac{\text{numerator}}{\text{denominator}}$$

digit *(dígito)* symbols used to write numbers (M1, p. 2)

Example 0, 1, 2, 3, 4, 5, 6, 7, 8, 9 are digits.

digital clock *(reloj digital)* a clock that shows time with only numerals or digits (M16, p. 62)

Distributive Property of Multiplication *(propiedad distributiva de multiplicación)* the rule that says when you multiply a sum by a number the product is the same as when you multiply each addend by the number and add the products (M10, p. 38)

Example $4 \times (5 + 2) = (4 \times 5) + (4 \times 2)$

divisible *(divisible)* a word that describes a number that you divide by another number, when the quotient is a whole number and there is no remainder (M12, p. 46)

Example 32 is **divisible** by 4 because the answer is a whole number (8) and there is no remainder.

dollar *(dólar)* a unit of money that is worth 100 cents (M4, p. 14)

E

edge *(arista)* the line segment that is formed where two faces meet (M25, p. 98)

elapsed time *(tiempo transcurrido)* the amount of time between the start and the end of an activity (M16, p. 62)

Example The **elapsed time** between 8:30 and 9:00 is 30 minutes.

endpoint *(extremo)* the point at either end of a line segment or the point at one end of a ray (M21, p. 82)

equal groups *(grupos iguales)* groups that have the same number of items (M7, p. 26)

equal to (=) *(igual a)* when something is the same as something else (M2, p. 6)

Example Four quarters are **equal to** (=) $1.00.

equation *(ecuación)* a number sentence that uses the equals sign (=) (M14, p. 54)

Example $2 + 1 = 3$ is an **equation**.

equilateral triangle *(triángulo equilátero)* a triangle with all sides the same length (M22, p. 87)

equivalent fractions *(fracciónes equivalentes)* fractions that name the same amount (M27, p. 106)

Example The fractions $\frac{1}{2}$ and $\frac{4}{8}$ are **equivalent fractions** because they name the same amount.

$$\frac{1}{2} = \frac{4}{8}$$

estimate *(estimación)* an approximate number that is close to the exact amount (M6, p. 22)

Example $13 + 29$ is about 40. 40 is an estimate.

evaluate *(evaluar)* to find the value of an expression (M13, p. 50)

exact answer *(respuesta exacta)* the actual sum, difference, product, or quotient (M6, p. 22)

Example $13 + 29 = 42$ 42 is the **exact answer**.

expression *(expresión)* numbers and symbols which are used to show problems (M13, p. 50)

Example 4×3 is an **expression**.

extend *(extender)* to make something longer (M15, p. 58)

F

face *(cara)* the flat surface of a solid figure (M25, p. 98)

fact family *(familia de operaciones)* sets of facts that are related because they use the same numbers (M7, p. 26)

Example: $4 + 3 = 7$; $7 - 3 = 4$
$3 + 4 = 7$; $7 - 4 = 3$

fluid ounce (fl oz) *(onza líquida)* a way to measure liquid (M18, p. 71)

Example This measuring cup measures up to one cup or 8 **fluid ounces**.

1 cup

foot (ft) *(pie)* a customary unit that we use to measure length or distance; 12 inches = 1 foot (M17, p. 67)

Example A ruler is one **foot** long.

formula *(fórmula)* a set of symbols that show a math rule (M24, p. 94)

Example The **formula** for area is length × width.

fraction *(fracción)* a number that can describe a part of a whole or part of a group or set of things (M26, p. 102)

Example The **fraction** $\frac{1}{2}$ shows one-half of the pie

G

gallon (gal) *(galón)* a customary unit that we use to measure capacity; 4 quarts = 1 gallon (M18, p. 71)

geometry *(geometría)* the study of points, lines, angles, and shapes (M21, p. 82)

gram (g) *(gramo)* a metric unit that we use to say how heavy an object is (M18, p. 71)

Example The mass of this paperclip is about one **gram**.

1 gram (g)

graph *(gráfico/a)* a chart or diagram that uses pictures, bars, or lines to show information (M20, p. 78)

greater than (>) *(mayor que)* when something is bigger, longer, or taller than something else (M2, p. 6)

Example The number 82 is **greater than** (>) the number 9.

group/set *(grupo/conjunto)* a number of things that go together (M26, p. 102)

H

halfway between *(en el punto medio entre)* in the middle of two things or numbers (M3, p. 10)

Example The number 5 is **halfway between** 1 and 10.

hexagon *(hexágono)* a polygon with six sides (M22, p. 87)

hold *(tener una capacidad de)* how much a container can have inside it (M18, p. 70)

Example This bucket can **hold** 10 gallons of water.

hundredths *(centésimos)* 1 of 100 equal parts that make up a whole (M30, p. 118)

Example $0.78 = 78$ **hundredths**

I

Identity or Zero Property of Addition *(propiedad de identidad de la suma)* the rule that says when you add zero to any number, the sum is always that number (M5, p. 19)

Example $8 + 0 = 8$; $9 + 0 = 9$

Identity Property of Multiplication *(propiedad de identidad de la multiplicación)* the rule that says that when 1 is multiplied by any number, the product is always that number (M8, p. 30)

Example $4 \times 1 = 4$; $8 \times 1 = 8$

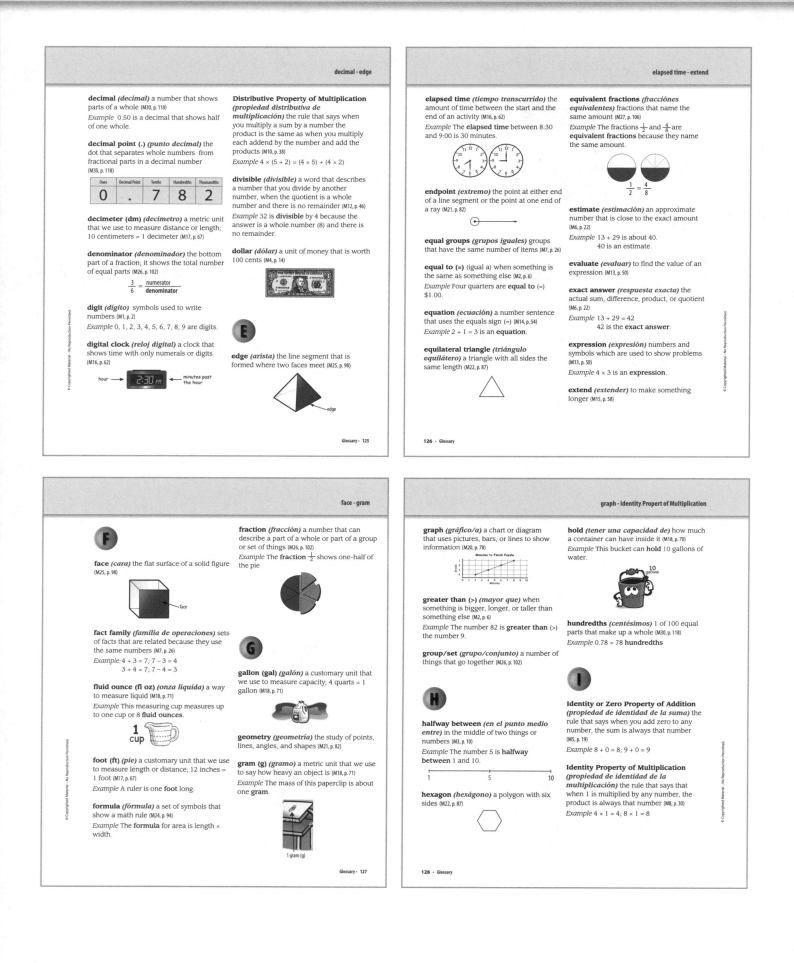

GLOSSARY

improper fraction *(fracción impropia)* a fraction with a numerator that is greater than or equal to its denominator (M28, p. 110)
Example This number is an example of an **improper fraction**.

$$\frac{7}{5}$$

inch (in) *(pulgada)* a customary unit that we use to measure length or distance (M17, p. 67)

inequality *(desigualdad)* a number sentence that uses < or > (M14, p. 54)
Example 2 + 1 < 4 is an **inequality**.

input/output (function) table *(tabla (función) de insum-producto)* a table that shows pairs of related numbers (M15, p. 58)

intersecting lines *(rectas secantes)* lines that cross (M21, p. 83)

interval *(intervalo)* the difference between two numbers on a scale (M20, p. 78)

Kinds of Milk Our Class Drinks

inverse operation *(operaciones inversas)* opposite operations, such as division and multiplication or addition and subtraction (M7, p. 26)
Example 12 + 6 = 18 is the **inverse operation** of 18 − 6 = 12.

isosceles triangle *(triángulo isósceles)* a triangle with two sides the same length (M22, p. 87)

K

kilogram (k) *(kilogramo)* a metric unit that we use to measure mass; 1,000 grams = 1 kilogram (M18, p. 71)

kilometer (km) *(kilómetro)* a metric unit that we use to measure distance or length; 1,000 meters = 1 kilometer (M17, p. 67)

L

left/left over *(residuo)* something that is extra (M11, p. 42)
Example 41 divided by 3 is 13. I have 2 **left over**.

---

less than (<) *(menor que, menos que)* when something is smaller or shorter than something else (M2, p. 6)

like denominators *(denominadores comunes)* fractions with the same denominator (M29, p.114)
Example $\frac{1}{12}$ and $\frac{4}{12}$ have **like denominators**.

line *(recta)* a straight path that goes in both directions without endpoints (M21, p. x)

line plot *(diagrama lineal)* a chart that uses Xs to sort data on a number line (M19, p. 74)

Goals Scored

line segment *(segmento de recta)* a part of a line (M21, p. 82)

linear units *(unidads lineales)* units that measure length, height, width, or distance (M17, p. 66)
Example Centimeters, inches, and miles are **linear units** because they measure length, height, width, or distance.

liter (L) *(litro)* a metric unit that we use to measure capacity; 1,000 milliliters = 1 liter (M18, p. 71)

1 liter (l)

M

make change *(dar cambio)* to give back the extra money when a person buys an item and pays more than the price of the item (M4, p. 14)
Example The book costs $1.75. I paid $2.00. The cashier has to **make change** and give me back 25 cents.

mass *(masa)* metric unit of measurement for the amount of matter, or material, in an object (M18, p. 70)
Example The **mass** of these grapes is 10 grams.

10 grams

mean *(media)* the average; the number you get when you add the numbers in a group and divide the sum by the number of addends (M19, p. 75)

---

median *(mediana)* the middle number in a set of data (M19, p. 75)

mental math *(cálculo mental)* math you do in your head without the help of a pencil, paper, or calculator (M5, p. 18)

meter (m) *(metro)* a metric unit that we use to measure distance or length; 100 centimeters = 1 meter (M17, p. 67)

metric *(métrico/a)* a system of measurement used in many countries (M17, p. 66)
Example Meters and centimeters are used to measure length in the **metric** system.

mile (mi) *(milla)* a customary unit that we use to measure length or distance; 5,280 feet = 1 mile (M17, p. 67)

milliliter (mL) *(mililitro)* a metric unit that we use to measure capacity (M18, p. 71)

1 milliliter (ml)

millimeter (mm) *(milímetro)* a metric unit we use to measure distance or length (M17, p. 67)

mixed number *(número mixto)* a number that has two parts: a whole number and a fraction (M28, p. 110)
Example The number below is a **mixed number**.

$$4\frac{5}{8}$$

mode *(moda)* the number in the data that you see most often (M19, p. 75)

multiple *(múltiplo)* the product of two numbers (M9, p. 34)
Example The **multiples** of three are: 3, 6, 9, 12, 15, 18, 21, 24, and 27.

x	0	1	2	3	4	5	6	7	8	9
1	0	1	2	3	4	5	6	7	8	9
2	0	2	4	6	8	10	12	14	16	18
3	0	3	6	9	12	15	18	21	24	27

N

net *(neto)* a pattern that can be used to make a model of a solid figure (M25, p. 98)

numerator *(numerador)* the top part of a fraction; it shows the number of parts you are counting (M26, p. 102)

$$\frac{3}{6} = \frac{numerator}{denominator}$$

O

obtuse angle *(ángulo obtuso)* an angle that is larger than a right angle (M21, p. 83)

obtuse triangle *(triángulo obtuso)* a triangle that has one obtuse angle (M22, p. 87)

octagon *(octágono)* a polygon with eight sides (M22, p. 87)

order *(ordenar)* to arrange numbers from least to greatest or from greatest to least (M2, p. 6)

ounce (oz) *(onza)* a customary unit that we use to measure weight; 16 oz = 1 lb (M18, p. 71)
Example A piece of bread weighs about one ounce.

outlier *(externo)* a number that is different from the rest of the numbers (M19, p. 75)

overestimate *(sobreestimación)* an estimate that is greater than the exact amount (M12, p. 46)

P

parallel lines *(líneas paralelas)* lines that never cross and are always the same distance apart (M21, p. 83)

parallelogram *(paralelogramo)* a quadrilateral that has two pairs of equal sides that are parallel (M22, p. 87)

partial product *(producto parcial)* a a product that you get when you break apart one factor and multiply one of the broken-apart numbers by the other factor (M10, p. 38)
Example 4 × 28 = ?
  4 × (20 + 8) = ?
  4 × 20 = 80
  4 × 8 = 32
  80 + 32 = 112, so
  4 × 28 = 112
80 and 32 are **partial products**.

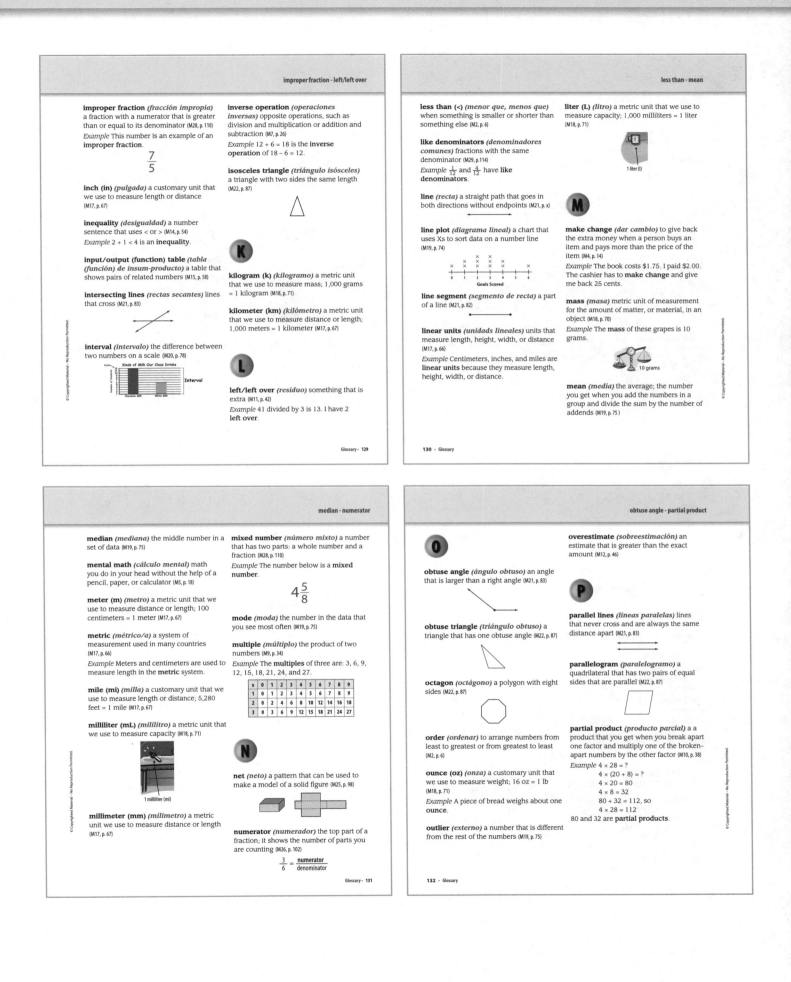

GLOSSARY

pattern *(patrón)* a set of numbers or objects in a certain order which helps you predict what will come next (M9, p. 34)
Example: A, B, C, A, B, C, ___
The next letter in the **pattern** is A.

pentagon *(pentágono)* a polygon with five sides (M22, p. 87)

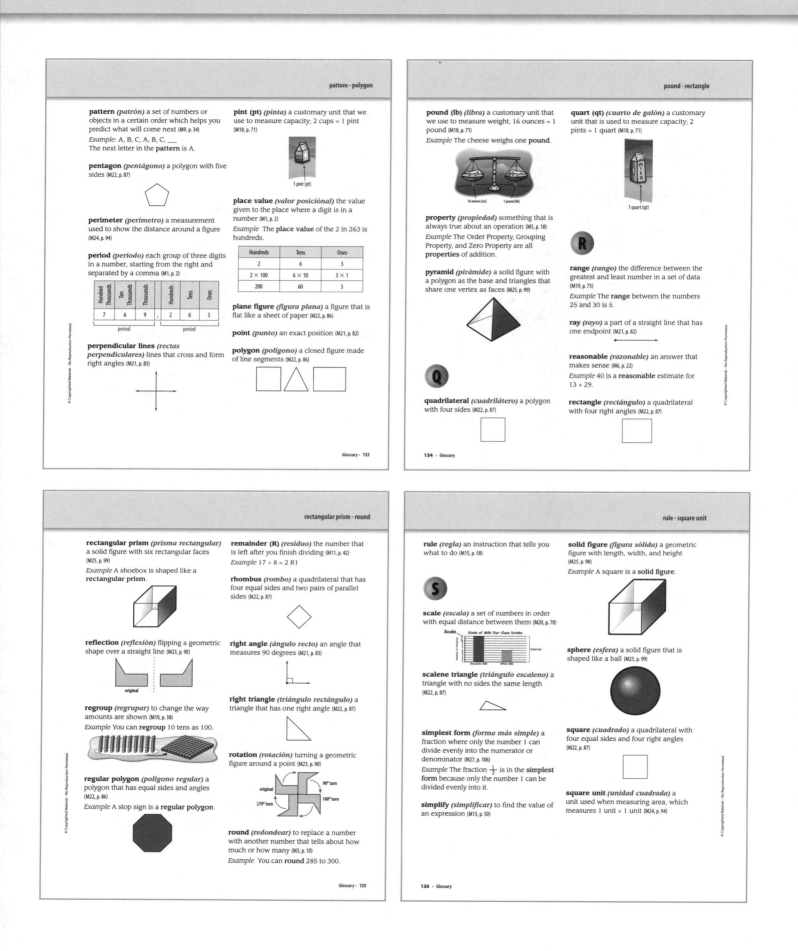

perimeter *(perímetro)* a measurement used to show the distance around a figure (M24, p. 94)

period *(período)* each group of three digits in a number, starting from the right and separated by a comma (M1, p. 2)

Hundred Thousands	Ten Thousands	Thousands	Hundreds	Tens	Ones
7	6	9	2	6	3
period			period		

perpendicular lines *(rectas perpendiculares)* lines that cross and form right angles (M21, p. 83)

pint (pt) *(pinta)* a customary unit that we use to measure capacity; 2 cups = 1 pint (M18, p. 71)

1 pint (pt)

place value *(valor posiciónal)* the value given to the place where a digit is in a number (M1, p. 2)
Example The **place value** of the 2 in 263 is hundreds.

Hundreds	Tens	Ones
2	6	3
2 × 100	6 × 10	3 × 1
200	60	3

plane figure *(figura plana)* a figure that is flat like a sheet of paper (M22, p. 86)

point *(punto)* an exact position (M21, p. 82)

polygon *(polígono)* a closed figure made of line segments (M22, p. 86)

Glossary · 133

---

pound (lb) *(libra)* a customary unit that we use to measure weight; 16 ounces = 1 pound (M18, p. 71)
Example The cheese weighs one **pound**.

16 ounces (oz)   1 pound (lb)

property *(propiedad)* something that is always true about an operation (M5, p. 18)
Example The Order Property, Grouping Property, and Zero Property are all **properties** of addition.

pyramid *(pirámide)* a solid figure with a polygon as the base and triangles that share one vertex as faces (M25, p. 99)

Q

quadrilateral *(cuadrilátero)* a polygon with four sides (M22, p. 87)

quart (qt) *(cuarto de galón)* a customary unit that is used to measure capacity; 2 pints = 1 quart (M18, p. 71)

1 quart (qt)

R

range *(rango)* the difference between the greatest and least number in a set of data (M19, p. 75)
Example The **range** between the numbers 25 and 30 is 5.

ray *(rayo)* a part of a straight line that has one endpoint (M21, p. 82)

reasonable *(razonable)* an answer that makes sense (M6, p. 22)
Example 40 is a **reasonable** estimate for 13 + 29.

rectangle *(rectángulo)* a quadrilateral with four right angles (M22, p. 87)

134 · Glossary

---

rectangular prism *(prisma rectangular)* a solid figure with six rectangular faces (M25, p. 99)
Example A shoebox is shaped like a **rectangular prism**.

reflection *(reflexión)* flipping a geometric shape over a straight line (M23, p. 90)

original

regroup *(regrupar)* to change the way amounts are shown (M10, p. 38)
Example You can **regroup** 10 tens as 100.

regular polygon *(polígono regular)* a polygon that has equal sides and angles (M22, p. 86)
Example A stop sign is a **regular polygon**.

remainder (R) *(residuo)* the number that is left after you finish dividing (M11, p. 42)
Example 17 ÷ 8 = 2 R1

rhombus *(rombo)* a quadrilateral that has four equal sides and two pairs of parallel sides (M22, p. 87)

right angle *(ángulo recto)* an angle that measures 90 degrees (M21, p. 83)

right triangle *(triángulo rectángulo)* a triangle that has one right angle (M22, p. 87)

rotation *(rotación)* turning a geometric figure around a point (M23, p. 90)

original   90° turn
            180° turn
270° turn

round *(redondear)* to replace a number with another number that tells about how much or how many (M3, p. 10)
Example You can **round** 285 to 300.

Glossary · 135

---

rule *(regla)* an instruction that tells you what to do (M15, p. 58)

S

scale *(escala)* a set of numbers in order with equal distance between them (M20, p. 78)

Scale   Kinds of Milk Our Class Drinks
                                    Interval

scalene triangle *(triángulo escaleno)* a triangle with no sides the same length (M22, p. 87)

simplest form *(forma más simple)* a fraction where only the number 1 can divide evenly into the numerator or denominator (M27, p. 106)
Example The fraction ⅟ is in the **simplest form** because only the number 1 can be divided evenly into it.

simplify *(simplificar)* to find the value of an expression (M13, p. 50)

solid figure *(figura sólida)* a geometric figure with length, width, and height (M25, p. 98)
Example A square is a **solid figure**.

sphere *(esfera)* a solid figure that is shaped like a ball (M25, p. 99)

square *(cuadrado)* a quadrilateral with four equal sides and four right angles (M22, p. 87)

square unit *(unidad cuadrada)* a unit used when measuring area, which measures 1 unit × 1 unit (M24, p. 94)

136 · Glossary

---

250 · Glossary

GLOSSARY

stem-and-leaf plot *(diagrama de tallo y hoja)* a chart that organizes data by place value (M19, p. 74)

Stem	Leaves
0	8 8 8 9 9 9 9
1	0 0 0 0 0 1 1 1 1 1 7 7

stem = tens digit   leaves = ones digit

Age of Book Club Members

straight angle *(ángulo recto)* an angle that measures exactly 180° (M21, p. 83)

survey *(encuesta)* when you get information by asking people questions (M19, p. 74)

symbol *(símbolo)* a sign that represents something else (M13, p. 50)
Example + – × ÷ are **symbols** used in math.

symmetry *(simetría)* when a figure has two halves that match exactly (M23, p. 90)
Example The two halves of this heart have **symmetry**. They match exactly.

T

tally chart/tally table *(tabla de conteo)* a way to show data using tally marks (M19, p. 74)

tenths *(décimos)* 1 of 10 equal parts that make up a whole (M30, p. 118)
Example 0.7 = 7 tenths

thousandths *(milésimos)* 1 of 1,000 equal parts that make up a whole (M30, p. 118)
Example 0.782 = 782 thousandths

ton (T) *(tonelada)* a customary unit used to measure weight; 2,000 pounds = 1 ton (M18, p. 71)

to the nearest *(a la más cercana)* to the closet number (M3, p. 10)

transformation *(transformación)* the movement of a geometric figure in one of three ways: translation, reflection, or rotation (M23, p. 90)

translation *(translación)* moving a geometric figure to a different position along a straight line (M23, p. 90)

original

trapezoid *(trapecio)* a quadrilateral with exactly one pair of parallel sides (M22, p. 87)

Glossary · 137

---

triangle *(triángulo)* a polygon with three sides (M22, p. 87)

U

underestimate *(estimación por defecto)* an estimate that is less than the exact amount (M12, p. 46)

units of measure *(unidades de medición)* amounts that we use to find the size of things (M17, p. 66)
Example Miles, centimeters, and yards are all different **units of measure**.

unknown *(incógnita)* another name for a variable, a number that is not known (M13, p. 50)

unlike denominators *(denominadores diferentes)* fractions that have different denominators (M29, p. 14)
Example $\frac{1}{2}$ and $\frac{1}{4}$ are fractions with **unlike denominators**.

unreasonable *(desrazonable)* when an answer does not make sense or does not seem right (M6, p. 22)
Example 20 is an **unreasonable** answer to the problem 19 + 20.

V

value *(valor)* how much something is worth (M1, p. 2)
Example The **value** of this ring is $5,000.

variable *(variable)* a symbol that stands for a unknown number (M13, p. 50)
Example In the expression 5 + n, n is the **variable**.

vertex/vertices *(vértice/ vértices)* a point where three or more edges meet on a solid figure; a point where two rays of an angle meet (M21, p. 83)

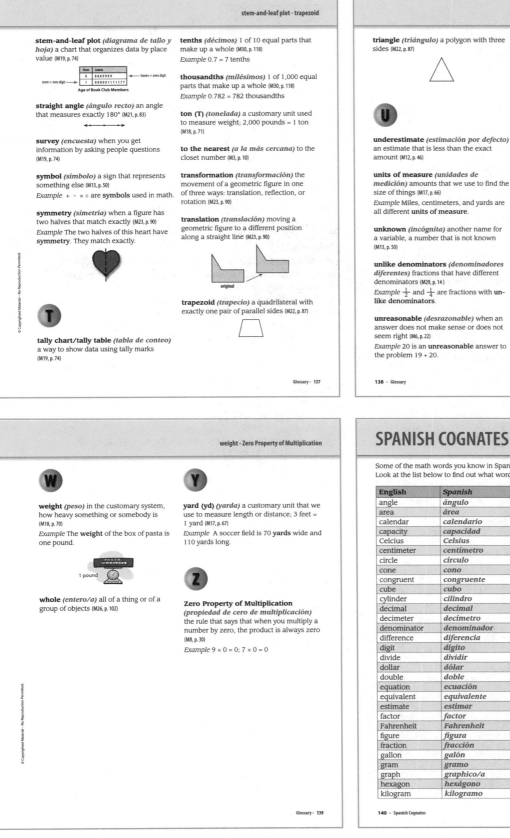
vertex

volume *(volumen)* the measure of how much space is inside a solid figure (M25, p. 98)

138 · Glossary

W

weight *(peso)* in the customary system, how heavy something or somebody is (M18, p. 70)
Example The **weight** of the box of pasta is one pound.

1 pound

whole *(entero/a)* all of a thing or of a group of objects (M26, p. 102)

Y

yard (yd) *(yarda)* a customary unit that we use to measure length or distance; 3 feet = 1 yard (M17, p. 67)
Example A soccer field is 70 **yards** wide and 110 yards long.

Z

Zero Property of Multiplication *(propiedad de cero de multiplicación)* the rule that says that when you multiply a number by zero, the product is always zero (M8, p. 30)
Example 9 × 0 = 0; 7 × 0 = 0

Glossary · 139

SPANISH COGNATES

Some of the math words you know in Spanish can help you learn math words in English. Look at the list below to find out what words you already know in both languages.

English	Spanish	English	Spanish
angle	*ángulo*	kilometer	*kilómetro*
area	*área*	line segment	*segmento de línea*
calendar	*calendario*	liter	*litro*
capacity	*capacidad*	meter	*metro*
Celcius	*Celsius*	mixed number	*número mixto*
centimeter	*centímetro*	multiplication	*multiplicación*
circle	*círculo*	numerator	*numerador*
cone	*cono*	octagon	*octágono*
congruent	*congruente*	order	*orden*
cube	*cubo*	ounce	*onza*
cylinder	*cilindro*	parallelogram	*paralelogramo*
decimal	*decimal*	pentagon	*pentágono*
decimeter	*decímetro*	perimeter	*perímetro*
denominator	*denominador*	pint	*pinta*
difference	*diferencia*	plane	*plano*
digit	*dígito*	point	*punto*
divide	*dividir*	polygon	*polígono*
dollar	*dólar*	prism	*prisma*
double	*doble*	product	*producto*
equation	*ecuación*	quotient	*cociente*
equivalent	*equivalente*	ray	*rayo*
estimate	*estimar*	rectangle	*rectángulo*
factor	*factor*	regroup	*reagrupar*
Fahrenheit	*Fahrenheit*	rhombus	*rombo*
figure	*figura*	similar	*similar*
fraction	*fracción*	solid	*sólida*
gallon	*galón*	sum	*suma*
gram	*gramo*	order	*ordenar*
graph	*graphico/a*	triangle	*triángulo*
hexagon	*hexágono*	volume	*volumen*
kilogram	*kilogramo*	yard	*yarda*

140 · Spanish Cognates

INDEX

INDEX

INDEX

INDEX

S

scalene triangle, 174–175
similar figures, 180–181
skip counting and multiplication, 68–69
solid figures and volume, xxxii, 194–201
    Assessing, Activating, and Building Background Knowledge
      (BP2), 194, 195, 196, 197, 198, 199, 200, 201
    dimensions, 196–197
    faces and edges, 196–197
    formulas, 196–197
    length, width, and height, 196–197
    making models and measuring space inside, 194–195
    net, 196–197
    patterns, 196–197
    solving word problems, 200–201
    using riddles to describe, 198–199
solving algebraic equations, 106–113
solving problems. See problem solving strategies
square, 174–175
square units, 188–189
standard form for numbers, 4–5, 236–239
stem-and-leaf plot, 148–149
straight angle, 166–167
Structure Analysis activity, 246
student learning system, vi
substitution, 92–93, 108–109
subtraction, 34–49
    difference, 36–37, 44–45
    estimation, 42–49
    mental math models, 34–35
    solving problems by breading apart or compensating, 40–41
    vocabulary, 36–37
surveys, 148–149
symmetry, 180–181

T

tally chart, 148–149
Teacher/Tutor Resource Book (TTRB), vii
    Lesson 1: Understand the Main Idea, xxii, xxiii
    Lesson 2: Learn the Vocabulary, xxiii
    Lesson 3: Use More Language, xxiv
    Lesson 4: Solve Math Problems, xxv
    Scope and Sequence tables, xxviii–xxxii
    Teacher Transparencies, viii
three-dimensional figures, 196–197
Tic-Tac-Toe activity, 244
time, xxx, 122–129
    A.M./P.M., 124–125
    analog/digital clocks, 124–125
    clock time and calendar time basics, 122–123
    elapsed, 124–127
    Higher-Order Thinking (BP5), 122, 123, 125, 126, 127, 129
    midnight and noon, 124–125
    solving problems using appropriate units of, 128–129
    vocabulary, 124–125
transformations and symmetry, xxxi, 178–185
    congruent figures, 180–181
    describe movements and test for symmetry, 178–179
    flip/slide/turn, 180–181
    fold, 178–179
    Hands-On Activities (BP6), 178, 179, 180, 181, 183
    identifying true/false statements with always, sometimes, and never, 184–185
    reflection/translation/rotation, 180–181
    similar figures, 180–181
    turns, types of (by degrees), 180–181
    vocabulary, 180–181
    writing sentences using related words, 182–183
trapezoid, 174–175
triangle, 174–175
True-or-False Trivia activity, 244

two-dimensional figures, 196–197

U

undo/undoes and inverse operations, 52–53
units, measurement, 130–133, 138–141, 188–189

V

value
    of algebraic expressions, 100–101
    of digits in numbers, 4–5
    of money, 28–29
variables, 100–103, 106–109, 188–189
Venn diagrams, 222
verbs. See language
vertex/vertices, 166–167, 172–173, 196–197
vocabulary
    addition/subtraction mental math, 36–37
    algebraic equations, 108–109
    algebraic expressions, 100–101
    capacity and weight measurement, 140–141
    collecting and organizing data, 148–149
    comparing/ordering numbers, 12–13
    counting money and making change, 28–29
    data and graphs, 156–157
    decimals, 236–237
    division, 52–53, 60–61, 68–69, 84–85
    estimation, 44–45
    fractions, 204–205, 212–213, 220–221, 228–229
    linear measurement, 132–133
    mental math and multiplication/division estimation, 92–93
    multiplication, 52–53, 60–61, 68–69, 76–77
    patterns and functions, 116–117
    perimeter and area, 188–189
    place value, 4–5
    rounding whole numbers, 20–21
    time, 124–125
    transformations and symmetry, 180–181
    See also language
Vocabulary Cards, viii
volume, 196–197. See also solid figures and volume

W

weight, 140–141. See also capacity and weight measurement
whole numbers
    comparing/ordering, 10–17
    place value, 2–9
    rounding, xxviii, 18–25
word form for numbers, 4–5, 236–239
Worksheets, viii

Z

Zero Property of Addition, 35–38
Zero Property of Multiplication, 60–61
zeros and mental math/estimation, 94–95